POLLUTION HANDBOOK 2001

NSCA POLLUTION HANDBOOK

National Society for Clean Air and Environmental Protection

© National Society for Clean Air and Environmental Protection

First Published January 1985
Updated and reprinted
1986, 1987, 1988, 1989
Revised 1990, 1991, 1992, 1993, 1994,
1995, 1996, 1997, 1998, 1999, 2000

Printed and published in Great Britain by
The National Society for Clean Air and Environmental Protection
44 Grand Parade, Brighton BN2 2QA
Tel: 01273 878770 Fax: 01273 606626 Email: admin@nsca.org.uk

ISBN 0 903 474 49 2

POLLUTION HANDBOOK 2001 - UPDATE

This edition of the Pollution Handbook was finalised between September and December 2000 and thus most legislative and other developments in pollution control up to the latter date are included in the main part of this book. Summarised below are developments which were, however, too late for inclusion in the appropriate chapter.

CHAPTER 1

Sustainable development (1.3, p4):

The National Assembly for Wales adopted a statutory sustainable development scheme on 16 November; among other things, this requires that sustainable development considerations be integrated into all aspects of the Assembly's work.

Community strategies (p5):

Part I of the Local Government Act 2000 requiring councils to prepare community strategies was brought into force in England on 18 October 2000. Guidance on preparing community strategies was expected late 2000/early 2001.

Integrated Pollution Prevention & Control (1.13.1, p12):

Draft amendment Regulations for England and Wales were issued for consultation in December 2000. These make a number of changes to Part 1 of Schedule 1; it is proposed to transfer the following installations from Part B to Part A2: composite wood-based board manufacture, metallurgical slag grinding, and large plant for the manufacture of new rubber tyres.

New (i.e. not in operation before 31 March 2001) Part B installations or mobile plant which become Part A2 as a result of the Regulations must apply for a Permit before being brought into operation; similarly existing Part B installations transferring to A2 under the Regulations may not make a substantial change without a Permit; Guidance (p13) for the paper, pulp and board manufacturing industries was published by the Environment Agency in November 2000 – existing installations in this sector were required to apply for a permit between 1.12.00–28.2.01.

CHAPTER 2

Climate Change (2.3.1a, p45):

The final version of the UK's Climate Change Programme was published in November 2000. The Programme is aimed at cutting UK emissions of greenhouse gases by 23% below 1990 levels by 2010; this should result in a reduction in carbon dioxide emissions of 19% by 2010.

As from 1 April 2001, all commercial and industrial companies will be subject to the Climate Change Levy in respect of electricity, gas, coal and LPG purchases.

Persistent Organic Pollutants (2.3.3f, p49):

Agreement on the UNEP sponsored Convention banning, or in some cases restricting, the production and use of certain POPs was agreed in December 2000 in South Africa. The Convention requires ratification by 50 countries before becoming legally binding.

EU Air Quality – Carbon Monoxide & Benzene (2.4.1bii):

This Directive has now been formally adopted and was published in the Official Journal of 13 December 2000 (OJ L313, Vol. 43); it must be brought into force by December 2002.

EU Air Quality - Ozone (2.4.1c, p53):

Environment Ministers adopted a Common Position on the draft Directive setting target values for ozone in November 2000; for human health a target value of 120 mg/m^3 averaged over 8 hours, with no more than 25 exceedences per year is to be achieved by 2010 (the Commission had proposed no more than 20 exceedences). The Directive now returns to the European Parliament for a second reading.

EU Regulation on Substances that Deplete the Ozone Layer (2.4.4, p54):

Hydrochlorofluorocarbons (HCFC) – amendment to existing text: the use of HCFCs in all solvent applications is banned from 1 January 2002 (not 2003); the use of HCFCs in foam blowing is to be phased out by 1 January 2004. Exports to countries party to the Montreal Protocol will be permitted until 31 December 2009. DETR/DTI Guidance on the new Regulation was published in October 2000.

EU Acidification Strategy (2.4.5a, p55):

EU Environment Ministers adopted a Common Position on the draft Directive on national emissions ceilings and on large combustion plant in November 2000. Both Directives now return to the European Parliament for a second reading.

Genetically Modified Organisms
(2.16.5, p89):

The *Genetically Modified Organisms (Contained Use) Regulations 2000* (SI 2831) came into force on 15 November 2000, replacing earlier 1992 Regulations; they apply in England, Scotland and Wales.

CHAPTER 3
Assessment & Management of Environmental Noise *(3.2.2, p112):*

Environment Ministers reached a Common Position on this draft Directive in December 2000.

Noise from Outdoor Equipment
(3.2.3, p113):

The DTI is consulting on the draft Regulations to implement this EU Directive, which need to be in place by 3 July 2001.

Noise Limits for Aircraft *(3.18.1, p127):*

New noise limits for aircraft departing from Heathrow, Gatwick and Stansted are due to come into effect. From 25 February 2001 the day-time limit is reduced to 94 dBA; the night-time limit is reduced to 87 dBA with effect from 25 March 2001 for the period 2330-0600; for the period 2300-2330 and 0600-0700, the limit remains 89 dBA.

CHAPTER 4
Basel Convention *(4.9.2, p144):*

The DETR announced in December 2000 that the UK had signed the 1999 Protocol to the Convention which establishes a liability and compensation system for damage resulting from transboundary movements of hazardous waste. New UK legislation putting in place a liability regime will be needed before the UK is in a position to ratify the Protocol.

Contaminated Land – Wales *(4.28.3, p172):*

The Welsh Assembly has issued draft Regulations and Guidance for consultation, similar to those already in place in England and Scotland; the new Regulations are not expected to be in place before summer 2001, with local authorities then allowed 15 months to publish their contaminated land strategies.

CHAPTER 5
Enforcement Notices (Discharge Consents) – Scotland *(5.15.3b, p203):*

New sections 49A and 49B of the *Control of Pollution Act 1974* were brought into force on 1 January 2001; s.49A enables SEPA to serve an enforcement notice if it is of the opinion that conditions of a discharge consent are being contravened; s.49B enables a person on whom an enforcement notice is served to appeal against the notice to Scottish Ministers. *The Control of Pollution (Registers) and (Consents for Discharges) (Secretary of State Functions) Amendment Regulations 2000* (SSI 432), which also came into force on 1 January 2001 detail the appeal procedure. These Regulations also require details of enforcement notices, convictions etc to be put on the public register.

Drinking Water Regulations *(5.17.1c, p209):*

New Regulations to implement the 1998 EU "Drinking Water Directive" – *The Water Supply (Water Quality) Regulations 2000* (SI 3184) began coming into force on 1 January 2001, with final parts coming into force on 1 January 2004. The Regulations, which apply in England and Wales, will replace the 1989 Regulations which will be progressively repealed. The new Regulations are summarised on page 209.

The Pollution Handbook is widely used by central and local government, industry, pollution control specialists, consultants, researchers and students. It aims, therefore, to provide an overview of environmental and pollution control legislation and related issues that is accessible to readers with widely varying knowledge and expertise. The Pollution Handbook does not set out to provide a detailed statement of the law and specialist professional advice should always be sought in dealing with specific problems, or before taking legal action. NSCA can accept no legal responsibility for any inaccuracies which may have arisen.

NSCA is always happy to receive comments and suggestions on both the content and layout of the Pollution Handbook.

Loveday Murley
Editor
18 January 2001

CONTENTS

INTRODUCTION

CHAPTER 1: INTEGRATED POLLUTION PREVENTION & CONTROL AND OTHER PRINCIPLES OF CONTROL

IMPLEMENTATION AND ENFORCEMENT AUTHORITIES

AIR QUALITY MANAGEMENT

REGULATION OF INDUSTRIAL EMISSIONS

REGULATION OF AGRICULTURAL POLLUTION

REGULATION OF POLLUTION FROM ROAD VEHICLES

RADIATION

CONTROL OF PROCESS ODOURS

CHAPTER 3: NOISE POLLUTION

GENERAL NEIGHBOURHOOD NOISE

REGULATORY CONTROLS - NOISE NUISANCE

ENTERTAINMENT NOISE

INDUSTRIAL AND CONSTRUCTION SITE NOISE

ROAD TRAFFIC NOISE

AIRCRAFT NOISE

RAIL NOISE

OCCUPATIONAL NOISE

LOW FREQUENCY NOISE

CHAPTER 4: WASTE POLLUTION

WASTE - GENERAL

THE EUROPEAN UNION & WASTE MANAGEMENT

IMPLEMENTATION AND ENFORCEMENT AUTHORITIES

WASTE ON LAND: REGULATORY CONTROLS

CONTAMINATED LAND

PESTICIDES

APPENDICES

(NB Appendix numbers follow chapter numbers)

1   IPC AND OTHER PRINCIPLES OF CONTROL

2   AIR POLLUTION

3   NOISE POLLUTION

[No appendices in 2001 Pollution Handbook]

4   WASTE POLLUTION

Integrated Pollution Control

Integrated Pollution Prevention & Control

Statutory Nuisance

Environmental Information

Environmental Assessment

1.1 INTRODUCTION

The principles underlying the UK approach to pollution control evolved over many years, with the term "Best Practicable Means" (BPM) providing the fundamental basis for almost 150 years. With integrated pollution control (IPC), came the requirement to select the "Best Practicable Environmental Option" and "Best Available Techniques Not Entailing Excessive Cost"; the need to apply a holistic approach in controlling pollution is now being taken a step further with the implementation of the EU Directive on Integrated Pollution Prevention and Control (IPPC) which requires the use of "Best Available Techniques" in controlling pollution. Sustainable Development, waste minimisation and the "polluter pays principle" are also key principles in the development of environmental policy and legislation – and all are applicable to the control of pollution across all environmental media - air, noise, waste and water pollution.

The first part of this chapter of the *Pollution Handbook* therefore explains some of the general principles of control which are applicable to all or some of the subsequent chapters and describes the main bodies concerned with the implementation and enforcement of UK pollution control legislation.

The second part of this chapter describes the legislative requirements of Integrated Pollution Control (IPC) and Integrated Pollution Prevention and Control (IPPC) which will eventually replace IPC when the transfer of existing installations to the new regime is completed in 2007. Finally this chapter covers those areas of UK pollution control, such as statutory nuisance and access to environmental information, which are of relevance in the control of air, noise, waste and water pollution.

1.2 EARLY CONTROLS

1.2.1 Alkali Acts & Best Practicable Means

Most of the UK's early pollution control measures were enacted as a result of the Industrial Revolution of the late 18th and 19th centuries, although both air and water pollution had been identified as problems many hundreds of years before (see chapters 2 and 5 respectively). The concept of "Best Practicable Means" (BPM) - which for many years was a fundamental principle of pollution control legislation - was often used to describe the whole approach of UK anti-pollution legislation towards industrial emissions, and indeed controlling other types of pollution, including noise. (See also chapter 2, 2.2.1 and chapter 3, 3.7.5)

The concept of BPM originated in a law applying in Leeds in 1842 under which a fine could be imposed on offenders who had not used the Best Practicable Means to prevent or abate smoke nuisance. In 1874 an amendment to the *Alkali Act 1863* required the use of BPM to prevent the discharge of all noxious or offensive gases arising from alkali works.

A schedule to the *Health and Safety (Emissions into the Atmosphere) Regulations 1983* (revoked in December 1996) listed all those processes ("works") which had to be registered with the pollution inspectorate; as an essential prior condition to registration, operators of scheduled works had to satisfy the inspectorate that the works were provided with the BPM for preventing the escape of noxious or offensive substances, and for rendering all such emissions harmless and inoffensive. BPM took into account the cost of pollution abatement and its effect on the viability of the industry concerned.

The essential elements of BPM so far as emissions to air were concerned could be defined as follows:

- no emission could be tolerated which constituted a recognised health hazard, either short or long term;

- emissions in terms of both concentration and mass, had to be reduced to the lowest practicable amount taking into account local conditions and circumstances, current state of knowledge on control technology and effects of substance emitted, financial considerations, and the means to be employed;

- having secured the minimum practicable emissions, the height of discharge should be arranged so that the residual emission was rendered harmless and inoffensive by dilution and dispersion.

The principle was extended to noise control. Under s.72 of the *Control of Pollution Act 1974*, it is a defence to prove that the BPM has been used to mitigate the effects of excessive noise from, for example, a factory. Section 80(7) of the *Environmental Protection Act* also allows a defence of BPM in respect of an action for nuisance from industrial, trade or business premises.

When working out the control details for any particular type of process, the pollution inspectorate would discuss ways of reducing emissions with representatives of the industry concerned, using their knowledge of control techniques and their own technical expertise. The conclusions were published in *Notes on Best Practicable Means*, which described treatment plant to be used and its maintenance, methods of operations and possibly a "presumptive limit" for emissions. Presumptive emission limits presumed that if an industry was discharging to the prescribed limit, then it would be meeting the BPM requirement. However, the intention was not that industry should pollute up to the limit, but rather that they should do whatever was practicable to reduce emissions below the limit.

BPM notes issued early in 1988 reflected for the first time European Community legislation on industrial emissions, in particular the 1984 framework Directive on air pollution from industrial plant (84/360/EEC); BPM notes were not enshrined in legislation so the limits could be tightened by the inspectorate as required to keep up with advances in abatement technology, or in scientific understanding of the effects of pollutants.

1.2.2 Pollution Inspectorates

(a) England and Wales

Until 1 April 1987, the Alkali Inspectorate (renamed HM Industrial Air Pollution Inspectorate in 1983) was responsible for regulating processes scheduled under the Alkali Acts. From 1984-1987 the Inspectorate, together with the Factory Inspectorate, came under the Health and Safety Executive. Before that and from 1 April 1987 to 1 April 1996, the Inspectorate came under the direct control of the Department of the Environment (now Department of the Environment, Transport and the Regions).

On 1 April 1987 a unified HM Inspectorate of Pollution (HMIP) was established with the aim of providing a more integrated approach to pollution control; an important area of its work was to develop a method for determining the Best Practicable Environmental Option (BPEO) for dealing with industrial processes and the wastes which they produce. HMIP was a statutory body and brought together the inspectorates for air pollution, radiochemicals and hazardous waste; it was also responsible for the control of water pollution from particularly polluting processes. Thus HMIP was primarily responsible for enforcement of legislation under Part I of the *Environmental Protection Act 1990* and under the *Radioactive Substances Act 1993*. HMIP also had responsibilities under the *Alkali etc Works Regulation Act 1906, Control of Pollution Act 1974, Town and Country Planning (Assessment of Environmental Effects) Regulations 1988, Control of Industrial Air Pollution (Registration of Works) Regulations 1989* and *Air Quality Standards Regulations 1989*.

On 1 April 1996, HMIP's responsibilities were transferred to the Environment Agency (see 1.7.1 below).

(b) Scotland

Until 1 April 1996 HM Industrial Pollution Inspectorate (HMIPI) was responsible for enforcing legislation controlling emissions from industrial premises, for the *Radioactive Substances Act 1993* and for the implementation of IPC (together with the River Purification Authorities). The Inspectorate also provided scientific and technical advice on industrial pollution generally, radioactive waste management and environmental radioactivity. HMIPI contributed to the work of the Hazardous Waste Inspectorate (Scotland), which was responsible for the oversight of waste management in Scotland. Both HMIPI and the HWI worked within the Scottish Office.

On 1 April 1996 HMIPI's responsibilities were transferred to the Scottish Environment Protection Agency (see 1.7.2 below).

GENERAL PRINCIPLES

1.3 SUSTAINABLE DEVELOPMENT

The term "sustainable development" has now become the starting point - or key principle - in formulating environmental policy and legislation. It was first introduced in the 1987 report of the World Commission on Environment and Development, *Our Common Future* (the Brundtland Report); this defined sustainable development as "meeting the needs of the current generation without compromising the ability of future generations to meet their own needs".

Many governments worldwide and the European Union have embodied the concept of sustainable development into policy making. In 1993 the European Commission published its *Fifth Action Programme on the Environment - Towards Sustainability*. This Programme covers 1993-2000 (proposals for a 6th Action Programme are under discussion) and stresses the need for governments, industry and communities to become involved in and take responsibility for the protection of their environment. At their meeting in June 1997 EU Heads of State amended the Maastricht Treaty to strengthen the Union's commitment to the principles of sustainable development - see also Appendix 6.

In May 1999, the Government published its strategy for sustainable development, *A Better Quality of Life* (Cm 4345), which replaced and updated *Sustainable Development - the UK Strategy* published in 1994. In order to achieve a better quality of life for current and future generations, the Strategy highlights the need for integrated policies with the aim of ensuring

* social progress which recognises the needs of everyone;
* effective protection of the environment;
* prudent use of natural resources;
* maintenance of high and stable levels of economic growth and employment.

The Strategy includes some 150 indicators, as well as 15 "headline" indicators, which can be used to measure progress towards achieving the objectives set out in the Strategy. Of the headline indicators seven relate to the environment: climate change; air quality; road traffic; river water quality; wildlife; land use; and waste. *Quality of Life Counts* (December 1999) provides a baseline assessment of all the indicators against which progress can be measured.

Both the Environment Agency and SEPA are charged with contributing towards attaining the objectives of sustainable development in carrying out their functions; Ministerial Guidance addressed to the Environment Agency, published in November 1996, outlines how this should be done, with similar Guidance being addressed to SEPA; see also 1.7.1(a) below.

Under the *Government of Wales Act 1998* (s.121), the Welsh Assembly is required to make a scheme on how it proposes to promote sustainable development principles in carrying out its work and to publish annual reports on progress. *A Sustainable Wales – Learning to Live Differently,* a draft of which was published in January 2000 outlines how the Assembly will implement this duty and how success will be measured. Included is a requirement for all papers submitted to the Assembly to include an assessment of implications for sustainable development and how it is to be implemented.

The Local Government Act 2000, which received Royal Assent in July 2000, requires all local authorities in England and Wales to prepare a community strategy for promoting or improving the economic, social and environmental well-being of their community and which contributes to the achievement of sustainable development in the UK. In preparing its strategy, the local authority should consult and involve appropriate people and must have regard to any guidance from the Secretary of State. Finally, *the Greater London Authority Act 1999* requires the Mayor to draw up a number of strategies for London (including on air quality, noise, municipal waste management) and to have regard to the effect of those strategies on the achievement of sustainable development in the UK.

1.4 POLLUTER PAYS PRINCIPLE (PPP)

A key principle of the European Union's environment policy is that the cost of preventing pollution or of minimising environmental damage due to pollution should be borne by those responsible for the pollution. The principle originates from the proceedings of the UN Conference on the Human Environment, Stockholm 1972; in the European Community PPP was first mentioned in the First Action Programme on the Environment (1973-77) (see Appendix 6). As a signatory to the Treaty of Rome, the UK accepts the principle of PPP.

Amongst the elements of the principle as set out by the EU are:

- *payments* in the form of grants or subsidies from the public purse which may be made towards: investment in anti-pollution installations and equipment; the introduction of new processes; and the costs of operating and maintaining anti-pollution installations.

- *charges* which may be levied directly as taxes on the process which generates the pollution, or alternatively as the purchase price of a licence which entitles the holder to generate specific quantities of pollutants.

The cost recovery schemes implemented in the UK under which operators meet the costs of regulation for, for example, Integrated Pollution Control and Integrated Pollution Prevention and Control, air pollution control, waste management licensing and discharge consents under water regulations, are in line with the principle that the polluter should pay.

Environmental taxes, used by a number of EU Member States, are another means of charging for pollution control, or encouraging the use of less polluting alternatives; however, these must not be incompatible with the functioning of the Single European Market. Commission Communication COM(97) 9 outlines the circumstances in which such taxes may be used and those in which they are not permissible.

1.5 BEST PRACTICABLE ENVIRONMENTAL OPTION

The use of the "Best Practicable Environmental Option" (BPEO) as a means of controlling pollution was first proposed by the Royal Commission on Environmental Pollution in its fifth Report (1976), *Air Pollution Control: An Integrated Approach.* It suggested that a unified pollution inspectorate should be established whose aim would be "to achieve the best practicable environmental option taking account of the total pollution from a process and the technical possibilities for dealing with it". In its 12th Report (1988), *Best Practicable Environmental Option,* the RCEP described its concept of BPEO in more detail, including guidelines on its implementation. It defined the BPEO as

> "the outcome of a systematic and decision-making procedure which emphasises the protection and conservation of the environment across land, air and water. The BPEO procedure establishes, for a given set of objectives, the option that provides the most benefit or least damage to the environment as a whole, at acceptable cost, in the long term as well as in the short term".

In applying for an IPC authorisation under Part I of the *Environmental Protection Act 1990,* process operators were required to demonstrate that their chosen abatement technique represented the BPEO; and in implementing Integrated Pollution Control the Environment Agency and Scottish Environment Protection Agency were required to set conditions which were commensurate with the BPEO. This specifies the pollution control technology which is the best practicable for the environment as a whole considering

- the total impact on water, land and air pathways together;
- the ability of the pathway to absorb the pollutant in the light of critical loads, where appropriate;
- the principles of sustainable development.

Technical Guidance Note E1 (Environmental), *Best Practicable Environmental Option Assessments for Integrated Pollution Control* (Stationery Office, 1997) describes a methodology for undertaking BPEO assessment for IPC in a consistent manner which is compatible with the requirements of the *Environmental Protection Act 1990.* Volume I provides guidance for assessing harm and comparing options for specific industrial processes to determine BATNEEC having regard to BPEO, as well as outlining the economic information required to gauge the practicality of process options. Volume II contains data that the Environment Agency has put together to support the methodology.

1.6 BEST AVAILABLE TECHNIQUES (BAT)

1.6.1 Euro-BATNEEC and BAT

Best Available Technology Not Entailing Excessive Cost (BATNEEC) was first used in the European Union (EU) Framework Directive on combating air pollution from industrial plant (84/360/EEC). This requires that "all appropriate preventative measures against air pollution have been taken, including the application of best available technology, provided that the application of such measures does not entail excessive cost". "Technology" is interpreted as that which operating experience has adequately demonstrated to be the best technology commercially available as regards the minimisation of emissions to atmosphere; it should also be proven to be economically viable when applied to the industrial sector concerned.

The EU Directive on Integrated Pollution Prevention and Control (IPPC) (see 1.12 below), requires competent authorities to ensure that "installations are operated in such a way that all the appropriate preventive measures are taken against pollution, in particular through the application of best available techniques . . ." This is defined as

> "the most effective and advanced stage in the development of activities and their methods of operation which indicates the practical suitability of particular techniques for providing in principle the basis for emission limit values designed to prevent and, where that is not practicable, generally to reduce emissions and the impact on the environment as a whole.
>
> - "available techniques" means those techniques which have been developed on a scale which allows implementation in the relevant industrial sector, under economically and technically viable conditions, taking into consideration the costs and advantages, whether or not the techniques are used or produced inside the Member State in question, as long as they are reasonably accessible to the operator;
>
> - "best" means, in relation to techniques, the most effective in achieving a high general level of protection of the environment as a whole;
>
> - "techniques" includes both the technology used and the way in which the installation is designed, built, maintained, operated and decommissioned."

This definition has been incorporated in the *Pollution Prevention and Control (England and Wales) Regulations 2000,* which came into force on 1 August 2000 (and similar in Scotland) (see 1.12.2 below). The European Commission is producing BAT Reference Documents (BREF Notes) defining BAT for the individual sectors covered by the IPPC Directive. The Environment Agency will then use these for producing IPPC guidance notes.

1.6.2 UK-BATNEEC

The *Environmental Protection Act 1990* requires the use of Best Available Techniques Not Entailing Excessive Cost (BATNEEC) to minimise releases from all Part A processes (prescribed for Integrated Pollution Control) and Part B processes (prescribed for air pollution control) - see Appendix 1.1.

Integrated Pollution Control: A Practical Guide published by the Department of Environment and Welsh Office in 1993 and updated in 1996 defines BATNEEC as follows:

Best means most effective in preventing, minimising or rendering harmless polluting releases. There may be more than one set of techniques that achieves comparable effectiveness - i.e. there may be more than one set of "best" techniques.

Available should be taken to mean procurable by the operator of the process in question. It does not imply that the technique has to be in general use, but it does require general accessibility. It includes a technique which has been developed (or proven) at pilot scale provided this allows its implementation in the relevant industrial context with the necessary business confidence. It does not imply that sources outside the UK are "unavailable". Nor does it imply a competitive supply market. If there is a monopoly supplier the technique counts as being available provided that the operator can procure it.

Techniques embrace both the plant in which the process is carried on and how the process is operated. It should be taken to mean the components of which it is made up and the manner in which they are connected together to make the whole. It also includes matters such as numbers and qualifications of staff, working methods, training and supervision and also the design, construction, lay-out and maintenance of buildings, and will affect the concept and design of the process.

Not Entailing Excessive Cost (NEEC) needs to be taken in two contexts, depending on whether it is applied to new processes or to existing processes.

So far as new processes are concerned, there will always be a presumption towards the use of BAT and BATNEEC, although the following principles should also be applied:

- the cost of the best available techniques must be weighed against the environmental damage from the process; the greater the environmental damage, the greater the costs of BAT that can be required before costs are considered excessive;

- the objective is to prevent damaging releases or to reduce such releases so far as this can be done without imposing excessive costs; if after applying BATNEEC serious harm would still result, the application can be refused; and

- as objective an approach as possible to the consideration of what is BATNEEC is required. The concern is with what costs in general are excessive; the lack of profitability of a particular business should not affect the determination.

With regard to existing processes, the main concern will be to establish timetables for upgrading to new plant standards, or as near as possible to such standards, or close down. Other factors to be taken into account for plant existing before July 1987 include:

- the plant's technical characteristics;
- its rate of utilisation and length of remaining life;
- the nature and volume of polluting emissions;
- the desirability of not entailing excessive cost for the plant concerned, having regard to the economic situation of undertakings belonging to the category in question.

The BATNEEC for specific processes is described in the process guidance notes for both Part A and Part B processes (listed in Appendices 1.3 and 2.1).

BATNEEC will be superseded by BAT (see above) as existing processes and new installations are permitted under the new Pollution Prevention and Control regime (see 1.12.2).

IMPLEMENTATION AND ENFORCEMENT AUTHORITIES

The main bodies involved in implementation and enforcement of pollution control legislation are given below, together with an outline of their responsibilities. More specific detail is given in the individual chapters.

1.7 ENVIRONMENT AGENCIES

Proposals for establishing independent environment agencies in England and Wales and in Scotland were published for consultation in 1991 and confirmed in July 1992. Such Agencies would, it was suggested, be better able to develop a consistent and cohesive approach to environmental protection across all media as envisaged by the implementation of Integrated Pollution Control and taking account of the principles of sustainable development. The Agencies, which formally took over their pollution control and other functions on 1 April 1996, were established by the *Environment Act 1995*, Part I. The Act received Royal Assent on 19 July 1995. In exercising their powers, s.39 of the Act requires both Agencies to take into account the likely costs and benefits of exercising (or not exercising) a power.

1.7.1 Environment Agency, England & Wales

The Environment Agency (in Welsh - Asiantaeth yr Amgylchedd) took over the responsibilities of HM Inspectorate of Pollution, the National Rivers Authority and the waste regulatory functions of local authorities on 1 April 1996. It is a non-departmental public body; members of the board are appointed by the Secretary of State for the Environment, Transport and the Regions, the Secretary of State for Wales and by the Minister of Agriculture,

Fisheries and Food. The Agency's head office in Bristol is responsible for policies, standards, ensuring a consistent approach to environmental protection and overall financial control. There are eight regional offices arranged on the basis of water catchment areas for water management and political boundaries for pollution control and prevention and waste regulation; these latter have been drawn as close as possible to water catchment boundaries, using district rather than county boundaries where these provide a better match. In Wales, however, the boundary follows that of the Principality. The pollution control boundary is also the local "public face" of the Agency. Area offices within each region are largely responsible for the operational side of the Agency's work.

(a) Aims and Objectives (s.4)

The principal aim of the Agency in discharging its functions to protect and enhance the environment is to make a contribution towards "attaining the objective of achieving sustainable development" (s.4(1) of the Act); section 4(2) requires Ministers to give the Agency statutory guidance on its objectives (including guidance on its contribution to sustainable development) to which the Agency must have regard. This was formally issued in November 1996 and requires the Agency:

- to adopt, across all its functions, an integrated approach to environmental protection and enhancement which considers impacts of substances and activities on all environmental media and on natural resources;

- to work with all relevant sectors of society, including regulated organisations, to develop approaches which deliver environmental requirements and goals without imposing excessive costs (in relation to benefits gained) on regulated organisations or society as a whole;

- to adopt clear and effective procedures for serving its customers, including the development of single points of contact through which regulated organisations can deal with the Agency;

- to operate to high professional standards, based on sound science, information and analysis of the environment and processes which affect it;

- to organise its activities in ways which reflect good environmental and management practice and provide value for money for those who pay its charges and to taxpayers;

- to provide clear and readily available advice and information on its work;

- to develop a close and responsive relationship with the public, local authorities, representatives of local communities and regulated organisations.

In making a contribution towards the objective of attaining sustainable development the Agency should:

- take a holistic approach to the protection and enhancement of the environment;

- ensure that the longer term implications and effects of actions, particularly those which appear irreversible, or reversible at high cost over a long time, are fully taken into account;

- maintain biodiversity;

- protect the global atmosphere, having regard to UK commitments under the UN Convention on Climate Change and the Montreal Protocol;

- where possible, discharge its regulatory functions in partnership with business in ways which maximise the scope for cost-effective investment in improved technologies and techniques and encourage business to adopt high environmental objectives and standards;

- develop close and responsive relationships with all sectors of the community, maximising their contributions to the achievement of sustainable development;

- become a recognised centre of knowledge and expertise and provide readily accessible advice and information on its work and best environmental practice.

(b) Functions (ss.5-10)

In considering or formulating proposals relating to its functions (except pollution control - see next para) the Agency or Ministers should ensure that these will *further* the conservation and enhancement of natural beauty, flora and fauna etc (s.7(1)(a) of the Act).

In carrying out its pollution control responsibilities, the main objective is to prevent or minimise, remedy or mitigate the effects of pollution of the environment (s.5(1)); as well as ensuring it has sufficient information regarding the level, or potential level, of pollution of the environment, the Agency must also follow developments in technology and techniques for abating and preventing pollution or its effects. In formulating or considering proposals for pollution control the Agency or Ministers should have regard to the *desirability* of conserving and enhancing natural beauty, flora and fauna etc (s.7(1)(b)). Section 81 of the Act also requires the Environment Agency to have regard to the National Air Quality Strategy in discharging its pollution control functions.

With regard to water, the Agency also has a duty "to promote the conservation and enhancement of the natural beauty and amenity of inland and coastal waters ...; the conservation of flora and fauna ... dependent on an aquatic environment; and the use of such waters and land for recreational purposes."

(c) Pollution Control Responsibilities

- Authorisations, licences and consents for emissions, discharges and disposals to air, water and land; monitoring compliance and enforcement, including prosecutions under IPC and water legislation; permitting of installations and enforcement of

regulations under Integrated Pollution Prevention and Control (IPPC);

- Waste management licensing, including the registration of carriers; regulating the import and export of waste and control over the movement of waste, and the regulation of special waste; regulation of radioactive waste accumulation and disposal; assessing waste disposal needs and priorities; production of technical guidance on waste management;

- Regulation of contaminated land designated as "special sites"; report on the state of contaminated land and, as necessary, produce site-specific guidance for local authorities;

- Monitoring environmental conditions and publishing relevant statistics; research; advice to government in setting environmental quality and other standards and proposals for pollution prevention measures;

- Advice and guidance to industry and others on best environmental practice.

The Agency is also responsible for administering registration and exemption schemes for producer responsibility in accordance with regulations, and monitoring and enforcement of associated obligations (*Environment Act,* ss.93-95 - see chapter 4, 4.20.2). In 1998, the Environment Agency adopted a new Enforcement and Prosecution Policy ; as well as outlining the circumstances under which the Agency will normally prosecute, the document sets out the following general principles under which it operates in relation to enforcement and prosecution; these are:

- Firm but fair regulation;

- Proportionality: enforcement action should be proportionate to the risks posed to the environment and to the seriousness of any breach of the law;

- Consistency: while this is important, variables such as environmental impact and offending history can also be taken into account;

- Transparency - as to why enforcement action has been taken;

- Targeting - of regulatory effort at those areas presenting the greatest risk to the environment.

(d) Consultation (ss.8 & 11-14)

Under s.8 of the Act, the Nature Conservancy Council for England, the Countryside Council for Wales or National Park (or Broads) Authority should notify the Environment Agency of any sites of special interest which might be affected by any of the Agency's activities or an authorisation. Where such notification has been received, the Agency must consult the relevant body before carrying out or authorising the activity. The Agency is also required to consult certain bodies before issuing a permit, authorisation, or discharge consent (this chapter 1.13.1(b), 1.14.2(b) and chapter 5, 5.15.3(a), respectively).

The Agency is required to set up and consult Regional Environment Protection Advisory Committees (REPACs), Regional and Local Fisheries Advisory Committees and Regional Flood Defence Committees in England and Wales. Members of the REPAC will normally include a representative from the fisheries and flood defence committees, industry, local authorities, environmental organisations and persons with a particular interest in the air and land aspects of the Agency's work.

An Advisory Committee for Wales advises the Secretary of State on matters relating to the Agency's functions in Wales.

The Environment Agency and the local authority associations (now the Local Government Association) have signed a Memorandum of Understanding (1997) covering those aspects of environmental protection for which they both have some responsibility, these include: air quality; waste management and contaminated land; water resources and flood defence; planning; and information provision. Through the Memorandum, the parties are committed to

- making their workings as **transparent** as possible to each other;
- the free exchange of **information** for the discharge of their statutory responsibilities;
- the principle of **consultation**, both formal and informal, on any issue which affects the other;
- **cooperating** with each other at all levels for the well-being of the environment.

The Environment Agency has also signed (May 1998) a Memorandum of Understanding with the Association of Chief Police Officers; this aims to ensure effective cooperation during incidents in which the environment may be at risk of harm.

(e) Pollution Inventory

The Agency maintains an Inventory of over 150 pollutants released to air, water and land from the (approx.) 2,000 industrial sites it regulates in England and Wales. Operators of IPC processes are required to submit annual reports on releases of individual substances by 31 January of each year for the previous year. The Pollution Inventory, which can be accessed on www.environment-agency.gov.uk, enables the public to find out about pollution from industries in their own locality. The Inventory is to be extended to include data from other factories and sites the Agency regulates, including landfill and sewage treatment plants, and industries covered by IPPC.

The Agency will also need to collate data on emissions of 50 substances from installations covered by IPPC for inclusion in the European Pollutant Emission Register (EPER), which has been established under the IPPC

Directive (see 1.12). The first reports are due in June 2003 covering 2001.

1.7.2 Scottish Environment Protection Agency

Plans for establishing a Scottish Environment Protection Agency (SEPA) were also issued for consultation in 1991.

As from 1 April 1996 SEPA took over the responsibilities of HM Industrial Pollution Inspectorate, the River Purification Authorities and the Hazardous Waste Inspectorate; SEPA also took over responsibility from local authorities for waste regulation and for the control of industrial air pollution under Part I of the EPA; it is also responsible for the control of all installations regulated for Integrated Pollution Prevention and Control. For operational purposes, Scotland has been divided into three regions (West, East and North), each with a Regional Board to which SEPA may delegate certain functions subject to the approval of the Secretary of State. Regional boundaries have been based on river catchment areas and matched as far as possible with the boundaries of unitary authorities. SEPA's headquarters are in Stirling.

(a) Aims and Objectives

Under s.31 of the Act, the Secretary of State for Scotland will give SEPA Guidance, to which it must have regard, on the objectives to be pursued in carrying out its functions; this will include Guidance on SEPA's contribution to attaining the objective of sustainable development.

In considering or formulating proposals relating to its functions, SEPA and the Secretary of State have a duty to have regard to the desirability of conserving and enhancing the natural heritage of Scotland, and of protecting and enhancing buildings, sites and objects of interest (e.g. historic, architectural) and the effect which any proposals might have on the natural heritage etc (s.32).

In carrying out its pollution control responsibilities, the main objective is to prevent or minimise, remedy or mitigate the effects of pollution of the environment (s.33(1)); as well as ensuring it has sufficient information regarding the level, or potential level, of pollution of the environment, SEPA must also follow developments in technology and techniques for abating and preventing pollution or its effects. Section 81 of the Act also requires SEPA to have regard to the National Air Quality Strategy in discharging its pollution control functions.

With regard to water, SEPA has a duty (s.34) to promote the cleanliness of rivers, inland, ground and tidal waters in Scotland and to promote the conservation and enhancement of the natural beauty and amenity of inland and coastal waters and the conservation of flora and fauna dependent on an aquatic environment.

Where land has been designated as a Natural Heritage Area or Scottish Natural Heritage considers an area of land to be of special interest, and which could be affected by an activity or authorisation of SEPA, it should notify SEPA of the fact. Where SEPA has received such notification, it must consult Scottish Natural Heritage prior to carrying out or authorising any activity on the land in question (s.35). SEPA and SNH have signed a formal Memorandum of Understanding which sets out arrangements for the coordination of their respective activities.

(b) Pollution Control Responsibilities

These are similar to those outlined for the Environment Agency, with the addition of the regulation of Part B processes for air pollution under Part I of the *Environmental Protection Act 1990*. SEPA is also responsible for regulating all installations under the *Pollution Prevention and Control (Scotland) Regulations 2000*.

Arrangements will need to be made in Scotland for collecting emissions data as required by the Decision establishing the European Pollutant Emission Register (see 1.12 below).

1.8 NORTHERN IRELAND

The Department of Environment (Northern Ireland) has overall responsibility for environmental protection and pollution control, conservation, and historic buildings and monuments. It aims "to protect and conserve the natural and built environment and to promote its appreciation for the benefit of present and future generations".

On 26 November 1997 *The Industrial Pollution Control (Northern Ireland) Order 1997* (SI 2777, NI 18) was made. It introduces a system of pollution control similar to the IPC and air pollution control regimes operating in the rest of the UK, although there are three tiers of control:

- "integrated central control": Part A processes with high pollution potential are regulated for IPC by the Industrial Pollution and Radiochemical Inspectorate (IPRI) within the DOE(NI); the IPRI is also responsible for control, disposal and transport of radioactive substances;

- "restricted central control": Part B processes with the potential to cause serious air pollution will be regulated for air pollution control, also by the IPRI;

- "local control" Part C processes with significant but less potential for air pollution will be regulated for air pollution control by district councils.

The Northern Ireland Order, and subsequent Regulations, are referred to as appropriate in the section on Integrated Pollution Control in this chapter (see 1.14), and in the section on local air pollution control in chapter 2 (see 2.12). The Regulations implementing the new legislation came into force on 2 March 1998; new processes were required to apply for an authorisation immediately; existing processes will transfer to the new regulatory regime by sector, with the final group required to apply for an authorisation by 31 December 2002.

Arrangements will need to be made in Northern Ireland for collecting emissions data as required by the Decision establishing the European Pollutant Emission Register (see 1.12 below).

1.9 LOCAL AUTHORITIES

Local authorities - usually environmental health departments or pollution control departments - have a wide range of responsibilities covering the whole spectrum of pollution control and environmental protection; these are detailed in the individual chapters of this book.

The local authority associations (now the Local Government Association) and the Environment Agency have signed a Memorandum of Understanding (1997) covering those areas of environmental protection for which they both have some responsibility - see 1.7.1(d) above.

The Public Health (Control of Disease) Act 1984 gives Port Health Authorities which have been constituted as a Port Health District similar responsibilities and powers to local authorities for legislation relating to public health and the control of pollution (including Part B processes under the *Environmental Protection Act 1990* and Part B installations under the *Pollution Prevention and Control (England and Wales) Regulations 2000*.

1.10 HEALTH AND SAFETY EXECUTIVE

The HSE, which is the executive arm of the Health and Safety Commission, is also involved with pollution legislation in that it enforces health and safety law for the majority of industrial premises for the protection of both the workforce and the general public. It operates mainly under the *Health and Safety at Work etc Act 1974* and regulations arising from the Act, e.g. the *Control of Substances Hazardous to Health Regulations 1999* (see chapter 2) and the *Noise at Work Regulations 1989* (see chapter 3). The HSE is also the licensing authority for nuclear installations (see chapter 4).

The HSE and the Environment Agency have signed a formal agreement which aims to minimise duplication in the regulation of industrial processes. HSE regulates industrial processes to protect workers and for safety issues.

1.11 BRITISH STANDARDS INSTITUTION

The BSI is an independent national organisation incorporated by Royal Charter. Through a Memorandum of Understanding with the Government, it is the national standards making body and produces all national standards. These include product and performance specifications, codes of practice, management systems, methods of testing, measurement, analysis and sampling, guides and glossaries. These standards are voluntary unless quoted in legislation, in which case they become mandatory. BSI also tests goods and services for industry and government.

The BSI has for some time participated in the work of the International Standards Organisation (ISO) and many ISO standards have been adopted as parallel British Standards. More recently there has been a shift in focus to European work, and the European Committee for Standardisation (CEN). Once a European Standard has been agreed, the BSI adopts it as a dual-numbered BS and withdraws any conflicting British Standards. Whilst it is not currently mandatory for UK bodies to use the European Standards, it is strongly advisable to do so as this provides a means of ensuring compliance with relevant European Directives.

INTEGRATED POLLUTION PREVENTION AND CONTROL

1.12 EU DIRECTIVE 96/61/EC

On 24 September 1996, EU Environment Ministers formally adopted a Directive on Integrated Pollution Prevention and Control (96/61/EC). It came into force on 30 October 1996 and had to be implemented by 30 October 1999 when it applied to all new installations and those undergoing a substantial change. Existing installations (i.e. operating before 31 October 1999 or for which an authorisation existed or had been requested and the installation was brought into operation by 31 October 2000) must comply with the Directive by 31 October 2007. Existing installations wishing to carry out a substantial negative change (i.e. one with significant negative effects on human beings or the environment) between implementation of the Directive and 31 October 2007 must apply for a permit covering that part of the installation to be substantially changed.

The main purpose of the IPPC Directive is "to achieve integrated prevention and control of pollution" from listed activities. This is to be done by preventing, or where that is not practicable, reducing emissions to the air, water and land by potentially polluting industrial and other installations "so as to achieve a high level of protection of the environment taken as a whole".

Annex I to the Directive lists the industrial activities to which the Directive applies; these are: energy industries; production and processing of metals; mineral industry; chemical industry; waste management; and other activities. This latter category includes pulp production, paper and board production, pretreatment or dyeing of fibres, tanning, slaughterhouses and disposal of animal carcases, various food processes and intensive poultry and pig rearing installations.

An application for a permit must be made to the competent authority (i.e. enforcing authority); where there is more than one "competent authority" (e.g. Environment Agency and local authorities), steps must be taken to ensure an integrated approach to the procedure for granting a permit. Conditions attached to the permit will relate to the operation of the plant, including emission limit values for certain substances and preparations listed in Annex III to the Directive based on best available techniques (BAT) (see 1.6.1 above); local environmental conditions, geographical location and other technical characteristics must be taken into account; other conditions should cover consumption of raw materials, energy efficiency, heat, noise, light and vibration, accident prevention, and waste management practices to avoid pollution following closure of the site. Permit conditions should ensure that there will be no breach of EU environmental quality standards or other EU legislation and ensure "a high level of protection for the environment taken as a whole". The permit must also contain monitoring requirements, specifying measurement methodology and frequency. Permits should be reviewed periodically and where necessary updated in line with BAT or to tighten permit conditions for various reasons. The Directive allows for Member States to use "general binding rules" as an alternative to individually tailored conditions. Public consultation requirements and access to permits and other data are similar to those under Part I of the *Environmental Protection Act 1990*.

Technical Guidance - or "Best Available Techniques Reference Documents" - are currently being drafted on behalf of the Commission and, once finalised, must be taken into account by competent authorities. BREFs for the following sectors have now been finalised: iron and steel (03/00), cement and lime (03/00), non-ferrous metals (05/00) and pulp and paper manufacture (07/00); final drafts are available for industrial cooling systems, chlor-alkali production, ferrous metal processing and the manufacture of glass. Further information can be found on the website of the Euro IPPC Bureau - http://eippcb.jrc.es. The Bureau has been established to ensure full exchange of information between Member States on BAT.

European Pollutant Emission Register

A Decision establishing the Register, which is required under the IPPC Directive, was approved in July 2000. Member States are required to collect data from IPPC facilities* on emissions of 50 substances present in quantities above specified thresholds; data for 2001 (or 2002 or 2003 if unavailable for 2001) must be sent to the Commission by June 2003; the Register is to be updated every three years, with emissions data for 2004 required in June 2006. Information on the Register is to be publicly available.

*This is defined as an "industrial complex with one or more installations on the same site where one operator carries out one or more [IPPC] activities".

1.13 POLLUTION PREVENTION CONTROL ACT 1999

This Act, which received Royal Assent on 27 July 1999 enables Regulations to be made implementing the 1996 EU Directive on Integrated Pollution Prevention and

Control (IPPC) - see next section. In so doing, it provides for the repeal of Part I of the *Environmental Protection Act 1990* which covers Integrated Pollution Control and Local Air Pollution Control - this will be done once all existing IPC and LAPC processes have transferred to control under the *Pollution Prevention and Control (England and Wales) Regulations 2000* (PPCR) and similar for Scotland.

The PPC Act also makes provision for waste licences issued under the *Control of Pollution Act 1974* and which had expired to be treated as though they were still in force (see chapter 4, 4.19.3), and for improved environmental regulation of off-shore gas and oil installations (see chapter 5).

1.13.1 Pollution Prevention and Control Regulations 2000

(England & Wales: SI 1973; Scotland: SSI 323)

The Regulations for England and Wales were brought into force on 1 August 2000, with the similar Regulations for Scotland coming into force on 28 September 2000; implementation of the Regulations belatedly fulfils the requirement to transpose the EU's IPPC Directive into national legislation, which should have been done by 31 October 1999.

The Regulations apply to all installations, including mobile plant, carrying out an activity listed in Annex 1 to the Directive. These are listed in Schedule 1 to the Regulations and are further categorised as A1 and A2 (Scotland: Part A)*; the Schedule has not been reproduced in this edition of the Handbook but can be accessed on The Stationery Office legislation website – www.legislation.hmso.gov.uk/si/si2000/20001973. Installations carrying out A1 activities, which include many of those currently regulated under Part I (IPC) and II (waste) of the EPA, as well as intensive farming units and food industries, are regulated by the Environment Agency in England and Wales; installations carrying out A2 activities - mainly those currently regulated for LAPC - are regulated by local authorities. Where a site consists of a single installation carrying out A1, A2 and Part B activities, it will normally be permitted as an A1 installation by the Environment Agency. Similarly installations carrying out A2 activities and a directly related non-IPPC waste management activity licensed under Part II of the EPA, will also be regulated by the Environment Agency. Installations with both Part A2 and B activities will be permitted as A2 installations by the local authority. Non-IPPC waste management activities at Part B installations will continue to be licensed by the Environment Agency and the Part B installation by the local authority.

[* Note: In **Scotland** all installations and mobile plant are regulated by the Scottish Environment Protection Agency. Schedule 1 attached to the Scottish Regulations therefore lists Part A activities to be regulated for IPPC and Part B activities for air pollution control.]

Part A2 installations and mobile plant in England and Wales are regulated by the local authority in whose area they are, or will be situated or (mobile plant) operated. Part B installations in England and Wales are regulated by the local authority in whose area they are or will be situated; Part B mobile plant are normally regulated by the local authority in which the operator has his principal place of business. Where the principal place of business is outside England and Wales and the plant has not yet been operated in England and Wales, the Regulator will be the local authority in which it first operated, or in whose area it is intended to first operate; or where the plant is already covered by a permit, the local authority which first granted the permit. (Regulation 8(5)).

The Secretary of State may direct (regs.8(6)-(7)) that responsibility for an A2 or Part B installation in England or Wales be transferred to the Environment Agency in respect of a specific installation ("specific direction") or a general class of installation ("general direction"). In the former case, the Secretary of State should notify the Agency, local authority and operator of the installation concerned, and in the latter case the Agency and all local authorities; the notice, which should also be advertised in the London Gazette and locally, should include the date on which the Direction takes effect and, where appropriate, its duration. Regulation 8(8) enables the Secretary of State to direct that responsibility for an installation comprising A1 and A2 activities or A2 and waste management activities be transferred to local authorities.

The Regulations follow the Directive's definition of an installation as

(i) a stationary technical unit where one or more activities listed in Part 1 of Schedule 1 are carried out; and

(ii) any other location on the same site where any other directly associated activities are carried out which have a technical connection with the activities carried out in the stationary technical unit and which could have an effect on pollution.

New or substantially changed installations in England and Wales (i.e. those brought into operation or undergoing substantial change on or after 31 October 1999) had to apply for IPPC permits within five months of the Regulations taking effect – i.e. before 1 January 2001; in Scotland such installations have until 1 April 2001 to apply for a permit. Existing installations (in operation before 31 October 1999, or for which an authorisation was granted or requested before 31 October 1999 and brought into operation before 31 October 2000) are being phased in by sector between December 2000 and March 2007 (Sc: 2001-2007), in accordance with the timetable in Schedule 3 to the Regulations. Exceptions to this are:

- where it is proposed to make a "substantial change" - defined by the Directive as "a change in operation which in the opinion of the competent authority may have significant negative effects on human beings or the environment"; an application for a permit should be made ahead of the phase-in date for the sector for that part of the installation affected by the change.

- where an installation is comprised of two IPPC linked activities - i.e. one activity depends on the other for its operation - with different phase-in dates; an application for a permit should be made at the earlier date. However an operator may apply to the Regulator for the phase-in date to be that of the primary activity undertaken (Sch.3, Part 1, para 2(4) & (5).

- where an operator of IPC or LAPC processes on a single site, but with different phase-in dates, wishes to bring both within PPC at the same time under a single permit.

The PPC Regulations also apply to, and list (also in Schedule 1), Part B installations - these are largely those prescribed under current EPA regulations, but which are not required to be regulated for IPPC. These will continue to be regulated for air pollution, in England and Wales by local authorities and in Scotland by SEPA. Existing Part B installations and mobile plant in England and Wales will transfer to PPC between 1 April 2002 and 1 April 2004 – Sch. 3, para 10(1) specifies the relevant date – and will be permitted on the basis of "deemed applications"; in such instances the Regulator will notify the operator within two months of the date of the deemed application that it has been made and the conditions to be attached. Deemed applications will be determined within 12 months of the date on which they are deemed to have been made; where the Regulator fails to determine the application within that period, and the applicant notifies the Regulator in writing that he treats the failure as such, then the application is deemed to have been refused. The operator will have the usual right of appeal to the Secretary of State if he does not agree with the conditions being imposed. In **Scotland** the relevant date for Part B installations and mobile plant is 31 December 2002 (Sch. 3, para 10).

Operators of new (i.e. E & W: brought into operation on or after the relevant date in Sch. 3, para 10(1); Sc: 31 December 2002) Part B installations or mobile plant should apply for a PPC Permit in accordance with the timetable for existing Part B installations.

The Offshore Combustion Installations (Prevention and Control of Pollution) Regulations, a draft of which was issued in January 2000, will implement the IPPC Directive for offshore combustion installations with an aggregate thermal input exceeding 50 MW. The Regulations, which cover the whole of the United Kingdom, will require existing installations to apply for a permit by 30 October 2007. The Regulations are within the remit of the Department of Trade and Industry.

Guidance

The Environment Agency has produced a "Regulatory Package" aimed at providing guidance to applicants on preparing and submitting applications for Part A1 installations; this contains:

- **Application form** covering permits, variations, transfers and surrenders;

- **Guide for applicants** including step by step help on completing the application form;

- **Sectoral technical guidance** – this is still being developed for each sector but will provide important advice on determining BAT; it will provide an inventory of emissions resulting from proposed techniques and how to assess the impact of those emissions on the environment.

- **General technical guidance** for use when no sectoral guidance is available; and also includes advice on those aspects of the IPPC requirements which have not formed part of the IPC application process, such as energy efficiency, noise and vibration, accident and environmental management systems.

- **Guidance on the preparation of site reports;**

- **Permit template**.

The Agency is to prepare statutory Guidance Notes for each sector which will be based on the BAT Reference Notes now being drafted by the European Commission. As well as defining the Best Available Techniques for the sector concerned, they will include indicative standards for both new and existing installations, with a timetable for upgrading for the latter. The Regulator will, however, need to justify setting a condition which is significantly different from the indicative standard. The Guidance will be amended and updated as appropriate to reflect new developments in technology. Generic guidance covering such issues as energy efficiency, site remediation and noise is also being drafted for use by Regulators in permitting new installations and those applying for a substantial change; in addition it is suggested that Regulators will still be able to use the guidance in the current IPC and LAPC Guidance Notes.

The DETR's *Integrated Pollution Prevention and Control – A Practical Guide*, a first edition of which was published in July 2000, provides guidance on how the Regulations should be interpreted in applying for a permit and the issues to be aware of or taken into consideration in making an application. A second edition of the Guide is to be published early in 2001. SEPA has published a similar guide for use in Scotland.

(a) Application for a Permit (Reg.7-9 & Sch.4, Part 1)

An application for a PPC permit to operate an existing installation or mobile plant should be made on the relevant form to the appropriate Regulator during the three month period prescribed in the Regulations (Sch.3; there are some differences between E+W and Scotland); it should be accompanied by the prescribed fee (A1 - *Environment Act*, s.41 - see 1.15.1(b) or A2 - E&W reg.22, of PPCR). The Regulations allow applications to be submitted electronically with the permission of the Regulator. For new installations, the *IPPC Practical Guide* suggests that an application for a permit be submitted prior to the start of construction, thus ensuring that operational and management techniques meet the requirements of the Regulations. For novel or very complex installations, it is suggested that a "staged" application procedure be used; the use of this procedure must be agreed with the Regulator beforehand, with applications submitted at the design stage of each phase of the construction. The applicant will still need to submit a consolidated version of all the applications for determination.

Where different parts of an installation are run by different operators, each will need to apply for a permit covering their part of the installation.

The application, in demonstrating that adequate environmental management systems are in place, should include the following information (with similar requirements in Scotland):

- All applications: full details of the operator (including name, address, ultimate holding company, registered office etc), and for a Part A installation or mobile plant - address, national grid reference, map or plan showing the site - and, for an installation, its location on the site, together with the name and address of any local authority in which the installation is situated.

- Part B mobile plant – name and address of local authority in which operator has his principal place of business, or if this is outside England and Wales, the local authority in which the plant was first operated in England and Wales, or if it has not yet been operated in England and Wales, the local authority in which it is first intended to operate it.

- Part A installation and mobile plant: report on the condition of the site, identifying any substances in, on, or under the site which might pose a pollution risk; care must be taken in the preparation of this report as contamination identified on closure of the site and not recorded on the earlier report will be assumed to have occurred during operations on the site. The Agency is to produce guidance on characterisation and assessment of sites.

- All applications: description of the installation or mobile plant - the scheduled activities to be carried out.*

- Part A: raw and auxiliary materials, other substances and energy to be used or generated in carrying on the activity.*

- All applications: nature, quantities and sources of likely emissions to each environmental medium (Part B to air only) and possible significant effects on the environment. For a Part A installation emissions are defined as "direct or indirect release of substances, vibrations, heat or noise ... into the air, water or land"; for a Part B installation emissions are defined as "the direct or indirect release of substances or heat ... into the air" (Reg.2).*

- All applications: technology and techniques to be used to prevent, or if this is not practicable, to reduce emissions.*

- All applications: proposals for monitoring emissions.

- Part A: measures to be taken for prevention and recovery of waste generated by the operation of the installation.

- Part A: relevant information obtained as a result of carrying out an environmental assessment in accordance with EU Directive 85/337 on the assessment of the effects of certain public and private projects on the environment (see 1.24.1).

- Part A: any additional information which the applicant wishes the Regulator to take into account in considering the application.

- All applications: where the permit is to authorise a specified waste management activity, any additional information which the applicant wishes the Regulator to take into account in considering whether the applicant is a fit and proper person as defined in, and required by, Regulation 4.

- All applications: where the permit is to cover an installation or mobile plant for which there are general binding rules (see d below), whether the applicant wishes the permit to be based on these or for specific conditions regarding its operation to be included on the permit.

- Part A: a non-technical summary of the application.

*Instead of these details, applications for waste oil burners less than 0.4 MW should give full details of the type of appliance to be used, fuel to be used, height and location of any chimney through which waste gases will be carried away and their efflux velocity, and the location of the fuel storage tanks for the appliance (Sch.4, para 3).

The Regulator has four months (or longer as agreed) in which to determine the application, beginning with the date on which the application was received; this period will normally begin when the Regulator accepts the application as being "duly made" – i.e. it is complete and has all the information the Regulator requires for making a determination; exceptions to this are (Sch.4, paras 4 & 15)

- applications referred to the Secretary of State – see below;
- if the Regulator requests additional information, the four month period will begin on the date on which the further information is received.
- where a person has been consulted over off-site conditions, the four month period will begin after the period allowed for representations;
- where issues of commercial confidentiality or national security have been determined, the four month period will begin after the 28 day period allowed for advertising the application (which itself begins 14 days after the issue has been decided).

Within 28 days (beginning 14 days after making the application) the applicant should publish details of the application in one or more local newspapers covering the area in which the installation is located, and for a Part A installation or mobile plant in the *London Gazette* (*Edinburgh Gazette*, as appropriate) as well. The advertisement should state where the application can be inspected and that any views on the application should be sent in writing to the Regulator within 28 days of the date of the advertisement; it should also note that any representations received will be put in the public register unless a request is made that they should not. Applications for waste oil burners less than 0.4 megawatts or the unloading of petrol at service stations do not have to be advertised (Sch.4, paras 5-8).

Copies of all applications will be put in the public register (E&W: Reg.29 & Sch.9; Sc: Reg.27 & Sch.9). An applicant may, however, request that certain information is excluded on the grounds of commercial confidentiality (Reg.31; Sc: Reg.29); the Regulator has 28 days in which to determine the request but if he fails to do so within that period, it is deemed not to be commercially confidential (Reg.31(4); Sc: Reg.29(4)), but will not be entered in the register for 21 days following notification to the applicant. The applicant has a right of appeal during that period with information subject to appeal not entered in the Register until seven days after determination or withdrawal of the appeal. Requests for exclusion on the grounds of national security are determined by the Secretary of State.

(b) Determination of Application (E & W: Reg.10; Sc: Reg.7. Sch.4, Part 2)

Within 14 days of receiving an application for a permit, the Regulator should send a copy of it to all statutory consultees, who have 28 days in which to make any representations to the Regulator. The following are statutory consultees for Part A installations and mobile plant:

- The Health authority in which the installation or mobile plant is to be operated;
- The Food Standards Agency;
- Where an emission may affect an SSSI, the Nature Conservancy Council for England, the Countryside Council for Wales, or Scottish Natural Heritage, as appropriate;
- Sewerage undertaker, harbour authority, local fisheries committee (E&W), as appropriate - i.e. where the installation may involve the release of a substance affecting their area of responsibility;
- The Environment Agency in respect of applications for A(2) installations; the relevant local authority in respect of A(1) applications (E&W). The local authority in which the installation is situated (Scotland only).
- The relevant planning authority, in respect of applications involving a waste management activity (E&W);

- The Secretary of State for Wales if the installation or mobile plant is to be operated in Wales.

The Health and Safety Executive should be consulted in respect of permit applications for both Part A and B installations for which a nuclear site licence (see chapter 4, 4.31.1) or major accident prevention policy document (under the COMAH Regulations – see 2.16.1) is required. The Regulations also enable the Secretary of State/Scottish Ministers to direct that other persons should be consulted.

The Nature Conservancy Council for England, Countryside Council for Wales, Scottish Natural Heritage should also be consulted in respect of applications for a Permit covering a Part B installation where an emission to air could have an adverse effect on an SSSI. The relevant Petroleum Licensing Authority should be consulted in respect of Part B applications covering the unloading of petrol at petrol stations.

Applications for permits in respect of waste oil burners under 0.4 megawatts do not have to be sent to statutory consultees (Sch.4, para 10).

Where it is proposed to issue a permit which includes off-site conditions (Sch.4, para 11), the Regulator should by notice consult the owner, lessee or occupier of the land; again 28 days should be allowed for representations.

The Secretary of State has the right to call in certain classes of, or individual, applications for determination (Sch.4, para 14); in such cases the Regulator should inform the applicant that his application has been forwarded to the Secretary of State, together with any representations received. Both the applicant and the Regulator may request a hearing; a request for a hearing should be made in writing within 21 days of being informed that the application has been forwarded to the Secretary of State. Such applications will then be considered by the Secretary of State who will then direct the Regulator as to whether a permit should be granted and, if so, with what conditions.

Where the Secretary of State becomes aware that the operation of an installation is likely to have significant negative effects on the environment of another Member State, he should send a copy of the permit application to the Member State concerned to enable bi-lateral consultations to take place. The application should be forwarded to the Member State at the time it is advertised (or as soon as possible after becoming aware of the likely effects of the installation, or when requested by the Member State). In those cases where an application has not been forwarded to the Secretary of State for determination, he should advise both the Regulator and the applicant that the permit application has been forwarded to another Member State. The four month determination period does not then begin until completion of the bi-lateral consultations; any representations made by another Member State must be taken into account when determining the application. (Sch.4, paras 17 & 18)

(c) Permits (E&W: Reg.9-15; Sc: Reg.6-11)

In determining an application for a permit, the Regulator must take into account whether the applicant will operate the installation or mobile plant in accordance with the permit and any conditions attached to it. If the permit is to authorise a waste management activity, the Regulator must be satisfied that the applicant is a "fit and proper person" - this is defined in Reg. 4 and is similar to s.74 of the *Environmental Protection Act 1990* (see chapter 4, 4.19.8 of this Handbook).

An application for a permit should be refused if the Regulator is of the opinion that

- the installation will have an unacceptable environmental impact;
- poor management systems, or lack of technical competence, will result in non-compliance with the permit or its conditions;
- where the permit covers a specified waste management activity, that this will not be in the hands of a fit and proper person.

All permits and conditions attached thereto must ensure that the installation will be operated in such a way as to ensure no significant pollution is caused and that all necessary preventative measures against pollution are taken; there is an implied condition in all permits that operators will use the Best Available Techniques (see 1.6 above) to prevent or reduce emissions. The BAT for an installation will take account of both technical and operational matters. When considering technical issues, the geographical location and local environmental conditions will be of relevance; so far as the operation of the plant is concerned, while not a mandatory requirement, certification to a recognised environmental management system such as ISO 14001 or the EU's Eco-Management and Audit Scheme will be evidence that the installation will be run satisfactorily. Schedule 2 to the PPC Regulations lists the issues to be taken into consideration in defining BAT for the installation, with further guidance, including basic principles for determining BAT, provided in the *IPPC Practical Guide* (DETR, 2000). Further guidance on BAT is to be provided in the forthcoming sectoral guidance.

It should be noted that despite not being explicitly included, as in BATNEEC, the costs and benefits of a particular technique should be taken into account when deciding on the best available technique.

For Part A installations and mobile plant, conditions should also ensure

- energy is used efficiently;
- waste production is avoided in accordance with the framework Directive on waste (see chapter 4, 4.6) or where waste is produced it is recovered or, if that is not possible, is disposed of in such a way as to avoid any impact on the environment;

- measures are in place to prevent accidents and to limit their consequences; incidents or accidents which cause, or may cause, significant pollution must be reported to the Regulator without delay.
- transboundary pollution is minimised;
- protection of soil and groundwater and appropriate management of waste generated by the installation;
- suitable emissions monitoring equipment is in place; measurement methodology, frequency, and evaluation procedure should also be set out; the operator must provide the Regulator with data to enable compliance monitoring and provide regular reports on results of emissions monitoring;

All permits (A and B installations) will also include emission limit values (ELVs) for all pollutants likely to be emitted in significant quantities; these will be based on BAT and in the case of Part A installations will also take into account their potential to transfer pollution to another environmental medium. In setting an ELV account may also be taken of the technical characteristics of the installation, its geographical location and local environmental conditions. Conditions should also ensure no breach of EU environmental quality standards and thus where such legislation requires a stricter ELV, then this should be set. Account will also need to be taken of the effect of the installation's emissions on local air quality and the achievement of national air quality objectives.

In setting a condition regulating a discharge to water from an A(2) installation or mobile plant in England or Wales, the local authority must have regard to any notice from the Environment Agency specifying an emission limit value and may not include a less stringent value, though it may include a stricter one. However, in setting conditions relating to noise from A1 installations, the *IPPC Practical Guide* only notes that local authorities "have expertise in setting standards for noise control", although the Environment Agency must justify its reasons for not following local authority advice in respect of noise; it also suggests that conditions relating to the control of noise and vibration should be commensurate with the best practicable means. Activities at an installation regulated by the PPC regulations are exempt from statutory nuisance legislation; non-PPC regulated activities, e.g. barking dogs and burglar alarms, however, are not.

A Permit for a Part A installation or mobile plant may include an off-site condition requiring the operator to carry out work which requires consent from another person (e.g. the owner of the land); in such cases (which will have followed consultation) where rights have been granted to carry out the work, compensation may be payable (Sch. 6).

Permits are to be periodically reviewed (E&W: Reg.15; Sc: Reg.11) and, in particular, when

- developments in best available techniques make further emissions reductions feasible without imposing excessive costs;
- significant pollution from an installation requires

existing emissions limits to be reviewed;

- operational safety necessitates change in techniques to be used.

Permit conditions included to ensure compliance with the *Groundwater Regulations 1998* (chapter 5, 5.15.2b) should be reviewed every four years.

General Binding Rules (E & W: Reg.14; Sc: Reg.10)

The IPPC Directive permits Member States to make "general binding rules" (GBRs) which can be used instead of site-specific conditions, to permit certain types of installation and mobile plant which share a number of similar characteristics. This Regulation enables the Secretary of State (or Scottish Ministers) to make GBRs for Part A installations or mobile plant so long as he is satisfied that this will result in the operation of an installation under such rules providing the same "high level of environmental protection and integrated prevention and control of pollution" as if it were permitted using specific conditions. The Secretary of State may, by notice, also revoke or vary GBRs. GBRs are currently being developed for intensive pig and poultry installations and for parts of the food and drink processing industry; consultation documents are expected in early 2001.

In applying for a Permit, an operator of a Part A installation or mobile plant for which GBRs exist may request the Regulator to include in the Permit a "general binding rules condition" covering the operation of the installation or mobile plant; for Regulatory and enforcement purposes, GBRs are treated as though they are site-specific conditions. It should be noted that not all installations within a sector for which GBRs have been developed may be suitable for permitting in this way; for instance if the site is close to an SSSI or other sensitive location, site-specific conditions will need to be included.

In making, revoking or varying GBRs, the Secretary of State should, as well as serving a copy of the rules or notice of revocation or variation on the Environment Agency and local authority Regulators, endeavour to bring them to the attention of all operators in the sector concerned. He should also publish a notice in the London Gazette.

(d) Variations (E&W: Reg.17, Sch.7; Sc: Reg.13, Sch.7)

Before making any change to the operation of the installation, Regulation 16 (Sc: Reg.12) requires the operator to notify the Regulator of the planned change, giving 14 days' notice; this does not however apply if the operator intends to apply for his permit or the conditions to be varied under Reg.17 (Sc: Reg.13). Thus a Reg.16 (Sc: Reg 12) notification could be used for minor operational changes which will not result in a breach of the conditions of the permit. While not a requirement of the Regulations, the *IPPC Practical Guide* suggests that Regulators should acknowledge receipt of the notice, either sanctioning the change or requiring the operator to apply for a variation of his permit prior to carrying out the change. However, if nothing is heard from the Regulator, then the operator

may at the end of the 14 day period make the planned change.

For more substantial changes – i.e. one which may have significant negative effects on human beings or the environment - or if there is any doubt about the effect of the planned change in the operation of the installation, then application should be made to vary the permit.

Conditions attached to a permit may also be varied by the Regulator at any time - e.g. following periodic review of the Permit, to update to take account of new developments in BAT, or following notification from the operator that he is intending to make a change to the way in which the installation is operated; or an operator may apply to the Regulator to vary the conditions of a Permit.

An application to vary conditions of a permit should be made in writing to the Regulator and should be accompanied by the prescribed fee (A1: *Env. Act*, s.41 or A2: PPC Reg.22). It should include full details of the operator, the installation or mobile plant and the proposed changes, and an indication of the variations being requested. Where a substantial change is being proposed, a report in compliance with the 1985 EU environmental assessment Directive (as amended) should accompany the application.

Where the Regulator is proposing to vary the conditions of a permit, or an application to do so has been made, it should serve a variation notice on the operator (in the case of an application for variation, within 14 days of receiving it). This should specify the variations to be made and the date or dates on which they are to take effect. Where a variation fee has not already been paid (i.e. Regulator-instigated variations), the notice will also specify the fee to be paid and by when.

The operator should then advertise the application for variation, or proposed variation notice, in a local newspaper and in the case of a Part A installation in the *London Gazette* (*Edinburgh Gazette*, as appropriate) within 28 days of receiving the notification from the Regulator. The advertisement should include the name of the operator, address of the installation, brief details of activities carried on and proposed changes. It should say where the application or variation notice can be seen (i.e. the location of the public register) and that any representations should be made in writing to the Regulator within 28 days; it should also note that such representations will be put in the register unless a specific request is made that this should not be done. The Regulator will also, within 14 days, notify statutory consultees sending a copy of the application or proposed variation notice, inviting representations, also within 28 days.

Applications for variations or proposed variation notices in respect of waste oil burners under 0.4 MW do not have to be notified to statutory consultees or advertised unless the Regulator decides otherwise and notifies the operator of this; in which case the normal consultation procedure will be followed. Applications or proposed variation notices in respect of the unloading of petrol at service stations do not have to be advertised; and neither do those served to comply with a Direction from the Secretary of State, or those modifying a previous proposed variation notice.

Where the Regulator is proposing to include an off-site condition in the variation notice, it should, before serving the notice, notify the owner, lessee or occupier of the land; 28 days should be allowed for representations, which should then be considered by the Regulator before serving the variation notice.

The Secretary of State may direct the Regulator to forward a specific application, or class of application, for variation for his determination. The Regulator should notify the applicant that the application has been forwarded to the Secretary of State; both the applicant and the Regulator have 21 days to make a written request for a hearing. Once the Secretary of State has determined the application, he will notify the Regulator and, if approving the application, direct the Regulator as to the conditions to be included.

Applications for variations, except those forwarded to the Secretary of State, will normally be determined within four months of receipt - three months for those that do not require advertising or notifying to statutory consultees.

Where an application for variation is proposing a substantial change in the operation of an installation which is likely to have a significant negative effect on the environment of another Member State, the Secretary of State should send a copy of the application or proposed variation notice to the other Member State at the same time that it is advertised. Such applications will not then be determined until consultations with the Member State concerned have been completed, at which time the Regulator's four month determination period begins.

(e) Transfer of Permits (E&W: Reg.18; Sc: Reg.14)

Where it is proposed to transfer all or part of a permit to another operator, the current and future operators (the "proposed transferee") should make a joint application to the Regulator, together with the prescribed fee (A1 installations & mobile plant – *Env Act* 1995, s.41; A2 & B – PPCR, Reg. 22) giving full details of them both, and in the case of a partial transfer, a map or plan of the installation showing which parts are to be transferred.

The Regulator has two months, or longer if agreed with the applicants, to determine the request, which should only be agreed if the Regulator is sure that the proposed transferee will operate the installation (or part installation) in accordance with the permit and its conditions; where the transfer involves a waste management activity, the Regulator should be satisfied that the proposed transferee is a fit and proper person (Reg.4). Transfers of whole permits will be effected through the endorsement of the permit with the new operator's details; in the case of partial transfers, a new permit will be issued to the new

operator covering the transferred parts of the installation, with the original permit being returned to the first operator, endorsed to show the extent of the transfer.

Where a partial transfer is effected, it may be necessary for the conditions of the permit to be varied to reflect the new operating responsibilities.

(f) Application to Surrender a Permit (E&W: Reg.19-20; Sc: Reg.15-16)

If an operator ceases, or intends to cease, all or part of his operations at a Part A installation or mobile plant, he should make an application to the Regulator to surrender all or part of the permit. The application and appropriate fee should include full contact details of the operator and in the case of a partial surrender, a site map or plan identifying the surrender unit. A site report should accompany the application; this should identify any changes in the condition of the site from those reported at the time of applying for a permit, and a description of the steps taken to avoid any pollution risks or to return the site to a satisfactory state.

The Regulator has three months (or longer as agreed with the operator) in which to determine the application to surrender; if the Regulator is satisfied with the condition of the site and that no further steps to avoid any pollution risk need to be taken, it should by notice accept the application, stating the date on which surrender takes effect; if it is not satisfied, it should specify the further steps to be taken to return the site to a satisfactory condition. In the case of a partial surrender, the Regulator may vary the conditions attached to the permit to take account of the surrender. Failure to determine the surrender within the agreed period will be deemed a refusal if the applicant notifies the Regulator that he treats it as such.

Where an operator of a Part B installation or mobile plant ceases, or intends to cease, all or part of his activities, he should notify the Regulator of the surrender of all or part of his permit and the date on which it is to take effect. Such notification should include full contact details for the operator and, in the case of partial surrender, a site map or plan identifying that part affected by the surrender. Permits covering Part B installations or mobile plant surrendered or partially surrendered cease to have effect on the date of the notification, unless the Regulator notifies the applicant that it is of the opinion that it is necessary to vary the conditions of a permit which is only being partially surrendered. In this case the Regulator will serve a variation notice and the partial surrender will take effect from the date on which the varied conditions take effect.

(g) Revocation of Permits (E&W: Reg.21; Sc: Reg.17)

The Regulator may, by notice, revoke all or part of a permit, to take effect not less than 28 days after the date on which the notice was served; a partial revocation may apply to either the operation of part of the installation or to some of the activities carried on at the installation. The

Regulator may also serve a revocation notice in relation to a permit authorising specific waste management activities at an installation if it appears that those activities are no longer in the hands of a fit and proper person (because that person has been convicted of a relevant offence - see chapter 4, 4.19.8), or that the activity is no longer managed by a technically competent person.

As well as stating the date on which the revocation (or partial revocation) is to take effect, it should specify, in the case of partial revocation, the activity or operations covered by the revocation.

If the Regulator considers certain steps need to be taken at a Part A installation or mobile plant to avoid a pollution risk or to return the site to a satisfactory condition once operations have ceased or partially ceased because of a revocation notice, the notice should say so and specify the steps (not already required by conditions attached to the permit) to be taken. Those sections of a permit requiring specific action on cessation of operations remain in force until the Regulator is satisfied that the necessary remedial action has been taken and has issued a certificate to this effect.

A revocation notice may be withdrawn before the date on which it takes effect.

(h) Fees and Charges (E&W: Reg.22)

Regulation 22 enables the Secretary of State to make a scheme covering fees and charges for those installations regulated by local authorities - i.e. A2 and Part B installations, covering fees for permit applications, variations, transfers and surrenders, as well as subsistence charges. Non-payment of subsistence charges may result in revocation of a Permit. For the time being, fees for Part B processes will continue to be based on the scheme made under the *Environmental Protection Act 1990* (chapter 2, 2.12.4).

The Local Authority Permits for Part A Installations and Mobile Plant (England and Wales) Fees and Charges Scheme 2000 came into force on 2 August 2000, setting fees as follows for A2 installations:

• Application for permit*
Fee to local authority Regulator: £1,664 per activity;
Fee to Environment Agency if permit is to authorise discharge to controlled water: £645 per discharge.

• Subsistence charges (annual)*
Charge payable to local authority Regulator: £1.035 per permitted activities;
Charge payable to Environment Agency: 56% of annual charge that would be payable under a Consent to Discharge under Part III of the Water Resources Act 1991.

*Where Permit also covers a Part B activity, the fee or charge levied under the Environmental Protection Act 1990 is also payable.

• Variation of permit
Fee to local authority Regulator: £1,060;

Fee to Environment Agency if variation relates to discharge consent: £645.

• Transfer of permit (whole/partial)
Fee to local authority Regulator: £166/£499;
Fee to Environment Agency if relates to discharge consent: £65/£194.

• Surrender of permit
Fee to local authority Regulator: £499;
Fee to Environment Agency if relates to whole or partial surrender of discharge consent: £194.

Fees and charges for A1 installations (Sc: Part A) are levied under a scheme made under the *Environment Act 1995,* s.41 (see this chapter 1.15.1).

(i) Enforcement (E&W: Reg.23-25; Sc: Reg.18-20)

The Regulator may issue an **enforcement notice** if he is of the opinion that an operator is not complying with his Permit or its conditions. The notice should state the contravention – or potential contravention - the remedial steps to be taken, and the period within which this must be done. The notice may be withdrawn at any time.

If the Regulator is of the opinion that the operation of an installation or mobile plant, or the way in which it is being operated, involves a serious risk of pollution, he can issue a suspension notice (see also next section (j)). A **suspension notice** may also be issued on the operator of an installation or mobile plant if the Regulator is of the opinion that he is no longer a fit and proper person on the grounds that waste management activities have ceased to be in the hands of a technically competent person. The notice should detail the pollution risk involved in operating the installation, the remedial action and the period within which this should be done. The notice should also state that, until the notice is withdrawn, the permit ceases to authorise the operation of the installation or the carrying out of specified activities; where the permit is to continue to have effect, the notice will authorise the carrying out of certain activities and specify the additional steps to be taken in carrying them out.

A suspension notice will be withdrawn once the steps taken to remove the pollution risk have been taken or in the case of waste management activities, they are back in the hands of a technically competent person.

(j) Powers to Remedy or Prevent Pollution
(E&W: Reg.26; Sc: Reg.21)

The Regulator may, if he is of the opinion that an emergency situation exists, take steps to deal with any serious risk of pollution instead of issuing a suspension notice, recovering the costs from the operator of the installation concerned. If the operator can show that the situation did not warrant emergency action being taken by the operator, no costs are recoverable.

The Regulator may also take action to deal with any pollution caused by an offence under Reg.32 (Sc: Reg.30)

- see below (m) Offences, having given the operator seven days' notice. Costs are recoverable from the operator.

(k) Appeals (E&W: Reg.27 & Sch.8; Sc: Reg.22 & Sch.8)

There is a right of appeal to the Secretary of State/Scottish Ministers in the following instances - any appeal should be made within six months of the decision being appealed against:

- refusal of permit or disagreement with conditions attached to it;
- refusal to vary conditions of a permit or disagreement with variation notice;
- rejection of transfer application; or disagreement with variation of conditions as a result of the transfer;
- rejection of surrender application, or disagreement with variation of conditions attached to Permit following partial surrender.

An appeal may also be made against the following:

- revocation notice - before the date on which the notice takes effect; revocation notices do not take effect until the appeal has been determined or withdrawn;

- variation, enforcement and suspension notices - within two months of the date of the notice; these notices are not suspended pending the outcome of an appeal.

There is no right of appeal against a notice or decision implementing a Direction from the Secretary of State/Scottish Ministers.

The appeals procedure, including the Secretary of State's (Scottish Ministers) right to appoint someone else to determine the appeal under s.114 & Sch.20 of the *Environment Act 1995* - is similar to that under IPC - see later this chapter, 1.14.2(h).

(l) Public Registers (E&W: Reg.29-31; Sc: Reg. 27-29. Sch. 9)

As with IPC and LAPC, the Regulators have a duty to maintain public registers containing details of applications for permits, permits, variations, transfers and surrenders of permits, appeals, enforcement, revocation and suspension notices etc. Local authority registers will also include details of permits etc relating to installations or mobile plant in their area for which the Environment Agency is the Regulator. The Regulations relating to the operation of the registers are similar to those for registers operating under the *Environmental Protection (Applications, Appeals and Registers) Regulations 1991,* as amended - see this chapter, 1.14.2(a) & (i), but with one major difference: where a request has been made that certain information be omitted from the register on the grounds of commercial confidentiality and the Regulator fails to determine the request within 28 days (or an agreed longer period), then the request is deemed to have been refused. If the Regulator refuses a request for confidentiality (or it is deemed to have been refused), the applicant has 21 days in which to appeal to the Secretary of State.

The Secretary of State may direct that specific information or information related to specific issues should not be put on the Register in the interests of national security. Regulators should notify the Secretary of State of any such information they exclude from the Register. He may also direct that information related to certain issues affecting national security be referred to him for decision on inclusion on the Register. An operator may also apply to the Secretary of State for information to be excluded on grounds of national security.

(m) Offences (E&W: Reg.32; Sc: Reg.30)

It is an offence to operate an installation without a permit, in contravention of a permit or of its conditions, to fail to comply with the terms of an enforcement or suspension notice, or to fail to comply with a court order requiring remedial action following conviction. Summary conviction in these cases may result in a fine not exceeding £20,000 and/or six months' imprisonment. Conviction on indictment may result in a fine and/or up to five years' imprisonment, depending on the offence.

Other offences, such as giving misleading or false information to the Regulator, making false entries in any records which are required to be kept, forging documents etc, may result in a fine not exceeding the statutory maximum on summary conviction, or a fine and/or up to two years' imprisonment on conviction on indictment.

(n) Information, Directions and Guidance (E&W: Reg.28, 36-37; Sc: Reg.26, 23-24)

The Secretary of State may, by notice, require the Regulator to furnish him with such information as he may require to discharge his obligations in relation to European Community or international agreements.

Directions from the Secretary of State/Scottish Ministers to Regulators may relate to any aspect of their functions under the Regulations; they may be either general or specific and may direct them as to the way in which they are or are not to exercise their powers.

Where the Secretary of State receives information from another Member State in relation to the operation of an installation outside the UK which is likely to have significant negative effects on the environment in England or Wales, he should direct the Environment Agency to bring it to the attention of anyone likely to be affected, providing those people with an opportunity to comment. (A similar arrangement applies in Scotland.)

Regulators have a duty to comply with any Directions, which should be in writing, and which may be varied or revoked by further Direction.

The Secretary of the State/Scottish Ministers may also issue Guidance to the Regulators relating to the carrying out of any of their functions under the Regulations; Regulators are required to have regard to any such Guidance.

1.14 ENVIRONMENTAL PROTECTION ACT, PART I

Proposals for an integrated approach to pollution control were first put forward by the Royal Commission on Environmental Pollution in their fifth report (*Air Pollution Control: An Integrated Approach; 1976*). The report drew attention to the cross-media movement of pollution, and the case was also made for a unified inspectorate "to ensure an integrated approach to difficult industrial problems at source, whether these affect air, water or land". Various consultation papers reviewing the control of air pollution and the establishment of HM Inspectorate of Pollution (HMIP) in England and Wales in April 1987 (see 1.2.1 above) culminated in the inclusion of Integrated Pollution Control (IPC) in the *Environmental Protection Act 1990*, Part I.

IPC covers all major solid, liquid and gaseous emissions to air, land and water from the most polluting and complex industrial processes - Part A processes. Thus, IPC recognises that reduction of a release to one environmental medium could well have implications for another. In cases of releases to more than one environmental medium from processes under central control, the enforcing authority must set conditions to ensure that the Best Practicable Environmental Option (BPEO) - see 1.5 above - is secured to minimise pollution to the environment as a whole. Thus it should also be borne in mind that the objective is to set conditions which protect the environment - not workers: health and safety legislation is designed to protect workers.

From 1 April 1996 the Environment Agency in England and Wales and the Scottish Environment Protection Agency became the enforcing authorities for IPC.

Integrated Pollution Control (IPC) was progressively implemented from 1 April 1991 in England and Wales and from 1 April 1992 in Scotland with the various categories of processes required to apply for an authorisation within specified dates; the final tranche of processes had to apply for an authorisation before the end of January 1996. Prior to authorisation under the EPA, processes continued to be regulated under the *Alkali Act 1906* and regulations under it - this was finally repealed in England and Wales in December 1996.

Part I of the EPA also covers the control of air pollution from Part B processes by local authorities in England and Wales and by SEPA in Scotland - see chapter 2. This Part of the EPA will be revoked once all processes prescribed for either IPC or LAPC have transferred to control under the *Pollution Prevention Control (England and Wales) Regulations 2000* (and similar in Scotland).

Northern Ireland

In Northern Ireland, processes with high pollution potential are regulated for integrated central control under the Industrial Pollution Control (Northern Ireland) Order 1997. The enforcing authority is the Industrial Pollution and Radiochemical Inspectorate (IPRI), within the Environment and Heritage Service, an agency of the Department of the Environment (NI). The IPRI is also responsible for regulating processes with the potential to cause serious air pollution ("restricted central control") - see chapter 2.

Reference to the appropriate article of the Northern Ireland legislation is given throughout this section and is shown as follows: (NI: IPCO, Art.0).

1.14.1 Environmental Protection (Prescribed Processes and Substances) Regulations 1991 (SI 472) (as amended)

> Note – these Regulations and the *Environmental Protection (Applications, Appeals and Registers) Regulations 1991* (see next section) no longer apply to new installations coming into operation, or those undergoing substantial change, on or after 31 October 1999; they will need to apply for a permit under the *Pollution Prevention and Control Regulations 2000* – see 1.13.1; existing processes contine to be regulated under the EPA until their transfer to PPC – see Schedule 3.

(Similar Regulations - The Industrial Pollution Control (Prescribed Processes and Substances) Regulations (Northern Ireland) 1998 (Statutory Rules of Northern Ireland no. 30) - have been made under Article 3 of the Industrial Pollution Control (NI) Order 1997; they came into force on 2 March 1998.)

These Regulations made under s.2 of the Act came into force in England and Wales on 1 April 1991 (Scotland - 1 April 1992). Schedule 1 of the 1991 Regulations (as amended) lists the processes prescribed for Integrated Pollution Control - Part A Processes - and those subject to control of air pollution only - Part B Processes - (Appendix 1.1).

The 1992 and 1993 amendment Regulations mainly relate to the definitions of prescribed processes in Schedule 1 attached to the 1991 Regulations - see Appendix 1.1. 1994 Amendment Regulations (SI 1271) are also mainly concerned with Schedule 1: some processes have been transferred from Part A to Part B or vice versa, some exempted from authorisation and some brought within the authorisation process for the first time. Although a consolidated version of the Regulations has been published, it should be noted that this is not a legal document; the original Regulations and subsequent amendments should be consulted where issues of legality, etc are concerned. 1995 Amendment Regulations (SI 3247, effective 8 January 1996) make further changes to the schedule of prescribed processes.

As a general rule where a site in England and Wales contains both Part A and Part B processes, the Part B processes falling within the same section of the Schedule as the Part A processes will be scheduled for control by the Environment Agency (in Scotland both Part A and Part B processes are controlled by SEPA). Where operations at a site involve a number of processes falling within the same IPC section, a single authorisation will be issued if all the processes form an integral part of the end product or purpose of the operation. Processes falling within different sections of Schedule 1 will require separate authorisations (except for those in different sections of Chapter 4 - chemical industry, where only one authorisation is required).

Schedules 4 and 6 of the 1991 Regulations list the substances to be controlled for air or land releases; Schedule 5 - releases to water - has been replaced by a new Schedule in the 1994 amendment Regulations (Appendix 1.2). The list for air applies to both IPC and air pollution control, and the lists for water and land releases to IPC. There is a requirement to use the Best Available Techniques Not Entailing Excessive Cost (BATNEEC - see 1.6 above) to minimise or prevent the release of all substances, whether prescribed or not, to the environment.

The timetable for bringing existing (i.e. in operation in the 12 months prior to April 1991 or 1992 in Scotland) Part A processes within IPC was also given in the 1991 Regulations. The final tranche of processes (Chapter 6 industries - see Appendix 1.1) were required to apply for authorisation between 1 November 1995 and 31 January 1996.

It is an offence to operate a process without an authorisation or in contravention of any conditions of the authorisation (EPA, ss.6(1) and 23; NI: IPCO, Art.6(1) and 23(1)(a)). Existing processes which applied for an authorisation within the appropriate period or were awaiting the outcome of an appeal could continue to operate.

Northern Ireland

Schedule 1 to the 1998 Regulations describes the prescribed processes to be regulated for Integrated Central Control (Part A processes); it also lists those for Restricted Central Control (Part B) and Local Control (Part C) - see chapter 2. While the processes prescribed for control are very similar to those in the rest of the United Kingdom, it is of course necessary to refer to the Schedule itself for details of classification.

As from 2 March 1998, all new processes had to apply for an authorisation from the relevant authority. Schedule 3 to the Regulations lists the dates within which existing processes must apply for an authorisation, with the first tranche required to apply before 31 December 1998. Others will be required to apply for authorisation as specified in Schedule 3, with the final tranche required to apply before 31 December 2002. Existing processes are defined as those operating in the 12 months before 2 March 1998; or the plant for which was in the course of construction, or for which contracts for construction had been exchanged in the 12 months to 2 March 1998; or are currently regulated under the *Alkali Act 1906*.

Schedules 4, 5 and 6 list the prescribed substances for release, respectively to air, water and land. These are identical to Schedules 4, 5 and 6 of the GB Regulations - see Appendix 1.2.

1.14.2 Environmental Protection (Applications, Appeals and Registers) Regulations 1991 (SI 507), as amended

> See boxed note at section 1.14.1 above.

(Similar Regulations - The Industrial Pollution Control (Applications, Appeals and Registers) Regulations (Northern Ireland) 1998 (SR NI 29) - have been made under The Industrial Pollution Control (Northern Ireland) Order 1997. They came into force on 2 March 1998.)

These Regulations came into force in England and Wales on 1 April 1991 (Scotland - 1 April 1992); they detail the procedure for applying for an authorisation and for a variation of the authorisation for both Part A and Part B processes as laid down by ss.6-15 of the EPA (as amended by the *Environment Act 1995*). The Regulations also cover the appeals procedure and the establishment of public registers of information. The 1996 Amendment Regulations (SI 667), which came into force on 1 April 1996, amend the 1991 Regulations with regard to advertising and consultation on applications and information to be placed on the public register. They also require companies applying for an authorisation for the first time and those seeking a variation to disclose the name of their parent company.

IPC adopts a preventative approach to pollution control. Before a prescribed process can be operated, prior authorisation must be obtained which will contain the specific conditions which must be met in operating the process.

As from 1 April 1991 in England and Wales (1 April 1992 in Scotland), all proposed new, and substantially changed existing, Part A processes required an IPC authorisation. (All large combustion plant, whether new or existing required an authorisation from 1 April 1991.) Authorisations for existing Part A plant were phased in over four years from 1 April 1992. Prior to authorisation existing plant could continue to operate under existing approvals, providing an application was made within the relevant period and pending a decision on that application. During that time they were not subject to IPC charges. The application procedure and charging structure are set out below.

It should be noted that the procedure for regulating processes for air pollution is much the same as that for Integrated Pollution Control (NI: Integrated Central Control) - see chapter 2.

Northern Ireland

The 1998 Regulations are similar to those applying in England, Scotland and Wales.

The Industrial Pollution Control (Authorisation of Processes) (Determination Periods) Order (Northern Ireland) 1998 (SR NI 30) varies the periods contained in the

IPCO within which enforcing authorities should determine applications for authorisations. For existing Part A processes the period is extended from six to nine months. For new Part A processes the period is six months unless a longer period is agreed. Where a request is made for certain information on an application to be excluded from the public register for reasons of national security or commercial confidentiality, the period of determination does not begin until the request has been determined or withdrawn.

(a) Applications (NI: IPCO, Art.6 & Sch. 1, Part I)

Applications for an IPC authorisation should be made on a form available from the enforcing authority. Prior to preparing an application - or at an early stage in its preparation - it is suggested that process operators should discuss it with the enforcing authority, thus ensuring that it will meet the requirements of the legislation.

In the case of planned new processes, operators are advised to make an application for an authorisation on the basis of design plans prior to construction of the plant. Where a novel or very complex process is under design, it is again suggested that the enforcing authority be involved at an early stage, and the use of a "staged" application procedure agreed - i.e. the application for an authorisation is submitted in stages as the plans for the process develop (Integrated Pollution Control: A Practical Guide, DOE/WO, 1996). The actual construction of the plant will be subject to separate approval under planning legislation - see 1.22.

In addition to general information about the plant (including the name and address of its parent company or ultimate holding company), and a description of the process, the application should have regard to the relevant IPR Process Guidance Note (England and Wales; see below and Appendix 1.3); it should also include:

- name and address of the local authority in which the process is to be carried on or, in the case of mobile plant, the local authority in which the applicant's principle place of business is located;

- a list of prescribed substances (and any other substances which might cause harm if released into any environmental medium) used in connection with or resulting from the process; the likely quantity and nature of releases from the process assuming the technology and controls have been fitted and are operational;

- description of the techniques to be used for preventing or minimising the release of prescribed substances and rendering harmless any substances which are released - i.e. the operator must show that the best available techniques not entailing excessive cost will be used (see 1.6.2 above);

- details of any proposed release of such a substance into any environmental medium and an assessment of the environmental consequences; where an IPC process releases substances to more than one environmental medium, an assessment must be undertaken to demonstrate that the application represents the Best Practicable Environmental Option (BPEO) (see 1.5 above); where the BPEO has not been selected, e.g. on cost grounds, this must be justified;

- proposals for monitoring the release of substances;

- in the case of existing plant, identification of areas requiring upgrading to comply with BATNEEC and new plant standards, together with provisional programme of improvements. (A detailed programme should be submitted within six months of receiving authorisation.)

The application plus eight copies must be sent to the enforcing authority; this will enable copies to be sent (within 14 days) to statutory consultees who will normally have 28 days (NI: 42 days) in which to comment; statutory consultees are

- the Health and Safety Executive
- Sewerage undertakers (sewerage authority in Scotland)
- Ministry of Agriculture, Fisheries and Foods, England, Secretary of State for Wales/Scotland (as appropriate)
- English Nature, Scottish Natural Heritage, Countryside Council for Wales (as appropriate)
- Harbour authority (if appropriate)
- the local authority in whose area the process (except mobile plant) will be carried on
- the local fisheries committee where the process may involve a discharge into territorial or coastal waters within its area.

In Northern Ireland, statutory consultees for Part A processes are:

- Department of Economic Development
- Department of Agriculture
- Department of the Environment, for processes which may involve a release into any underground strata or waterway, into a sewer, or of any substance into any environmental medium
- relevant district council
- relevant harbour authority for processes which may result in the release of any substance into the harbour.

Incomplete applications, those with insufficient information or accompanied by an incorrect fee will be returned to the applicant and it will be deemed as not having been submitted. In such instances it would be important for the applicant to resubmit the application as soon as possible so as not to risk prosecution for operating without an authorisation.

In submitting the application, the applicant may request that certain information should not be put in the register on the grounds of commercial confidentiality or national security (EPA, ss.21 & 22; NI: IPCO, Arts.21 & 22). Any request for exclusion should be accompanied by a full statement justifying the request. The enforcing authority has 14 days to consider the request. If it agrees, then the relevant information will be withheld (though it will be sent to the HSE); if the request is refused, the applicant has 21 days in which to appeal to the Secretary of State (see below); during this period the information in dispute will not be added to the register. Following determination or withdrawal of an appeal in respect of commercial confidentiality, a further seven days must elapse before the information is put in the register (Env. Act 1995, Sch. 22, para 58(2); IPCO, Art.22(5)). It should be noted that if the enforcing authority fails to respond to the request for information to be withheld within 14 days, then it automatically becomes commercially confidential (s.22(3) of the EPA; NI: IPCO, Art.22(3)).

Following acceptance of the application and resolution of any issues of commercial confidentiality, copies must be filed in the public register (see below), as the public also have a right to comment on the application - see also below (b) public consultation.

The Secretary of State (NI: DOE) may request the enforcing authority to forward a particular application, or class of applications, to him for determination (EPA, Sch. 1, para 3; NI: IPCO, Sch. 1, Part I, para 3). The enforcing authority should inform the applicant that this has been done; both parties have 21 days in which to request the Secretary of State to arrange either a local inquiry or a hearing in connection with the application.

Under the *Environmental Protection (Authorisation of Processes) (Determination of Periods) Order 1991* an application must be determined within four months from the day on which it is received or from when any issues of commercial confidentiality or national security are resolved (NI: 6 months - IPCO, Sch. 1, Part I, para 5); a longer determination period may, however, be agreed with applicants.

(b) Public Consultation

The public have a right to be consulted about applications for authorisations and proposals to vary an authorisation. Thus, the process operator must publish an advertisement in a local newspaper not less than 14 days but not more than 42 days following an application for authorisation or notification of, or application for, a variation. Applications for authorisations must also be advertised in the *London Gazette (Edinburgh Gazette or Belfast Gazette* - as appropriate). Applications or variations for mobile plant do not have to be advertised.

As well as brief details of the process, the advertisement should state where a copy of the application can be seen; it should also state that copies of any representations received will be put on the public register unless a request is made in writing that they should not. In such cases a statement will be put in the register saying that such a request has been made (without identifying the person making the request).

The Environment Agency has initiated a procedure for extending public consultation on applications for environmental licences which raise matters of significant local concern. Under the new procedure, the Agency consults widely with local public and relevant representative groups both on the application and on its proposed decision; its final decision is then published together with the reasons for that decision. In some cases the Agency will hold public meetings where the applicant would have to make a presentation on its application. Applications to be subject to enhanced consultation are likely to include: large industrial plant (e.g. power stations, chemical plants, steel works); hazardous waste incinerators; burning waste as a fuel; operating new nuclear facilities; increasing discharges of radioactive substances; landfill sites; processes leading to significant discharges to bathing waters, and those likely to be of major public concern or which have, in the past, led to complaints.

(c) Integrated Pollution Regulation Notes

England & Wales

In addition to giving guidance on what constitutes the BATNEEC for each process, IPR Notes (see Appendix 1.2) include "achievable release levels (ARL)" for new plant using best available techniques. For existing plant a timetable for improvements towards meeting ARLs or for decommissioning the plant will normally form part of the authorisation. IPR Notes also include details of any environmental quality standards, European Union and international obligations etc which should be met (see chapter 2, 2.4); advice on techniques for pollution abatement and compliance monitoring is also given. Inspectors may take account of "site specific issues", such as the locality of the process with regard to emission effects.

A series of Technical Guidance Notes (see Appendix 1.4) provide guidance and background detail on a range of technical subjects and will be of interest to process operators, contractors used by the enforcing authorities and other regulatory bodies. Subjects dealt with by TG Notes include BPEO assessments, monitoring emissions of pollutants at source, solvent vapour emissions and pollutant abatement technology.

Scotland

IPR Notes do not apply in Scotland; guidance on the implementation of IPC in Scotland issued by the Scottish Office (*A Practical Guide - Central Control, 1992*) notes that the IPR notes for England and Wales "represent an important source of information for the Scottish enforcing authorities and for applicants". It says that enforcing authorities will take note of their contents but may also prepare separate notes for Scotland. The Guide therefore suggests that applicants should discuss with the enforcing authorities the likely standards to be imposed and frame applications accordingly. General notes of guidance outlining information to be given on application forms are available from the Scottish Office.

Northern Ireland

For Part A processes, operators in Northern Ireland should refer to IPR Guidance Notes produced by the Environment Agency. The IPRI has produced guidance notes for Part B processes in Northern Ireland.

(d) Authorisations

In granting an authorisation and setting conditions, the enforcing authority must have regard to any Directions from the Secretary of State implementing, for example, EU and other international obligations (EPA, s.7(b); NI: IPCO, Art.30), and to the National Air Quality Strategy (s.81 of the *Environment Act 1995* and see chapter 2, 2.9). Conditions may specify emission levels (including, where appropriate, for noise to prevent nuisance), the breaching of which constitutes an offence. Enforcing authorities are required to ensure that operators are using BATNEEC, that the conditions imposed will prevent or minimise release of the most polluting substances, and that any that are released are rendered harmless. There is also an implied condition (a residual duty) in all authorisations that operators will use BATNEEC to prevent or minimise pollution at all stages of plant design and operation. Conditions should not be attached regulating the final disposal of waste to land (EPA, s.28; NI: IPCO, Art.28); this activity will require a waste management licence under Part II of the EPA (NI: Part II of *Pollution Control and Local Government Order 1978* or *Waste & Contaminated Land Order 1997*, when implemented). However, authorisations under Part I of the EPA (NI: IPCO) for waste disposal and recycling processes should take account of the objectives of the waste framework Directive, including not causing nuisance through noise and odour (see also chapter 4, 4.6).

Authorisations should ensure compliance with any quality objectives or standards, emission limits and with national emission plans set by the Secretary of State for Environment, Transport and the Regions (e.g. for compliance with the EU Large Combustion Plant Directive (EPA, s.3(5) - see chapter 2, 2.4.4); where the release of a substance is likely to affect more than one environmental medium, the authorisation must have regard to the BPEO.

If the enforcing authority is not convinced that an applicant will be able to carry on the process in compliance with the conditions to be imposed, it must refuse the application for an authorisation (EPA, s.6(4); NI: IPCO, Art.6(4)). An application for an authorisation should also be refused if the enforcing authority considers that a prescribed release might contribute or result in failure to achieve a statutory water quality objective (EPA, s.28(3)); *The Industrial Pollution Control Order 1997* extends this to cover pollution of any waters in Northern Ireland (Art.28(3)).

Authorisations may be transferred to another person who should notify the enforcing authority within 21 days (EPA, s.9; NI: IPCO, Art.9). However it is advisable to consult the enforcing authority prior to purchase of the plant to ensure that it has no objections to the transfer. A copy of the transfer notice will be put in the public register.

All authorisations also contain a condition requiring operators to provide annual reports to the Environment Agency of releases of around 150 specified substances; the reports are due by 31 January covering the previous year. The data gathered forms the basis of the Agency's new pollution database which replaces the Chemical Release Inventory established by the former HM Inspectorate of Pollution.

Authorisations have to be reviewed not less than every four years to take account of technological developments and to reflect new guidance notes. However where the timing of the review falls within two years of the relevant date for the process to transfer to control under the *Pollution Prevention and Control Regulations 2000*, then the process of permitting as an IPPC installation will take the place of the review (para 5.6, *IPPC: A practical guide*, DETR, 2000)

(e) Variations

Conditions of an authorisation may be varied either at the request of the enforcing authority or of the operator.

Section 10 of the EPA (NI: IPCO, Art.10) empowers the enforcing authority to serve a variation notice in which it may vary conditions attached to an authorisation - for example, improved pollution control techniques and technology might make tighter emission limits feasible. The notice will specify the changes which the enforcing authority has decided should be made and the date(s) on which the variations are to take effect (unless the notice is withdrawn). Sch. 22, para 51(3) of the *Environment Act 1995* amends s.10 of the EPA to permit the enforcing authority to serve a notice varying a variation notice; this should specify the changes the enforcing authority wishes to make to the first variation notice and the date these are to take effect. The process operator must advise the enforcing authority of the way in which it is intended to meet the revised conditions. If the change is "substantial" (see below), then the normal application procedure for an authorisation will be followed and a fee become payable. There is a right of appeal (see (h) below) except if the variation notice implements a Direction from the Secretary of State.

Section 11 of the EPA and the *Environmental Protection (Applications, Appeals and Registers) Regulations 1991* (NI: IPCO, Art.11 and 1998 Regulations) apply where an operator wishes to make a change to the way in which the process is carried out and which could have implications for the authorisation. Such a request may be made when the process is already in use or at the design or construction stage. As a first step, the operator should send the enforcing authority written details of the changes being requested. If the enforcing authority considers that the changes require the conditions attached to the authorisation to be varied, then the operator must submit a formal application. An application to make a substantial change will then follow the procedure outlined above for applying for an authorisation; note: the application should include the name and address of the parent or ultimate holding company if this information is not already on the public register. There is a right of appeal if the enforcing authority refuses a s.11 variation (see below).

Statutory consultees (see (a) applications above) should be consulted concerning both proposed s.10 and s.11 variations and a copy of all representations received put in the public register, together with any received from the public - see above (b) public consultation.

Applications for variations (except those referred to the Secretary of State) must be determined within four months of receipt unless a different period is agreed. An application for a variation will be deemed to have failed if the enforcing authority fails to determine it within the agreed period and the applicant notifies the enforcing authority that he considers the failure to determine as refusal of the application (Env. Act 1995, Sch. 22, para 93(10)).

The *Environment Act 1995* (Sch. 22, para 93(5)) amends Schedule 1 of the EPA to permit the Secretary of State to call in applications for variations for determination. In doing so, he may either arrange for a local inquiry or give both the applicant and the enforcing authority the opportunity of a hearing.

Minor or "relevant" changes will be considered by the enforcing authority, without consulting statutory consultees, and any changes to conditions to be attached to the authorisation notified to the operator. "Relevant" changes relate to the way in which the process is carried on which may affect the substances released or affect the amount or characteristic of any substance released. "Substantial" changes are defined in the EPA (s.10(7); NI: IPCO, Art.10(8)) as those resulting in substantial changes "in the substances released from the process or in the amount or any other characteristic of any substance so released".

Copies of all variations and relating documentation must be put in the public register.

(f) Revocation of Authorisation

Following 28 days written notice, the enforcing authority may revoke an authorisation for failure to pay the annual subsistence charge, or if it has reason to believe that the process has not been carried on at all or carried on for 12 months; prior to the notice taking effect, the enforcing authority may either withdraw the notice or vary the date on which revocation is to take effect. (EPA, s.12; NI: IPCO, Art.12)

(g) Enforcement

If the enforcing authority believes conditions of an authorisation are being breached it can take any of the following actions under ss.13-14 of the EPA (NI: IPCO, Arts.13-14):

- serve an enforcement notice (s.13) reinforcing an existing condition or requiring the operator to remedy the cause of the breach of condition within a specified period; Sch. 22, para 53 of the *Environment Act 1995* amends the EPA to permit the enforcing authority by written notice to withdraw an enforcement notice.

- where it is felt that the continued operation of the process involves "an imminent risk of serious pollution of the environment", serve a prohibition notice requiring the operator to close down all or part of the process and take the necessary steps to stop the risk (s.14); written notice of the withdrawal of a prohibition notice will be given by the enforcing authority when it is satisfied that the necessary action to deal with the problems has been taken.

Where there is no immediate environmental risk, the enforcement officer will usually discuss the remedial action needed, and confirm it in writing. Prosecutions will normally only be undertaken for serious pollution incidents and contraventions of the law, including operating without an authorisation, failure to comply with formal remedial requirements, failure to supply information or supplying false information, and obstructing an enforcement officer. In deciding whether or not to prosecute, the Agency will usually take such factors into account as the environmental effect of the offence, how foreseeable it was, compliance record of offender, deterrent effect of prosecution and personal circumstances of the offender. (Environment Agency Enforcement and Prosecution Policy, November 1998)

(h) Appeals

Section 15 of the EPA (NI: IPCO, Art.15) provides for a right of appeal against a decision of the enforcing authority to the Secretary of State (except when the decision implements a Direction from the Secretary of State - *Environment Act 1995*, Sch. 22, para 54(2)) in the following instances:

- refusal of authorisation or disagreement with conditions attached to the authorisation;
- terms of variation notice served by enforcing authority under s.10;
- refusal of request for variation of authorisation under s.11;
- revocation of authorisation;
- terms of enforcement or prohibition notice.

Section 22 (NI: IPCO, Art.22) provides a right of appeal with regard to decisions relating to whether information should be considered as commercially confidential and thus excluded from the public registers (see above - applications).

Where an appeal is lodged against a revocation notice or decision of the enforcing authority that information is not commercially confidential, implementation of the notice or decision is deferred pending determination or withdrawal of the appeal. All other notices take effect from the specified date and disputed conditions remain in place pending determination or withdrawal of the appeal. An appeal against conditions of an authorisation or refusal of an authorisation or variation must be made within six months, or in the case of enforcement, variation and prohibition notices, within two months. Where a revocation notice has been served, the appeal should be lodged before the date the notice takes effect. Appeals against a refusal to exclude information from the public register should be made within 21 days.

The Secretary of State may determine the appeal himself or appoint someone else for this purpose (*Env. Act 1995*, s.114 & Sch. 20). With effect from 1 September 1997 the Secretary of State delegated his powers for processes in England to the Planning Inspectorate. He has, however, reserved the right to recover appeals relating to the following for determination himself:

- processes or sites of major importance;
- those giving rise to significant public controversy or legal difficulties;
- those which can only be decided in conjunction with other cases over which inspectors have no jurisdiction;
- those which raise major or novel issues of industrial pollution control which could set a policy precedent;
- those which merit recovery because of the particular circumstances.

Appeals relating to issues of commercial confidentiality (s.22 of EPA) are also determined by the Secretary of State.

In Northern Ireland Article 15(3) and Schedule 2 of the *Industrial Pollution Control Order 1997* enables the DOE(NI) to refer appeals, or parts thereof, to the Planning Appeals Commission.

The Regulations (NI: 1998 Regulations) specify the information to be sent to the Secretary of State (England: Planning Inspectorate; NI: DOE) by the operator; this should include a notice of appeal, a statement setting out the reason for the appeal and a statement as to whether the appellant wishes the matter to be dealt with through written representations or by a hearing. A copy of these three documents should also be sent to the Agency/SEPA and the Secretary of State - or Planning Inspectorate - advised that this has been done. The Secretary of State (or Planning Inspectorate) should also be sent a copy of the application and of the authorisation (where this exists), together with any relevant correspondence and notices. Appeals may only be dealt with in writing if both parties agree; if either party request that the matter be dealt with by a hearing, then one will be arranged. A local inquiry may be held in connection with the appeal, either at the instigation of the Secretary of State's appointee or the Secretary of State may direct that a local inquiry be arranged (*Env. Act 1995*, Sch. 22, para 54).

Within 14 days of receiving notice of the appeal, the enforcing authority must send details of it to statutory consultees and others who submitted comments on the original application for the authorisation - they have 21 days in which to send any further comments to the Secretary of State (or Planning Inspectorate). These will then be copied to both the enforcing authority and the appellant and will also be put in the public register unless a written request is made that this should not happen. In such cases a statement will be added to the register saying that representations concerning the appeal have been received and are subject to a request to exclude from the register.

Where the matter is to be decided in writing, the enforcing authority must submit its comments to the Secretary of State (or his appointee) within 28 days of receipt of the appeal notice. The appellant will then have 17 days to comment on the statement. Both sides have 14 days from the date of receipt to comment on any other statements submitted in connection with the appeal.

Where a hearing is to be held, the Secretary of State (or Planning Inspectorate) will notify the appellant and the enforcing authority of the time, date and place - a minimum of 28 days notice will be given; details must be advertised in the local press and also sent to statutory consultees etc giving not less than 21 days notice. In the case of mobile plant, notice of the hearing must be given in the place in which the plant was operating when the enforcement/prohibition notice was served. Any further statements relating to the appeal should be submitted within six weeks of the appeal being lodged or not less than 21 days before the hearing (whichever is first). Most hearings will be held wholly or partly in public, unless matters of commercial confidentiality are involved (when the hearing will always be in private).

Following determination, copies of the decision and any report are sent to the appellant, the enforcing authority and statutory consultees; copies of the decision only are sent to others involved. In those cases where the Secretary of State has recovered an appeal, the Inspector will report to the Secretary of State who will then make a decision on the appeal. Documents relating to the determination of the appeal are put in the public register.

If an appeal is withdrawn, the enforcing authority should advise all those who were originally given notification of it.

(i) Public Registers

Sections 20-22 of the EPA (as amended by the *Env. Act 1995*, Sch. 22, paras 57-58) are concerned with the establishment of registers of IPC (and air pollution control - see chapter 2) information to be maintained by the enforcing authorities. Articles 20-22 of the *Industrial Pollution Control (Northern Ireland) Order 1997* contain similar provisions.

The 1996 Amendment of the *Applications, Appeals and Registers Regulations* (NI: IPCO, Art.20(1) and 1998 Regulations) list the documentation to be placed in the register:

- documentation relating to an application for an authorisation or for variation of the conditions of an authorisation; and subsequent information relating to the application for an authorisation requested by the enforcing authority;
- copy of advertisement relating to application for authorisation or variation or notification by enforcing authority to vary an authorisation; representations made as a result of the advertisement unless a request is made that they should not be put on the register; in such cases a statement to this effect should be put on the register without identifying the person making the request;
- authorisations and their conditions;
- written notice of transfer of authorisation to another person;
- revocation, variation, enforcement or prohibition notices issued by the enforcing authority; notification by the enforcing authority of withdrawal of enforcement or prohibition notice;
- documentation relating to an appeal, its determination and any accompanying reports;
- details of convictions relating to carrying on of a prescribed process with or without an authorisation;
- monitoring data collected by the enforcing authority or submitted by an operator as a condition of the authorisation; where such information is omitted on grounds of commercial confidentiality, then the enforcing authority should put a statement on the register confirming or otherwise compliance with the relevant condition of the authorisation;
- information given to the enforcing authority on or after 1 April 1996 in compliance with a condition of an authorisation, variation, enforcement or prohibition notice;
- reports by the enforcing authority relating to the environmental consequences of a prescribed process in the locality of premises where the prescribed process is carried on under an authorisation;
- Directions from the Secretary of State.

Information affecting national security or which is accepted as being commercially confidential may be withheld and a note to this effect added to the register. The onus is on operators to prove that disclosure of specific information would be prejudicial to their commercial interests. If the enforcing authority does not agree that information is commercially confidential, the operator may appeal to the Secretary of State; the information in dispute will not be put on the register until the appeal is determined and if it is determined as not being commercially confidential, a further seven days must elapse before its entry on the Register. Exclusion of data from the register on the grounds of commercial confidentially lasts for four years after which it will be added to the register unless a further four year exclusion is applied for and agreed.

Local authorities in England and Wales have copies of entries relating to IPC processes in their area in their registers, and also maintain registers for air pollution processes - Part B processes - under their control (see chapter 2). Registers held by district councils in Northern Ireland will also contain particulars of authorisations granted by the DOE's Chief Inspector (Industrial Pollution and Radiochemical Inspectorate).

Applications for an authorisation or variation which have been advertised in a paper should be put on the register within 14 days of receipt by the enforcing authority; notifications to vary an authorisation (which are also advertised) should also be put on the register within 14 days of notifying the operator. The Regulations do not specify the time within which other information should be placed in the register although guidance issued by the Department of Environment (now DETR) suggests that this should be done "as soon as possible". Information held on the registers may be inspected by the public free of charge and copies of entries obtained on "payment of a reasonable charge".

Information will be removed from the register in the following circumstances:

- withdrawal of application for authorisation prior to determination - all particulars to be removed not less than two months but within three months after the date of withdrawal;
- if a process ceases to be a prescribed process following amendment of the Prescribed Processes and Substances Regulations - all particulars to be removed not less than two months but within three months of the date on which the process ceases to be prescribed;
- monitoring information relating to a process - four years after entering in the register;
- information relating to a process which has been superseded - four years after the later information has been entered in the register.

1.14.3 Offences

It is an offence (EPA, s.23; NI: IPCO, Art.23) to operate a prescribed process without an authorisation or to contravene any conditions attached to an authorisation or other enforcement notice without reasonable excuse. Other offences include making a false or misleading statement and obstructing an inspector. Summary conviction carries a maximum fine of £20,000 and/or three months imprisonment, and conviction on indictment an unlimited fine and/or two years imprisonment.

1.15 ENVIRONMENT ACT 1995
1.15.1 Fees and Charges

Sections 41-43 of the Act, which came into force on 21 September 1995, enable the Environment Agency and SEPA to make schemes (to be approved by their respective Secretary of State) for the recovery of costs in respect of granting and ensuring compliance with environmental licences. Such costs include:

- activities relating to issuing authorisations and permits (including applications, variations, transfers and surrender of permits);
- carrying out compliance monitoring and enforcing controls; enforcement action;
- sampling and analysis of releases;
- operation of the public registers of information;
- administrative expenditure in support of the above functions, including salaries, travel and subsistence costs, office services, etc.

Charges are levied according to the number of components a process contains. Levels of charges are reviewed each year. Where an authorisation is issued part way through the year, the charge will be calculated on a pro-rata basis. The financial year runs from 1 April - 31 March.

(a) IPC - England and Wales

Fees are set out in *The Environment Act (Environmental Licences) (Integrated Pollution Control) Charging Scheme*, revised annually, and which covers:

- Application fee (covering consideration of each IPC application);
- Subsistence charge (payable annually, covering the cost of inspection, monitoring and enforcement);
- Substantial variation fee (normally applied to the number of components in the process as it would be following the proposed change). Variations necessitated by a non-substantial change to a process do not incur a charge, the costs being recouped through the annual subsistence charge.

The cost of any routine monitoring, e.g. to verify an operator's monitoring, is charged monthly in arrears to the operator concerned. Ad hoc and reactive monitoring is covered by the subsistence charge.

If an operator withdraws an application within 56 calendar days of its receipt by the Environment Agency, then the fee will normally be refunded, though the Agency retains the right not to do so. Non-payment of statutory fees or charges may result in revocation of an operator's authorisation.

Scotland

A similar charging scheme applies in Scotland, where fees are generally higher than in England and Wales.

Northern Ireland

The Industrial Pollution Control (Industrial Pollution, Radiochemicals Inspection) (Fees and Charges Scheme) (Northern Ireland) 1998, made under Article 8 of the *Industrial Pollution Control (Northern Ireland) Order 1997* covers charges in respect of applications for authorisations and variations and subsistence charges.

(b) IPPC - England & Wales

In August 1999 the Environment Agency published proposals for an interim charging scheme covering installations to be regulated by the Agency under PPC. This scheme, to be based on either time and materials or use of existing scheme structures, is to run from 31 October 1999 to 31 March 2001, during which time a new scheme will be developed for introduction from 1 April 2001. Charges will be levied per activity, with an installation usually comprising a number of activities.

The interim charging scheme applies to:

- new installations applying for PPC permits;
- existing installations undergoing substantial change, and thus being brought completely or partially within PPC;
- sectors requiring to apply for PPC permit before 31 March 2001.

A charging scheme covering those installations regulated by local authorities in England and Wales will be made under Reg.22 of the *Pollution Prevention and Control (England & Wales) Regulations 2000*. This will cover charges for applications for permits, annual subsistence charge; variations, transfer and partial transfers and surrenders of permits. Where an A2 installation involves a discharge to water, there will be an additional charge to cover Environment Agency costs.

Scotland

Charges for IPPC installations in Scotland are levied under a scheme made under the *Pollution Prevention and Control (Scotland) Regulations 2000*, which came into force on 28 September 2000. As a first step an interim charging scheme has been made covering the period to 31 March 2001. This covers new installations and existing installations undergoing a substantial change.

1.15.2 Powers of Entry

Sections 108-109 of the Act empower "a person who appears suitable to an enforcing authority to be authorised in writing ..." to enter premises where they have reason to believe a prescribed process is being or has been operated (with or without an authorisation) or where they believe there is a risk of serious pollution. Authorised persons may take photographs, samples etc of substances, and require access to relevant information and records. The authorised person may render harmless any substance or article from which it is considered there is imminent danger of serious harm; a written and signed report of what has been done and why should be given to a responsible person on the premises and a copy of the report served on the owner of the substance or article (if different).

Except in an emergency, a warrant should be obtained if entry has been or is likely to be refused and it is probable that force will be needed to gain entry.

Similar powers for inspectors in Northern Ireland are contained in Articles 17 and 18 of the *Industrial Pollution Control (Northern Ireland) Order 1997*.

NUISANCE

There are three types of nuisance: statutory nuisance where a particular nuisance has been made so by statute; and public and private nuisance which are within Common Law.

1.16 STATUTORY NUISANCE

Various Acts of Parliament have covered statutory nuisances; these included the *Public Health Act 1936* which was often used in respect of odour (see chapter 2, 2.35.1); the *Clean Air Act 1956* (now *Clean Air Act 1993*) in respect of smoke (see chapter 2, 2.14.2); the *Control of Pollution Act 1974* (noise nuisance - see chapter 3, 3.7); and in Scotland, until 1 April 1996, ss.16-26 of the *Public Health (Scotland) Act 1897*.

1.16.1 Environmental Protection Act, Part III

Part III of the *Environmental Protection Act 1990*, as amended by the *Noise and Statutory Nuisance Act 1993* (see chapter 3, 3.8) contains the main legislation on statutory nuisance and enables local authorities and individuals to take action to secure the abatement of a statutory nuisance. *The Noise Act 1996* enables action to be taken in respect of noise nuisance from dwellings between 11.00 pm and 7.00 am (see chapter 3, 3.9.1).

Part III of the EPA applied in England and Wales from 1 January 1991 and in Scotland from 1 April 1996 as a result of implementation of s.107 and Schedule 17 of the *Environment Act 1995*; these extend the relevant provisions of the EPA to Scotland.

Section 79 of the EPA, as amended, defines the following statutory nuisances:

a) any premises in such a state as to be prejudicial to health or a nuisance;

b) smoke emitted from premises so as to be prejudicial to health or a nuisance;

c) fumes or gases emitted from premises so as to be prejudicial to health or a nuisance (from private dwellings only);

d) any dust, steam, smell or other effluvia arising on industrial, trade or business premises and being prejudicial to health or a nuisance;

e) any accumulation or deposit which is prejudicial to health or a nuisance;

f) any animal kept in such a place or manner as to be prejudicial to health or a nuisance;

g) noise emitted from premises so as to be prejudicial to health or a nuisance;

ga) noise that is prejudicial to health or a nuisance and is emitted from or caused by a vehicle, machinery or equipment in a street or in Scotland, road;

h) any other matter declared by any enactment to be a statutory nuisance. (See, for example, s.259, *Public Health Act 1936* regarding ponds and watercourses – *Pollution Handbook*, chapter 5, 5.13)

Action for nuisance defined in (b), (d), (e) or (g) or paragraph (ga) above may only be taken against a process regulated for IPC, LAPC (Part I of EPA) or IPPC with the consent of the Secretary of State (s.79(10), as amended by *Pollution Prevention and Control Act 1999*, Sch. 2, para 6).

Action for smoke emissions can be taken under the *Clean Air Act 1993* (CAA) in certain instances and cannot therefore be dealt with as a statutory nuisance under the EPA. These instances are:

* smoke emitted from a chimney of a private dwelling in a smoke control area (s.20 of CAA);

* dark smoke from a chimney of a building or a chimney serving the furnace of a boiler or industrial plant attached to a building or installed on any land (s.1 of CAA);

* smoke from a railway locomotive steam engine (s.43 of CAA);

* dark smoke caused by industrial or trade burning (s.2 of CAA).

Also excluded from statutory nuisance action are dust, steam, smell etc (d above) from a railway locomotive steam engine and noise (g above) from aircraft other than model aircraft. Crown defence premises and those occupied by visiting forces are excluded from action under (b)-(g) above. Statutory nuisance legislation cannot be used to take action against land which is in a contaminated state (EPA, s.79(1A), *Env. Act 1995*, Sch. 22, para 89, effective 1 April 2000).

It should be noted that the EPA interprets "premises" as including "land". Equipment (ga above) includes musical instruments. Guidance from the Department of the Environment, Transport and the Regions (Env. Circular 9/97, WO 42/97) suggests that loudspeaker tannoys, loudhailers, radios and "ghetto-blasters" should also be regarded as equipment.

There is a defence (ss.80(8) & 82(10) of the EPA) of Best Practicable Means in respect of nuisance from industrial, trade or business premises. This is interpreted as practicable given local conditions, technical knowledge and financial implications; means includes design, installation and maintenance of plant, buildings and structure and periods of operation.

Steam railway locomotives and recreational steam vessels are exempt from nuisance action in respect of steam and smoke; steam road vehicles (such as traction engines and steamrollers) used on a public highway are also exempt.

So far as action to deal with bonfire smoke is concerned, in certain instances it would be possible to use the *Highways (Amendment) Act 1986*: this makes it an offence to light a fire, permit or direct one to be lit, the smoke from which injures, interrupts or endangers anyone using a highway.

(a) Action by Local Authorities

Local authorities have a duty to inspect their areas from time to time to detect whether a nuisance exists or is likely to occur or recur (s.79(1) of EPA). (Port Health Authorities have the same powers to take action for nuisance, except for noise.) An authority must also take such steps as are reasonably practicable to investigate any complaint of statutory nuisance from a person living in its area. Section 81(2) enables a local authority to take action against a statutory nuisance outside its area if it appears to be affecting any part of its area.

Where the local authority is satisfied that a statutory nuisance exists, or is likely to occur or recur, it must serve an abatement notice on the person responsible for the nuisance or if that person cannot be found, on the owner or occupier of the premises (s.80(1)). If the nuisance is as a result of a structural problem, then the notice should be served on the owner of the premises. The *Noise and Statutory Nuisance Act 1993* amends the procedure for serving an abatement notice in respect of a nuisance from or caused by an unattended vehicle, machinery or equipment (VME) on the street to enable the notice to be affixed directly to it (see chapter 3, 3.8.1).

The notice should impose all or any of the following requirements (s.80(1)):

a) the abatement of the nuisance or prohibiting or restricting its occurrence or recurrence;

b) the carrying out of such works and other steps necessary to abate the nuisance.

The notice should specify the time or times within which the requirements of the notice must be complied with; it should also state that there is a right of appeal and that any appeal against a notice should be made within 21 days to the Magistrates' Court (Sheriff in Scotland) - see below.

Failure to comply with the terms of an abatement notice without reasonable excuse may result in prosecution in the Magistrates' Court (Sheriff in Scotland) (s.80(4)). Conviction may result in a maximum fine of £5,000, plus a daily fine of £500 for each day on which the offence continues after conviction. Where the conviction is for noise from industrial, trade or business premises, the maximum fine is £20,000.

If an abatement notice is not complied with, the local authority may take the necessary steps to abate the nuisance itself (s.81(3)). In the case of action to abate a noise nuisance (s.79(g) of the EPA), this can include seizure of the noise-making equipment - s.10(7) and Sch.1 of the *Noise Act 1996* (this Act does not apply in Scotland); the procedure is set out in chapter 3, 3.9.2.

Any expenses reasonably incurred by a local authority in England and Wales in abating or preventing the recurrence of a statutory nuisance may be recovered by them from the person responsible for the nuisance (s.81(4)). The *Noise and Statutory Nuisance Act 1993* adds a new s.81A to the EPA enabling local authorities in England and Wales to charge interest from the date of serving the payment notice until full payment is received. If no payment has been received after 21 days, then the expenses plus accrued interest become a legal charge on the property. The charge on the property remains until the debt has been paid in full; if the property is sold, then the charge passes to the new owners. The person on whom the notice is served may appeal to the county court within 21 days of its service. New s.81B of the EPA enables local authorities in England and Wales to require the debt to be paid in instalments over a period of up to 30 years.

(b) Action by Individuals

Action to abate a statutory nuisance may also be taken by an individual through the Magistrates' Court (Sheriff in Scotland) (s.82 of EPA). The nuisance must exist or be likely to recur. Prior to taking action, the complainant must notify the alleged nuisance-maker that it is intended to take court action.

If proved, the court will serve an order which

a) requires abatement of the nuisance within a specified time, and the carrying out of any necessary works; and/or

b) prohibits a recurrence of the nuisance and requires the carrying out of any necessary works within a specified time to prevent a recurrence.

Again, failure to comply with an order without reasonable excuse is an offence and results in a fine, plus a daily fine for each day on which the offence continues after conviction.

1.16.2 The Statutory Nuisance (Appeals) Regulations 1995 (SI 2644)

An appeal against an abatement notice served under ss.80 and 80A of the *Environmental Protection Act 1990* (as amended by the *Noise and Statutory Nuisance Act 1993*) should be lodged with the Magistrates' Court within 21 days of service of the notice.

These Regulations, applicable in England and Wales, came into force on 8 November 1995, replacing 1990 Regulations; the 1995 Regulations are very similar to the 1990 Regulations, their main effect being to add further grounds for appeal against an abatement notice. The Regulations also outline the procedure to be followed when the appellant claims the notice should have been served on another person, and the action which the court may take to give effect to its decisions. Similar Regulations - the *Statutory Nuisance (Appeals) (Scotland) Regulations 1996* (SI 1076) - came into force on 2 May 1996 in Scotland.

Grounds for appeal include:

- unreasonable amount of time given for complying with a notice, or unreasonable requirements;

- an error or other irregularity in the notice;

- that it could or should have been served on someone else; in this instance the appellant should give a copy of the appeals notice to any other person referred to in it;

- in the case of a notice served on a trade or business premises that the best practicable means was used to prevent or counteract the effects of the nuisance. This can be used in defence of the following nuisances: premises in such a state as to be prejudicial to health etc; smoke emitted from a chimney; dust, steam, smell or other effluvia; the manner or place in which animals are being kept; noise; and noise from or caused by vehicles, machinery or equipment;

An appeal may also be lodged if it is felt that the requirements of an abatement notice in respect of noise from premises or VMEs are more onerous than the terms of a valid consent (e.g. for construction work or for the use of loudspeakers).

Where an appeal has been lodged, the notice will be suspended pending determination of the appeal if compliance would result in expenditure or the noise was caused due to carrying out a task imposed by law, except

- where there is a risk of injury to health;

- the cost of carrying out the work required by the notice is not considered disproportionate to the expected benefit;

- there is no point in suspending the notice because of its limited duration.

The Court also has powers to dismiss an appeal, or quash or vary the terms of an abatement notice.

1.17 PUBLIC NUISANCE

A public nuisance is both a tort (civil wrong) and a crime punishable by law, whereas private nuisance is a tort, a wrong for which there is remedy by compensation or damages. Where nuisance is alleged, the court will consider a variety of elements including the nature of the facts complained of, the location, and whether or not the complainant has lost the right to complain through acquiescence. The harm, inconvenience or discomfort suffered by the complainant must be material, and continuing or recurrent; the courts will also take into account the nature of the locality: what is acceptable in an area of substantial industrial activity may not be acceptable in the heart of a residential area; and indeed what is acceptable in a rural area may not be acceptable in an urban situation. Public nuisance takes into account primarily the number of persons affected. The nuisance should affect "all persons who come within the sphere of its operation".

In cases of public nuisance, criminal prosecution can be made by the Attorney General or other enforcing bodies including local authorities' environmental health departments; civil proceedings can be instituted by the Attorney General alone or at the request of a local authority or individual. Section 222 of the Local Government Act 1972, provides that a local authority "in the case of civil proceedings may institute them in their own name".

1.18 PRIVATE NUISANCE

Private nuisance actions are more common than public nuisance cases and rely on damage or unreasonable interference with an individual's right to use and enjoy their property. Action may be brought by the aggrieved person in the civil court (either the County or the High Court). Only the occupier of the land or person having a requisite interest is entitled to sue. This may include owner occupiers and tenants but not relatives or visitors even if living with the occupier.

In any proceedings, the person causing the nuisance will be responsible whether or not the nuisance arises from the property he/she occupies, provided that it affects the plaintiff's property. Ownership of land does not necessarily mean that the owner will be held responsible for the actions of others who may cause nuisance. However, the occupier of property may be liable for nuisance even if he/she did not cause it, if he/she allows it to continue during his/her occupation. Remedial action is principally an injunction (a court order restraining the convicted person from committing or continuing the act or omission complained about) and damages.

Eight important principles have been established in court in relation to private nuisance:

a) there must be material interference with property or personal comfort;

b) it is no defence for the defendant to show that all reasonable steps and care have been taken to prevent the nuisance;

c) the nuisance need not be injurious to health;

d) temporary or transient (noise) nuisance will not generally be accepted as a nuisance;

e) the courts do not seek to apply a fixed standard of comfort;

f) it is no defence to show that the plaintiff came to the nuisance;

g) the courts will not interfere with building operations conducted in a reasonable manner;

h) contrary to the general rule in the law of tort, malice may be a significant factor.

Generally speaking, nuisances caused by a person or organisation carrying out a duty imposed by statute are exempt from nuisance action.

ACCESS TO ENVIRONMENTAL INFORMATION

The establishment of public registers under, among others, the *Environmental Protection Act 1990*, has made a wide range of environmental information held by enforcement authorities publicly available. Information on the registers includes applications for (and actual) authorisations and consents, enforcement notices, monitoring results. Only matters of genuine commercial confidentiality and national security may remain secret. Among the areas covered by registers are Integrated Pollution Control, industrial air pollution control, waste management, water pollution and radioactive substances. In addition, the *Environment and Safety Information Act 1988* provides for the maintenance of registers of notices relating to environmental and public safety matters issued under, for example, the *Health and Safety at Work Act 1974* and the *Food and Environment Protection Act 1985*.

1.19 EU DIRECTIVE ON PUBLIC ACCESS TO ENVIRONMENTAL INFORMATION

In 1990, the European Union adopted a Directive on Public Access to Environmental Information (90/313/EEC) which had to be implemented by 31 December 1992. Under the Directive members of the public are entitled to have access to all information about the environment held by government and public authorities in their own or another Member State (unless exempt on the grounds of commercial confidentiality or national security). The Directive defines this as information relating to the state of water, air, soil, fauna, flora, land and natural sites, as well as information relating to

- activities (including those which give rise to nuisances such as noise) or measures adversely affecting, or likely to affect these; and

- activities or measures designed to protect these, including administrative measures and environmental management programmes.

Information must be supplied within two months of a request; reasons for refusal must be given and there must be a right of appeal.

The Commission published a proposal in July 2000 for a new Directive on public access to environmental information, which will replace the 1990 Directive. The new Directive – COM(2000) 402 - will update the current Directive to take account of developments in information technology and to specify more clearly information access procedures; it will also enable the Community to ratify the UNECE Convention on Access to Environmental Information - see next section.

The new Directive will widen the scope of "environmental information" to include "information in any form on the state of the environment; on factors, measures or activities affecting or likely to affect the environment and on those designed to protect it, on emissions, discharges and other releases into the environment, on the cost benefit and economic analyses used within the framework of such measures or activities; and on the state of human health and safety...". The definition of public authorities, to whom the Directive applies, includes bodies carrying out functions or providing services directly or indirectly related to the environment. Environmental information held on behalf of public authorities is also covered by the Directive. The Directive requires information to be made available within one month of a request being made, two months for particularly complex requests.

Information should only be withheld in those circumstances where the benefits of non-disclosure, or protection of the public interest, clearly outweigh the public interest in the information. Information held by public authorities on emissions, discharges and other releases to the environment which relate to Community legislation may not be withheld for reasons of commercial or industrial confidentiality. Authorities will be allowed to charge a "reasonable" amount for supplying information and should publish a schedule of charges; request for payment in advance will not be allowed. Where a request for information is refused, the authority must give its reasons in writing; where access is refused, there should be a right of appeal either through the courts or a body set up to deal with appeals.

1.20 UNECE CONVENTION ON ACCESS TO INFORMATION

This Convention, the full name of which is the Convention on Access to Information, Public Participation in Decision Making and Access to Justice in Environmental Matters, was adopted in June 1998 in Aarhus, Denmark; it covers information held by public authorities and it will enter into force after ratification by 16 countries – as at August 2000 eight had done so. The UK is expected to do so in the summer of 2001 and to implement it through Regulations under the *Freedom of Information Bill* (see 1.21.2 below). The Convention covers:

- **access to information** - the definition of environmental matters is rather wider than that in either the 1990 EU Directive or the UK Regulations, and includes issues which may form part of the decision making process connected with the environmental issue, such as land use planning, health and safety and economic issues; information on biological diversity and genetically modified organisms are also covered by the Convention. Criteria for withholding information are very tightly defined; information should normally be released within one month of a request and there is a right of appeal in the event of refusal. Citizens can apply for information held by the authorities in their own or another country which is a party to the Convention.

- **public participation** - the Convention lists projects where this would be obligatory; they include developments relating to waste management, energy and chemical industries and intensive farming. The public should be given the opportunity to comment either directly or through a representative body, and the results of such consultation taken into account as much as possible.

- **access to justice** - the Convention aims to make it easier for people to take action through the courts or other public authorities if they feel that national environmental law is being contravened. "Adequate and effective remedies" must be available if the case is proved.

1.21 UK LEGISLATION

1.21.1 Environmental Information Regulations 1992 (SI 3240)

In the UK, the 1990 EU Directive has been implemented through the above Regulations made under the *European Communities Act 1972*, as amended by 1998 Regulations (SI 1447). The 1992 Regulations came into force on 31 December 1992 and apply in England, Scotland and Wales with similar Regulations, which came into force in March 1993, applying in Northern Ireland. The Regulations place a duty on all those to whom they apply to make arrangements for dealing with requests for environmental information. The definition of environmental information is similar to that in the Directive; it includes all relevant information, as well as that collected before 31 December 1992 and information held in all forms - e.g. written, visual, aural, databases, computer records, registers and reports.

As of 31 December 1992, all information relating to the environment held by central and local government and other bodies with regulatory responsibilities for the environment became publicly accessible. This includes information held by bodies such as the Environment Agency and SEPA, Health and Safety Executive, English Nature, Countryside Council for Wales and Scottish Natural Heritage.

As well as exemptions for reasons of commercial confidentiality, international relations and public and national security, the Regulations exclude: internal communications and unfinished documents; judicial matters; personal data (unless the individual consents to disclosure); volunteered information; material which has been or is of issue in legal proceedings or enquiries (including disciplinary enquiries); and material whose disclosure could itself lead to environmental damage.

The Regulations provide for the information to be made available in the most appropriate manner, e.g. registers and annual reports; all those to whom the Regulations apply must publish, from time to time, details of the main areas in which they hold unrestricted environmental information and a contact point for gaining access to it.

A request for information should be dealt with as soon as possible and within two months; reasons for refusal - such as the information is covered by one of the exemptions - must be given; other grounds for refusal include: that the request was too general or unreasonable; it is considered outside the scope of the Regulations; or the body does not have the requested information. There is no formal appeals system against refusal. Department of the Environment (now DETR) guidance suggests appealing to the head of the body concerned, to the local government ombudsman (in dealings with a local authority), to one's MP, or if all else fails, taking action in the courts. The *Freedom of Information Bill* (see below) includes provision for the appointment of an Information Commissioner with powers to order the release of information.

As is the case with the public registers, inspection in person of publicly held information is free of charge. Where a request for information is met by providing copies of documents, a reasonable charge may be made to cover copying and associated staff costs.

It should also be noted that in those instances where other environmental legislation requires more or less information to be made publicly available than these Regulations, the legislation requiring greater public access takes precedence.

It is also possible to request access to environmental information under the 1994 Code of Practice on Access to Government Information. This is a non-statutory Code with different requirements and exemptions from the Regulations and can be used to try to gain access to information held by public bodies answerable to the Parliamentary Ombudsman. Where access to information is refused under the Code, the matter can be referred to the Parliamentary Ombudsman.

1.21.2 Freedom of Information Bill

This Bill, published in May 1999, would extend the right to official information on environmental (and other) matters to that held by courts and tribunals, the police, local councils and possibly to some private industries and utilities carrying out public functions. It would apply in England and Wales and in Scotland to those bodies not dealing with devolved issues.

Those covered by the Bill will be required to disclose information on request and within 20 days; in deciding whether to accede to a request, the authority will be required to consider whether the public interest in disclosure outweighed that of withholding; exemptions are likely to include such issues as national security, international relations, commercial confidentiality, investigations into possible criminal offences, accident investigations, or documents relating to the "formulation or development of government policy". An Information Commissioner will be appointed with powers to determine appeals where access to information has been refused and to order the release of information; decisions relating to what is or is not in the public interest will, however, continue to be taken by Ministers. The Bill will enable Regulations to be made implementing the 1998 UNECE Convention (1.20 above), when the *Environmental Information Regulations 1992* would be repealed.

PLANNING CONTROL AND ENVIRONMENTAL ASSESSMENT

1.22 PLANNING - GENERAL

Most new industrial developments - defined as "the carrying out of building, engineering, mining or other operations in, on, over or under land, or the making of any material change in the use of any building or other land" - require planning permission from the local planning authority. Applications for developments and projects with permitted development rights covered by the EU environmental assessment Directive (see 1.24.1a below) must be supported by an environmental statement, prepared on the basis of an environmental assessment. The public has a right to comment on planning applications which are advertised in the local press and copies placed on the planning register.

In considering the application, the planning authority will aim to ensure that there is no significant clash between domestic, commercial, industrial, agricultural or aesthetic interests and will approve or reject the application accordingly. While not primarily concerned with potentially polluting emissions, the planning authority will of course also take into account the overall effect of the proposed development on the neighbourhood.

When consent is given, it is usual to impose conditions relating to the construction and use of a new structure, or a changed use of an old one. Once a consent has been given for a particular use described under the Use Classes Order, that use cannot be changed from one class to another without obtaining a new permission from the planning authority.

If the application is refused, or granted subject to conditions which the applicant feels are unacceptable, there is a right of appeal to the Secretary of State. The appeal may be determined either by a written procedure, or by an inspector holding a public inquiry to determine the facts. The inspector will then report back with recommendations to the Minister who must make the final decision. With some particularly large or controversial projects, the Minister may call in the application for determination by holding a public inquiry.

The *IPPC Practical Guide* (DETR, 2000) advises developers of new industrial sites on which it is proposed to operate an installation carrying out an IPPC activity to liaise with the enforcing authority at an early stage in the project. This will ensure that new installations are developed to meet the legislative requirements of Integrated Pollution Prevention and Control (see 1.13.1 above).

The main pieces of legislation in England and Wales covering planning are the *Town and Country Planning Act 1990* (and Regulations and Orders made under it) and the *Planning (Hazardous Substances) Act 1990* (and 1992 Regulations - see below). These Acts have both been amended by the *Planning and Compensation Act 1991*. In Scotland, the principal planning legislation is the *Town and Country Planning (Scotland) Act 1997*. In Northern Ireland, the relevant legislation is the *Planning (Northern Ireland) Order 1991* and the *Planning General Development Order (Northern Ireland) 1993* (as amended).

Planning Departments also need to have regard to the objectives of the National Air Quality Strategy when considering planning applications for new developments; if there is a likelihood that a new development could lead to an air quality standard being breached, then the application should be refused. LAQM.G4(00), *Air Quality and Land-Use Planning* (May 2000), (Sc: LAQM G4(S)00)) provides guidance for local planning departments on this issue.

Planning Policy Guidance Notes

To assist planning authorities - and indeed applicants - there are a number of policy statements relating to planning and development issues. Planning Policy Guidance Notes (PPG) and Mineral Policy Guidance Notes are the main sources of information, providing advice on the points which should be taken into account when considering whether a particular type of development or activity would be appropriate for the locality. They are not statutory documents but nevertheless can play a very influential role in the operation of the planning system especially when considering draft development plans or in local planning appeals. PPG 1 (March 1992) covers general policy and principles and is currently under revision; other PPGs cover issues as diverse as noise, renewable energy and tourism and transport (see bibliography). They are published by the Department of the Environment, Transport and the Regions and the Welsh Office (often jointly) and by the Scottish Office. In Northern Ireland, planning policy guidance is contained in Planning Policy Statements (see bibliography).

PPG 23 on *Planning and Pollution Control* (1994) aims to inform planners on the various pollution controls with specific relevance to those industrial developments likely to pose a pollution risk. A main objective of this PPG is to provide guidance on avoiding duplication between planning and pollution controls, and it is to be revised to reflect the potential influence of air quality management areas on planning applications. PPG 24 on Planning and Noise (1994) outlines how noise should be taken into account in the planning process (see chapter 3, 3.5.1).

Planning Policy Guidance Notes are published on the DETR's website at www.planning.detr.gov.uk; as well as PPGs, the site includes minerals policy guidance notices, regional policy guidance notes, a list of research reports and best practice advice.

1.23 PLANNING - HAZARDOUS SUBSTANCES

The *Planning (Hazardous Substances) Act 1990* consolidates and amends certain provisions of the *Town and Country Planning Act 1971* and the *Housing and Planning Act 1986*. Under the Act, the presence of a hazardous substance on, over or under land above a specified quantity (the controlled quantity) will require a consent from the hazardous substances authority (HSA). The Act provides for local authorities to be appointed as the HSA; they will be required to take into account the current and contemplated use of the land, its surroundings etc in considering applications. The Act provides for public registers to be maintained containing full details of applications, consents, conditions etc.

The Act has now been implemented in England and Wales through the *Planning (Hazardous Substances) Regulations 1992* (SI 656), which came into effect on 1 June 1992. Similar Regulations - the *Town and Country Planning (Hazardous Substances) (Scotland) Regulations 1993* (SI 323) - came into effect in Scotland on 1 May 1993, with the *Planning (Hazardous Substances) Regulations (Northern Ireland) 1993* covering Northern Ireland.

Storage of certain hazardous substances above the controlled quantity, singly or in aggregate if of the same generic EC classification (specified in the Regulations) requires a consent from the HSA; the procedure for obtaining a consent is set out in the Regulations. This is similar to the procedure for applying for an authorisation under Part I of the *Environmental Protection Act 1990* - i.e. a prescribed form must be used for the application which must be accompanied by the appropriate fee; the application must be publicised locally and statutory consultees asked for their views. In the case of refusal of an application, there is a right of appeal to the Secretary of State. Applications, consents and their conditions, modifications, revocations etc will all be put on a public register.

The Regulations do not apply to controlled wastes or radioactive waste which are subject to control under the *Environmental Protection Act 1990* and *Radioactive Substances Act 1993*. Nor do they cover the storage of explosives where the licensing system is administered by the Health and Safety Executive. Contravention of the Regulations is subject to a maximum fine of £20,000 on summary conviction or an unlimited fine on conviction on indictment.

The *Planning (Control of Major-Accident Hazards) Regulations 1999* (SI 981), which came into effect in England and Wales on 20 April 1999, amend both the *Planning (Hazardous Substances) Act* and the Regulations which implement those requirements of the 1996 EU Directive on the Control of Major Accident Hazards (see chapter 2, 2.16.1) relating to the use of land-use controls in the siting of new hazardous installations, including the consent requirements. Planning authorities must take land-use controls into account when considering modifications to sites or other new developments in the vicinity of such sites; they must also comply with the Directive's objectives that development decisions take account of the need to ensure danger to human health or the environment from accidents at major hazard sites is minimised. Similar Regulations for Northern Ireland (2000 - SR 101) came into force on 24 April 2000, and in Scotland on 6 July 2000 (2000 - SSI 179).

1.24 ENVIRONMENTAL ASSESSMENT

1.24.1 European and International Measures

(a) Assessment of Certain Public and Private Projects

European Union Directive 85/337/EEC on the assessment of the effects of certain public and private projects on the environment was implemented in England, Scotland and Wales through 1988 Regulations and in Northern Ireland in 1989; it requires an environmental impact statement to be prepared on all proposed developments which might have a significant effect on the environment. The statement should include a full description of the project; this might include measures to be taken to avoid, reduce or remedy any adverse effects of the development, and supporting data to enable full assessment by the public and various authorities. Annex I of the Directive lists types of projects for which EA is mandatory; a second list, Annex II, includes projects which "shall be made subject to an assessment where Member States consider their characteristics so require".

In March 1997 Environment Ministers formally adopted Directive 97/11/EC amending the 1985 Directive. This Directive, which had to be implemented by 14 March 1999, gives more guidance as to the information to be provided by developers; it requires public consultation prior to authorisation of a project subject to environmental assessment (rather than before start of the work); the decision of the determining authority, together with reasons for it and measures required to offset any adverse impacts, must be made public.

Annex I now lists 20 types of project subject to mandatory EA (see box). Additional criteria for deciding whether or not an Annex II project should be subject to EA include: (a) is the project likely to have "significant" environmental effects (on the basis of preset thresholds); and (b) is it likely to have a "significant effect" on an area designated a special protection zone under other EU legislation. Annex II lists 50 types of project including: agriculture, extractive, energy, metal processing, glass making, chemical, food, textile, leather, wood, paper and rubber industries, tourism and leisure. It also includes the modification or expansion of authorised or completed Annex I or II projects "which could have a major or negative impact on the environment". Member States must put in place a formal mechanism for determining whether a particular Annex II project should be subject to EA - the outcome and the reasons for it must be made public.

Projects for which EA is Mandatory

(Annex I to Directive 97/11/EC)

- Power stations with a heat output of 300 MW or more, nuclear power stations and nuclear reactors (including decommissioning and dismantling);
- Crude oil refineries; facilities for gasification and liquefaction of coal or bituminous shale;
- Asbestos plants;
- Construction of motorways and express roads and widening of existing dual and single carriageways where new or widened section is more than 10 km in length;
- Long distance railway lines and airports with a planned runway length of 2100 metres or more;
- Inland waterways and inland waterway ports which allow the passage of vessels over 1,350 tonnes;
- Developments for the disposal of special waste, including incinerators, chemical waste treatment and landfill facilities, radioactive waste disposal sites and toxic waste facilities; non hazardous waste facilities with capacity of more than 100 tonnes per day;
- Projects for the reprocessing of irradiated nuclear fuels, for the production or enrichment of fuel, and the processing or storage of nuclear waste;
- Integrated chemical facilities (producing inorganic or organic chemical products, fertilisers, biocides, pharmaceuticals or explosives;
- Groundwater abstraction or artificial groundwater recharge with annual volume of at least 10 million cubic metres;
- Plant for the transfer of water between river basins;
- Waste water treatment plant with capacity exceeding 150,000 population equivalent;
- Extraction of oil (> 500 tonnes per day) and natural gas (> 500,000 m³ per day);
- Gas, oil and chemical pipelines > 800 mm diameter and > 40 km in length;
- Dams storing in excess of 10 million cubic metres;
- Intensive pig and poultry rearing units;
- Industrial plant for production of pulp from timber or similar fibrous materials;
- Quarries and open cast mines > 25 hectares and peat extraction sites exceeding 150 hectares;
- Construction of overhead power lines with voltage of 220 kV or more and length > 15 km;
- oil, petrochemical or chemical products storage facilities with capacity of > 200,000 tonnes.

(b) Assessment of Certain Plans and Programmes on the Environment

Published in December 1996 this proposal for a Directive (COM(96) 511), amended by COM(99) 73, would require an environmental assessment to be carried out, and an environmental statement prepared, before the adoption by public authorities of, or national legislation for, land-use development plans and programmes likely to have significant environmental effects; in the UK this would include structure plans and unitary development plans and local plans; it would not apply to plans submitted to the Commission under the Structural Funds Regulation (EEC 2081/93), to those plans which are not subject to formal adoption or legislation in the Member State concerned, or to plans or programmes determining "the use of small areas at local level". The statement would need to include:

- environmental characteristics of any area which might be significantly affected;
- existing environmental problems;
- likely significant adverse environmental effects of implementing the plan or programme and measures to prevent, reduce or offset those effects;
- possible alternative ways of achieving the plan's objectives and why these are not considered appropriate.

The Directive includes requirements for consulting environmental authorities and other interested bodies, with the general public also being given an opportunity to comment; relevant member states would need to be consulted over those projects likely to have transboundary effects.

The text of the Directive is now to be finalised in conciliation committee of members of the Council of Ministers and the European Parliament. Outstanding issues include the scope of the Directive; the Council want to restrict it to national, regional and local plans in certain sectors (including, agriculture, forestry, fisheries, energy, industry, transport, waste, telecommunications, tourism, and land use), with other sectors considered on the basis of whether the plan or programme was likely to have a significant environmental effect. Parliament and the Commission want the Directive to apply to the Community's structural funds. It is hoped to agree the draft to enable adoption in early 2001.

(c) UNECE Convention

A Convention on Environmental Impact Assessment in a Transboundary Context (Espoo Convention) came into force in 1998, 90 days after ratification by 16 countries (2000 – 28 ratifications). It applies solely to those projects with possible transboundary effects (e.g. off-shore oil production, new reservoirs or dams); it gives those likely to be affected by a project the right to be notified about the project, to participate in the EIA and then to be consulted about the transboundary impacts and measures to mitigate them.

The Convention was ratified by the European Community on 24 June 1997 and by the UK on 10 October 1997. The terms of the Convention have been taken account of in the amended EU Directive - see (a) above.

1.24.2 UK Regulations

The *Town and Country Planning (Environmental Impact Assessment) (England and Wales) Regulations 1999* (SI 293) which came into force on 14 March 1999 implement the 1997 Directive; earlier 1988 Regulations (SI 1199), and subsequent amendments, which implemented the 1985 Directive have been revoked. Similar Regulations apply in Scotland (the *Environmental Impact Assessment (Scotland)*

Regulations 1999 - SI 1) and in Northern Ireland *(the Planning (Environmental Impact Assessment) Regulations (Northern Ireland) 1999* - SR 73).

In accordance with the Directive, environmental assessment of Annex I (Schedule 1 in the Regulations) projects is mandatory (see earlier box). Also in accordance with the Directive, the Regulations detail the formal screening process for determining whether an Annex II project requiring planning permission should be subject to environmental assessment; the Regulations set statutory "exclusive" thresholds for most Annex II projects, below which an EA would not normally be required, subject to a power for the Secretary of State to determine that a particular project should be subject to EA; higher non-binding indicative thresholds where an EA may be required have been set out in DETR Circular 02/99 for all Annex II projects, with developments being considered on a case by case basis. EA would however, normally be required for projects within SSSIs or other sensitive locations or which could have a significant effect on the environment.

As a first step in determining whether a development falls within the Directive - i.e. is an EIA development - the developer may ask the planning authority for a "screening opinion"; the planning authority should normally determine the request - the Regulations set out both the procedure and criteria to be used - within three weeks, or such longer period as is agreed. If it does not, or the developer disagrees with the planning authority's decision, a "screening direction" may be sought from the Secretary of State. Where a decision has been made that a development is an EIA development, the developer should be notified that an environmental statement will be required. The Regulations enable the developer to seek an opinion - a "scoping opinion" from the planning authority or from the Secretary of State - a "scoping direction" - on the type of information which is required to be included in the environmental statement. Statutory consultees - bodies which should be consulted over planning applications, the Environment Agency, the principal council for the area, the Countryside Commission, the Nature Conservancy Council for England or the Countryside Council for Wales - should be consulted prior to adoption of the scoping opinion or direction.

The environmental statement, together with the planning application should be submitted to the local planning authority, who should notify statutory consultees of its receipt. In giving approval for an EIA development, the planning authority (or Secretary of State) should make publicly available a statement outlining the reasons for their decision and the measures to be taken to avoid adverse environmental impacts.

The Regulations also provide for copies of environmental statements to be placed on the planning register and to be made publicly available, for appeals, and for consultation with EU Member States about projects with significant transboundary effects.

Various Regulations cover those projects (such as new rail line developments, harbour projects, off-shore and on-shore pipelines) for which authorisation is granted under other regulatory regimes and Parliamentary Private Bills (rather than planning law). These include the *Offshore Petroleum Production and Pipelines (Assessment of Environmental Effects) Regulations 1999* (SI 360), which came into force on 14 March 1999, replacing 1998 Regulations (SI 968). The Regulations require mandatory assessment of certain projects relating to the extraction of oil and natural gas and gas, oil and chemical pipelines above the threshold (see box), as well as other projects below the threshold which are likely to have significant environmental effects. Similar Regulations implementing the 1997 Directive have been made with respect to the following: fish farming in marine waters (E, S, W: 1999, SI 367; NI: 1999, SR415); highways (E, W: 1999, SI 369); forestry (E & W: 1999, SI 2228; S: 1999, SI43; NI: 2000, SR 84); harbour works (E, S, W: 1999, SI 3445); decommissioning nuclear reactors (1999, SI 2892); electricity works (E & W: 2000, SI 1927; S: 2000, SSI320). Further Regulations covering other types of development are expected.

DETR Circular 02/99, *Environmental Impact Assessment*, provides guidance on the Directive and application of the Regulations in England and Wales.

ENVIRONMENTAL MANAGEMENT AND AUDIT SYSTEMS

A responsible attitude towards the environment is now recognised by many businesses - industrial, manufacturing or service - to be not only good for the environment but also good for their business in terms of how they are viewed by their customers. In 1992 the British Standards Institution published BS 7750, *Environmental Management System,* which outlined the steps to be taken in developing an environmental management system. A revised version, compatible with the Eco-Management and Audit Regulation (1.21.2 below), was published in 1994 and formally recognised by the Commission in 1996. BS 7750 was withdrawn in September 1997 following agreement on international standard ISO 14001 (see below).

1.25 ENVIRONMENTAL MANAGEMENT

ISO 14001:1996 and supporting documents, developed by the International Standards Organisation, provide guidance on implementing an environmental management system. They provide general guidelines on principles, systems and supporting techniques and outline the requirements for companies wishing to certify to the standard. A number of other documents in the series outline standards for environmental auditing. These standards have been formally recognised by the Commission with the draft proposal (see below) amending the 1993 EU Regulation setting requirements compatible with ISO 14001. ISO 14001 is itself under revision; issues under discussion include a mandatory requirement for environmental reports to be made publicly available, as is the case under EMAS, clarification of what is meant by continuous environmental improvement and a more explicit requirement to comply with environmental legislation. A revised version of the standard is due 2001/02.

Companies or organisations wishing to be certified under ISO must ensure that their environmental management system takes account of the following:

- the development of an environmental policy;
- a commitment to comply with relevant environmental legislation and regulations;
- products or services are produced, delivered and disposed of in an environmentally friendly manner - and thus any adverse effects on the environment are minimised;
- expenditure on environmental protection is timely and effective, and that planning for future investment and growth reflects market needs on the environment - that best available technology is used where appropriate and economically viable;
- the principles of sustainable development;
- objectives and targets aimed at continuous environmental improvement; evaluation procedures; staff training and awareness.

Where the company has identified a "significant environmental effect" this should be entered on a register. All participating companies should carry out an environmental audit at least every three years or annually if there is "particular potential to cause environmental harm".

Certification for compliance with the standard is voluntary and may cover all or part of a company's sites or operations. In the UK certification is carried out by external assessors ("certifiers") who are formally accredited under a scheme run by the UK Accreditation Service. UKAS, which is also responsible for accrediting verifiers for the environmental statements required under the Eco-Management and Audit Regulation (see below), is the national accreditation body for the UK. It was formed as a result of amalgamation of the National Certification Accreditation Board (NACCB) and the National Measurement Accreditation Service (NAMAS).

1.26 ENVIRONMENTAL AUDITING

In 1993, the European Union approved a Council Regulation allowing Voluntary Participation by Companies in the Industry Sector in a Community Eco-Management and Audit Scheme (EMAS). The Regulation (1836/93), which came into force in May 1995, aims to encourage industrial companies to continually evaluate and improve their environmental performance. At their meeting in February 2000, Environment Ministers adopted a common position on a proposal to amend the Regulation (COM(98) 622) with a view to making it compatible with ISO 14001 and extending its coverage to non-industrial companies and organisations (e.g. agricultural and financial sectors) whose activities can have a direct or indirect effect on the environment. Organisations will still be able to register one or all their sites; where more than one is registered, each will have to comply with the Regulation; organisations operating in a number of Member States would have to register in each country. The European Parliament, in adopting the proposal on a second reading, also adopted a number of amendments; these include strengthening requirements on those carrying out environmental audits, and permitting financial inducements as a means of increasing participation in the scheme.

The Institute of Environmental Assessment is the UK Registration Authority; companies may choose whether or not to participate in the scheme and indeed whether to register all or only some of their sites. Under the 1993 scheme, companies registering under EMAS are required to carry out an assessment of operations at each site and the impact on the environment. This would form the basis of an environmental protection system (including an environmental policy, environmental management system and audit programme). Issues to be covered include energy policy, waste and water management, product planning, safety, staff training and involvement in environmental issues, information to be made public and complaints handling; objectives and targets should be set with a view to "reasonable continuous improvement of environmental performance" reducing environmental impacts to levels commensurate with the use of best available technology. The new Regulation deletes reference to BAT but defines continual improvement as "the process of enhancing, year by year, the measurable results of the EMS related to an organisation's management of its significant environmental impacts, based on its environmental policy, objectives and targets. . ." An environmental audit must be carried out not less than every three years and the resulting environmental statement verified; in the intervening years an environmental statement should be published. The new Regulation will also require verification of the annual statements if it reports any changes from the 3-year statement.

Accredited verifiers ensure compliance with all aspects of the Regulation and validate the environmental statement if satisfied with the way the company has complied with the Regulation. The verifier and the auditor should be independent of each other.

Companies satisfying the requirements of the Regulation and registering under the Scheme can use a "statement of participation". This cannot be used on actual products or packaging, or to advertise the product. Under the new Regulation a logo is to be introduced as a means of promoting EMAS more widely; organisations will be able to use this in advertising their products, services and activities.

The UK Accreditation Service is responsible for accrediting verifiers for the environmental statements.

1.27 ENVIRONMENTAL LIABILITY

1.27.1 EU Proposals

In March 1993 the European Commission published for discussion a Green Paper (COM(93) 47) on Remedying Environmental Damage. The rationale for the document is the principle that the polluter should pay for any damage caused to the environment; the paper proposed strict (or no fault) liability where the polluter is known and the establishment of a compensation fund to cover damage where the polluter is not known or where damage is the result of pollution and cannot be attributed to a single party. The Green Paper has now been succeeded by a White Paper – COM(2000) 66 – published in February 2000. This confirms the principle that the "polluter should pay" and suggests that a liability regime would also enhance two other important principles of environmental protection – prevention and the precautionary principle, and thus result in more responsible behaviour on the part of business.

The White Paper concludes that a framework Directive, which takes account of the following, would be the most appropriate way forward

- only damage identified after the Directive entered into force would be covered;

- it would not apply to diffuse sources of pollution (such as air pollution), liability for which cannot easily be apportioned;

- it should cover both environmental damage, which includes harm to biodiversity, contamination of land, etc and "traditional" damage to health and property;

- the activities to be covered by an environmental liability regime include those covered by EU legislation dealing with emission limits for hazardous substances; dangerous substances and preparations; prevention and control of risks from accidents; transfrontier shipment and disposal of hazardous and other waste;

- in the case of biodiversity it should cover harm to biodiversity protected under EC legislation on habitats, wild birds and protection of other natural resources through the Natura 2000 network;

- strict liability would be applied where damage has been caused by a dangerous activity (as defined by the directive, but including damage arising from potentially dangerous activities, such as an activity carried on under the IPPC or GMO Directives); liability for damage to biodiversity from non-dangerous activities, or from an activity not otherwise covered by EU legislation, would be fault based. If the polluter could not be identified, the State should pay compensation or for restoration. An issue to be decided is whether a permit-granting authority should bear some responsibility if an operator can prove that the damage has been caused by an activity specifically allowed by a permit;

- Authorities in Member States would be responsible for ensuring restoration of damage to the environment; however, public interest groups meeting certain criteria would have the right to seek a judicial review in those cases where it is felt the State has not acted at all or not acted "properly" and in certain circumstances to claim against the polluter; such groups would also have the right, in urgent cases, to ask courts for an injunction to require an alleged polluter to stop a particular activity to prevent significant damage or further damage to the environment.

The White Paper also considers ratification of the Council of Europe Convention (see below) as a possible way forward, but concludes that it would need to be complemented by an EU measure to bring more clarity and precision to the areas covered by the Convention. Thus a tailor-made Directive would provide more legal certainty. In considering a transboundary liability scheme, the White Paper concludes that this could lead to inconsistency – compensation could be claimed for an activity which caused damage in another Member State, but the same activity causing damage from within the State could escape claims for compensation if it was not covered by a national scheme.

Comments were invited on the White Paper until 1 July 2000 – both the DETR and the Scottish Executive invited comments on the White Paper; a proposal for a framework Directive or other measure is not expected to be ready until late in 2001.

1.27.2 The Lugano Convention

The Council of Europe has already agreed (March 1993) a Convention on Civil Liability for Damage Resulting from Activities Dangerous to the Environment (the Lugano Convention). Although some countries have signed the Convention, it requires ratification by three before it comes into force. (In Paying for our Past, DOE, 1994, it was stated that there were no plans for the UK to sign the Convention.) The Convention applies to a wide range of industries, including research laboratories dealing with genetically modified organisms, who will be liable for any "intolerable" damage caused even though pollution legislation has been complied with. It provides for compensation to persons and property and for economic loss as a result of environmental damage; operators are required to have insurance cover and the Convention provides for environmental organisations to take legal action in pursuit of the Convention's requirements.

Air Quality Management

Regulation of Industrial Emissions

Smoke Control

Regulation of Pollution from Road Vehicles

Radiation

Odour

EARLY CONTROLS

2.1 INTRODUCTION

The development of air pollution control legislation in the UK has been a gradual process with most of it resulting from the Industrial Revolution of the late 18th and 19th centuries; air pollution was, however, first acknowledged to be a problem many hundreds of years earlier.

Coal was already used in England by the year 852 and a record of "Seacoales Lane" in London dates from 1228. The use of coal was prohibited in London in 1273 as being prejudicial to health; however the practice must have continued for early in the 14th century a Royal Proclamation prohibited the use of seacoal by artificers (craftsmen) in their furnaces. In 1648, Londoners petitioned Parliament to prohibit the importation of coal from Newcastle because of the injuries they experienced. After complaints of smoke from his neighbour, one baker was ordered to erect a chimney "so high as to convey the smoake clear of the topps of the houses".

In 1661 John Evelyn published his tract *Fumifugium or The Smoake of London Dissipated*. This suggested practical schemes to improve the air over London. These were ignored and it was not until 1819 that Parliament appointed a committee to enquire to what extent persons using steam engines and furnaces could erect them in a manner less prejudicial to the public health and comfort. However, nothing of significance emerged from the committee's deliberations.

2.2 ALKALI ACTS AND BEST PRACTICABLE MEANS

The Industrial Revolution, which was based on coal as the energy source, brought a worsening of urban squalor and appalling air pollution. Around 1860, discharges to the air from an early alkali works devastated the surrounding country, corroding material and tools and destroying vegetation and crops. Air pollution from the works could no longer be ignored. Following overwhelming public complaint and a Parliamentary Enquiry, the first *Alkali etc Works Act* was passed in 1863. This made no attempt to control smoke, but required that 95% of the offensive emissions should be arrested. The remainder, after adequate dilution, might be allowed to pass to atmosphere. This tolerance replaced the unworkable prohibition of all previous enactments and allowed a rapidly growing chemical industry the freedom to develop. The same Act set up a national inspectorate to enforce the legislation. The improvement in pollution levels was dramatic: acid emissions from alkali works were reduced from an annual rate of almost 14,000 tonnes to about 45 tonnes.

The second *Alkali Act* (1874) required, for the first time, the application of the Best Practicable Means (BPM) to prevent the escape of noxious or offensive gases. The Act was subsequently extended to all the major industries that pollute the air. The requirement applied whether the escapes arose indirectly from any part of the process or plant, or directly from the exit flues. The requirement also applied to "fugitive" or "uncontained" emissions; these could include gases or vapours leaking from process storage tanks, pumps, compressors, coking plant or streams of liquid effluent; they could also include dust from roadways, stockpiles or even materials carried out of works on the wheels of vehicles. The 1874 Act also introduced the first statutory emission limit - for hydrogen chloride (0.2 grains per cubic foot).

2.2.1 Scheduled Processes

A series of Acts then followed which were eventually consolidated by the *Alkali etc Works Regulation Act 1906*. This linked together a schedule of carefully defined and chosen processes - works - with an equally carefully chosen list of "noxious and offensive gases". The types of works scheduled were those thought most likely to cause pollution problems and included a substantial part of the chemical industry, petroleum refineries, petrochemicals, electricity generation, coal carbonisation, iron and steel works, non-ferrous metals, mineral processing works etc.

The *Public Health (Smoke Abatement) Act 1926* empowered ministers to make various additions to the list of scheduled works and noxious and offensive gases by an order laid before Parliament for approval and given legislative effect as a statutory instrument. As industrial technology advanced, seven such orders extended control over various processes between 1928 and 1963. These orders were consolidated in 1966 in the *Alkali etc Works Order*. In 1974 the *Health and Safety at Work etc Act* was passed. It was essentially an enabling measure and was intended to repeal the 1906 Act entirely, replacing it by regulations made under the 1974 Act, e.g. the *Health and Safety (Emissions into the Atmosphere) Regulations 1983*. The remaining sections of the 1906 Act were repealed in England and Wales on 16 December 1996 following completion of authorisation of all prescribed processes under Part I of the *Environmental Protection Act 1990* (see chapter 1, 1.14 and chapter 2, 2.12).

The legislation was administered in England and Wales by HM Inspectorate of Pollution (or its forerunners), with almost identical legislation in Scotland administered by HM Industrial Pollution Inspectorate. The control of scheduled processes by the Inspectorate had three distinct aspects:

Registration: Under the *Health and Safety (Emissions into the Atmosphere) Regulations* (SI 943, repealed December 1996) scheduled works had to be registered annually. As an essential prior condition to the first and all subsequent registrations, every scheduled works had to be provided, to the satisfaction of the chief inspector, with the Best Practicable Means for preventing the escape of any noxious or offensive substances, and for rendering all such emissions harmless and inoffensive. The *Control of Air Pollution (Registration of Works) Regulations 1989* (SI 318, repealed December 1996) specified the information that should be contained in applications to HM Inspectorate of Pollution for the registration of scheduled works under the *Alkali etc Works Regulation Act 1906* and the *Health and Safety at Work etc Act 1974* and in the register of works (which had to be made available for public inspection).

Inspection: Following registration, it was a requirement that the Best Practicable Means must always be in use, and that pollution control equipment must be maintained in good and efficient working order. Under the *Health and Safety at Work etc Act 1974,* inspectors were authorised to enter premises for examination or investigation without prior announcement. The emphasis was on prevention rather than cure.

If the inspector believed that provisions of the 1974 Act (or the *1906 Alkali Act*) were being contravened, an improvement notice could be issued specifying the problem, the period during which it should be put right and if appropriate, the remedial measures to be taken. Where toxic emissions were involved the process would generally be suspended or drastically curtailed. Inspectors could also issue a prohibition notice if there was believed to be a risk of personal injury.

Presumptive Limits: The remaining aspect of control was the setting, via the Notes on Best Practicable Means, of presumptive limits which specified the amount of pollutant per cubic metre of gas that could be emitted from the chimney stack. Although they were non-statutory limits, there was normally a presumption that if the limit was being met, then the legislation was being complied with in that the Best Practicable Means were being used. The fact that BPM Notes were non-statutory documents allowed the inspectorate to tighten emission limits in line with advances in abatement technology or scientific understanding of the effects of pollutants. For many processes there were, in addition, other limits based on subjective assessment, such as smoke emission or other visibility criteria. Most of the processes covered by the Act were prescribed for Integrated Pollution Control under Part I of the *Environmental Protection Act 1990* (see chapter 1, 1.14).

2.2.2 Smoke Control

While the *Public Health (Smoke Abatement) Act 1926* had enabled the Alkali Inspectorate to extend its influence to industrial smoke, there was no measure to control the far more widespread problem of smoke from domestic chimneys. Other legislation enabled smoke to be dealt with as a possible nuisance, but was largely ineffective because a nuisance had first to be proved in court. Thus the atmosphere of Britain's urban areas was still characterised by the pervading pall of smoke and sulphur fumes from countless stacks, chimneys and funnels. The lack of winter sunshine, the prevalence of pea-soup fogs, black buildings and even black snow, had become accepted as the price of progress and bronchitis, exacerbated by smoke and sulphur, was a common illness.

It was not until the infamous London smog of December 1952, which lasted for five days, that any real action was taken. The first casualties of the fog were prize cattle brought to London for the Smithfield Show - one died, 12 had to be slaughtered and some 160 required veterinary treatment. Even an opera performance at the Sadlers Wells Theatre had to be stopped after the first Act as the audience could not see the stage! More seriously, some 4,000 additional deaths were directly attributed to the episode.

The Government appointed a committee, under the chairmanship of Sir Hugh Beaver, to study the problem of air pollution. Its terms of reference were "to examine the nature, causes and effects of air pollution and the efficacy of present preventive measures; to consider what further measures are practicable; and to make recommendations". The committee issued two reports, the first in 1953 and the second in 1954; these recognised that the constituent parts of the problem were gaseous and particulate emissions, and recommended immediate legislation to reduce smoke, grit and dust.

The eventual result was the *Clean Air Act 1956* which was later amended and extended by the *Clean Air Act 1968.* These Acts (covering England, Scotland and Wales, with a similar 1964 Act for N. Ireland) constituted the operative legislation against pollution by smoke, grit and dust from domestic fires and other commercial and industrial processes not covered by the *Alkali Acts* and other subsequent pollution legislation. They regulated the combustion of solid, liquid and gaseous fuels and controlled the heights of new industrial chimneys that are not scheduled elsewhere. The legislation also prohibited the emission of "dark" smoke from any chimney, provided for Government funding for the conversion of domestic grates to smokeless operation, and regulated the fuels that could be burned on them.

The 1956 and 1968 Acts have now been consolidated and their provisions re-enacted in the *Clean Air Act 1993* which came into force on 27 August 1993. This applies in England, Scotland and Wales only. (s.30 - regulations about motor fuel - also applies in Northern Ireland: see 2.14.4 below.) In Northern Ireland, the 1964 Act has been replaced by the *Clean Air (Northern Ireland) Order 1981.*

INTERNATIONAL AND EUROPEAN INITIATIVES

2.3 INTERNATIONAL INITIATIVES

2.3.1 Environment and Development

Many pollution problems - depletion of the ozone layer, global warming, export of hazardous wastes and so on - are recognised as global problems requiring global solutions. Here the United Nations Organisation and its agencies, such as the United Nations Environment Programme (UNEP), have an important role in providing a forum for discussion and cooperation on global environmental problems. UNEP itself was founded in 1973 following the UN Conference on the Human Environment held in 1972 where the 113 participating countries expressed concern over the rapidly deteriorating environment.

A further conference - the United Nations Conference on Environment and Development (UNCED, or the Earth Summit) - was held in June 1992 in Brazil. This conference was a direct result of the UN Commission on Environment and Development whose report *Our Common Future* (often called the Brundtland Report, after its Chairman Gro Harlem Brundtland), was published in 1987. This identified the importance of "sustainable development" in eradicating poverty and halting further environmental degradation and moving to sustained economic growth.

The Earth Summit in Brazil was attended by world leaders, ministers, officials and representatives of environment non-governmental organisations from over 160 countries. The main aim of the Conference was to find ways to "halt and reverse the effects of environmental degradation" while increasing efforts "to promote sustainable and environmentally sound development in all countries". As well as establishing a Sustainable Development Commission and endorsing a *Declaration of Principles* for the pursuit of sustainable development as the prime means of alleviating Third World poverty and global environmental degradation, two important conventions were agreed (see below); The conference also agreed a *Statement of Principles* for the sustainable management and conservation of forests and funding for new environmental aid for developing countries.

(a) Framework Convention on Climate Change (Climate Treaty)

Developed countries are required to take measures aimed at returning emissions of greenhouse gases (in particular carbon dioxide) to 1990 levels by 2000 and to provide assistance to developing countries. Other obligations include compiling inventories of emissions, producing and publishing national programmes of measures to limit emissions and to promote research and public education about climate change. The Convention came into force on 21 March 1994 following ratification by 50 countries; as at May 2000 the Convention had been ratified by 184 countries, including both the European Community and the UK.

In December 1997, in Kyoto, Japan, parties to the Climate Treaty agreed to make legally binding cuts in emissions of six greenhouse gases - carbon dioxide, methane, nitrous oxide, hydrofluorocarbons, perfluorocarbons and sulphur hexafluoride. Between 2008-2012 developed countries will reduce their emissions by an average of 5.2% below 1990 levels (for the first three substances; any year between 1990-1995 for the last three). Different targets have been set for individual countries - e.g. EU 8%, Switzerland 8%, USA 7%, Japan 6%. The Protocol also permits emissions trading between countries as a means of meeting targets, although rules for doing this have still to be finalised. The Protocol will come into force 90 days after ratification by 55 countries which together account for 55% of the 1990 carbon dioxide emissions of developed countries. As at August 2000, 29 countries had ratified the Protocol; it is hoped that enough countries will have ratified it to enable it to come into force by 2002.

In 1997 UK levels of carbon dioxide were 8% lower than in 1990. The Government has pledged to reduce emissions of carbon dioxide by 20% of their 1990 level by 2010; this will be achieved through greater energy efficiency, renewable forms of power generation, and development of an integrated transport policy (Prime Minister's statement to House of Commons, June 1997).

Climate Change - the UK Programme, published January 1994, outlines a number of voluntary actions which various sectors (e.g. individuals, industry and commerce and the public sector) can take to reduce energy consumption and also government measures. Voluntary actions include encouraging energy conservation and efficiency; better use of transport and use of fuel efficient cars; central government can play its part by encouraging voluntary action, support for renewable energy, and regulatory and/or economic instruments where necessary. In March 2000, the Government (together with the devolved administrations) published a draft revised Climate Change Programme; this aims for a 21.5% cut in greenhouse gas emissions, as well as the 20% cut in carbon dioxide emissions to which the Government is already committed.

The draft programme takes account of already agreed policies which will help to reduce carbon dioxide emissions such as the climate change levy (which takes effect in 2001), negotiated agreements with the energy intensive industries and voluntary agreements with car manufacturers to cut engine emissions; among its further proposals for reducing greenhouse gas emissions are:

- action to cut emissions in all sectors of the UK (including business, public, transport, domestic, agriculture, forestry and land use);
- improved energy efficiency in the home;

- more clarity for business – carbon emissions trading to be seen as part of the longer-term solution to cutting greenhouse gas emissions; encouragement for UK-based carbon offset projects.

The consultation period on the draft programme ended on 2 June 2000 and it was hoped to publish the final programme before the end of 2000, with a view to enabling UK ratification of the Kyoto Protocol soon after.

The UK's *Home Energy Conservation Act 1995* should also result in reduced carbon dioxide emissions; this Act requires local authorities to report to the Secretary of State on how "significant energy savings" - initially 30% - can be made from residential properties, including homes in multiple occupation, in their area. (See also below, 2.4.2 - carbon dioxide)

(b) Convention on Biological Diversity

This aims to protect and preserve endangered plants and species on land and in the oceans and has three main goals: the conservation of biodiversity; the sustainable use of the components of biodiversity; and the fair and equitable sharing of the benefits arising from the use of genetic resources. The Convention came into force on 29 December 1993 following ratification by 30 countries, and became legally binding 90 days later. As at August 2000, there were 178 ratifications. Countries will each draw up a list of "protected areas". Use of resources in protected areas - e.g. exploitation of plants for medicines - would need to be paid for with financial assistance additional to current levels of development assistance. It has been signed and ratified by the EC and the UK.

A Protocol to the Convention – the Cartagena Protocol on Biosafety – had, as at 26 May 2000, been signed by 68 parties to the Convention (including the UK and the European Community), but will require ratification by 50 before coming into force 90 days later; the Protocol addresses the potential risks of transboundary movements (through trade or by accident) of living genetically modified organisms (LMOs). Exporters will be required to obtain the prior informed consent – or, the term used in the Protocol, Advanced Informed Agreement – from the importing state. Detailed information about the shipment, including an environmental and health risk assessment must be provided and authorisation obtained from the importer prior to its arrival. Importing countries have 270 days to reach a decision (though they can ask for longer) and must inform the Biosafety Clearing House (which is to be established) of their decision. The Clearing House will maintain details of shipments and of risk assessments. The Protocol includes labelling requirements and enables importing countries to adopt a "precautionary" approach in deciding whether or not to authorise a shipment – thus if there is any scientific uncertainty, they can refuse to proceed with the shipment.

(c) Agenda 21

A huge document setting out an "environmental work programme" into the 21st century. It aims to provide guidance for governments in establishing environmental policies that meet the needs of sustainable development; it covers all areas of pollution, energy policy, population and development issues. In the UK, local authorities have been encouraged to adopt their own Agenda 21 - i.e. a strategy for sustainable development at local level - in consultation with business and community groups. One of the main tasks of the Sustainable Development Commission is to ensure progress on Agenda 21.

2.3.2 Ozone Layer

Concern over depletion of the stratospheric ozone layer, particularly over Antarctica, was first raised in the 1970s. Increasingly scientific evidence pointed to the fact that the growing consumption of chlorine based chemicals - such as chlorofluorocarbons - may be largely to blame for the continuing damage to the ozone layer. It also became clear that action was needed on an international basis to protect the ozone layer from further damage to avert a more serious situation. More recently, preliminary results for research being carried out by the European Arctic Stratospheric Ozone Experiment reveal that ozone amounts in the Northern Hemisphere are also falling, thus confirming the need for urgent measures if further damage is to be halted.

The ozone layer which forms part of the earth's stratosphere, lies about 15-20 km above the earth's surface. Ozone molecules absorb some of the sun's ultraviolet radiation, thus acting as a protective filter. Research shows that increased ultraviolet light on earth as a result of ozone depletion can increase the risk of skin cancer and eye cataracts, depress the human immune system, and harm aquatic systems and crops.

A series of meetings held under the auspices of the UN Environment Programme culminated in Montreal in September 1987 with the signing of an Agreement on Substances that deplete the Ozone Layer - the Montreal Protocol. This has now been ratified by over 170 governments worldwide and committed industrialised nations to reduce consumption of CFCs by 50% by 1999 and to freeze production of halons in 1992. In 1992 methyl bromide, hydrochlorofluorocarbons and hydrobromofluoro-carbons were included in the Protocol, with further controls on the first two substances being agreed in 1995, and the timetable for methyl bromide being tightened further in 1997. Further restrictions on HCFCs and methyl bromide were agreed in December 1999 and bromochloromethane added to the list of restricted substances.

The Protocol is reviewed regularly and in the light of scientific evidence revised and strengthened. It currently provides for the following:

- **Chlorofluorocarbons:** based on 1986 consumption levels, 75% reduction by 1 January 1994; phase out by 1 January 1996. Less developed countries to freeze production and consumption at 1995/7 average levels, 50% cut in 2005, phase out by 2010.

- **Halons:** based on 1986 levels, phase out by 1 January 1994; less developed countries – as for CFCs.

- **Carbon Tetrachloride:** Based on 1989 levels, 85% reduction by 1 January 1994; phase out by 1 January 1996.

- **1,1,1-trichloroethane:** based on 1989 levels, 50% reduction by 1 January 1994; phase out by 1 January 1996.

- **Methyl Bromide:** for developed countries, freeze on use at 1991 levels from 1 January 1995; 25% reduction by 1 January 1999, followed by 50% reduction by 1 January 2001, 70% by 1 January 2003 and phase out by 1 January 2005, subject to exemption for critical agricultural uses. Less developed countries are to reduce use by 20% by 2005 using a baseline of the average of 1995-98 consumption and phase out by 2015. Quarantine and pre-shipment fumigations to be limited to 21 days before export, with obligation to report quantity used for such purposes, imports and exports to any country not a party to the 1994 amendments on methyl bromide are prohibited.

- **Hydrochlorofluorocarbons:** developed countries, freeze at 2.8% of CFC and HCFC consumption in 1989 from 1 January 1996 levels; 35% reduction by 2004 and freeze in production; 65% by 2007; 90% by 2010; 99.5% by 2013; phase out by 2020, subject to limited exemptions for existing equipment to 2030. Less developed countries are to freeze their consumption of HCFCs in 2016 at 2015 levels and phase out entirely by 2040; freeze production in 2016 using average of 2015's production and consumption levels.

- **Hydrobromofluorocarbons:** phase out from 1 January 1996.

- **Bromochloromethane:** production and consumption banned from 2002.

In ratifying the original Protocol, which came into force in August 1992, governments commit themselves to its requirements. The European Community has implemented the latest revisions to the Protocol through Regulation 2037/2000/EC - see below 2.4.4.

In the case of the first four substances listed above, limited production for essential uses will be allowed after the phase out dates. An annual list of critical uses in developed countries is to be published by UNEP from 2004. Criteria to be taken into account in considering whether a use is essential include:

- the use must be necessary for the health and safety of society or critical for its functioning;

- no alternatives which are technically and economically feasible and which are acceptable on health and safety grounds;

- insufficient recycled material, both in terms of quantity and quality, available.

In 1997, parties to the Protocol also agreed that with effect from 1 January 2000, imports and exports of new and recycled CFCs and halons, methyl bromide and HCFCs will require licensing. It is hoped this will curb the illegal trade in these substances.

The UK has been able to meet the requirements of the Protocols basically through the voluntary cooperation of industry and consumers in reducing their use of CFCs - see also 2.4.4.

2.3.3 Convention on Long-Range Transboundary Air Pollution

This Convention, which was adopted in Geneva in 1979 and came into force in 1983, was drawn up under the auspices of the UN Economic Commission for Europe (which comprises more than 50 countries in Eastern and Western Europe and the USA and Canada). The Convention was the result of concern - particularly from Norway and Sweden - that the long-range transport of certain pollutants (mainly sulphur dioxide and nitrogen oxides) was having an adverse effect on the environment of their countries. The Convention says that countries shall "endeavour to limit and, as far as possible, gradually reduce and prevent air pollution, including long range transboundary air pollution". This should be achieved through the "use of best available technology that is economically feasible".

The Convention also deals with the long-range transport of nitrogen and chlorine compounds, polycyclic aromatic hydrocarbons, heavy metals and particles of various sizes.

Critical Loads

There is a commitment that subsequent reductions in emissions of both sulphur dioxide and nitrogen oxides will be negotiated "taking into account the best available scientific and technical developments . . . and internationally accepted critical loads". The "critical loads" approach takes account of the level of pollutant that a receptor - e.g. ecosystem, human being, plant or material - can tolerate without suffering long term adverse effect according to current knowledge.

Critical loads maps covering the whole of Europe are being drawn up by the European Evaluation and Monitoring Programme (EMEP) under the LRTAP Convention. In the UK the Department of the Environment, Transport and the Regions (DETR) is preparing maps showing the levels of deposition at which soils in the UK are vulnerable to acidity. Other maps show actual estimates of deposition and where this is likely to exceed the critical load.

In its revised Air Quality Guidelines for Europe (1999, in press), the World Health Organisation has recommended the following critical levels and loads:

- *Sulphur dioxide:* critical level 10-30 μg/m³ (annual) depending on type of vegetation; critical load 250-1500 eqS/ha/yr depending on the type of soil and ecosystem.

- *Nitrogen oxides:* critical level 30 μg/m³ (annual); critical load 5-35 kgN/ha/yr depending on the type of soil and ecosystem.

- *Ozone:* critical level 0.2-10 ppm.h (5d-6m) depending on type of vegetation, (Accumulated exposure Over a Threshold of 40 ppb).

(a) Sulphur Protocol

The Helsinki Protocol adopted in 1985 came into force in 1987; it required signatories to reduce national sulphur emissions, or their transboundary fluxes by 30% on 1980 levels, by 1993. This Protocol was ratified by 22 countries, but not the UK or the European Community (although some individual Member States did do so). All signatories to the Protocol achieved reductions of more than 30%, as did a number of non-signatories including the UK with a reduction of 37% by the end of 1993 (45% by the end of 1994).

This Protocol has now been renegotiated using data based on critical loads assessments; countries are required to reduce, by the year 2000, their sulphur emissions to meet a UNECE-wide target of 60% of the gap between sulphur emissions and the critical load. Particularly sensitive areas of Scandinavia, Germany and The Netherlands where natural and unattributable emissions exceed the critical load have been excluded from the calculations.

Individual countries' target reductions are based on their contribution to acid deposition over the areas included in the calculations. To meet the 60% target, the UK has agreed to reduce its own sulphur dioxide emissions by 50% by 2000, 70% by 2005 and 80% by 2010 (on 1980 levels). (To meet the target by the year 2000 would have required the UK to reduce its emissions by 79%, a target to which the UK would not agree.)

The new Protocol was officially signed in Oslo in June 1994 and came into force on 5 August 1998; parties to the Protocol must submit their national strategies for meeting their targets to the UNECE monitoring committee within six months of ratification. As at March 2000, this Protocol had been ratified by 21 countries (including the UK who did so on 17 December 1996), plus the European Community (April 1998).

At the time of ratification, the UK Government also published its national strategy for meeting the requirements of the Protocol: briefly, this suggests that current emissions reduction and control programmes will ensure the 2000 and 2005 targets are met, with advances in technology helping to meet the 2010 target. At the end of 1996 UK emissions of sulphur dioxide were 59% lower than in 1980 (*Digest of Environmental Statistics,* No. 20, 1998).

(b) Nitrogen Oxides Protocol

The 1988 Sofia Protocol, which came into effect in 1991, freezes nitrogen oxides emissions, or their transboundary fluxes, by 1994 using a 1987 baseline. As at March 2000, this Protocol had been ratified by 26 countries (including the UK, 1990), plus the European Community (1993). In 1994 UK NOx emissions were 11% lower than in 1987, and by the end of 1996 had fallen a further 10% (*Digest of Environmental Statistics,* No. 20, 1998).

(c) Protocol to Abate Acidification, Eutrophication and Ground Level Ozone

This "multi-effect protocol" covering nitrogen oxides, sulphur dioxide, VOCs and ammonia was finalised in Gothenburg, Sweden in November 1999 and as at March 2000 had 28 signatories (including the UK), but no ratifications. The Protocol will come into force 90 days after the 16th ratification.

Critical loads have been used as a basis for setting national emissions ceilings, to be met by 2010, based on 1990, to combat acidification, eutrophication and tropospheric ozone formation. Parties to the Protocol have signed up to a national emissions ceiling, which requires them to reduce total emissions of each of the pollutants to their ceiling level or below by the end of 2010. Emissions ceilings for the UK are

- sulphur dioxide – 625 kilotonnes/year
- nitrogen oxides – 1181 kilotonnes/year
- VOCs – 1200 kilotonnes/year
- ammonia – 297 kilotonnes/year

The Protocol also sets emission limits for both stationary and mobile sources (including combustion plant, electricity plant, dry cleaning, cars and lorries) and requires the use of best available techniques to meet limits. Parties to the Protocol "may apply different emission reduction strategies that achieve equivalent overall emission levels for all source categories together".

(d) VOC Protocol

A further Protocol under the LRTAP Convention signed in Geneva in 1991 to control emissions of volatile organic compounds (VOCs) or their transboundary fluxes came into force on 29 September 1997; as at March 2000 it had been ratified by 19 countries, including the UK which did so in June 1994.

VOCs are defined as "all organic compounds of anthropogenic nature, other than methane, that are capable of producing photochemical oxidants by reactions with nitrogen oxides in the presence of sunlight". VOCs are involved in the formation of ground level ozone and in depletion of the ozone layer. They also contribute to the greenhouse effect in that methane and photochemical oxidants produced from the use of VOCs are both greenhouse gases. Thus they have both local and regional/transboundary effects.

The new Protocol obliges most parties to secure a 30% overall reduction in their VOC emissions by 1999, using 1988 as a base (or another year between 1984 and 1990 to be specified when acceding to the Protocol). Other basic obligations include requirements, two years after the Protocol enters into force

- to apply national or international emission standards to new sources of VOCs, taking account of guidance on control technologies given in the Protocol;

- to apply national or international measures to products that contain solvents and promote the use of products with low or nil content; and to foster public participation in VOC emission control.

no later than five years after entering into force

- to apply economically feasible best available technologies to existing stationary sources in those areas where ozone standards are exceeded or transboundary fluxes originate;

- to implement techniques to reduce VOC emissions from petrol distribution and motor vehicle refuellings and to reduce the volatility of petrol.

So far as these latter obligations are concerned, a European Union Directive controlling VOC emissions during petrol storage and distribution was adopted in late 1995 - see 2.22.9. Another Directive (99/13), agreed in March 1999, limits emissions of VOCs due to the use of organic solvents in certain activities and installations - see below 2.4.5(c).

In November 1993, the UK Government published its strategy for meeting its commitments under the Protocol, which it was hoped would result in a 36% reduction in emissions of VOCs by 1999. The strategy includes: setting of emission limits in conditions attached to authorisations for both Part A and Part B processes regulated under the *Environmental Protection Act 1990*; implementation of EU measures to reduce evaporative emissions during petrol storage and distribution; information to the public on reducing usage - and thus emissions - of household products containing VOCs. By the end of 1996, the UK had achieved a 20% reduction in VOC emissions on 1988 levels (*Digest of Environmental Statistics,* No. 20, 1998).

(e) Heavy Metals

This Protocol was signed in June 1998 at Aarhus, Denmark, and will come into force 90 days after ratification by 16 countries; as at March 2000 it had been ratified by three. It requires emissions of cadmium, lead and mercury to be reduced to below their 1990 levels (or an agreed year between 1985 and 1995). It also aims to cut emissions from new and existing industrial sources and waste incinerators by laying down strict limit values based on the use of best available techniques. In April 2000, the European Commission published a proposal for a decision (COM(2000) 217) to ratify the Protocol on behalf of the Community.

(f) Persistent Organic Pollutants

This Protocol was also signed in June 1998 at Aarhus, Denmark, and will come into force 90 days after ratification by 16 countries; as at March 2000 it had been ratified by three. It aims to phase out production and use of a defined list of substances as well as imposing requirements to eliminate discharges, emissions and losses, and to ensure safe disposal methods. The list covers 16 substances in three categories:

- pesticides (aldrin, dieldrin, endrin, chlordane, DDT, hexachlorocyclohexane, heptachlor, chlordecone, mirex and toxaphene);

- industrial chemicals (PCBs, hexachlorobenzene and hexabromobiphenyl);

- by-products and contaminants (dioxins, furans and PAHs).

Annexes to the Protocol set emission limit values, as well as outline best available techniques for the various industrial sectors which emit substances covered by the Protocol.

UNEP is also sponsoring negotiations on a legally binding convention to ban or restrict the production and use of POPs; The substances to be included are much the same as those covered by the UNECE Protocol. The convention, once agreed and in force, would be worldwide rather than just the member countries of the UNECE. It is unlikely to be finalised before mid-2001 at the earliest, pending agreement on outstanding issues which include financial aid for developing countries to enable them to switch to substitute products.

(g) Evaluation and Monitoring Programme

A 1984 Protocol, which was ratified by the UK in 1985 and by the European Community in 1986, provides funding for the programme of monitoring and evaluation of the long-range transport of air pollution (EMEP). EMEP comprises some 100 monitoring stations in 25 countries which provide data on all Convention substances.

2.3.4 World Health Organisation

The World Health Organisation's recommended air quality guidelines are used as a basis for setting EU standards and were also taken into account by the UK Expert Panel on Air Quality Standards when making recommendations for UK air quality standards (see this chapter, 2.10.2). Originally published in 1987, as *Air Quality Guidelines for Europe*, WHO's recommendations are not mandatory but are generally accepted as being levels not to be exceeded if healthy air quality is to be maintained. In 1993 WHO began reviewing the guidelines in the light of new scientific data and at a Consultation meeting in October 1996 revised guidelines (see Table 2.1) were agreed; a fully revised version of *Air Quality Guidelines for Europe* is currently in press (1999).

Table 2.1: WHO Air Quality Guidelines

(This table includes only those pollutants for which EU standards exist or are being proposed)

Substances	Time-weighted average	Averaging time
Classical air pollutants		
Nitrogen dioxide	200 µg/m³	1 hour
	40 µg/m³	annual
Ozone	120 µg/m³	8 hour
Sulphur dioxide	500 µg/m³	10 minutes
	125 µg/m³	24 hour
	50 µg/m³	annual
Carbon monoxide	100 mg/m³	15 minutes
	60 mg/m³	30 minutes
	30 mg/m³	1 hour
	10 mg/m³	8 hours
Particulate matter	exposure-effect information to be provided giving guidance on major health impacts for short and long term exposures at various levels	
Organic pollutants		
PAH (benzo-a-pyrene)	8.7×10^{-5} (ng/m³)$^{-1}$	UR*/lifetime
Benzene	6×10^{-6} (µg/m³)$^{-1}$	UR/lifetime
Inorganic pollutants		
Lead	0.5 µg/m³	annual
Arsenic	1.5×10^{-3} (µg/m³)$^{-1}$	UR/lifetime
Cadmium	5 ng/m³	annual
Mercury	1.0 µg/m³	annual

*UR is the excess risk of dying from cancer following lifetime exposure.
Source: WHO Website: www.who.uk

2.4 THE EUROPEAN UNION AND AIR POLLUTION CONTROL

The need to reduce emissions from all sources is a major thrust of the European Union's policy to improve air quality. More recently the global threats of climate change and depletion of the ozone layer have been an important factor in shaping EU policy. Details of EU measures to reduce traffic-related pollution are summarised later in this chapter at 2.22.

In 1998 the Commission published a discussion paper, *Clean Air for Europe*, which proposes integrating all the EU's air pollution control programmes into a single strategy. This, it is suggested, would help to ensure that targets and policies for reducing emissions from, for example, vehicles or industrial sources, did not conflict.

A summary of the institutions of the European Union, its legislative procedures and a list of the Directives on air pollution are given in Appendix 6 and 6.2, respectively.

2.4.1 Air Quality

(a) Assessment and Management

On 27 September 1996 a framework Directive on ambient air quality assessment and management (96/62/EC) was formally adopted; it came into force on 21 November 1996, and had to be implemented by Member States by 21 May 1998. A main aim of the Directive is to protect human health and the environment by avoiding, reducing or preventing harmful concentrations of air pollutants; this will be achieved through

- the definition and fixing of objectives for air quality and setting of limit values and/or alert thresholds (and/or target values for ozone);
- assessing air quality in a uniform manner;
- making information available to the public;
- maintaining or improving ambient air quality.

The framework Directive requires the Commission to propose "Daughter" Directives setting air quality objectives, limit values, alert thresholds, guidance on monitoring, siting and measurement methods for individual pollutants as follows:

- Sulphur dioxide, nitrogen dioxide, fine particulate matter (PM₁₀), suspended particulate matter and lead by 31 December 1996; published October 1997 and formally adopted as Directive 99/30 on 22 April 1999 - see (b)(i) below.

- Ozone by 1 March 1998 in accordance with Article 8 of the 1992 ozone Directive; proposal expected end 1998; COM(99) 125 published 9 June 1999 - see (c) below.

- Benzene and carbon monoxide - proposal should have been brought forward no later than 31 December 1997; COM(98) 591 published December 1998 - see (b)(ii) below.

- PAHs (benzo-a-pyrene as indicator), cadmium, arsenic, nickel compounds (classified as carcinogens) and mercury - as soon as possible but not later than 31 December 1999.

Pollutants to be considered at a further stage are dioxins, VOCs, methane, ammonia, nitric acid and PAHs (general). Proposals for other substances to be covered by daughter Directives will be considered on the basis of new scientific evidence on environmental or health effects.

Factors to be taken into account when setting limit values and alert thresholds include: degree of exposure of population (including sensitive groups); climatic conditions; sensitivity of flora and fauna and of historic heritage; economic and technical feasibility; and long-range transmission of pollutants. The World Health Organisation's guidelines (see above, 2.3.4) will also be used as a basis for setting air quality objectives.

Criteria for monitoring, modelling and estimation techniques will be fixed for individual pollutants. Monitoring will be mandatory in population centres of more than 250,000, in those areas where the level of the pollutant is above a certain proportion of its limit value, and in other areas where limit values are exceeded. Member States must designate the national, regional or local authorities to be responsible for implementation of the Directive and also accredit laboratories for quality

Table 2.2: EU Air Quality Standards

Sulphur Dioxide and Suspended Particulates: EU Directive 80/779/EEC

Limit values (to be met by 1.4.83)

Sulphur dioxide
- 120 µg/m³ if smoke less than 40 µg/m³; 80 µg/m³ if smoke more than 40 µg/m³ – one year (median daily values)
- 180 µg/m³ if smoke less than 60 µg/m³; 130 µg/m³ if smoke more than 60 µg/m³ – winter (median of daily values)
- 350 µg/m³ if smoke less than 150 µg/m³; 250 µg/m³ if smoke more than 150 µg/m³ – year, peak (98 percentile of daily values)

Smoke
- 80 µg/m³ – one year (median of daily values)
- 130 µg/m³ – winter (median of daily values)
- 250 µg/m³ – year, peak (98 percentile of daily values)

Guide values

Sulphur dioxide
- 100-150 µg/m³ – 24-hour mean
- 40-60 µg/m³ – one year mean

Nitrogen dioxide: EU Directive 85/203/EEC

Limit value (to be met by 1.7.87)
- 200 µg/m³ – one year (98 percentile of 1-hour mean)

Guide values
- 50 µg/m³ – 1 year (50 percentile of 1-hour mean)
- 135 µg/m³ – 1 year (98 percentile of 1-hour mean)

Lead in the air: EU Directive 82/884/EEC

Limit value (to be met by 9.12.87)
- 2 µg/m³ annual mean

assurance and assessment.

Member states must assess ambient air quality on the basis of the limit values and alert thresholds set, drawing up action plans indicating measures to be taken in the short term where there is a risk that these may be exceeded. Certain measures are required depending on measured air quality:

- in zones where levels exceed or are likely to exceed the limit value, plus the margin of tolerance (i.e. the percentage of the limit value by which the value may be exceeded) - plans and programmes to achieve the limit value within the specific time limit must be drawn up and implemented and the public given details of them;

- in zones where the levels are lower than the limit value - these levels should be maintained and the best ambient air quality compatible with sustainable development maintained;

- where the alert threshold is exceeded, steps must be taken to inform the public and a report sent to the Commission within three months of the episode, with details such as duration and levels of pollutants recorded.

(b) Air Quality Standards

The adoption in July 1980 of a Directive on health protection standards for levels of sulphur dioxide and suspended particulates in air resulted in an important change in UK policy. In effect, the Directive introduced into the UK the first air quality standards and was thus a break with the UK's tradition of setting non-statutory emission standards, via the pollution inspectorate. Similar Directives for nitrogen oxides and lead followed. The Directives fixed limit values (and non-mandatory guide values), all of which have now to be met.

Following adoption of the new Directive setting limit values for sulphur dioxide, oxides of nitrogen, particulate matter and lead (see below), various articles of these Directives were repealed on 1 January 2000; the remainder (including those articles relating to limit values) will be repealed on 1 January 2005 (or 1 January 2010 in the case of the nitrogen dioxide Directive). The current standards are shown in Table 2.2.

These standards have been implemented in the UK through *Air Quality Standards Regulations* - see this chapter, 2.8. The widespread introduction of smoke control areas (see 2.14.3 below) has played a major part in reducing levels of smoke.

(i) Directive Relating to Limit Values for Sulphur Dioxide, Oxides of Nitrogen, Particulate Matter and Lead

The first Daughter Directive - 99/30 - under the Air Quality Assessment and Management Directive (see above) was published in October 1997; it was formally adopted on 22

April 1999 and must be implemented by July 2001. The Government and devolved administrations were due to issue a consultation paper outlining their proposals for implementing it, and the framework Directive, during 2000.

The Directive sets limit values for the above pollutants with the aim of avoiding, preventing or reducing their harmful effects on human health and on the environment as a whole (Table 2.3). Where the limit value is likely to be exceeded on more than the permitted number of days per year then action programmes setting out plans to meet the limit value by the target date must be drawn up; where the limit value is exceeded, steps must be taken to ensure it is met by the target date; where air quality is below the limit value, it should not be allowed to deteriorate. When the alert threshold for sulphur dioxide or nitrogen dioxide is exceeded, specified information must be made available to the public. Information (updated hourly, or every three months for lead) on ambient concentrations of all the pollutants should be made available to the public, including exceedances of the public indicator threshold (i.e. the hourly or daily limit values below). The Directive recognises that some Member States may not be able to meet some of the limit values because of climatic or other special circumstances. The Commission is to review the Directive before 30 September 2003.

Table 2.3: Forthcoming EU Air Quality Standards (99/30)

Sulphur dioxide

- *Hourly limit value for the protection of human health:* 350 μg/m³, not to be exceeded more than 24 times per calendar year (pcy) target date: 1.1.05.

- *Daily limit value for the protection of human health:* 125 μg/m³, not to be exceeded more than 3 times pcy; target date: 1.1.05.

- *Alert threshold:* 500 μg/m³ measured over 3 hours.

- *Annual limit value for the protection of ecosystems:* 20 μg/m³; target date: 2 years after Directive enters into force.

Nitrogen dioxide

- *Hourly limit value for the protection of human health:* 200 μg/m³, not to be exceeded more than 18 times pcy; target date: 1.1.10.

- *Annual limit value for the protection of human health:* 40 μg/m³; target date: 1.1.10.

- *Alert threshold:* 400 μg/m³ measured over 3 hours.

- *Annual limit value for the protection of vegetation:* 30 μg/m³; target date: 2 years after Directive enters into force.

Particulate matter (PM$_{10}$)

Stage 1:

- *Daily limit value for the protection of human health:* 50 μg/m³, not to be exceeded more than 35 times pcy; target date: 1.1.05;

- *Annual limit value for the protection of human health:* 40 μg/m³; target date: 1.1.05.

Stage 2:

- *Indicative daily limit value for the protection of human health:* 50 μg/m³, not to be exceeded more than 7 times pcy; target date: 1.1.10.

- *Indicative annual limit value for the protection of human health:* 20 μg/m³; target date: 1.1.10.

Lead

- *Annual limit value for the protection of human health:* 0.5 μg/m³; target date: 1.1.05.

(ii) Carbon Monoxide and Benzene

The Commission published its second proposal for a "daughter Directive" under the AQMA Directive in December 1998, and Environment Ministers adopted a Common Position on it on 10 April 2000. COM(98) 591 (amended by COM(2000 223) establishes a limit value of 10 mg/m³ (8.5 ppm) averaged over 8 hours for carbon monoxide to be achieved by 1 January 2005; for benzene a limit value of 5 μg/m³ (about 1.66 ppb) averaged over a calendar year and to be achieved by 1 January 2010 is proposed; for those countries which would have difficulty in meeting the limit, a five year derogation is to be allowed but benzene concentrations must not be allowed to exceed a yearly average of 10 μg/m³.

The carbon monoxide proposal accords with WHO Guidelines, and also with EU policy on the environment and on protecting human health. The benzene proposal is based on a limit which is both achievable and considered to offer a high level of protection for human health.

The Directive specifies the number of and siting of measurement stations, as well as reference methods for air quality measurements. Member States are required to supply regular and up-to-date information to the public and appropriate organisations, and to draw up action plans where limit values are exceeded. The Commission is expected to review the benzene limit by 2004.

(c) Monitoring and Information - Ozone

In September 1992 a Directive on Air Pollution by Ozone (92/72/EEC) was adopted; it includes requirements for a monitoring network, exchange of information and for a warning system for when ozone concentrations exceed thresholds above which there is considered to be a health risk (see Table 2.4). The values, which should not be exceeded, are based on WHO recommendations:

Table 2.4: EU Ozone Thresholds

	μg/m³	or	as ppb
Health protection			
8 hour mean	110		55
Vegetation protection			
1 hour mean	200		100
24 hour mean	65		32.5
Population information			
1 hour mean	180		90
Population warning			
1 hour mean	360		180

When the population thresholds are exceeded (see table) information must be available "on a sufficiently large scale as soon as possible to enable the population concerned to take all appropriate preventive protective action". Such information should include the area affected, forecast of length of episode and whether ozone levels are likely to increase further; information on what health precautions are advisable (e.g. the need to avoid strenuous exercise) should also be given.

This Directive has been implemented in the UK through the *Ozone Monitoring and Information Regulations 1994* - see this chapter, 2.9. In the UK ozone levels are monitored and information is made available to the public (see section 2.10.1).

In June 1999, the Commission published its proposals for a Directive setting target values for ozone (COM(99) 125; this is the third proposal to be published under the 1996 Air Quality Assessment and Management Directive (see 2.4.1a), and also forms part of the Commission's acidification strategy (see 2.4.5a). A target value for the protection of human health of 120 µg/m³ to be achieved as far as possible by 2010 is proposed, and should not be exceeded on more than 20 days per calendar year, averaged over 3 years; the Directive specifies the information to be made available to the public when ozone levels reach an information threshold of 180 µg/m³ and an alert threshold (aimed at sensitive sections of the population) of 240 µg/m³, both averaged over an hour. A target value for the protection of vegetation of 17000 µg/m³ .h, averaged over 5 years and also to be achieved as far as possible by 2010 is also proposed. Long term objectives of 120 µg/m³ for the protection of human health and 6000 µg/m³ for the protection of vegetation are also proposed.

Member States will be required to identify zones and agglomerations where either the target values or long term objectives are unlikely to be met within the specified period, and to draw up action plans or programmes in accordance with the Directive. Member States should also identify those zones and agglomerations in which the long term objective is already met and should ensure that air quality is maintained in those areas.

The proposal requires the public to be given regular information about ozone levels, monitoring and for the results of such monitoring to be made publicly available.

(d) Exchange of Air Pollution Data

Decision 97/101/EC approved in January 1997 establishes a "reciprocal exchange of information and data from networks and individual stations measuring ambient air pollution within Member States". This supersedes an earlier 1982 Decision which aimed to achieve equality throughout the Community and harmonise measurements and, subsequently, techniques. The new scheme covers all the pollutants listed in the air quality assessment and management Directive (see above); Member States are required to submit to the Commission data collected and validated in accordance with the Decision; data for the year must be sent by October of the following year. The data will be stored by the European Environment Agency; a request for access to the data may be made to the EEA or to a Member State.

2.4.2 Carbon Dioxide

The members of the European Union have agreed that emissions of carbon dioxide (CO_2) - the major greenhouse gas, accounting for 66% of global greenhouse effect - should be stabilised at 1990 levels by 2000. This was in line with a commitment made at the 1992 Earth Summit and confirmed in the Framework Convention on the Climate - see above 2.3.1a. In April 1998 the EU (together with individual Member States) signed a Protocol to the Convention (the Kyoto Protocol); this commits the members of the EU to reducing emissions of six greenhouse gases by 8% based on 1990 levels between 2008-2012. In June 1998 Member States agreed on how to apportion the 8% target cut and, as a result, the UK is to reduce its emissions by 12.5%.

The EU also has in place a number of other measures aimed at stabilising CO_2 emissions; these include:

- **reducing energy demand:** Directive to improve Energy Efficiency (93/76) implements the programme of Specific Actions for Vigorous Energy Efficiency (SAVE) and could reduce growth in CO_2 emissions by about 25%; the Directive requires, inter alia, regular inspections of cars and boilers; energy audits for business; thermal insulation of new buildings; certification of CO_2 emissions related to energy consumption in buildings. Decision 96/737, adopted in December 1996 outlines a multi-annual programme for the promotion of energy efficiency (SAVE II) from 1996-2000. It includes measures to improve energy efficiency and to encourage the exchange of experience and information at all levels.

- **monitoring CO₂ emissions:** Council Decision 99/296/EC amends Decision 93/389 ; it details "A Monitoring Mechanism for Community CO_2 and other Greenhouse Gas Emissions" and extends the scope of the earlier Decision to cover all emissions of greenhouse gases, including those not covered by the Montreal Protocol; it requires stabilisation of CO_2 emissions at 1990 levels by 2000, the drawing up of national programmes for meeting EU commitments under the Kyoto Protocol, monitoring in this respect and reporting to the Commission. National programmes should include actions to increase energy conservation and efficiency, encourage a switch to low or no carbon fuels and implement Community legislation. Member States are required to report on and publicise their policies and ·actions to limit emissions of CO_2 and other greenhouse gases and to evaluate the impact of these measures.

- **reducing CO₂ emissions from cars:** The Commission has brokered agreements with European, Japanese and South Korean car manufacturers to reduce emissions from new cars - see 2.22.7.

2.4.3 Methane

Methane - CH_4 - is the second most important greenhouse gas (after carbon dioxide), accounting for 18% of the global greenhouse effect. In November 1996, the Commission published a Strategy Paper (COM(96) 557) for reducing methane emissions from the three sectors chiefly responsible for emissions: agriculture (45% of EU emissions), waste (32%) and energy (23%). It is hoped that the measures proposed for these sectors (see below) will lead to a reduction in methane emissions of 30% by 2005 and 41% by 2010.

- **Agriculture:** promotion of research and incentives to reduce emissions from, in particular, cattle and sheep; animal manure management, e.g. anaerobic digesters or covered lagoons.

- **Waste:** promotion of measures to encourage separate collection of organic wastes, composting and recycling; new anaerobic landfills to be equipped with methane recovery and use systems; wherever possible, existing landfills to be retrofitted with methane collection and use systems; otherwise encourage flaring.

- **Energy:** CH_4 reduction schemes promoting best available recovery techniques in coal mines. For natural gas, a minimum leakages standard and increased control frequency of pipelines.

In 1996 UK methane emissions totalled just over 3.7 thousand tonnes, with landfill and agriculture accounting for 46% and 28% respectively of the total (*Digest of Environmental Statistics*, No. 20, 1998).

2.4.4 Substances that Deplete the Ozone Layer

Over the past decade there have been a number of EU measures aimed at controlling the use of chlorofluorocarbons (CFCs) and other substances that deplete the ozone layer; in June 1988, the Council of Environment Ministers agreed on a Decision to ratify the Montreal Protocol of 11 September 1987 to the Vienna Convention for the protection of the ozone layer; this initiative had originated from the United Nations Environment Programme. The Protocol came into force on 1 January 1989 and aimed to achieve a 50% reduction in CFC use by 1999; the Protocol has since been strengthened on a number of occasions and the timetable for phasing out the production and use of the various ozone depleting chemicals tightened. Regulation 3093/94/EC (adopted in December 1994), which consolidated and repealed Regulations 594/91 and 3952/92, extended controls on ozone depleting chemicals to cover hydrochlorofluorocarbons (HCFC), hydro-bromofluorocarbons (HBFC) and methyl bromide.

The 1994 Regulation has now been replaced by a new Regulation (2037/2000), which came into force on 1 October 2000. This implements, and in some cases goes further than, the latest revisions to the Montreal Protocol (see above 2.3.2).

The current schedule, leading to the phase-out of the main ozone depleting chemicals, is as follows:

- **Chlorofluorocarbons (11, 12, 113, 114, 115):** production banned from 1 January 1995. Supply and use banned from 1 October 2000.

- **Other Fully Halogenated CFCs (13, 111, 112, 211, 212, 213, 214, 215, 216, 217):** as for other CFCs.

- **Halons:** production banned from 1 January 1994. Halons 1211 and 1301 (used in firefighting) are to be phased out by 31 December 2002. The supply and use of halon 1011 (bromochloromethane) is banned from 1 October 2000.

- **Carbon Tetrachloride:** sale and use banned from 1 October 2000.

- **1,1,1-trichloroethane:** sale and use banned from 1 October 2000.

- **Methyl Bromide:** using 1991 as a base level, 60% reduction on production and consumption from 1 January 2001, 75% reduction in from 1 January 2003, with elimination by 1 January 2005.

- **Hydrochlorofluorocarbons:** 2.8% cap on consumption, leading to phase out in 2020. The use of HCFCs in new air conditioning equipment and refrigeration equipment is banned from January 2001. The use of new HCFCs is banned in existing refrigeration and air conditioning equipment from 1 January 2010, and on all, including recycled HCFCs from 2015 (this latter date to be reviewed by 31 December 2008); their use in solvents and polyurethane foams is banned from 1 January 2003. Exports to countries who have not signed the Montreal Protocol are to be banned from 1 January 2004.

- **Hydrobromofluorocarbons:** production banned from 1 January 1996.

The limits apply both to the amounts of CFCs which can be produced within the European Union and to the amounts imported. Limited exceptions (to be updated annually) to the timetable will be allowed where substitutes have not been found for "essential uses", e.g. medical uses, in particular metered dose inhalers for asthma and other lung diseases - see also 2.3.2; in a communication published in November 1998, the Commission advised that essential use status for MDIs containing CFCs is to be phased out to 2003. "All practicable precautionary measures" have to be taken to ensure no leakages of ozone depleting substances from various commercial and industrial installations and manufacturing processes.

An export licensing system is to be introduced, similar to that included in the Montreal Protocol, as a means of halting the illegal trade in CFCs etc; the import of products containing ozone depleting substances is banned as is the export of ozone depleting substances and products containing them.

The *Environmental Protection (Controls on Substances that Deplete the Ozone Layer) Regulations 1996 (SI 506)* which came into force on 26 March 1996 implement the requirements of the 1994 EU Regulation; non-compliance with the Regulations is an offence and subject to a maximum fine of £5,000 on summary conviction or an unlimited fine on conviction on indictment.

Voluntary agreements between the UK Government and the aerosols, air conditioning & refrigeration, fire protection, and the foam industries ensure that where HFCs are used, any emissions to atmosphere will be minimised. The industries concerned have also agreed not to use HFCs where emissions are unavoidable if safe, practical and more environmentally acceptable alternatives exist. In September 1999, the Government announced that metered dose inhalers containing CFCs would be phased out over three years; CFCs are to be replaced by HFC-134a which is not an ozone depleter and also has significantly lower global warming potential.

2.4.5 Industrial Emissions

(a) Strategy to Combat Acidification

There has been considerable concern about the effects of acid deposition on parts of the EU for many years and various measures aimed at reducing discharges of pollutants thought to contribute to the problem have been put in place. These provide a framework for reduction of industrial air pollution and propose specific emission limits for pollutants such as sulphur dioxide, nitrogen oxides and suspended particulates. The EU's long-term objective, as stated in the Fifth Environmental Action Programme is that there should be no exceedance of critical loads for acidification anywhere in the EU. On the basis of measures in place prior to 1997, however, the Commission estimates that about nine million hectares of the Community will still exceed critical loads in 2010. In an effort to cut this deficit to 4.5 million hectares, the Commission published in March 1997 a Draft Communication on a Community Strategy to Combat Acidification (COM(97) 88); the main elements of the Strategy are:

- A proposal for a Directive - COM(99) 125) - *setting national emission ceilings for critical atmospheric pollutants for each Member State* for sulphur dioxide, nitrogen oxides, ammonia and VOCs was published on 9 June 1999 and a Common Position agreed on 22 June 2000; the second reading in the European Parliament is expected early in 2001. National emission ceilings are set for the four pollutants for each Member State, to be achieved by 2010; the UK figures (actual for 1990 in brackets) are:

  – sulphur dioxide: 585 kilotonnes (1990: 3,805)
  – nitrogen oxides: 1,167 kilotonnes (1990: 2,839)
  – VOCs: 1,200 kilotonnes (1990: 2,667)
  – ammonia: 297 kilotonnes (1990: 329)

The Directive will require Member States to draw up programmes by October 2002 for reducing emissions of the pollutants from all sources (including energy, transport, industry and agriculture) and to send these to the Commission; national programmes should be reviewed, and where necessary revised, by 1 October 2006. Member States will be required to submit annual emission inventories to the Commission, as well as projections to 2010. The Commission is to review progress towards meeting national targets in 2004 and 2008 and will, if necessary, propose revisions to the ceilings.

- Proposal for a Council Directive on the *sulphur content of certain liquid fuels;* this was formally adopted on 26 April 1999 and had to be implemented by 1 July 2000. Directive 99/32 maintains the limit for the sulphur content of gas oil at 0.2% by weight (as set in Directive 93/12 - see 2.22.8) as a minimum standard, reducing to 0.1% from 1 January 2008. The sulphur content of heavy fuel oils (used mainly in refineries, power stations and industry) will be limited to 1% by weight from 1 January 2003; the UK average is 2.3% (DETR, 1997). Operators of combustion plant burning heavy fuel oil with a sulphur content of more than 1% may continue to do so as long as total SO_2 emissions do not exceed 1700 mg/m^3. Member States which contribute very little (or nothing) to acidification have a derogation to use gas oils with a sulphur content of between 0.1-0.2%, and heavy fuel oils with a sulphur content up to 3% until 1 January 2013. Refineries may also continue to burn high sulphur fuels so long as total emissions do not exceed 1700 mg/m^3 (existing plant) or 1000 mg/m^3 (new plant).

The Directive has been implemented in England and Wales, and in Scotland through Regulations made under the *European Communities Act 1972.* As well as making it an offence to use heavy fuel oils and gas oils exceeding the sulphur limits in the Directive, the Regulations detail sampling requirements to confirm compliance – see this chapter, 2.15.

- Ratification of *UNECE Sulphur Protocol*: this was ratified by the Community in April 1998 – Decision 98/686 (see also 2.3.3a above).

- Revision of the 1988 *Large Combustion Plant Directive:* see (b) below.

- To negotiate for the inclusion of *"sulphur dioxide control areas"* in the current revision of the IMO's MARPOL Convention controlling maritime pollution (see also 5.21); in such areas ships would be required to use marine bunker fuel oil with a sulphur content not exceeding 1.5%. Both the Baltic and North Seas have now been declared "SOx Emission Control Areas", although the reduced sulphur limit will not be enforced until the decisions have been ratified by countries together representing at least half the world's tonnage – see chapter 5, 5.21.

(b) Large Combustion Plant

In 1988 agreement was reached on the Large Combustion Plant Directive (88/609/EEC) which commits Member

States to specific reductions in emissions of sulphur dioxide and nitrogen oxides from large fossil fuel burning plant (50 MW or more) - mainly power stations. The UK is committed to reducing sulphur dioxide emissions from existing plant (i.e. licensed prior to 1 July 1987) in steps of 20, 40 and 60% of the 1980 baseline by 1993, 1998 and 2003 respectively. Reductions in nitrogen oxides emissions of 15% by 1993 and 30% by 1998 had also to be achieved. Emission limits for sulphur dioxide and nitrogen oxides for new plant are included in an annex to the Directive.

The UK is on target to meet its commitments under the Large Combustion Plants Directive. By the end of 1996 UK sulphur dioxide emissions from LCP were 57% lower than in 1980 - i.e. 17% ahead of the 1998 target. Emissions of nitrogen oxides from LCP were 44% lower than 1980 - an improvement of 14% over the 1998 requirement (*Digest of Environmental Statistics*, No. 20, 1998). During the period 1980-93, total EU emissions of SO_2 and NO_x reduced by 52.5% and 45.8% respectively. See also 2.3.3a & b for the UK's commitments under the sulphur and nitrogen oxides protocols to the UNECE Convention on Long-Range Transboundary Air Pollution.

The 1988 Directive did not cover sulphur dioxide emissions from new solid fuel plant between 50-100 MW as agreement could not be reached on the limit to be applied to these plant. However in December 1994 an amendment Directive (94/66) covering such plant was adopted; this came into force on 24 June 1995 and sets an emission limit of 2000 mg/m³ for such plant (i.e. those authorised to start after 1 July 1987). Proposals for a Directive covering emissions from small (up to 50 MW) combustion plant are under discussion.

In June 2000, Environment Ministers reached agreement on a Common Position on the proposed amendments of the 1988 Directive, (COM(98) 415, published in July 1998, amended by COM(99) 611); it is expected to receive a second reading in the European Parliament in early 2001. As well as taking account of technical developments since the adoption of the 1988 Directive, it aims to contribute to the goals of the acidification strategy in a cost effective manner and thus reduce health risks from LCP emissions. Emission limits which individual plant must meet are to be based on the age of the plant, with those licensed since 1990 when the original Directive came into force required to meet the strictest limits. The next band would encompass those that started operating in July 1987 up 1990; pre-July 1987 plant would be required to meet the same limits by January 2008; alternatively Member States may choose to draw up an emissions reduction plant covering all such plant operating in 2000 - the plan should ensure that their total emissions do not exceed the total allowed for such plant in 2008. Member States may exclude these "old" plant from the need to meet emission limits or the emissions plan if the operator gives an undertaking (by June 2004) that the plant will not operate

for more than 20,000 hours after January 2008.

The strictest emission limit values for SO_2 and NO_x, based on best available techniques, will cover new large (i.e. over 50 MWth) combustion plant (including gas turbines, biomass and combined heat & power plants); for solid and liquid fuel plant with a capacity of less than 100 MW, an emission limit of 850 mg/m³ SO_2 is proposed, and 200 mg/m³ for those over 300 MW; emission limits for plant between 100-300 MW would be on a scale within the upper and lower limits. An emission limit of 400 mg/m³ NOx is proposed for solid fuel plant with a capacity of less than 100 MW and 300 mg/m³ for plant between 100-300 MW. Large combustion plant over 50 MW will be required to comply with the Integrated Pollution Prevention and Control Directive (see chapter 1, 1.12).

In the UK, a National Emissions Plan drawn up by the Secretary of State for the Environment under s.3 of the *Environmental Protection Act 1990* establishes emission limits and allocates quotas for the main sectors responsible for emissions - power stations and refineries, and for other industries. For power stations specific quotas/limits have been established for National Power, PowerGen, Scotland and N. Ireland. For refineries and other industry, quotas/limits are set for England/Wales and Scotland. The emission limits will be met by a variety of means including flue gas desulphurisation and the use of lower sulphur fuels. The *Large Combustion Plant (New Plant) Directions 1995* require conditions to be set in IPC authorisations ensuring compliance with the 1988 and 1994 Directives. In Scotland, the *Large Combustion Plant (Control of Emissions) (Scotland) Regulations 1991* (SI 562) implement the earlier Directive. In 1995 the National Emissions Plan was amended to make allowance for the transfer by National Power to Northern Ireland Electricity of some its surplus SO_2 and NO_x quota in 1995 and 1996. The Plan was further amended in December 1996 to ensure that future allocations of emissions quota for both SO_2 and NO_x were more closely in line with regulatory consents under IPC and thus based on BATNEEC.

Following consultation, the Environment Agency announced new controls on emissions of sulphur dioxide from coal and oil fired power stations to take effect, through variations to IPC authorisations, from 1 February 2000. The new controls will result in a reduction of approximately 60% (from 1996/7) of SO_2 and particulate matter by 2005. The Agency's Decision Document *Controls on Emissions from Coal- and Oil-Fired Power Stations* (December 1999) sets A-Limits for individual power stations and B-Limits to be met by all power stations owned by a particular generator. The Agency Decision also states that

- operators should give priority to using those of their power stations equipped with flue gas desulphurisation equipment;
- operators who use FGD plant who are increasing their market share will be allowed an agreed amount of

flexibility in their Limit so long as the plant is being operated in an environmentally acceptable manner and in accordance with their IPC authorisation;

- operators installing FGD plant will be allowed some flexibility in their B-Limit during the last two years of construction;

- operators of existing FGD plant had to submit plans for upgrading by October 2000;

- all operators must submit a case for fitting FGD to reduce pollution from generating units expected to operate for more than 40% of the year beyond 2001.

(c) Solvent Emissions

In March 1999 Environment Ministers adopted Council Directive 99/13 on the limitation of emissions of volatile organic compounds due to the use of organic solvents in certain activities and installations; it has to be implemented by April 2001. The aim of the Directive, which will mainly apply to the paint coatings and pharmaceuticals industries, is to reduce emissions of VOCs by approximately 50% by 2010, based on 1990 levels, from various activities listed in an Annex to the Directive.

Annex III specifies annual thresholds for solvent consumption for the activities and emission limits. The Directive gives Member States the option of meeting the overall reduction target through the establishment of a national plan for existing installations: this would enable Member States to set their own reduction targets for sectors taking into account national patterns of emissions, while still meeting the overall objectives of the Directive – existing installations using solvents which are carcinogens, mutagens or reproductive toxicants cannot be included in a national plan. New installations are also excluded and are required to comply with emission limits for the sector concerned and to be registered with, or authorised by the appropriate authority upon implementation of the Directive by 1 April 2001; existing installations would have until 31 October 2007 to comply. Installations requiring a permit under the IPPC Directive would not also require authorisation under this Directive although they must comply with its requirements. Member States who already have measures reducing VOC emissions but which are incompatible with the Directive will have until 2010 to comply.

Consultative documents from the DETR (covering England & Wales) and the Scottish Executive propose (July 2000) implementing the Directive through Directions under the *Pollution Prevention and Control Act 1999* and the *Environmental Protection Act 1990;* these would require enforcing authorities to include conditions in permits and authorisations which meet the requirements of the Solvents Directive. Relevant Secretary of State Guidance on Local Authority Air Pollution Control will also be reviewed to ensure it takes account of the minimum requirements of the Directive.

(d) Major Accident Hazards

Following a major explosion at a chemical factory in Seveso, Italy, in 1976, which resulted in health and other environmental problems in the area, the EU adopted a Directive on the Major Accident Hazards of Certain Industrial Activities (82/501/EEC). This Directive, commonly known as the Seveso Directive, was amended in 1987 and 1988; on 3 February 1999 it (and the subsequent amendments) were repealed, the date by which Member States had· to have implemented its replacement - Council Directive 96/82/EC on the control of major accident hazards involving dangerous substances (Seveso 2), which was adopted on 9 December 1996. In the UK the required Regulations - the *Control of Major Accident Hazards Regulations 1999* - came into force on 1 April 1999 (see this chapter 2.16.1).

The 1982 Directive aimed, through laying down requirements for notification of major hazard sites, hazard and risk assessments, safety reports and emergency planning, to prevent major accidents which may cause serious damage to·the environment or human health. An amendment to the Directive (87/216/EEC) required owners of "top tier" sites - i.e. those storing above specified amounts of hazardous substances and those carrying out particularly toxic or hazardous activities - to provide information to the public on the nature of the hazard and on action to be taken in the event of an accident. The 1996 Directive aims to close some of the loopholes/shortcomings of the earlier Directives which were identified in the light of lessons learned from accidents since the 1982 Directive came into force; many of the accidents were felt to have been preventable given better management and operational procedures.

The 1996 Directive applies mainly to the chemical and petrochemical industries and to those which produce or use substances with flammable, toxic or explosive properties; warehouses and storage facilities for hazardous materials such as fuel oils and gases are included but nuclear and military installations are not. Land-use policies must take major hazard sites into account, and thus more attention must be given to the siting of potentially hazardous installations, ensuring that new installations are sited at an "appropriate distance" from residential or other areas used by the public; these aspects of the Directive have been implemented through the *Planning (Control of Major-Accident Hazards) Regulations 1999* in England and Wales and similar 2000 Regulations in Scotland - see chapter 1, 1.23.

The Directive defines "hazard" in terms of its potential to damage or harm human health and the environment (flora, fauna, water, soil etc); operators of those establishments where dangerous substances are present above a certain threshold (top tier sites) are required to identify possible hazards and to adopt appropriate management and staff training procedures and policies to prevent accidents or minimise harm caused by accidental releases. This information must be included in the detailed safety report required by the Directive to be submitted to the competent authority (in England, Scotland & Wales - the HSE, the Environment Agency or SEPA); this must also include "main possible major accident scenarios" and how they would be dealt with. The Directive also requires an on-site emergency plan to be prepared and sufficient information given to the competent authority to enable it to prepare an off-site emergency plan. The competent authority must identify those establishments where, because of their proximity or the combinations of substances, the occurrence of an accident becomes even more potentially dangerous.

Safety reports must be publicly available and inspected by the competent authority to ensure that they meet the Directive's requirements. The competent authority must reject the safety report if it is of the opinion that, on the basis of the report, the continued use (or the start up) of an installation would "involve an imminent risk of a major accident". The competent authority must carry out an inspection of the facility (using qualified and trained personnel) and prepare a report of any follow-up measures required, with a follow-up inspection taking place within three months.

Operators of lower tier establishments must notify the competent authority of the hazards and produce a Major Accident Prevention Policy; this should set out aims and principles for preventing major accidents and show that the policy is in place and being implemented.

2.4.6 Transport Policy

In 1992 the European Commission adopted a Green Paper on the *Impact of Transport on the Environment* (COM(92) 46 final). This outlines an EU strategy for "sustainable mobility" and highlights the expected growth in all forms of transport with a consequent rise in levels of pollution. Between 1990 and 2010, the Commission forecasts a growth in road/goods transport of 42%, in rail/goods transport of 33%, and in air/passenger transport of 74%. Private cars are predicted to increase 45% over the period 1987-2010 and vehicle kilometres 25% between 1990 and 2010.

The Green Paper while noting the EU's current and future legislative programmes on emission limits and standards, says that these will not be enough to contain likely environmental damage from increased transport. The Commission suggests the need for a more integrated approach to transport policy and policy in other areas on which transport has an impact, such as planning and economic policy.

Since 1970, the European Union has adopted a number of Directives aimed at reducing emissions of air pollutants from all classes of vehicle. These are summarised later in this chapter - see 2.22.

IMPLEMENTATION AND ENFORCEMENT AUTHORITIES

As was seen earlier in this chapter (section 2.2.1 and 2.2.2), HM Inspectorate of Pollution and its predecessors had most of the responsibility for controlling air pollution from a wide range of scheduled processes. The control of emissions from non-scheduled processes was the responsibility of local authorities, usually the environmental health department or its equivalent. *The Clean Air Acts* of 1956 and 1968 strengthened the powers of local authorities, previously contained in the *Public Health Act 1936,* to control such works, although it should be noted that the Acts covered only combustion processes and smoke, grit and dust emissions.

Implementation of Part I of the *Environmental Protection Act 1990* extended local authority powers to include the control of air pollution from a range of prescribed processes (see 2.12 below). Action to control smoke, dust, fumes and gases as a statutory nuisance can be taken under Part III of the EPA (see chapter 1, 1.16.1).

2.5 LOCAL AUTHORITIES
2.5.1 England and Wales

Local authorities became responsible for air pollution control under Part I of the *Environmental Protection Act 1990* (EPA) on 1 April 1991; processes prescribed for local authority control - Part B processes (see Appendix 1.1) - require an authorisation from their local authority.

In carrying out their functions under Part I of the EPA local authorities must have regard to the National Air Quality Strategy (new section 4(4A) of EPA, *Environment Act 1995,* Sch. 22, para 46(5)) - see this chapter 2.7; they also have a duty to keep themselves up-to-date with regard to techniques and technologies for preventing and reducing releases to air from Part B processes (new section 4(9) of EPA), *Env. Act 1995,* Sch. 22, para 46(9)).

Local authorities are also responsible for

- permitting of A2 installations under the *Pollution Prevention and Control (England & Wales) Regulations 2000,* and enforcement of the Regulations (see chapter 1, 1.13.1);
- air quality management and assessment (this chapter 2.7) under the *Environment Act 1995;*
- enforcing statutory nuisance legislation (see chapter 1, 1.16.1);
- enforcement of the *Clean Air Act 1993,* including the regulation of smoke, grit, dust and fumes from furnaces and for implementation and enforcement of smoke control (this chapter, 2.14);
- enforcing noise control legislation (see chapter 3)
- identification of and ensuring appropriate clean up of contaminated land under the *Contaminated Land (England) Regulations 2000* (and similar in Scotland) - see chapter 4.

The *Public Health (Control of Diseases) Act 1984* gives Port Health Authorities similar responsibilities to local authorities in relation to those sections of the *Clean Air Act 1993* and the *Environmental Protection Act 1990* relating to the control of air pollution.

A Memorandum of Understanding between the Environment Agency and local authority associations agreed in February 1997 outlines working arrangements and communications on all the various areas in which both have responsibilities, including air quality management, waste management and contaminated land - see chapter 1, 1.7.1d.

2.5.2 Scotland

Scottish local authorities have similar responsibilities to authorities in England and Wales. However they are not responsible for local air pollution control (Part B processes) under Part I of the *Environmental Protection Act 1990;* since 1 April 1996 these have been regulated by the Scottish Environment Protection Agency (SEPA) (*Env. Act 1995*, s.21(1)(h)). Similarly, SEPA, and not local authorities, will also be responsible for all installations regulated under Integrated Pollution Prevention Control (chapter 1, 1.13).

2.6 NORTHERN IRELAND

In Northern Ireland, the control of air pollution was the responsibility of the Department of the Environment under the *Alkali Act 1906.* The *Industrial Pollution Control (Northern Ireland) Order 1997,* which received Royal Assent on 26 November 1997, establishes a system of air pollution control similar to that operating in the rest of the UK. There are, however, two tiers of air pollution control:

- processes with the potential to cause serious air pollution are regulated by the Industrial Pollution and Radiochemical Inspectorate (IPRI) of the Environment and Heritage Service, an agency of the DOE;

- processes with significant but less potential for air pollution are regulated by district councils.

New processes (i.e. those coming into operation on 2 March 1998 or after) were required to apply for an authorisation immediately; existing processes are being brought within the new controls between 1 October 1998 and 31 December 2002.

Local authorities (district councils) are responsible for the control of domestic emissions and for emissions from commercial and industrial premises not covered by the *Alkali Act 1906,* for statutory nuisance and noise legislation.

AIR QUALITY MANAGEMENT

A report from the Committee on the Medical Effects of Air Pollutants (*Quantification of the Effects of Air Pollution on Health,* The Stationery Office, 1998) suggests that the short term impact of air pollution on health results in the premature death of between 12,000-24,000 vulnerable (i.e. the very old, very young or sick and those with respiratory diseases) people in Great Britain each year; the Committee also estimates that between 14,000 and 24,000 hospital admissions and readmissions may be associated with short term air pollution each year. The effects of air pollution on health have, however, been recognised for more than three centuries - in 1648 Londoners petitioned Parliament to ban the importation of coal from Newcastle because of its injurious effects.

National and EU legislation (as well as international agreements) over the years has tended to focus on reducing pollution from a particular sector, e.g. from industry or from motor vehicles. Now, however, the emphasis is on maintaining or, where necessary, improving local air quality to protect public health: targets or limit values are set for individual pollutants and action plans drawn up for those areas where there is a risk that standards might be, or are being, exceeded - see above, 2.4.1a, the EU ambient air quality assessment and management Directive, and 2.7 below, the Air Quality Strategy for England, Scotland, Wales and Northern Ireland. The UNECE Convention on Long-Range Transboundary Air Pollution (see 2.3.3), whose signatories include most European countries, aims to reduce levels of certain pollutants to protect, and to prevent further damage to, sensitive ecosystems.

This section of the *Pollution Handbook* outlines the provisions of Part IV of the *Environment Act 1995:* the Secretary of State is required to draw up a National Air Quality Strategy; local authorities are required to review and assess local air quality against standards and objectives in the National Air Quality Strategy and where necessary to declare an air quality management area. Brief details of the UK air quality monitoring networks and of the sources of research and advice on issues such as the health effects of pollutants on which Government policy is based are also given. Further sources of information on the effects of pollutants are listed in the bibliography at the back of this book.

2.7 ENVIRONMENT ACT 1995, PART IV

National Air Quality Strategy (s.80)

This section of the Act was brought into force on 1 February 1996; it requires the Secretary of State to formulate a national air quality strategy in consultation with the environment agencies, representatives of local authorities and of industry and other relevant bodies or persons considered appropriate. Following a period of consultation in 1996 the first Strategy, *The United Kingdom National Air Quality Strategy* was published in March 1997, with the objectives for each pollutant (apart from that for ozone) being given statutory force in the (now revoked) *Air Quality Regulations 1997* (SI 3043).

Proposals for amending the Strategy were published in January 1999 and a revised version, *The Air Quality*

Strategy for England, Scotland, Wales and Northern Ireland – Working Together for Clean Air, published in January 2000. This builds on the previous Strategy, outlining a national framework for reducing hazards to health from air pollution in the UK. Objectives for the eight main health-threatening pollutants (Table 2.5) have, as before, been set with regard to recommendations of the Government's Expert Panel on Air Quality Standards (see 2.10.2 below) and, apart from ozone, given statutory backing in Regulations - *the Air Quality (England) Regulations 2000* (SI 928 – effective 6 April 2000), and similar in Scotland (SSI 97 – effective 7 April 2000), and in Wales (SI 1940, W.138 – effective 1 August 2000). Local authorities must take account of these objectives when reviewing local air quality and, where necessary, draw up an air quality management plan if standards are being breached or are at risk.

The Strategy recognises that ozone is not easily controlled by local measures and that measures to reduce it will therefore need to be agreed at a European level. Further measures for achieving the objective for ozone (Table 2.6) will therefore be considered in the light of those agreed

Table 2.5: Objectives for the Purposes of Local Air Quality Management (included in the Air Quality Regulations 2000)

Benzene	16.25 µg/m³ (5 ppb) running annual mean to be achieved by 31.12.03;
1,3 Butadiene	2.25 µg/m³ (1 ppb) running annual mean to be achieved by 31.12.03;
Carbon monoxide	11.6 mg/m³ (10 ppm) running 8 hr mean to be achieved by 31.12.03;
Lead	0.5 µg/m³ annual mean to be achieved by 31.12.04; 0.25 µg/m³ by 31.12.08;
Nitrogen dioxide	200 µg/m³ (105 ppb) 1 hour mean to be achieved by 31.12.05, not to be exceeded more than 18 times a year (provisional objective) ;
	40 µg/m³ (21 ppb) annual mean to be achieved by 31.12.05 (provisional objective);
Particles (PM₁₀)	50 µg/m³ 24-hour mean to be achieved by 31.12.04, not to be exceeded more than 35 times a year;
	40 µg/m³ annual mean to be achieved by 31.12.04;
Sulphur dioxide	350 µg/m³ (132 ppb) 1 hour mean, to be achieved by 31.12.04; not to be exceeded more than 24 times per year;
	125 µg/m³ (47 ppb), 24 hour mean, to be achieved by 31.12.04, not to be exceeded more than 3 times per year;
	266 µg/m³ (100 ppb), 15 minute mean to be achieved by 31.12.05, not to be exceeded more than 35 times per year.

Table 2.6: National Objectives, for the purposes of LAQM (not in the Regulations)

Objective for the protection of human health	
Ozone	100 µg/m³ (50 ppb), daily max. of running 8-hour mean, to be achieved by 31.12.05; not to be exceeded more than 10 times per year (provisional).
Objective for the protection of vegetation and ecosystems	
Nitrogen Oxides	(assuming NOₓ is taken as NO₂) 30µg/m³ (16 ppb), annual mean, to be achieved by 31.12.00;
Sulphur Dioxide	20 µg/m³ (8 ppb), as both annual mean and winter average (1/10-31/3), to be achieved by 31.12.00.

under the recently agreed UNECE Multi-Pollutants Protocol (see 2.3.3c), and the EU's proposals for a new Ozone Directive and National Emissions Ceilings Directive (see 2.4.1c and 2.4.5a).

This Strategy also sets national objectives for nitrogen oxides and sulphur dioxide for the protection of vegetations and ecosystems to be achieved by the end of 2000; these objectives (see Table 2.6) apply in areas more than 20 km from an agglomeration and more than 5 km away from industrial sources regulated under Part I of the *Environmental Protection Act 1990;* motorways and built up areas of more than 5,000 people. Proposals for implementing these objectives will be included in proposals for implementing the EU's 1999 Directive which sets limit values for sulphur dioxide, oxides of nitrogen, particulate matter and lead (see 2.4.1i).

As well as setting AQ standards and objectives, the Strategy includes:

• an assessment of current air quality, and describes the international and European framework within which the Strategy has been drawn up (see 2.3 and 2.4 above);

• what the Government is doing to achieve the Strategy's objectives;

• the contribution which other sectors – including industry, transport, local government, the environment agencies - can make towards achieving the objectives of the National Strategy.

With regard to this latter point local authorities are advised (it is not a statutory requirement) to develop a local air quality strategy to ensure that air quality is integrated into planning and transport policy. This local strategy might cover: cooperation within and between local authorities; involving and informing business and the community; local statutory and voluntary measures.

The Environment Agency and SEPA are required to take account of the Strategy in carrying out their pollution control functions (s.81). Section 7(2) & (12) of the *Environmental Protection Act 1990,* as amended by the

Environment Act, Sch. 22, para 49(2) place the same obligation on local authorities in England and Wales.

The Greater London Authority Act 1999 (GLAA 1999) requires the Mayor of London to publish an air quality strategy for London containing proposals and policies for implementing the National Air Quality Strategy and achieving the statutory objectives in Greater London; it should also include an assessment of current and future air quality in Greater London. In drawing up the London Air Quality Strategy the Mayor should consult London local authorities and the Environment Agency. In carrying out their duties under the *Environment Act* London local authorities will need to have regard to the London Strategy as well as the National Strategy, DETR Guidance and any Directions from the Secretary of State.

While the Strategy covers Northern Ireland, it has no statutory force as the *Environment Act 1995* does not apply; however, some district councils in Northern Ireland are reviewing air quality on the basis of the Strategy.

A further review of the Strategy was to be commenced towards the end of 2000; it will take account of further research on impacts of air pollution on health and of the costs and benefits of the Strategy's objectives; objectives for other pollutants will be included where there is evidence of effects.

Local Authority Functions and Duties (ss.82-84)

These sections of the Act, which place a duty on local authorities to review air quality in their area, were brought into force on 23 December 1997. The review should include the likely future air quality within the relevant period and an assessment of whether air quality standards and objectives are being achieved, or are likely to be achieved measured against the National Air Quality strategy. LAQM Guidance G1(00) recommended that initial reviews and assessments should be completed by June 2000, and air quality management areas designated by October 2000, with at least one further review and assessment being completed before the end of 2003.

Any part of the authority's area in which standards or objectives are not being met, or are unlikely to be met within the relevant period set out in the *Air Quality Regulations 2000* should by Order be designated an "air quality management area". The Guidance outlines a three stage review and assessment process for local authorities:

- **Stage 1:** establish whether any "significant" existing or proposed sources of the regulated pollutants both within the area of the authority and outside which could result in it not meeting an air quality objective in part of its area; for this stage it is not necessary to carry out monitoring, air quality dispersion modelling or to construct an emissions inventory. (It is open for an authority to go straight to Stage 3 if it is considered that a particular pollutant source is likely to lead to an objective not being met in part of its area.)

- **Stage 2:** if on the basis of the information gathered during Stage 1, it is thought that there is a likelihood of not meeting any of the objectives in any part of the authority's area, a more detailed review and assessment should be carried out – this will include monitoring, modelling in areas where it is thought likely that the highest concentrations of the pollutants of concern will occur; if results show that the objective is likely to be met in such areas, then the authority will not need to declare an air quality management area (or proceed to Stage 3); if however, it is thought an objective will be exceeded, and thus an air quality management area designated, then a Stage 3 review and assessment must be carried out.

- **Stage 3:** a detailed assessment of current and future air quality based on the results of further more detailed monitoring and modelling must be prepared, leading finally, if it is still predicted that an objective will not be met on time, to formal proposals to designate an air quality management area. The Guidance suggests four months between consulting on proposals to designate an AQMA and its actual designation

Following formal designation by Order of an AQMA, the local authority must carry out a further assessment of the air quality in that area, identifying those standards or objectives which are not being met (or which are unlikely to be met within the relevant period) and the possible reasons. Within 12 months of designation, and in parallel with the aforementioned assessment, the local authority should draw up an action plan for each AQMA setting out the various measures, together with target dates, by which it aims to meet air quality standards. Following consultation on the plan, and its revision as appropriate, local authorities should aim to have the action plan in place within 12-18 months of designation of the AQMA. The plan may be revised as appropriate. AQM Orders may be varied by subsequent Order or revoked (where standards and objectives are being achieved or likely to be during the relevant period), but only following a further air quality review.

In carrying out its functions in respect of an air quality review, assessment or preparing an action plan, the local authority must consult:

- the Secretary of State,
- the appropriate Environment Agency,
- in England and Wales, any highway authority affected by the review or plan,
- any local authority with whom it shares a border,
- in England, any relevant county council,
- appropriate National Parks authority,

and, as the local authority considers appropriate, any public authorities with functions within the area, representatives of business interests, or any other bodies or persons (Sch.11 to the Act). *The Greater London Authority Act 1999* amends Sch.11 to require local authorities in Greater London and those adjoining a Greater London authority to, in addition, consult the Mayor.

Schedule 11 also specifies that the local authority should ensure the public have free access to the following documents, with copies obtainable at a reasonable charge:

- results of air quality review
- results of any assessment made
- any Order designating an Air Quality Management Area
- any action plan
- any Directions from the Secretary of State
- in England, proposals and statements submitted by a county council under s.86 or any Secretary of State Direction.

Although the National Air Quality Strategy covers Northern Ireland, district councils there are not formally required to carry out reviews and assessment of local air quality as Part IV of the *Environment Act* does not apply in Northern Ireland. The EU Directive on AQMA does however apply.

Guidance for local authorities

The DETR and National Assembly for Wales have published (March 2000) four guidance notes relating to local authorities' duties, which update and replace earlier 1997 guidance; similar guidance has been published by the Scottish Executive for local authorities in Scotland:

- Framework for review and assessment of air quality (LAQM.G1(00); G1(S)(00));
- Developing local air quality action plans and strategies: the main considerations (LAQM.G2(00); G2(S)(00));
- Air quality and transport (LAQM.G3(00); G3(S)(00));
- Air quality and land-use planning (LAQM.G4(00); G4(S)(00)).

In May 2000 DETR, the National Assembly for Wales and the Scottish Executive published four sets of technical guidance; they replace earlier 1998 Guidance which has been updated to reflect policy and scientific developments:

- Review and assessment: monitoring air quality (LAQM.TG1(00));
- Review and assessment: estimating emissions (LAQM.TG2(00));
- Review and assessment: selection and use of dispersion models (LAQM.TG3(00));
- Review and assessment: pollutant specific guidance (LAQM.TG4(00)).

Section 88(2) of the *Environment Act* requires local authorities to have regard to any guidance issued by the Secretary of State in carrying out their duties under this Part of the Act. London local authorities are also required to have regard to the London air quality strategy (*Greater London Authority Act 1999*, s.364).

The following air quality advice lines have also been set up to provide assistance to local authorities:

- ***Emissions*** – tel: 0207 793 1965; email: emissions.factors@london-research.gov.uk; operated by the London Research Centre.

- ***Modelling*** – tel: 0208 256 4972; email: modelhelp@stanger.co.uk; operated by Stanger Science & Environment.

- ***Pollutant specific guidance*** – tel: 0117 976 3837; email: aqm-review@uwe.ac.uk; operated by Air Quality Consultants and University of West of England.

- ***Monitoring*** – tel: 01235 463356; email: aqm.helpline@aeat.co.uk; operated by the National Environmental Technology Centre.

- ***Industrial sources*** – tel: 01306 743312; email: industrial.emissions@rsk.co.uk; operated by RSK.

Reserve Powers of Secretary of State (E & W) and of SEPA (s.85)

This section of the Act (brought into force on 23 December 1997) provides powers for the Secretary of State/SEPA (acting with the approval of the Secretary of State) to carry out or to have carried out a review of air quality within the area of a local authority; to assess whether air quality objectives and standards are being met; to identify those parts of a local authority's area where it seems objectives and standards are not being met; and to make an assessment of the possible reasons why they are not being met either within the area of the LA or within a designated area.

If it appears to the Secretary of State/SEPA that a local authority is not meeting its obligations under ss.82-84, or that AQSs or objectives are unlikely to be achieved, the Secretary of State/SEPA may direct the local authority to:

- arrange for an air quality review to be carried out as specified by the Directions;

- arrange for a new air quality review to be carried out, covering such area as directed or in the way specified by the Directions;

- to revoke or modify an Order made under s.81 of the Act;

- to prepare or modify its action plan or to implement any measures in its action plan.

The Greater London Authority Act 1999 amends the *Environment Act 1995* to give similar powers to the Mayor of London with regard to London local authorities; however such powers may only be exercised following consultation with the authority concerned and having regard to any Guidance issued under s.88(1) by the Secretary of State.

The Secretary of State/SEPA may also direct local authorities (other than those in Greater London, s.367(4) *GLAA 1999* amendment to s.85(5) of *Env. Act 1995*) to take account of European or international commitments in their action plan.

County Council Functions (s.86)

This section of the Act came into force on 23 December 1997 and applies in those districts in England covered by a district council which are also in an area comprising a county council.

The relevant county council may make recommendations to the district council with regard to the district council's duties under this part of the Act, which the district council must take into account.

Where the district council is preparing an action plan, the county council should submit its proposals, together with a statement outlining the timescale, for meeting air quality standards and objectives within the designated area. The *Air Quality (England) Regulations 2000* require the county council to submit its proposals within nine months of first being consulted by the district council on its action plan.

If the Secretary of State is of the opinion that the council is not meeting its obligations under this section of the Act, he may through Directions require the county council to

- submit its proposals and statement of timescale for meeting AQSs and objectives;

- to modify its proposals or statement in accordance with the Directions and to submit this to the district council;

- to implement any measures in an action plan as required by the Direction.

Directions may also require county councils to take steps to implement international or European obligations with regard to air quality.

Schedule 11 to the Act requires county and district councils in England to provide each other with information "as is reasonably requested" in pursuit of their respective duties and functions.

Where a local authority in London is drawing up an action plan in respect of a designated area, the Mayor of London should submit his proposals for the area to the authority, together with a statement outlining when he proposes to implement each of his proposals (new s.86A to *Env. Act 1995*, added by s.368 of GLAA 1999).

Regulations (s.87)

This section of the Act (brought into force on 1 February 1996) provides for regulations covering all aspects of this Part of the Act, including air quality standards; objectives for restricting levels of particular substances in the air; prohibiting or restricting specified activities, vehicle or mobile equipment access in general or in certain circumstances; communicating AQ information to the public; regulations may also relate to air quality reviews, assessments, orders designating AQ management areas and action plans; vehicle emission spot checks; offences, penalties (including fixed penalty offences) and appeals.

(a) Air Quality (England) Regulations 2000 (SI 928)

These Regulations came into force on 6 April 2000, with similar Regulations (SSI 97) taking effect in Scotland on 7 April and in Wales (SI 1940, W.138) on 1 August 2000. The 1997 Regulations (SI 3043) have been revoked.

The Regulations incorporate the objectives contained in the Air Quality Strategy for England, Scotland, Wales and Northern Ireland, against which local authorities must review and assess air quality (see above, s.80 of the Act); they also specify the period within which county councils in England must submit proposals to district councils for inclusion in an air quality action plan (see above, s.86 of the Act).

Further Regulations are to be made transposing the EU 1999 Directive relating to limit values for sulphur dioxide, oxides of nitrogen, particulate matter and lead (2.4.1bi).

(b) Road Traffic (Vehicle Emissions) (Fixed Penalty) Regulations 1997 (SI 3058)

These Regulations apply in England, Scotland and Wales and were brought into force on 26 December 1997, but currently only apply in the areas of seven local authorities (see 2.23.7). Following review, the Government is currently consulting (June 2000) on extending the Regulations to all local authorities in England and Wales. The 1997 Regulations empower authorised officers to check that emissions from road vehicles comply with Construction and Use Regulations and to issue fixed penalty notices to drivers of vehicles failing the test; they also enable fixed penalty notices to be issued to drivers who leave their vehicle engine running unnecessarily - see also this chapter 2.23.7.

2.8 THE AIR QUALITY STANDARDS REGULATIONS 1989 (SI 317)

These Regulations (amended 1993), made under the *European Communities Act 1972*, came into effect on 31 March 1989 and apply to England, Scotland and Wales. *The Air Quality Standards Regulations (Northern Ireland) 1990* (amended 1994 and 1996) containing similar provisions came into operation on 31 May 1990. The Regulations implement EU Directives setting air quality limit values and guide values for sulphur dioxide and suspended particulates (80/779/EEC), a limit value for lead in air (82/884/EEC) and air quality standards for nitrogen dioxide (85/203/EEC); these were the first EU Directives to lay down mandatory air quality standards - the standards are detailed earlier in this chapter, 2.4.1b. These Directives are to be superseded by the "daughter" Directive under the Air Quality Assessment and Management Framework Directive - see this chapter 2.4.1a.

The UK Regulations provided for specific areas to be temporarily exempted from complying with the air quality limits for suspended particulates and lead. With respect to the limit values for suspended particulates, a number of districts, mostly in the West Midlands, Yorkshire, North East England, and Glasgow in Scotland had until 1 April 1993 to comply, although programmes for meeting the Directive had to be drawn up in advance of this.

The Regulations require the Secretary of State to ensure that the amounts in the air of suspended particulates and sulphur dioxide (considered both separately and in association), lead, and nitrogen dioxide are measured and reduced below specified limit values. They do not apply to exposure to lead in the air as a result of a person's occupation, nor to nitrogen dioxide in the atmosphere at work or within buildings.

New Regulations will be required, before the implementation date of July 2001, to transpose the 1999 Directive setting limit values for sulphur dioxide, oxides of nitrogen, particulate matter and lead – see 2.4.1bi.

2.9 THE OZONE MONITORING AND INFORMATION REGULATIONS 1994 (SI 440)

These Regulations made under the *European Communities Act 1972* apply throughout the UK and came into force on 21 March 1994; they implement EU Directive 92/72 (see this chapter 2.4.1c).

The Regulations require the Secretary of State to either set up or designate monitoring stations for ozone - the Directive specifies the number and where they should be sited. Monitoring results must also be analysed and evaluated in accordance with the reference method (or method giving similar results) in the Directive.

When ozone levels exceed thresholds specified in the Directive, the public must be informed and health advice given.

2.10 AIR POLLUTION MEASUREMENT AND MONITORING

Measurements of air pollution have been made for many years in the UK, with monitoring (i.e. the systematic measurement of air pollution) begun in 1914 by the voluntary Committee for the Investigation of Atmospheric Pollution. This Committee included, among others, members from a few local authorities, the Coal Smoke Abatement Society (the forerunner of the National Society for Clean Air) and the Director of the Meteorological Office. Its work was put on an official footing in 1917, under the direction of the Met. Office with the aim of providing an adequate picture of smoke and sulphur dioxide, grit and dust in towns; this coordinating function was later passed to the Department of Scientific and Industrial Research, followed in turn by the Fuel Research Station, Warren Spring Laboratory and now the National Environmental Technology Centre (NETCEN) (part of AEA Technology).

In 1961, the National Survey of Air Pollution was set up to monitor concentrations of both smoke and sulphur dioxide; measurements were made at about 1,200 urban and rural sites throughout the UK by local authorities and other bodies.

An annual National Atmospheric Emissions Inventory is prepared each year for the Department of the Environment,

Transport and the Regions (DETR) by NETCEN. The Inventory covers black smoke, sulphur dioxide, nitrogen oxides, carbon monoxide, non-methane volatile organics, methane, carbon dioxide, lead, ammonia, metals and halogens; it provides estimates of pollution to atmosphere from all known sources and is used by government for policy formulation and for meeting European legislative requirements and international treaty obligations.

2.10.1 Monitoring Networks

In 1982, the National Survey was replaced by a more streamlined network - the UK Smoke and Sulphur Dioxide Monitoring Network. This Network comprises some 180 sites monitoring black smoke and sulphur dioxide, including sites monitoring in compliance with the EU Directive on air quality limit values and guide values for sulphur dioxide and suspended particulates (see 2.4.1b), with a similar number comprising the Basic Urban Network (some sites are common to both networks). Like its predecessor, this Network is equipped and operated by local authorities, industries and other bodies; it is coordinated by NETCEN who process and analyse the data on behalf of the DETR. Daily average concentrations of sulphur dioxide are measured using the acid titration method (BS 1747, Part 3) and smoke using the reflectance method (BS 1747, Part 11). Smoke and sulphur dioxide measurement data are available from the air quality archive website - http://www.aeat.co.uk/netcen/aqarchive/archome.html. The archive includes automatic and non-automatic monitoring data and the UK atmospheric emissions inventories, with some data going back to the 1960s.

Nitrogen dioxide is measured (using diffusion tubes) at approximately 1,200 urban background and roadside sites. In compliance with EU Directives, ground level concentrations of nitrogen dioxide and airborne lead are also monitored. Acid deposition and toxic organic micropollutants (dioxins, PCBs and PAHs) are also measured at a number of sites.

In January 1992 the Enhanced Urban Network (EUN) - now the Automatic Urban Network (AUN) - funded by the DETR, became operational, and a number of local authority sites were integrated into the Network. Sulphur dioxide, nitrogen oxides, carbon monoxide, ozone and particulate matter (PM_{10}) are monitored continuously using automatic instruments. The DETR also funds the Automatic Rural Network which monitors ozone by automatic UV absorption analysers. The main purpose of the sites is to provide up to date information on air quality which can be used to increase understanding of air quality problems, to assess personal exposure to air pollution and to assess the extent to which air quality standards and targets are met.

In April 1998, the Urban and Rural Networks were combined under a single Central Management and Coordination Unit, with Stanger Science and Environment (environmental consultants) being contracted to carry out day to day management and control of the combined Networks - the UK Automatic Urban and Rural Air Quality Monitoring Networks (AURN); there are over 100 monitoring sites, with more planned to ensure monitoring will comply with the EU Daughter Directive on SO_2, NO_2, PM_{10} and lead (see 2.4.1bi). Responsibilities include specifying the monitoring equipment, site housings, data handling and maintenance requirements; sites are operated mainly by trained staff within local authorities and data from the sites coordinated by NETCEN on behalf of the DETR. NETCEN is responsible for quality assurance and quality control in respect of the AUN and the National Physical Laboratory for the rural and London networks. Air quality information is logged on a central computer system which gathers and analyses data from all the sites.

The Hydrocarbons Network which consists of 12 sites, is also funded by the DETR and monitors 25 VOCs, including benzene and 1,3 butadiene. The National Physical Laboratory is the Central Management and Coordination Unit for this Network (as well as being responsible for quality assurance/quality control).

Measurement is carried out using the following methods:

- *Ozone*: UV absorption
- *Oxides of nitrogen:* Chemiluminescence
- *Carbon monoxide:* IR absorption
- *Sulphur dioxide:* UV fluorescence
- *PM$_{10}$:* Tapered element oscillating microbalance
- *Hydrocarbons:* Gas chromatography
- *VOCs:* Flame ionisation detector.

In 1990, the DOE (now DETR) established an air quality information service to advise the public both on the quality of the air and on any precautions which should be taken during pollution episodes. In November 1997, a new system was launched, with air pollution bands reflecting effects on health (Table 2.7 below). Data collected by the networks on ozone, sulphur dioxide, nitrogen dioxide, benzene, 1,3 butadiene, carbon monoxide and PM$_{10}$ is available via an air quality telephone line (freephone 0800 556677), on Ceefax (page 410-417) and Teletext (page 106); it is also sent to the media for inclusion in weather bulletins and is also available on the Internet (http://www.environment.detr.gov.uk/airq/aqinfo.html). Data from automatic monitoring networks from 1972 onwards and from non-automatic networks (the National Air Quality Archive), as well as data from the National Atmospheric Emissions Inventory can also be accessed at this website.

The DETR is expected to issue proposals for amending the air quality information service to ensure that information provided to the public meets the requirements of the EU's Daughter Directive on Air Quality (see 2.4.1 above).

2.10.2 Research and Advice

There are of course a wide range of independent and government sponsored bodies carrying out research in all areas relating to air pollution and air quality. Of particular interest to air quality are two groups set up under the auspices of the DOE (now DETR):

- *Quality of Urban Air Review Group* (QUARG): set up to review current knowledge of urban air quality and how it is assessed in the UK, especially in relation to public exposure and information to the public; QUARG makes recommendations to the Secretary of State for the Environment, Transport and the Regions as to any changes which need to be made to the monitoring networks, pollutants measured, advice to the public and identifies areas where more research is needed.

- *The Expert Panel on Air Quality Standards* consists of medical and air pollution experts. It was set up to advise the Government on health-based air quality standards for the UK; its recommendations are listed below:

  - *Benzene:* 5 ppb as a running annual average to be reduced to 1 ppb (1994);
  - *Ozone:* 50 ppb as a running 8 hour average (1994);
  - *1,3 butadiene:* 1 ppb measured as a running annual average (1994);
  - *Carbon monoxide:* 10 ppm measured as a running 8-hour average (1994);
  - *Sulphur dioxide:* 100 ppb measured over a 15 minute averaging period (1995);
  - *Particles (PM$_{10}$):* 50 µg/m³ measured as a 24-hour running average (1995);
  - *Nitrogen dioxide:* 150 ppb measured as an hourly average (1996);
  - *Lead:* 0.25 µg/m³ measured as an annual average (1998);

Table 2.7: Air Pollution Information "Bands"

Description "...air pollution"	low	Standard threshold moderate	Information threshold high	Alert threshold very high
Sulphur dioxide (ppb, 15 minute average)	Less than 100	100-199	200-399	400 or more
Ozone (ppb)	Less than 50 (8 hr running av)	50-89 (hourly average)	90-179 (hourly average)	180 or more (hourly average)
Carbon monoxide (ppm, 8 hr running average)	Less than 10	10-14	15-19	20 or more
Nitrogen dioxide (ppb, hourly average)	Less than 150	150-299	300-399	400 or more
Fine Particles (µg/m³, 24 hr running average)	Less than 50	50-74	75-99	100 or more

Low: Effects unlikely to be noticed even by individuals who know they are sensitive to air pollutants;
Moderate: Mild effects, unlikely to require action, may be noticed amongst sensitive individuals;
High: Significant effects may be noticed by sensitive individuals and action to avoid or reduce these effects may be needed;
Very high: The effects on sensitive individuals described for "high" levels of pollution may worsen.

- *Polycyclic Aromatic Hydrocarbons:* taking benzo[a]pyrene as a marker for the total mixture of PAHs in the UK, 0.25 ng/m³ measured as an annual average (1999).

These recommendations are reflected in the standards and objectives for air quality in the National Air Quality Strategy (see 2.7 above).

The Department of Health's Committee on the Medical Effects of Air Pollutants (COMEAP) is an expert body set up in 1992 to advise the government on the effects of environmental factors on health. It has published a number of reports including *Asthma and Outdoor Air Pollution* and *Non-Biological Particles and Health* (both 1995), and *Quantification of the Effects of Air Pollution on Health in the United Kingdom* (1998); its views help to inform the work of EPAQS when recommending air quality standards. It also provides advice on the type of information which should be provided to the public during air pollution episodes. COMEAP has also drafted guidance (2000) on assessing the health impacts of industrial emissions to enable regulators to respond, in particular, to concerns from nearby residents. This outlines a procedure for assessing such impacts – including looking at statistics for illness, mortality, monitoring and modelling and studies to determine causes of clusters of illness.

2.10.3 Methods of Measuring

Although some measurement methods are relatively cheap and simple, others may involve the expenditure of thousands of pounds on equipment, the training of personnel to operate the instruments, and the careful analysis of results.

The choice of measurement method depends to a large extent on the finance and expertise available, but above all it has to be practical and relevant to the airborne contaminant under investigation. In each case the technique consists of two essential components: sample collection, and sample analysis.

There are two basic systems: the indirect, where sample collection and analysis are carried out separately and independently, and the direct, where two operations are combined simultaneously to give a direct reading. The direct method is most useful where immediate warnings are required of imminent danger and alarm circuits can be triggered, e.g. to protect workers or to check the compliance of emissions with legislation.

Environmental standards and legislative requirements will affect not only the method used, but also the duration of the monitoring. Essentially, effective monitoring requires both a sound knowledge of the instrumental and analytical methods employed and a full understanding of the behaviour of the pollutants in question, in terms of both the physical and chemical processes that they undergo in time and space in the ambient atmosphere.

A number of reference books on various methods of measuring air pollution are listed in the bibliography.

2.11 INDOOR AIR QUALITY

Most people spend around 90% of their time indoors and the increasing use of double glazing and other energy conservation measures will generally mean less natural ventilation and the build up of a range of potentially harmful pollutants. Indoor pollution can arise from a number of sources: heating, ventilation or cooking appliances can generate carbon monoxide, nitrogen dioxide and VOCs; the solvents used in many cleaning products, household sprays and some paints; tobacco smoke which gives off a range of harmful chemicals including formaldehyde, nicotine, tar, carbon monoxide and oxides of nitrogen; wood products such as chipboard and some glues contain formaldehyde. Naturally occurring uranium, present in certain rocks such as granite, produces radon, a naturally radioactive gas, which if it seeps upwards can build up to dangerously high concentrations in houses – see 2.27 and 2.30.

The presence of pollutants in the home environment – apart from radon - is however largely in the control of the householder and there are no regulations covering indoor air pollution; there are of course regulations and/or guidance relating to matters such as ventilation in homes (e.g. in areas where radon might be a problem) and the siting and servicing of appliances such as gas cookers and heaters; householders too should ensure adequate ventilation. In the workplace, however, the *Control of Substances Hazardous to Health Regulations 1999* place strict controls on the use and storage of hazardous or toxic substances to ensure risks to health are prevented or minimised - see this chapter 2.16.2.

REGULATION OF INDUSTRIAL EMISSIONS

The *Environmental Protection Act 1990* gave local authorities powers to control air pollution from a range of prescribed (Part B) processes (see Appendix 1.1 and 2.12 below); in Scotland these powers were transferred to the Scottish Environment Protection Agency (SEPA) on 1 April 1996. Under the *Pollution Prevention and Control (England and Wales) Regulations 2000* (see chapter 1, 1.13.1) which came into force 1 August 2000 – with similar Regulations coming tinto force in Scotland on 28 September 2000 - some processes currently regulated for local air pollution control only will, between 2002-2006 become regulated for Integrated Pollution Prevention and Control. Other processes currently regulated for local air pollution control but which do not require to be regulated for IPPC, will continue to be regulated for air pollution but under the *Pollution Prevention and Control Regulations*; their transfer to the new Regulations will take place between 2002-2004 (Schedule 3 to the Regulations, Parts 1 and 2; Scotland 31 December 2002).

Much of the principal legislation for dealing with industrial smoke pollution is contained in the *Clean Air*

Act 1993 which came into force on 27 August 1993 and extends to England, Scotland and Wales only - 2.14 below. The provisions of this Act enabling local authorities to designate "Smoke Control Areas" also apply to residential areas; the content of motor fuel is regulated by Regulations made under s.30 of the Act (which also applies in N. Ireland). The *Clean Air Act 1993* is a consolidating Act and replaced the Clean Air Acts 1956 and 1968, Part IV of the *Control of Pollution Act 1974,* the *Control of Smoke Pollution Act 1989,* as well as various sections of a number of other Acts. *The Clean Air (Northern Ireland) Order 1981* provides similar controls for Northern Ireland.

Responsibility for making environmental legislation (including pollution control) in Scotland and Wales now rests with the Scottish Parliament and the Welsh Assembly, respectively, and in Northern Ireland will be the responsibility of the Northern Ireland Assembly. Prior to 1999, most pollution control legislation applying in England and Wales also covered Scotland, modified where necessary to take account of the Scottish administrative and judicial system.

In Northern Ireland the *Industrial Pollution Control (Northern Ireland) Order 1997* establishes a system of industrial air pollution control similar to that applying in the rest of the UK - see 2.6 above. Industrial emissions are currently regulated under the *Alkali Act 1906* - this will be repealed in Northern Ireland following full implementation of the new legislation.

2.12 ENVIRONMENTAL PROTECTION ACT 1990, PART I

Under the *Environmental Protection Act*, which received Royal Assent on 1 November 1990, local authorities were given new powers to control air pollution from a range of industrial processes, including mobile plant (i.e. those designed to move or to be moved on roads or otherwise). Part I of the Act also introduced Integrated Pollution Control for more potentially polluting industrial processes - this is regulated by the Environment Agency and the Scottish Environment Protection Agency (see chapter 1, 1.14).

As from 1 April 1991 (1992 in Scotland), all new Part B processes and existing processes which were substantially modified after 1 April 1991/2, had to apply immediately for an authorisation from their local authority. Existing Part B processes were required to apply for an authorisation within specified dates between 1991 and 1993.

In Scotland, the *Environment Act 1995* transferred responsibility for local air pollution control under Part I of the EPA to the Scottish Environment Protection Agency on 1 April 1996 (see chapter 1, 1.7.2).

Port Health Authorities in England and Wales have the same responsibilities and functions as local authorities for controlling local air pollution under Part I of the EPA.

The Department of Environment (now Department of the Environment, Transport and the Regions) has published five general guidance notes (see Appendix 2.1) which are intended to serve as a manual for local authorities on the operation of their air pollution control responsibilities. Issues covered include the procedure for applications for an authorisation, variations and appeals, as well as the establishment, content and access to the public registers. Revisions to general guidance notes are published in "upgrading guidance notes" - see Appendix 2.1.

The *Environment Act 1995,* Schedule 22, makes a number of amendments to the EPA and these are noted in the following text.

Part I of the EPA will be repealed once all Part B processes have transferred to control under the *Pollution Prevention and Control (England and Wales) Regulations 2000* (and similar Regulations in Scotland); transfer of existing Part B processes which are to become A2 installations and regulated for all emissions will be phased in between 2002-07; Part B processes falling outside the scope of the IPPC Directive will transfer to the new Regulations between 2002-2004, with existing processes being permitted on the basis of "deemed applications" - see chapter 1, 1.13.1. New processes are required to apply for a Permit – see chapter 1, 1,13.1.

Northern Ireland

The *Industrial Pollution Control (Northern Ireland) Order 1997* establishes a system of air pollution control similar to that applying in the rest of the UK. There are however two levels of air pollution control: Part B processes - those with the potential to cause serious air pollution - are regulated by the Industrial Pollution and Radiochemical Inspectorate (IPRI) of the Environment and Heritage Service, an agency of the Department of the Environment (NI); Part C processes - those with significant but less potential for air pollution - are regulated by district councils. (A third category, Part A processes - those with high pollution potential - are regulated for Integrated Pollution Control also by the IPRI.)

Reference to the appropriate article of the Northern Ireland legislation is shown as follows: (NI: IPCO, Art.0).

2.12.1 Environmental Protection (Prescribed Processes and Substances) Regulations 1991 (SI 472) (as amended)

(Similar Regulations - The Industrial Pollution Control (Prescribed Processes and Substances) Regulations (Northern Ireland) 1998 (Statutory Rules of Northern Ireland no. 30) - have been made under Article 3 of the Industrial Pollution Control (NI) Order; they came into force on 2 March 1998.)

These Regulations made under s.2 of the Act came into force on 1 April 1991 in England and Wales and a year later in Scotland. Schedule 1 to the 1991 Regulations, as amended, lists Part A processes to be regulated for

Integrated Pollution Control (see chapter 1, 1.13) and those to be regulated for the control of air pollution (Part B processes) (Appendix 1.1). Amendment Regulations (1992 - SI 614, 1993 - SI 1749 and SI 2405, 1994 - SI 1271 and 1995 - SI 3247) are mainly concerned with changing process descriptions or altering the categorisation of prescribed processes. 1996 Amendment Regulations (SI 2678) prescribe certain petrol storage and distribution processes for authorisation as Part B processes. (A consolidated version of the Regulations to 1994 was published in 1994, but it should be noted that this is not a legal document; thus, the original Regulations and subsequent amendment Regulations should always be consulted where matters of legality etc are concerned.)

In England and Wales, where both Part A and Part B processes within the same section of Schedule 1 are carried on at a site, the Environment Agency will normally be the regulatory body. Where a site has a number of processes in different sections of the Schedule, they will each require a separate authorisation.

Schedule 4 to the 1991 Regulations lists the substances to be controlled in relation to air pollution (see Appendix 1.2). There are separate lists for releases to land and water which apply to IPC. The Best Available Techniques Not Entailing Excessive Costs (BATNEEC - see chapter 1, 1.6.2) must be used to prevent or minimise the release of all substances - whether prescribed or not - to the environment to render them harmless.

The 1991 Regulations also detailed the dates within which existing processes had to apply for an authorisation; all existing (i.e. in operation prior to the 1991 or 1992 date from which they could apply for authorisation) have now been authorised. The subsequent amendment Regulations specify the dates by when existing processes coming under control as a result of the amendment Regulations had to apply for authorisation. Transitional arrangements permitted existing processes to continue operating prior to receiving (or being refused) an authorisation provided the application was made on time; in the event of a refusal existing processes could continue to operate pending the outcome of an appeal. Failure to apply for an authorisation renders the operator liable for prosecution under s.23(1)(a) of the EPA (NI: IPCO, Art.23(1)(a)).

It should be noted that certain processes, although included in the Regulations, are exempt; these include processes carried out at museums to demonstrate an historical activity; at an educational establishment or as part of a domestic activity in a private home. Prescribed processes releasing substances in "trivial" amounts (except where the release results in an offensive smell outside the premises) are also exempt, as are engines for propelling most forms of transport (e.g. aircraft, road vehicles, ships etc).

As noted above, the *Pollution Prevention and Control (England and Wales) Regulations 2000* which implement the 1996 EU Integrated Pollution Prevention and Control Directive came into force on 1 August 2000, and similar in Scotland on 28 September 2000). When all existing Part B (and Part A) processes have been brought within the new Regulations between 2001-07, Part I of the EPA and Regulations under it will be revoked - see chapter 1, 1.13.1.

Northern Ireland

Schedule 1 to the 1998 Regulations describes the prescribed processes to be regulated for Integrated Central Control (Part A) - see chapter 1; Restricted Central Control (Part B); and local control (Part C). While the processes prescribed for control are very similar to those in the rest of the United Kingdom, it is of course necessary to refer to the Schedule itself for details of classification.

As from 2 March 1998, all new processes had to apply for an authorisation from the relevant authority. Schedule 3 to the Regulations lists the dates within which existing processes must apply for an authorisation, with the first tranche required to apply before 31 December 1998. Others will be required to apply for authorisation as specified in Schedule 3, with the final tranche required to apply before 31 December 2002. Existing processes are defined as those operating in the 12 months before 2 March 1998, or the plant for which was in the course of construction or for which contracts for construction had been exchanged in the 12 months to 2 March 1998, or are currently regulated under the *Alkali Act 1906*.

Schedules 4, 5 and 6 list the prescribed substances for release, respectively, to air, water and land. These are identical to Schedules 4, 5 and 6 of the GB Regulations - see Appendix 1.2.

2.12.2 Environmental Protection (Applications, Appeals and Registers) Regulations 1991 (SI 507), as amended

(Similar Regulations - The Industrial Pollution Control (Applications, Appeals and Registers) Regulations (Northern Ireland) 1998 (SR NI 29) - have been made under The Industrial Pollution Control (NI) Order 1997. They came into force on 2 March 1998.)

These Regulations came into force in England and Wales on 1 April 1991 and a year later in Scotland; they detail the way in which applications for authorisations, variations and substantial changes are to be made for both Part A and Part B processes; they also set out the circumstances and procedures for appeals against decisions made by the enforcing authority and establish public registers of authorisations etc.

1996 Amendment Regulations (SI 667), which came into force on 1 April 1996, amend the 1991 Regulations with regard to advertising and consultation on applications, information to be placed on the public register and requirement to disclose name of parent or holding company on applications and variations.

With effect from 1 April 1996 responsibility for regulating

Part B processes in Scotland transferred to the Scottish Environment Protection Agency (SEPA).

These Regulations will be repealed once existing Part B (and Part A) processes have transferred to control under the *Pollution Prevention and Control (England and Wales) Regulations 2000* (and similar in Scotland).

Northern Ireland

The 1998 Regulations are similar to those applying in England, Scotland and Wales.

The Industrial Pollution Control (Authorisation of Processes) (Determination Periods) Order (Northern Ireland) 1998 (SR NI 30) - varies the periods contained in the IPCO within which enforcing authorities should determine applications for authorisations:

- Existing Part A and Part B Processes: 9 months, instead of 6; where a request has been made for certain information to be considered as of importance to national security or as commercially confidential, the determination period begins when such matters have been resolved;
- Part C, new waste or recovered oil burners: 2 months, instead of 6.

Where a request is made for certain information on an application for authorisation to be excluded from the public register for national security or commercial confidentiality reasons, the 6 months (or longer as agreed) period of determination does not begin until the request has been determined or withdrawn.

(a) Applications

(NI: IPCO, Art.6 & Sch. 1, Part I)

All processes prescribed for local air pollution control (see Appendix 1.1) must apply for an authorisation from the local authority in which the process will be carried on (or in Scotland from SEPA); in the case of mobile plant in England and Wales (i.e. plant designed to move or to be moved by road or otherwise), this will be the local authority in which the applicant's principal place of business is situated.

For planned new processes, it is recommended that an application for an authorisation be made at the design stage (i.e. before construction); this will avoid the possibility of unnecessary expenditure due to the enforcing authority not approving, for example, the abatement technology. The actual construction of the site will be subject to separate approval under planning legislation (see chapter 1, 1.22).

In addition to general information about the plant, its location, name and address of operator and description of the process, the application should also identify the parent or ultimate holding company and its address. In making an application for authorisation the process operator should take account of the appropriate Process Guidance Note (see below and Appendix 2.1) and should include the following details:

- list of prescribed substances (and non-prescribed substances which might cause harm if released to the environment) to be used in connection with, or resulting from, the process; details of likely quantities and natures of releases should be given assuming the technology and controls have been fitted and are operational;
- description of techniques to be used for preventing or minimising the release of prescribed substances and rendering harmless any which are released;
- details of any proposed release and an assessment of the environmental consequences;
- proposals for monitoring, sampling and measurement of air emissions;
- for existing plant, outline programme for upgrading to meet new plant standards for BATNEEC.

An application for an authorisation for a waste oil burner with a net rated thermal input of less than 0.4 MW need only provide a list of specific information related to the appliance.

The application, relevant fee and copies (if requested) must be sent to the appropriate enforcing authority. If the application is considered to be incomplete - e.g. lacking in detail, sent without a fee or an incorrect fee - it will be returned to the applicant. Supplementary information in respect of applications for new or substantially changed processes should be requested in writing with a deadline by when the information should be submitted (EPA, Sch. 1, para 1(3)).

In submitting the application, the applicant may request that certain information should not be put on the register on the grounds of national security or commercial confidentiality (EPA, ss.21 & 22; NI: IPCO, Arts.21 & 22); the request for exclusion, which the enforcing authority has 14 days to consider, should be accompanied by a full statement justifying it. If it agrees, then the relevant information will be withheld; if the enforcing authority refuses the request, the applicant has 21 days in which to appeal to the Secretary of State (see below), during which time the information will not be added to the register. Following determination or withdrawal of the appeal, a further seven days must elapse before the information is added to the register (Env. Act 1995, Sch. 22, para 58(2)). It should be noted that if the enforcing authority fails to respond within 14 days to the request for information to be withheld, then it automatically becomes commercially confidential (s.22(3) of the EPA and of the NI: IPCO). The period for determination of applications for which a request for commercial confidentiality has been made will begin from the date on which such matters have been resolved.

Following acceptance of the application and resolution of any issues of commercial confidentiality, the enforcing authority will file a copy of the application in the public register kept for the purpose (see below).

Copies of applications (except those for small waste oil burners will be sent to English Nature, Scottish Natural Heritage, and the Countryside Council for Wales (as appropriate) where an emission to air may affect a Site of Special Scientific Interest; these bodies - statutory consultees - will normally have 28 days in which to comment. Petroleum licensing authorities must be consulted over applications relating to petrol storage and distribution processes in their area (1996 Amendment to EP Prescribed Processes & Substances Regulations - SI 2678). Applications for mobile plant need only be sent to the consultees if the plant is likely to remain in the same place for at least six months and is within one kilometre of an SSSI; in such cases a copy of the application should be sent to the relevant branch/office which should be invited to comment in the usual way. The Health and Safety Executive should be advised that an application for an authorisation has been made (1996 Amendment Regulations).

In Northern Ireland, the Department of Economic Development is a statutory consultee for both Part B and Part C processes; the DOE(NI) should be consulted over applications relating to Part B and C processes where a release to air may affect an area of special scientific interest; the relevant district council is a statutory consultee in the case of a Part B process which may involve a release to air. Statutory consultees must be notified within 14 days of the application being received and have 42 days in which to comment.

The enforcing authority will normally have four months from the date of receipt to consider applications relating to new processes (14 days for new waste or recovered oil burners under 0.4 MW). Under the *Environmental Protection (Authorisation of Process) (Determination of Periods) (Amendment) Order 1994,* local authorities had nine months in which to decide applications for processes prescribed for their control as a result of the 1994 amendments to the *Prescribed Processes and Substances Regulations.*

The Secretary of State may request the enforcing authority to forward a particular application, or class of application, to him for determination. The enforcing authority should advise the applicant that this has been done; both parties have 21 days in which to request the Secretary of State to arrange either a hearing or a local inquiry in connection with the application (Schedule 1, para 3; NI: IPCO, Sch. 1, Part I, para 3).

(b) Public Consultation

The applicant must publish an advertisement in an appropriate local newspaper not less than 14 days and not more than 42 days after the application is made; this should include brief details of the application, where it can be seen in the public register and note that any comments made will be put on the public register unless a request is made for them to be excluded. A period of 28 days (NI: 42 days) will normally be allowed for receipt of any comments from the public. Applications relating to waste oil burners under 0.4 MW, petrol service stations and to mobile plant do not need to be advertised although a copy of the application will be placed on the public register.

(c) Process Guidance Notes

In addition to the General Guidance Notes covering various aspects of local authority air pollution control, Process Guidance Notes (PG Notes) cover each of the Part B process sectors - see Appendix 2.1. The Environment Agency are responsible for producing the guidance notes, which are issued under s.7 of the EPA, to assist enforcing authorities in drawing up authorisations and setting appropriate conditions of operation.

Process Guidance Notes provide guidance on what constitutes BATNEEC for each category of process; they will usually include details of emission limits and controls, monitoring, sampling and measuring of emissions, materials handling and storage. They may also include general requirements for staff training, maintenance and response to abnormal emissions.

The Notes set the standards to be met by new plant and say that existing plant should be upgraded to new plant standards "whenever the opportunity arises", with the timetable for upgrading taking account of criteria laid down in the 1984 EU Directive on combating air pollution from industrial plant. The PG Notes include an outside limit beyond which an upgrading programme may be extended "only in exceptional circumstances".

Process Guidance Notes are generally reviewed every four years with a view to updating to reflect advances in technology etc. General revisions and amendments are published in Additional Guidance Notes (AQ Notes) - see Appendix 2.2; these provide clarification on matters relating to PG Notes as well as general guidance on administrative procedures relating to the EPA. The Agency is currently reviewing all LAPC Guidance Notes to update them to take account of IPPC, the Air Quality Strategy and relevant EU Directives, as well as developments in BAT/BATNEEC.

A number of technical guidance notes have also been published by the Environment Agency (and earlier ones by HMIP). These provide background detail on a range of technical subjects - see Appendix 1.4. For instance, the TG note on *Guidelines on Discharge Stack Heights for Polluting Emissions* (published in 1993 by HMSO) covers a wide variety of pollutant discharges not dealt with by the *Memorandum on Chimney Heights,* which it complements; it is intended primarily as an aid for enforcing authorities (but is also of interest to industry) in setting conditions for authorisations.

Guidance Notes for Part C processes in Northern Ireland have been produced by the Department of Environment, Northern Ireland.

(d) Authorisations

In considering whether to grant an authorisation, and the conditions which should be attached to it, the enforcing authority will take into account comments from statutory consultees and members of the public, as well as other relevant legislation, Directions from the Secretary of State, the National Air Quality Strategy and Process Guidance Notes, setting conditions as appropriate to ensure compliance with them. Where the Part B process consists of a waste disposal or recovery process, the enforcing authority should also ensure that the objectives of the Framework Directive on waste will be achieved - see chapter 4, 4.6.

In addition to factual details and a general description of the process, authorisations will include specific conditions for the operation of processes. Authorisations and their conditions should be written clearly and precisely to ensure their enforceability. Implicit in all authorisations is a duty (a residual duty) to use BATNEEC (see chapter 1, 1.6.2) to prevent or minimise the release to air of any prescribed substances and to ensure that any emissions are rendered harmless. If it is felt necessary, emission standards for specific pollutants can be included as well as conditions for monitoring releases beyond the boundary of the plant. Reference to the need to adhere to other relevant legislation such as the *Clean Air Act 1993* and nuisance provisions of the EPA should also be noted on the authorisation; however conditions relating to aspects of pollution control other than air pollution should not be included; nor should conditions be included which are solely for the protection of health at work, or which relate to the final disposal of waste.

Authorisations for mobile plant will normally include a requirement for the operator to notify the enforcing authority in advance if it is proposed to relocate the plant, including details of the new location.

In general there is a requirement to review authorisations at least every four years, and immediately if complaints are felt to be the result of older standards in operation or if new information about the harmful effects of a pollutant becomes available. Copies of all authorisations will be placed on the public register (see below).

It is an offence (EPA, ss.6(1) & 23; NI: IPCO, Arts.6(1) & 23)) to operate a process without an authorisation or in contravention of any of its conditions, even if an appeal has been lodged against those conditions. If an authorisation has been refused and an appeal lodged, the process can continue to operate pending the outcome of the appeal. The enforcing authority must refuse to grant an authorisation if it is felt that the operator will be unable to meet the proposed conditions (EPA, s.6(4); NI: IPCO, Art.6(4)).

Operators of existing plant (i.e. those in operation prior to the date specified in the Regulations) are usually required to let the enforcing authority have a detailed upgrading plan within 6-12 months of receiving their authorisation.

If this is not possible because, for example, further investigation of the technological options is needed, then the operator is allowed to submit a paper detailing expected progress leading up to a date for submitting the final upgrading plan. The enforcing authority would then issue a variation notice (see below) incorporating the programme into the authorisation.

Authorisations may be transferred to another person, who should notify the enforcing authority within 21 days of taking it over (EPA, s.9; NI: IPCO, Art.9). Details should be put on the public register.

(e) Inspections

Guidance (AQ 4/95) from the Department of Environment (now DETR) suggests that local enforcing authorities should aim to carry out a full inspection of authorised processes (except small waste oil burners) in their area approximately every six months; the main purpose is to check compliance with conditions of an authorisation, with compliance monitoring and in response to complaints; such visits may be unannounced.

Sites will also usually be visited in connection with applications for an authorisation, variation, etc.

(f) Variations

Sections 10 and 11 of the Act provide for authorisations to be varied by the enforcing authority or the process operator respectively.

Section 10 of the EPA (NI: IPCO, Art.10) requires the enforcing authority to vary an authorisation if it is of the opinion that conditions in the existing authorisation do not comply with BATNEEC or meet other objectives for minimising air pollution. In this instance, the enforcing authority will serve a variation notice specifying the changes it has decided should be made and the effective date. The *Environment Act 1995*, Sch. 22, para 51 amends the EPA to enable the enforcing authority to serve a variation notice varying a variation notice; this should specify the changes the enforcing authority wishes to make to the original variation notice and when these are to take effect. A variation notice will also require the operator to notify the enforcing authority how it proposes to meet the new requirements. If in the opinion of the enforcing authority this will result in a substantial change in the substances released from the process, or in the amounts released, then a procedure similar to applying for an authorisation (including disclosure of parent or holding company where this information is not already on the public register) is followed and a fee becomes payable (see below); varied variation notices do not however have to be sent to statutory consultees or advertised (*Env. Act 1995*, Sch. 22, para 93(4)). Where the action proposed to meet the variation notice is not considered substantial, the enforcing authority must decide whether it is acceptable; the enforcing authority has the option of issuing an amended variation notice proposing different action. Minor changes to an authorisation are likely to be decided by the enforcing authority alone and any alterations to the conditions attached to an authorisation advised to the operator.

There is a right of appeal except if the variation notice implements a Direction from the Secretary of State (see below).

Under s.11 of the EPA (NI: IPCO, Art.11), process operators must inform the enforcing authority if any substantial changes to the process are planned or if it is to be transferred to another person. While not a formal requirement, operators are advised to notify the enforcing authority if it is proposed to make a "relevant change" to the process - e.g. changing the way in which the process is operated - which might affect the amount and nature of emissions. Again, minor changes would be considered by the enforcing authority and a request for a more substantial change would follow the procedure outlined above for making an application. A process operator may appeal to the Secretary of State if a variation under s.11 of the EPA is refused.

Applications for variations (except those referred to the Secretary of State) must be determined within four months of receipt unless a different period is agreed. An application for a variation will be deemed to have failed if the enforcing authority fails to determine it within the agreed period and the applicant notifies the enforcing authority that he considers the failure to determine as refusal of the application (*Env. Act 1995*, Sch. 22, para 93(10)).

The *Environment Act 1995* (Sch. 22, para 93(5)) amends Schedule 1 of the EPA to permit the Secretary of State to call in applications for variations for determination. In doing so, he may either arrange for a local inquiry or give both the applicant and the enforcing authority the opportunity of a hearing.

Copies of variation notices and changes in conditions attached to an authorisation will be put on the public register.

(g) Revocation of Authorisation

Following 28 days written notice, the enforcing authority may revoke an authorisation in the following circumstances (EPA, s.12; NI: IPCO, Art.12):

- failure to pay the annual subsistence charge;
- it has reason to believe that the process has not been carried on, or not carried on for 12 months.

Prior to the notice taking effect, the enforcing authority may either withdraw the notice or vary the date on which revocation is to take effect.

(h) Enforcement

If the enforcing authority believes conditions of an authorisation are being breached it can take any of the following actions under ss.13-14 of the EPA (NI: IPCO, Arts.13-14):

- serve an enforcement notice (s.13) reinforcing an existing condition or requiring the operator to remedy the cause of the breach of condition within a specified period; Sch. 22, para 53 of the *Environment Act 1995* amends the EPA to permit the enforcing authority by written notice to withdraw an enforcement notice.

- where it is felt that the continued operation of the process involves "an imminent risk of serious pollution of the environment", serve a prohibition notice requiring the operator to close down all or part of the process and take the necessary steps to stop the risk (s.14); written notice of the withdrawal of a prohibition notice will be given by the enforcing authority when it is satisfied that the necessary action to deal with the problems has been taken.

(i) Appeals

The Secretary of State may determine appeals himself or appoint someone else for this purpose (*Env. Act 1995*, s.114 and Sch. 20). In Northern Ireland the DOE may refer an appeal to the Planning Appeals Commission for determination or for consideration prior to determination by the DOE (IPCO, Art.15(3) & Sch. 2). With effect from 1 September 1997, the Secretary of State delegated his powers on appeals for processes in England to the Planning Inspectorate. He has however, reserved the right to recover appeals relating to the following for determination himself:

- processes or sites of major importance;
- those giving rise to significant public controversy or legal difficulties;
- those which can only be decided in conjunction with other cases over which inspectors have no jurisdiction;
- those which raise major or novel issues of industrial pollution control which could set a policy precedent;
- those which merit recovery because of the particular circumstances.

Operators of Part B processes have a right of appeal under s.15 of the EPA (NI: IPCO, Arts.15 & 22) to the Secretary of State (or Planning Inspectorate in England; DOE in NI) against the decision of the enforcing authority, including refusal to authorise a process or imposition of a particular condition, the serving of variation, enforcement or prohibition notices, or revocation of an authorisation. There is also a right of appeal under s.22 of the EPA in relation to issues of commercial confidentiality - these appeals are determined by the Secretary of State. There is however no right of appeal where the notice implements a Direction from the Secretary of State (*Env. Act 1995*, Sch. 22, para 54(2)).

An appeal against refusal of an authorisation or a variation or of conditions of an authorisation must be made within six months; for revocation notices, before the date on which the notice takes effect; for enforcement, prohibition or s.10 variation notices, within two months; appeals against a refusal to exclude information from the public register must be made within 21 days. Where an appeal has been lodged against a revocation notice or decision of the enforcing authority that information is not commercially confidential, implementation of the notice or decision is deferred pending determination of the appeal. All other notices or decisions take effect from the specified date; disputed conditions also remain in place pending the outcome of the appeal.

The Regulations specify the information to be sent to the Secretary of State (England: Planning Inspectorate) by the operator; this includes a notice of appeal; statement setting out the reason for the appeal; statement about whether the appellant wishes the matter to be decided by written representations or by a hearing; these three documents should be copied to the enforcing authority and the Secretary of State - or Planning Inspectorate - advised that this has been done. The Secretary of State (or Planning Inspectorate) should also be sent a copy of the application and of the authorisation (where this exists) and relevant correspondence and notices with the appeal documents.

Following notification that an appeal has been lodged, the enforcing authority must, within 14 days, notify the statutory consultees and others who commented on the original application for the authorisation and invite comments; the notice will also state that a copy of any representations made will be put on the public register unless a written request is made that this should not happen. Any representations must usually be submitted to the Secretary of State (or his appointee) within 21 days.

Both parties must agree to the matter being dealt with in writing but if either side requests a hearing, then this will be arranged. A local inquiry may also be held in connection with the appeal, either at the instigation of the Secretary of State's appointee, or the Secretary of State may direct that a local inquiry be arranged (*Env. Act 1995*, Sch. 22, para 54).

If the appeal is to be decided through written representations, the enforcing authority has 28 days (from receipt of the appeal) in which to submit any further statement; the appellant will then have 17 days on which to comment on this statement; both have 14 days on which to comment on any other representations submitted.

If a hearing is to be held, the Secretary of State (Planning Inspectorate in England) will notify the appellant and the enforcing authority of the date, time and place for the hearing (giving at least 28 days notice); not less than 21 days notice of it should be given in a local newspaper and the same notice given to statutory consultees, etc. In the case of mobile plant, notice of the appeal must appear in the place in which the plant was operating when the enforcement/prohibition notice was issued. Most hearings will be held wholly or partly in public, unless matters of commercial confidentiality are concerned (in which case the hearing will always be in private).

Following determination, copies of the decision and any report will be sent to the appellant, the enforcing authority and statutory consultees. In those cases where the Secretary of State has recovered an appeal, the Inspector will report to the Secretary of State who will then make a decision on the appeal. A copy of the decision only will be sent to others involved in the appeal. A copy of both the report and decision will be put on the public register.

(j) Public Registers

Sections 20-22 of the EPA (as amended by *Env. Act 1995*, Sch. 22, paras 57-58) are concerned with the establishment of registers of air pollution control (and IPC - see chapter 1) information to be maintained by the enforcing authorities. Articles 20-22 of the *Industrial Pollution Control (NI) Order* contain similar provisions.

The 1996 Amendment of the Applications, Appeals and Registers Regulations list the documentation to be placed in the register (NI: 1998 Regulations).

- documentation relating to an application for an authorisation or for variation of the conditions of an authorisation; and subsequent information relating to the application for an authorisation requested by the enforcing authority;

- copy of advertisement relating to application for authorisation or variation or notification by enforcing authority to vary an authorisation; representations made as a result of the advertisement unless a request made that they should not be put on the register in which case a statement to this effect should be put on the register without identifying the person making the request;

- authorisations and their conditions;

- written notice of transfer of authorisation to another person;

- revocation, variation, enforcement or prohibition notices issued by the enforcing authority; notification by the enforcing authority of withdrawal of enforcement or prohibition notice;

- documentation relating to an appeal, its determination and any accompanying reports;

- details of convictions relating to carrying on of a prescribed process with or without an authorisation;

- monitoring data collected by the enforcing authority or submitted by an operator as a condition of the authorisation; where such information is omitted on grounds of commercial confidentiality, then the enforcing authority should put a statement on the register confirming or otherwise compliance with the relevant condition of the authorisation;

- information given to the enforcing authority on or after 1 April 1996 in compliance with a condition of an authorisation, variation, enforcement or prohibition notice;

- reports by the enforcing authority relating to the environmental consequences of a prescribed process in the locality of premises where the prescribed process is carried on under an authorisation;

- Directions from the Secretary of State.

Information affecting national security or which is accepted as being commercially confidential may be withheld and a note to this effect added to the register. The onus is on the operator to prove that disclosure of specific information would be prejudicial to their commercial interests. Exclusion of data from the register on the grounds of commercial confidentially lasts for four years after which it will be added to the register unless a further four year exclusion is applied for and agreed.

Applications for an authorisation or variation which have been advertised in a paper should be put in the register within 14 days of receipt by the enforcing authority; notifications to vary an authorisation (which are also advertised) should also be put in the register within 14 days of notifying the operator. The Regulations do not specify the time within which other information should be placed in the register although guidance issued by the Department of Environment (now Department of the Environment, Transport and the Regions) suggests that this should be done "as soon as possible". Information held in the registers may be inspected by the public free of charge and copies of entries obtained on "payment of a reasonable charge".

Information will be removed from the register in the following circumstances:

- withdrawal of application for authorisation prior to determination - all particulars to be removed not less than two months but within three months after the date of withdrawal;
- if a process ceases to be a prescribed process following amendment of the *Prescribed Processes and Substances Regulations* - all particulars to be removed not less than two months but within three months of the date on which the process ceases to be prescribed;
- monitoring information relating to a process - four years after entering in the register;
- information relating to a process which has been superseded - four years after the more recent information has been entered in the register.

Local authority registers in England and Wales (but not Port Health Authorities) also have copies of entries relating to IPC processes in their area; they will also contain copies of authorisations covering Part A and Part B processes in a port health district in their area. In NI, registers of Part B processes are held by the DOE, with district councils having registers of Part C processes;

district councils also hold details of Part A and Part B processes in their area. In Scotland, registers of processes regulated for air pollution are maintained by the Scottish Environment Protection Agency.

2.12.3 Offences

It is an offence (EPA, s.23; NI: IPCO, Art.23) to operate, without reasonable excuse, a prescribed process without an authorisation, in contravention of a condition attached to an authorisation, or other variation, enforcement or prohibition notice. Summary conviction may result in a fine of up to £20,000 and/or up to three months imprisonment (*Env. Act 1995*, Sch. 22, para 59(3)). Conviction on indictment may result in an unlimited fine and/or two years imprisonment.

2.12.4 Fees and Charges

Section 8 of the *Environmental Protection Act 1990* enables the Secretary of State to set up a scheme enabling local enforcing authorities in England and Wales to recover costs related to carrying out their air pollution control responsibilities.

Operators of Part B processes are required to pay a fee when applying for an authorisation or to vary an existing authorisation. An annual subsistence charge (which may be paid in quarterly instalments) becomes payable each 1 April. In both cases a reduced charge will be made for small waste oil burners (less than 0.4 MW). The charge will cover compliance monitoring and enforcement costs, including sampling and analysis of emissions.

Fees and charges for air pollution control in England are set annually by the Secretary of State, and by the National Assembly of Wales for charges in Wales.

The Local Enforcing Authorities Air Pollution Fees and Charges Scheme (England) 2000 sets out the charges which applied in England from 1 April 2000:

Initial application for authorisation   £1,280

except

- where process comprises one or more waste oil burning appliance under 0.4 MWth   £120

- where process relates to the unloading of petrol into storage tanks at a service station   £120

Substantial change   £815

except

- where this results solely from implementing upgrading programme   £120

- where process comprises one or more waste oil burners under 0.4 MWth   £80

- where process relates to the unloading of petrol into storage tanks at a service station   £80

Annual subsistence charge   £796

except

- where process comprises one or more waste oil burners under 0.4 MWth   £121

- where process relates to the unloading of petrol into storage tanks at a service station   £121

- odorising of natural gas   £292

- the charge is paid in quarterly instalments £826

Initial application fees and annual subsistence charges for processes which comprise mobile crushing and/or screening plant are based on the number of authorisations held by the operator.

Non-payment of statutory fees or charges may result in revocation of an operator's authorisation.

Northern Ireland

A similar charging scheme will be made under Article 8 of the *Industrial Pollution Control (NI) Order 1997*.

2.13 ENVIRONMENT ACT 1995

Powers of Entry

Sections 108-109, (effective 1 April 1996) empower "a person who appears suitable to an enforcing authority to be authorised in writing ..." to act under these sections of the Act. The Act also requires that, except in an emergency, a warrant should be obtained if entry has been or is likely to be refused and it is probable that force will be needed to gain entry.

Similar powers for inspectors in Northern Ireland are contained in Articles 17 and 18 of the *Industrial Pollution Control (NI) Order 1997*.

Authorised persons (warranted officers) are empowered to enter premises where they have reason to believe a prescribed process is being or has been operated (with or without an authorisation) or where they believe there is a risk of serious pollution. They may take photographs, samples etc of substances, and require access to relevant information and records. The authorised person may render harmless any substance or article from which it is considered there is imminent danger of serious harm; a written and signed report of what has been done and why should be given to a responsible person on the premises and a copy served on the owner of the substance or article (if different).

2.14 CLEAN AIR ACT 1993

This Act covers England, Scotland and Wales, with s.30 (regulations on motor fuel) applying also to Northern Ireland. It came into force in August 1993 and consolidates the 1956 and 1968 *Clean Air Acts* (which were repealed); it also incorporates clean air legislation contained in other Acts such as the *Control of Pollution Act 1974*, the *Control of Smoke Pollution Act 1989* (which is also repealed) and the EPA. Regulations made under the earlier Acts still apply.

Similar controls in Northern Ireland are provided in the *Clean Air (Northern Ireland) Order 1981*.

It should be noted that Parts I, II and III of the Act do not apply to processes prescribed for control under Part I of the *Environmental Protection Act 1990* or to installations to be regulated under the Pollution Prevention and Control Act 1999 from the date on which an authorisation or permit has been granted, refused or refusal confirmed following an appeal (s.41, as amended by the *Pollution Prevention and Control Regulations 2000* (England & Wales, or Scotland, as appropriate).

Offences

Prosecutions for most offences under the *Clean Air Act 1993* are dealt with in the Magistrates' Court (Sheriff Court, Scotland); offences are subject to a fine on the standard scale as specified in the *Criminal Justice Act 1982/Criminal Procedure (Scotland) Act 1975*, both as amended; for offences under ss.10, 42 and 43, where conviction relates to an offence which is substantially a repetition or continuation of an offence for which the defendant has already been convicted, a cumulative fine of £50 per day may be substituted (s.50 of CAA).

2.14.1 Part I: Dark Smoke

Prohibition of Dark Smoke from Chimneys (s.1)

This section prohibits the emission of dark smoke from a chimney of any building; it also applies to chimneys not attached to a building serving furnaces of fixed boilers or industrial plant, and could include incinerators and crematoria. The Secretary of State may, by regulation, exempt prescribed lengths of emission from action under this section. Section 43 of the Act brings dark smoke emissions from railway engines within the scope of s.1.

There are four defences available in any proceedings for dark/black smoke emission. These are that the alleged emission was:

a) solely due to lighting a furnace from cold and all practicable steps had been taken to minimise emissions;

b) solely due to unavoidable mechanical failure of part of the plant, that this could not reasonably have been foreseen or if foreseen could not reasonably have been provided for and that the emission could not have been prevented after failure occurred;

c) solely due to unavoidable use of unsuitable fuel, suitable fuel not being available and the best available fuel being used; and all practical steps were taken to minimise the emission;

d) due to any combination of a, b and c.

It should be noted that these are not absolute defences and are available only if every practical effort is made to avoid and/or minimise emissions.

Prohibition of Dark Smoke from Industrial or Trade Premises (s.2)

Subject to certain exemptions, it is an offence to cause or permit the emission of dark smoke from industrial or trade premises (as distinct from chimneys). Unless the contrary is proved, an emission of dark smoke is deemed to have taken place if material is burned on those premises in circumstances where the burning would be likely to give rise to the emission of dark smoke. This can include night-time burning of cable and vehicles on open ground by removing the necessity for a local authority to prove by direct observation that dark smoke has been emitted.

"Industrial or trade premises" means premises normally used for industrial or trade purposes, or premises not normally so used, but which, at the time of the offence, were being used for industrial or trade burning, e.g. demolition sites. For the purposes of this section, land being used for commercial agriculture or horticulture constitutes trade premises (Code of Good Agricultural Practice for the Protection of Air, MAFF, 1998). Thus, for example, emitting dark smoke from the burning of tyres on a commercial farm would probably be an offence.

An offence under this section of the Act may result in a fine not exceeding £20,000 (Environment Act 1995, Sch. 22, para 195).

Meaning of "Dark Smoke" (s.3)

Where legal standards of emission are prescribed for smoke, they refer to "dark" and "black" smoke.

Dark smoke is defined by reference to a shade on the British Standard Ringelmann Chart (see Appendix 2.3) and means smoke which if compared ... with the Ringelmann Chart would appear to be as dark as, or darker than shade 2 on the chart.

Black smoke (defined in the *Dark Smoke (Permitted Periods) Regulations 1958* and in the *Dark Smoke (Permitted Periods) (Vessels) Regulations 1958*) means smoke which, if compared ... with the Ringelmann Chart, would appear to be as dark as, or darker than shade 4 on the chart.

Although legislation defines dark and black smoke by reference to colour shades on the Ringelmann Chart, the use of the Chart is not compulsory. The 1993 Act says that "for the avoidance of doubt, it is hereby declared that ... the court may be satisfied that smoke is or is not dark smoke ... [even if] there has been no actual comparison of the smoke with a chart of the type mentioned".

For an illustration and description of how to use the Ringelmann chart see Appendix 2.3.

2.14.2 Part II: Smoke, Grit, Dust, and Fumes

Installation of Furnaces (s.4)

Before installing a furnace (except a domestic furnace) in a building or fixed boiler, the local authority must be informed; any such furnace must be capable of being operated continuously without emitting smoke when burning fuel of a type for which the furnace was designed.

There is no definition of "furnace", but a practical interpretation of this word whenever it appears in clean

Table 2.8: The Dark Smoke (Permitted Periods) Regulations 1958 (SI 498)

These Regulations were made under s.1(2) of the 1956 Act. Similar 1958 Regulations apply in Scotland and 1965 Regulations in Northern Ireland.

Specified permitted periods of emission are as follows:
a) Aggregate emissions of dark smoke

Number of furnaces served by the chimney	Permitted emission of dark smoke in any period of eight hours	
	If not soot blowing during period	If soot blowing during period
One	10 mins	14 mins
Two	18 mins	25 mins
Three	24 mins	34 mins
Four or more	29 mins	41 mins

Where a single boiler or unit of industrial plant is fired by more than one furnace discharging into the same chimney, those furnaces shall be deemed to be one furnace.
b) Continuous emission of dark smoke
The continuous emission of black smoke in excess of four minutes, caused otherwise than by soot blowing, is prohibited.
c) Aggregate emission of black smoke
No emission of black smoke exceeding two minutes aggregate in any period of thirty minutes is allowed. There are thus three standards of emission which are acceptable in relation to any one chimney.
(Soot blowing is a method of cleaning deposited carbon from the internal surfaces of large industrial boilers. It includes the use of a jet of steam onto heat exchange surfaces on a regular, usually daily basis.)

Table 2.9: Clean Air (Emission of Dark Smoke) (Exemption) Regulations 1969 (SI 1263)

These Regulations (made under s.1(3) of the 1968 Act) apply to England and Wales. They exempt the emission of dark smoke caused by the burning of certain materials subject to specified conditions. The corresponding Regulations for Scotland are the *Clean Air (Emission of Dark Smoke) (Exemption) (Scotland) Regulations 1969*. In Northern Ireland, the *Clean Air (Emission of Dark Smoke) (Exemption) Regulations 1981 apply.*

Exempted Matter	Conditions*
1. Timber and any other waste matter (other than natural or synthetic rubber or flock or feathers) which results from.the demolition of a building or clearance of a site in connection with any building operation or work of engineering construction (within the meaning of section 176 of the Factories Act 1961).	A, B and C
2. Explosive (within the meaning of the Explosives Act 1975) which has become waste; and matter which has been contaminated by such explosive	A and C
3. Matter which is burnt in connection with:	
a) research into the cause or control of fire	C
or	
b) training in fire fighting.	C
4. Tar, pitch, asphalt and other matter which is burnt in connection with the preparation and laying of any surface, or which is burnt off any surface in connection with re-surfacing, together with any fuel used for any such purpose.	
5. Carcasses of animals or poultry which	A and C unless the burning is carried out
a) have died, or are reasonably believed to have died, because of disease;	by or on behalf of an inspector (within the
b) have been slaughtered because of disease; or	meaning of section 84 of the Diseases of
c) have been required to be slaughtered pursuant to the Diseases of Animals Act 1950	Animals Act 1950)
6. Containers which are contaminated by any pesticide or by any toxic substances used for veterinary or agricultural purposes; and in this paragraph "container" includes any sack, box or receptacle of any kind.	A, B and C

* Condition A	That there is no other reasonable safe and practicable method of disposing of the matter.
Condition B	That the burning is carried out in such a manner as to minimise the emission of dark smoke.
Condition C	That the burning is carried out under the direct and continuous supervision of the occupier of the premises concerned or a person authorised to act on his behalf.

air legislation is usually taken as "any enclosed or partly enclosed space in which liquid, solid or gaseous matter is burned, or in which heat is produced". Domestic furnaces are defined as those with a maximum heating capacity of less than 16.12 kilowatts.

Limits on Rate of Emission of Grit and Dust (s.5)

The Secretary of State may by regulation prescribe limits on the rates of emission of grit and dust from the chimneys of all furnaces (except domestic furnaces); it is a defence to prove that the best practicable means were used to prevent any emission in excess of the permitted rates.

The Clean Air Act (Emission of Grit and Dust from Furnaces) Regulations 1971 (SI 162)

These Regulations (which do not cover N. Ireland) were made under s.2(1) of the 1968 Act and apply to:

a) boilers;
b) indirect heating appliances (being heating appliances in which the combustion gases are not in contact with the material being heated);
c) furnaces in which the combustion gases are in contact with the material being heated but that material does not in itself contribute to the grit and dust in the combustion gases.

The Regulations do not apply to incinerators burning refuse or waste matter (solid or liquid) whether or not the resulting heat is used for any purpose. (Incinerators are prescribed processes under the *Environmental Protection Act* - see earlier this chapter and chapter 1, 1.14.) Schedules 1 and 2 of the Regulations tabulate the quantities of grit and dust which may be emitted, and where the rating of the boiler or furnace is intermediate between the tabulated values, the minimum permitted emission is obtained by interpolation (see Appendix 2.4).

Arrestment Plant for Furnaces (ss.6-9)

Section 6 requires all furnaces (except domestic furnaces) to be equipped with grit and dust arrestment plant approved by the local authority and the arrestors to be properly maintained and used if used for the following purposes:

a) to burn pulverised fuel; or
b) to burn, at a rate of 45.4 kg or more an hour, any other solid matter; or
c) to burn, at a rate equivalent to 366.4 kilowatts or more, any liquid or gaseous matter.

The Secretary of State may by regulation prescribe limits on the rates of emission of grit and dust from the chimneys of furnaces, and prescribe different limits for different cases and according to different circumstances. Such regulations would not however apply to furnaces begun, or an agreement for the purchase or installation entered into, before the implementation of the regulations.

Section 7 of the 1993 Act specifies under what circumstances exemptions from s.6 will be permitted:

a) The Secretary of State has power to provide in Regulations that furnaces of any particular class, whilst used for a prescribed purpose, should be exempted. Here the *Clean Air (Arrestment Plant) (Exemption) Regulations* 1969 are relevant (see below).

b) The local authority may, on application, exempt a specific furnace installation providing that it is satisfied that the emissions will not be prejudicial to health or a nuisance. The local authority must give a written decision within eight weeks, and an aggrieved applicant may appeal within a further 28 days, to the Secretary of State.

An offence occurs if a furnace is exempt and is then used for any purpose other than that prescribed in the exemption.

When considering an application for approval of a proposed arrestor plant (or an application for exemption from the need to install an arrestor plant) the local authority will have regard to the probable grit and dust burden in the flue gases, and to the known efficiency of the proposed arrestor plant so that it can compare the probable emissions with any standard which might at the time be in force or which is under consideration. It should be noted that arrestor plant, unless very well maintained at all times, rarely operate at full design efficiency after a few years in use.

Measurement of Grit, Dust and Fumes (ss.10-11)

Grit is defined in the *Clean Air (Emission of Grit and Dust from Furnaces) Regulations 1971* as particles exceeding 76 μm in diameter; the *Clean Air Act 1993* (s.64) defines fumes as any airborne solid matter smaller than dust. British Standard BS 3405 defines dust as small solid particles between 1-75 μm in diameter.

Under s.10 if a furnace (or range of furnaces served by one chimney) is used to burn:

a) pulverised fuel,
b) any other solid matter at a rate of 45.4 kg, or more per hour, or
c) any liquid or gaseous matter, at a rate equivalent to 366.4 kilowatts or more,

the local authority may serve a notice on the owner of the plant or occupier of the building, requiring grit, dust and fume emissions to be measured from time to time, to adapt the chimney for that purpose, to provide and maintain the necessary measuring apparatus, and to inform the local authority of measuring results. The occupier of the building is under a duty to permit the local authority to be present during the measuring and recording of emissions. The local authority may revoke its notice at any time.

Table 2.10: Clean Air (Arrestment Plant) (Exemption) Regulations 1969 (SI 1262)

These Regulations were made under s.4(1) of the 1968 Act.

Class of Furnace

1.   Mobile or transportable furnaces.

Purpose

a)   providing a temporary source of heat or power during any building operation or work of engineering construction (within the meaning of section 176 of the *Factories Act 1961*);

b)   providing a temporary source of heat or power for investigation or research;

c)   providing heat or power for the purpose of agriculture (within the meaning of section 109(3) of the *Agriculture Act 1947*).

Class of Furnace

2.   Furnaces other than furnaces designed to burn solid matter at a rate of 1.02 tonnes an hour or more, which fall within any of the following descriptions and in which the matter being heated does not contribute to the emission of grit and dust:

a)   furnaces burning liquid matter, gas, or liquid matter and gas;

b)   hand-fired sectional furnaces designed to burn solid matter at a rate of not more than 11.3 kg an hour for each square foot of grate surface;

c)   magazine type gravity-fed furnaces designed to burn solid matter at a rate of not more than 11.3 kg an hour for each square foot of grate surface;

d)   furnaces fitted with an underfeed stoker designed to burn solid matter at a rate of not more than 11.3 kg an hour for each square foot of the plan area of the combustion chamber;

e)   furnaces fitted with a chain grate stoker designed to burn solid matter at a rate of not more than 11.3 kg an hour for each square foot of the grate surface;

f)   furnaces fitted with a coking stoker designed to burn solid matter at a rate of not more than 11.3 kg an hour for each square foot of area covered by the fire bars excluding the solid coking plate.

Purpose

Any purpose except the incineration of refuse.

If the plant burns at a rate of:

a) less than 1.02 tonnes/hour of solid matter other than pulverised fuel, or
b) less than 8.21 Megawatts of liquid or gaseous matter,

the industrialist may serve a notice on the local authority requiring the authority from time to time to measure and record emissions at its own expense until such notice is withdrawn in writing.

The Clean Air (Measurement of Grit and Dust from Furnaces) Regulations 1971 (SI 161)

These Regulations were made under s.7(2) of the 1956 Act and prescribe the administrative process to invoke the above provisions (similar Regulations apply in Scotland):

a) A local authority must give at least six weeks' notice in writing to an industrialist requiring:

- adaptations to be made to the chimney or flues; and
- the provision of the necessary equipment, to enable measurements to be made in accordance with BS 3405 (Simplified) Method for Measurement of Particulate Emission Including Grit and Dust. The British Standard states the principles to adopt, sets out requirements to be met in designing apparatus and indicates basic sampling procedures.

b) When the sampling points have been installed and the equipment provided (or it is known that the firm are engaging a consultant who possesses the equipment), the local authority must give at least 28 days' notice in writing, requiring the tests to be carried out in accordance with the methods detailed in Measurements of Solids in Flue Gases (published by the Institute of Energy).

c) Before making the measurement the industrialist must give the local authority at least 48 hours' notice in writing of the date and time of the commencement of the tests.

d) The result of the test must be sent to the local authority within 14 days from the making of the measurements and the reports shall include:

- the date(s) of the test(s);
- the number of furnaces discharging into the chimney on that date;
- the results of the measurements expressed in lbs/hour of grit and dust emitted and, in the case of solid fuel fired plant, the percentage of grit in the solids.

A notice may require the making of measurements from time to time or at stated intervals, but not at intervals of less than three months unless, in the opinion of the local authority, the true level of emission cannot be determined without further measurement being made.

If an industrialist serves a "counter notice" on the local authority, he need only make adaptations to the chimney to enable the measurements to be made, including the provision of scaffolding where necessary, and the provision of facilities such as electrical connections to enable the measurements to be made. The local authority must provide the sampling equipment and conduct the test entirely at its own expense.

Information about Furnaces and Fuel Consumed (s.12)

Local authorities may serve a notice on the occupier requesting information about furnaces in a building and the fuel or waste being burned to be given to them within 14 days or longer.

Outdoor Furnaces (s.13)

This section notes that ss.5-12 apply to boilers or industrial plant furnaces attached to buildings or installed on land.

Height of Chimneys (ss.14-16)

At whatever height smoke and flue gases are discharged, gravity will eventually bring the larger particles of grit, dust and soot to the ground. Additionally, because of the natural turbulence of the atmosphere, a proportion of the gases and of the freely suspended fine particles will reach the ground although not affected by gravity. The higher the point of discharge and the greater the total heat content of the discharged gases, the more widespread and diluted will be the fine particles and gases by the time they reach ground level. The control of chimney heights enables local authorities to take into account a number of relevant factors in determining the height of a chimney. These include the need to avoid downdraught or downwash created by the chimney itself, or by buildings or topographical features; to avoid the ground level concentration of combustion products becoming prejudicial to health or a nuisance; in the case of smaller units to prevent the flue gases from entering nearby buildings in too high a concentration.

Under s.14 of the Act, unless the height of the chimney has been approved by the local authority and any conditions attached to approval adhered to, it is an offence to cause or knowingly permit a furnace to be used to

- burn pulverised fuel;
- burn at a rate of 45.4 kg or more an hour any other solid matter; or
- burn at a rate equivalent to 366.4 kilowatts or more any liquid or gaseous matter.

An application for chimney height approval must contain adequate information to enable the necessary calculations to be carried out. Additional information on the calculation of chimney heights is given in Appendix 2.5.

The local authority must consider an application for approval for a chimney height for a furnace and give a written decision within 28 days of its receipt, unless it is agreed in writing between the local authority and the applicant that a longer period may be allowed. Should the local authority fail to deal with the application within the agreed period, then approval without qualification will be deemed to have been given.

The local authority, however, must not approve the proposed chimney height unless it is satisfied that it will be sufficient to prevent, so far as is practicable, the smoke, grit, dust, gases or fumes emitted from the chimney from becoming prejudicial to health or a nuisance, having regard to:

a) the purpose of the chimney;
b) the position and descriptions of buildings near to it;
c) the levels of the neighbouring ground;
d) any other matters requiring consideration in the circumstances.

Any approval of the height of a chimney may be granted unconditionally or subject to conditions as to the rate and/or quality of emissions from the chimney. "Rate of emissions" is defined as the quantities of any specified substance which may be emitted in a period specified in the conditions attached to the approval, e.g. kg/hr of sulphur dioxide. Many other miscellaneous emissions may, of necessity, be considered for inclusion in conditions as to the rate of emission, but there will be cases where a limitation on "rate" alone will not sufficiently ensure against excessive pollution by materials other than normal combustion products; in those cases it might be appropriate to impose conditions as to the "quality" (i.e. concentration) of the emission. A limitation on the quality of emission would be appropriate if the products of combustion contain gases or acid mists resulting from abnormal reactions or breakdown of materials derived from chlorinated or sulphur-bearing compounds etc, or if products of combustion are mixed with waste gases from non-combustion processes.

There will also be occasions, particularly in relation to metallurgical processes, where the optical density of emissions may be regulated by reference to percentage obscuration or perhaps by reference to the Bacharach Scale (a scale of ten shades, from white to black, for the assessment of smoke in flues; a smoke stain is obtained by sampling flue gases through a filter paper in a prescribed manner, and graded according to the scale).

If the local authority decides not to approve the height of a chimney or to attach conditions to its approval, it must give the applicant a written notification of its decision, stating its reasons; it must additionally specify the lowest height, if any, which it is prepared to approve unconditionally and/or the lowest height it is prepared to approve with any specified conditions. The applicant may appeal against the decision to the Secretary of State within 28 days. The Secretary of State may confirm the local authority's decision, or may amend the height or conditions if this is thought to be appropriate. The Secretary of State must also give a written notification of the decision stating the reasons and, where a chimney height is not approved, specifying what height, with and/or without conditions would be approved.

Section 16 applies where plans have been submitted in accordance with building regulations to the local authority to erect or extend a building outside Greater London or in an outer London borough, and the plans include a chimney outside the scope of s.15 above (i.e. one not serving a furnace). It does not cover residences, shops or offices. Again, the local authority must reject the plans if it is thought that the proposed height of chimney will not be sufficient, so far as practicable, to prevent emissions of smoke, grit, dust or gases from becoming prejudicial to health or a nuisance. The factors to be taken into account are the same as listed above. There is a right of appeal against the local authority's decision to the Secretary of State.

The Secretary of State may by regulation exempt boiler or plant to be used for certain prescribed purposes from the above requirements so long as the chimney height has been approved for that purpose.

Clean Air (Heights of Chimneys) (Exemption) Regulations 1969 (SI 411)

These Regulations were made under s.6(1) of the 1968 Act. It is not necessary to apply for chimney height approval for any exempted boiler or plant specified in these Regulations. Such boiler or plant include those used:

a) as a temporary replacement for a boiler or plant which is under inspection or being maintained, repaired, rebuilt or replaced by another permanent boiler or plant;
b) as a temporary source of heat or power for building or engineering construction work;
c) as a temporary source of heat or power for investigation or research;
d) as an auxiliary plant used to bring other plant to an operating temperature;
e) as a mobile or transportable source of heat or power for agricultural operations.

Two other pieces of legislation are also of relevance where approval of chimney height is needed. These are

• **Building Act 1984:** Section 73 of this Act applies when a new building is erected which will over-reach the chimney of an adjoining building. Providing that the chimney of the lower building is in the party wall between it and the taller building, or is six feet or less from the taller building, the local authority may by notice require the person who erects the taller building to raise the height of the chimneys of the adjoining building if it is reasonably practicable to do so, so that the chimneys are the same height as the taller building or its chimneys, whichever is the higher. The notice will also require the owner or occupier of the adjoining building to allow the work to be done, but he may elect to do the work himself and charge the reasonable cost of so doing to the person on whom the notice was served. In the event of non-compliance with the notice, the local authority may do the work in default.

- **The Building Regulations 2000:** The Clean Air Act 1993 controls chimney heights only if the fuel consumption exceeds 45.4 kg or 366.4 kilowatts or more per hour. *The Building Regulations 2000* (SI 2531, effective 1 January 2001) consolidate and replace the 1991 Regulations and subsequent revisions. They apply to all chimneys, irrespective of the capacity of the fireplace, furnace, or type of building. Part J of Schedule 1 of the Regulations applies to fixed heat producing appliances designed to burn solid fuel, oil or gas, or are incinerators. Such appliances must have adequate provision for the discharge of the products of combustion to outside air, and be so constructed as to reduce to a reasonable level the risk of the building catching fire.

The relevant Regulations in Scotland are the *Building Standards (Scotland) Regulations 1990.* Part F deals with heat producing installations and storage of liquid and gaseous fuels.

Smoke Nuisances in Scotland (s.17)

This section was repealed on 1 April 1996 following implementation of s.107 and Schedule 17 of the *Environment Act 1995.* It enabled action to abate certain nuisances from smoke to be taken under the *Public Health (Scotland) Act 1897.*

2.14.3 Part III: Smoke Control

Creation of Smoke Control Areas (ss.18-19)

Section 18 allows a local authority to declare the whole or any part of its district a smoke control area by making a "Smoke Control Order". Before doing so it must publicise its intention, and the effect of the Order, in the *London Gazette (or Edinburgh Gazette)* and a local newspaper on two successive weeks. Unless postponed through resolution, the Order must come into effect not later than six months after it was made. The Order may specify to what area the Order applies, the types of buildings covered, and any exemptions (e.g. specified buildings or fireplaces).

Section 19 enables the Secretary of State (or in Scotland, the Scottish Environment Protection Agency, *Environment Act 1995,* Sch. 22, para 196) to direct a local authority to bring forward, within six months, proposals for making a Smoke Control Order for the purposes of abating smoke pollution in its area.

Local authorities may themselves subsequently revoke or vary Orders; Smoke Control Orders originally confirmed by the Secretary of State (Scotland, SEPA) can only be revoked or varied by a similarly confirmed Order.

Prohibition on Emission of Smoke in Smoke Control Area (ss.20-22)

When operative, it is an offence for an occupier of premises within a smoke control area to allow smoke emission from a chimney, unless the smoke is caused by the use of an "authorised fuel" (listed in Regulations - see Appendix 2.6a). It is recognised that there may be times when certain of these fuels may cause short periods of light smoke emission. Appliances which may be used in a smoke control area are defined in *Smoke Control (Exempted Fireplaces) Orders.* These conditionally exempt the emission of smoke from chimneys serving the various fireplaces (see Appendix 2.6b).

The implications of the law are that coal, oil and wood cannot be used as fuel in a smoke control area unless burnt on an exempted fireplace (unless they can be burnt without any emission of smoke). Refuse cannot be burnt in an incinerator in a smoke control area unless there is a specific exemption written into the Order, a general exemption for incinerators, or unless smokeless combustion can always be achieved. This prohibition would even apply to the simple incinerators which consist of a dustbin with a chimney.

The local authority may also include in the Smoke Control Order other exemptions, which it may feel are necessary, subject to reasonable conditions. One of these is to allow the lighting of domestic fires with sticks and paper if there is no gas in the dwelling.

Dealings with Unauthorised Fuel (s.23)

It is an offence to acquire for use or to sell by retail for delivery in a smoke control area any fuel other than an authorised fuel, unless in each case the premises or fireplace are exempt. It is a defence to prove that the sale for delivery of unauthorised fuel was carried out in the belief that either the building or the fireplace/boiler or plant was not covered by a Smoke Control Order.

In Northern Ireland, the sale or delivery of unauthorised fuels in smoke control areas is prohibited by *The Smoke Control Areas (Sale or Delivery of Unauthorised Fuel) Regulations (Northern Ireland) 1998* (SR 328). *The Sulphur Content of Solid Fuel Regulations (Northern Ireland) 1998* (SR 329) prohibit the sale or delivery within Northern Ireland of solid fuel with a sulphur content exceeding 2%.

Adaptation of Fireplaces (ss.24-29)

The local authority may serve a notice on the owner of a private dwelling in a smoke control area requiring work to be carried out to ensure compliance with a Smoke Control Order. So long as the work has been carried out to the local authority's satisfaction, it should repay seven-tenths of the reasonable cost of the adaptation, and it may repay all or any part of the remaining three-tenths. Grants are not available for "new dwellings" begun on or after 16 August 1964.

A local authority may designate as unsuitable any appliances for which suitable fuels are not fully available, and in those circumstances a grant is not available for installation of those appliances. The principles which local authorities must follow in assessing eligibility of works of adaptation for grant are contained in the Memorandum on Smoke Control Areas, as revised. The Department of Environment (now DETR) also set cost limits for local authority guidance in assessing "reasonable costs".

The Act enabled the Secretary of State to repay to the local authority a proportion of their expenditure in implementing a Smoke Control Order. Exchequer contributions for smoke control orders in England and Wales made after 31 March 1995 are not normally available. Claims for payments could be made up to 31 December 1996 for payment by 31 March 1997. In Scotland such grants were no longer available from 1 April 1993; applications for approval of schemes had to be submitted to the Scottish Office Environment Department by 31 March 1993 and contributions for all approved schemes claimed by 28 February 1995.

In Northern Ireland, grant-aid is apportioned as follows: DOE(NI) – 40% of approved costs; the council – 30%; and the householder/occupier – 30%.

2.14.4 Part IV: Control of Certain Forms of Air Pollution

Regulations about Motor Fuel (s.30)

This section enables the Secretary of State to make regulations limiting the composition and content of motor fuel and preventing or restricting the production, treatment, distribution, import, sale or use of any fuel which fails to comply with the requirements and which is for use in the United Kingdom. (See also this chapter, 2.23.) Before making any regulations the Secretary of State must consult representatives of manufacturers, users of vehicles, producers and users of fuel for motor vehicles as well as air pollution experts.

The Motor Fuel (Composition and Content) Regulations 1999 (SI 3107)

These Regulations, which came into force on 1 January 2000, replace 1994 Regulations (SI 2295) and apply throughout the UK. They implement Directive 98/70/EC relating to the quality of petrol and diesel fuels, which also bans the marketing of leaded petrol from 1 January 2000 (see 2.22.8).

The Regulations apply to both the distribution of fuel to, and the sale of fuel from, filling stations; the limits to be met are detailed later in this chapter at 2.22.8. Petrol stations with low throughput will not have to meet the summertime volatility requirements laid down in the Regulations until three deliveries of such fuel have been made. Fuel sold for tests and experimental purposes is exempt from the Regulations.

Sale of Leaded Petrol

Leaded petrol was withdrawn from general sale on 1 January 2000; the Directive allows for a limited amount of leaded petrol to be sold for use in old vehicles - i.e. classic and historic vehicles - and this is to be made available through a permit system under the Regulations. Producers of petrol for use in the UK and importers of petrol into the UK, who are also members of the Federation of British Historic Vehicle Clubs, may apply to the Secretary of State for a permit (or permits). Initially, permits are to be valid for one year to enable amendments to the system to deal with any problems; thereafter permits will be valid for three years.

An application for a permit should include full details of the applicant, evidence showing that he is a producer or importer of petrol into the UK and a registered member of the FBHVC. The applicant should also outline his retail distribution network for the sale of petrol, the areas in which it is intended to sell leaded petrol, and the number and location of nominated filling stations. They must also agree to sell leaded petrol for the duration of the permit. In common with other permit and environmental licence systems, the Regulations provide for permits to be varied, revoked or surrendered, as well as providing for appeals to the Secretary of State on any matters relating to a permit. It should be noted that permits may normally be surrendered on one month's notice; holders of single permits must however give six months' notice of their intention to cease the distribution and sale of leaded petrol - this is to enable the Secretary of State to find another permit holder.

Regulations about the Sulphur Content of Oil Fuel for Furnaces or Engines (s.31)

The Secretary of State is empowered to make regulations limiting the sulphur content of a wide range of fuel oils used in industry, commerce and in domestic boilers. The Secretary of State has a duty to consult similar to that outlined for s.30 above.

The Marketing of Gas Oil (Sulphur Content) Regulations 1994 (SI 2249)

These Regulations were revoked in England and Wales on 27 June 2000 following implementation of the *Sulphur Content of Liquid Fuels (England and Wales) Regulations 2000* (SI 1460), and on 30 June in Scotland following implementation of similar Regulations (SSI 169) – see below 2.15.

The 1994 Regulations, which now only apply in Northern Ireland, came into effect on 1 October 1994; they are enforced by local authorities and implement EU Directive 93/12/EEC relating to the sulphur content of certain liquid fuels (see this chapter, 2.22.8). Under the Regulations it is an offence to market gas oil with a sulphur content in excess of 0.2% by weight - Directive 99/32 amends Directive 93/12 to reduce the sulphur content of gas oil to

0.1% by weight from 1 January 2008 (see also 2.4.5a). The Regulations do not apply to gas oil in the fuel tanks of vessels, aircraft or motor vehicles crossing a frontier between a third country and an EU Member State, or to gas oil for processing prior to final combustion; aviation kerosene is also outside the scope of the Regulations. To ensure compliance with the Regulations, local authorities are required to check the sulphur content of gas oils on the market in their area.

Supplementary Provisions (s.32)

This section notes that anyone contravening or failing to comply with the provisions of Regulations made under ss.30 and 31 shall be guilty of an offence and liable to a fine, subject to any exclusion for liability included in the Regulations. Regulations made under ss.30 and 31 apply to fuel used in the public service of the Crown.

Cable Burning (s.33)

Cable burning for the purposes of recovering the metal is illegal unless the burning is carried out as part of a process subject to authorisation under Part I of the *Environmental Protection Act 1990* or an activity subject to permit under the *Pollution Prevention and Control Act 1999*.

2.14.5 Part V: Information about Air Pollution

Research and Publicity (s.34)

This enables local authorities to carry out or contribute towards the cost of, investigations and research relevant to air pollution. It can arrange lectures, addresses and discussions and publish information; organise exhibitions or other displays including films; prepare or contribute towards the cost of making a film or exhibition, etc. Care should be taken to ensure that any material published does not breach trade secrets, unless the written consent of the person providing the information has been obtained.

Obtaining Information (s.35)

In order to obtain information about emissions into the air - gaseous, liquid or solid or any combination (s.40) - the local authority may issue a notice under s.36 (see below); it can enter premises to measure and record emissions (either by agreement or using powers under s.56 of the Act which confers rights of entry and inspection); or it can agree with the occupiers of premises that they will measure and record emissions for the local authority. Private dwellings and caravans are excluded from this section.

The local authority may only use its powers of entry to measure and record emissions after serving and expiry of a 21 day notice on the occupier which

- specified the kind of emissions in question and how it was proposed to measure and record them;

- stated that it would monitor and record the emissions itself unless the occupier requested the local authority to serve a section 36 notice.

Investigation of emissions from processes subject to Part I of the *Environmental Protection Act 1990* or an activity regulated by permit under the *Pollution Prevention and Control Act 1999* may only be carried out following service of a s.36 notice or by contributing to the cost of such investigation, as provided for in s.34, without entering the premises.

In exercising its powers to obtain information, the local authority should set up a consultation committee of locally representative people with knowledge of air pollution problems or an interest in the local amenity; this should meet not less than twice a year to discuss the extent and way in which information collected should be made publicly available.

Notices Requiring Information about Air Pollution (s.36)

The local authority may by notice require an occupier of premises in its area to provide certain information about emissions of pollutants into the air at specified intervals. If the notice is served on a process for which authorisation under Part I of the EPA is required, only information certified by the appropriate enforcing inspector as being required under the EPA need be supplied. The person on whom a notice is served has six weeks within which to comply, or longer as agreed with the local authority.

Notices may require periodical returns or single event emission data; but if periodical returns are requested, the interval between returns shall be not less than three months, and no one return is to cover a period of more than one year.

Section 36 applies to all premises, including Crown premises, unless specifically exempted by the Secretary of State. The *Control of Atmospheric Pollution (Exempted Premises) Regulations 1977* (SI 18) covering England and Wales list government research establishments to which this section does not apply.

Failure to comply with a notice, without reasonable excuse is an offence, as is the furnishing of false information.

Appeal against Notice (s.37)

A person on whom a s.36 notice is served may appeal to the Secretary of State on the grounds that

- disclosure would unreasonably prejudice some private interest, or be contrary to public interest, or

- the information is not readily available and cannot readily be collected without incurring undue expenditure.

Following consultation with representatives of local

authorities, industry and air pollution experts, the Secretary of State may make regulations relating to the appeals process.

Regulations under the *Control of Pollution Act 1974 - the Control of Atmospheric Pollution (Appeals) Regulations 1977* (SI 17) - set out the information to be submitted with the appeal, allow the Secretary of State to withhold certain, secret information from the local authority and indicate how the appeal should be determined. If an appeal is upheld, the Secretary of State may direct the local authority to withdraw or to modify the notice, or to take steps to ensure that the prejudicial information is not disclosed to the public. Similar Regulations (1982) apply in Scotland.

Regulations about Local Authority Functions under ss.34, 35 and 36 (s.38)

Following consultation with representatives of local authorities, industry and air pollution experts, the Secretary of State may make regulations prescribing emissions for which a s.36 notice may be issued, the information which such a notice may require and the way in which such notice is to be given. Regulations may also specify under what circumstances local authorities may arrange for the occupier of premises to measure and record emissions and the apparatus which local authorities may provide and use for measuring and recording emissions. Regulations would also provide for the setting up of a public register.

The Control of Atmospheric Pollution (Research and Publicity) Regulations 1977 (SI 19) limit the information to be required. Notices may only relate to sulphur dioxide or particulates from processes where stock does not contribute to the emission, or gas or particulates where stock does contribute to the emission, or gas or particulates from non-combustion processes. Also laid down is the information which can be required in respect of such emissions. The Regulations contain provisions relating to the service of notices and the maintenance of a register of information under these Regulations. Similar Regulations (1982) apply in Scotland.

Provision by Local Authorities of Information for Secretary of State (s.39)

This section enables the Secretary of State, after consultation with a local authority, to direct it to monitor air pollution and to send the information to the Secretary of State. Any capital expenditure incurred by the local authority in providing and installing apparatus to be able to comply with a direction may be reclaimed from the Secretary of State.

2.14.6 Part VI: Special Cases

Relation to Environmental Protection Act 1990 (s.41)

Parts I-III of the *Clean Air Act 1993* (dark smoke; smoke, grit, dust and fumes; smoke control areas) do not apply to a process prescribed for control under Part I of the EPA from the date of authorisation, refusal of authorisation or confirmation of refusal following an appeal. This section is to be repealed by the *Pollution Prevention and Control Act 1999* (Sch.3).

Colliery Spoilbanks (s.42)

The owner of a mine or quarry from which coal or shale is, has been, or will be obtained must use all practicable means to prevent combustion of refuse from the mine or quarry and to prevent or minimise emissions of smoke and fumes from the refuse.

Table 2.11: The Dark Smoke (Permitted Periods) (Vessels) Regulations 1958 (SI 878)

Class of Case	*Permitted Period for Emission of Dark Smoke*
1. Emissions from a forced draught oil-fired boiler furnace, or an oil engine.	10 minutes in the aggregate in any period of two hours.
2. Emissions from a natural draught oil-fired boiler furnace, (except in the case falling within class 4 below).	10 minutes in the aggregate in any period of one hour.
3. Emissions from a coal-fired boiler furnace:-	
a) when the vessel is not under way (except in the cases falling within class 4 below).	10 minutes in the aggregate in any period of one hour.
b) when the vessel is under way.	20 minutes in the aggregate in any period of one hour.
4. Emission from a natural draught oil-fired boiler furnace or a coal-fired boiler furnace in the following cases:-	20 minutes in the aggregate in any period of one hour.
a) a vessel with funnels shortened for the purpose of navigating the Manchester Ship Canal;	
b) a tug not under way, but preparing to get under way or supplying power to other vessels or to shore installations;	
c) a vessel not under way but using main power for the purpose of dredging, lifting pumping or performing some other special operation for which the vessel is designed.	5 minutes in the aggregate in any period of one hour.
5. Emission from any other source.	

The nuisance provisions of the *Environmental Protection Act 1990* and Parts I-III of the *Clean Air Act 1993* may not be applied to smoke, grit or dust arising from combustion of mine refuse.

This section of the Act does not apply to refuse from a mine or quarry deposited before 5 July 1956 if it was no longer in use and ownership had passed from the mine or quarry owner.

Railway Engines (s.43)

Emissions from railway engines are subject to the dark smoke provisions of s.1 of the 1993 Act and owners of railway engines are required to use any practicable means for minimising emissions of dark smoke. The remainder of Part I, together with Parts II and III of the 1993 Act do not apply to smoke, grit or dust from railway engines. However emissions could be the subject of a statutory nuisance action under s.79 of the EPA (see chapter 1, 1.16.1).

The Dark Smoke (Permitted Periods) Regulations 1958 made under s.19 of the 1956 Act are also applicable.

Vessels (s.44)

Vessels in water not navigable by sea-going ships and in waters within the seaward limits of the territorial waters (including docks, ports, harbours and rivers) of the UK, must comply with the dark smoke provisions of s.1 of the 1993 Act. This section does not apply to ships in HM Navy or "Government Shipping" (e.g. merchant shipping) being used by the Navy.

The Dark Smoke (Permitted Periods) (Vessels) Regulations 1958 made under s.1(2) of the 1956 Act specify the types of emissions which will be permissible and the length of time. There are similar Regulations for Scotland (1958) and for Northern Ireland (1965).

A vessel is not under way when it is at anchor or made fast to the shore or bottom. However a vessel which is aground is deemed to be under way. The Regulations include a proviso that continuous emissions of dark smoke caused otherwise than by the soot blowing of a water tube boiler shall not exceed:

a) in the case of classes 1 and 2: 4 minutes;
b) in the case of natural draught oil-fired boiler furnaces in class 4: 10 minutes; and
c) in no case shall black smoke be emitted for more than 3 minutes in the aggregate in any period of 30 minutes.

Exemption for Purposes of Investigations and Research (s.45)

The local authority may exempt a particular chimney, boiler or furnace etc or the acquisition or sale of a specified fuel from various provisions of the Act, for example to enable investigations or research relevant to air pollution to be carried out without making the applicant liable to proceedings. If the local authority refuses the exemption, the applicant has a right of appeal to the Secretary of State for the Environment, Transport and the Regions.

Crown Premises (s.46)

In the event of excessive emissions of smoke, grit and dust from Crown premises, the local authority should notify the Minister responsible for the premises who should take appropriate action to prevent or minimise the emission. This includes premises within a smoke control area and those being used by visiting forces (except for Parts IV and V); ships in the Navy or Government Ships (e.g. merchant shipping) being used by the Navy are also subject to the Act.

2.14.7 Part VII: Miscellaneous and General

Application of Certain Provisions to Fumes and Gases (s.47)

This enables the Secretary of State to make regulations extending the scope of ss.4, 5, 6, 7, 11, 42, 43, 44 and 46 (covering variously grit, smoke and dust) to fumes or prescribed gases.

Power to give effect to International Agreements (s.48)

The Secretary of State may make Regulations relating to any of the provisions of Parts IV, V and VII of the 1993 Act to enable compliance with international agreements.

Administration and Enforcement (ss.49-62)

These sections of the Act are mainly administrative, relating to such matters as improper disclosure of information by an officer (s.49), penalties for offences under the Act (s.50), county court powers to authorise works and order payments (s.54) and general provisions as to enforcement (s.55).

Duty to Notify Occupiers of Offences (s.51)

Where an offence has been or is being committed under ss.1, 2 or 20 (prohibition of certain smoke emissions), the local authority's authorised officer must notify the occupier of the premises, either verbally or in writing "as soon as may be". If notification is given verbally this should be confirmed in writing before the end of four days following that on which the officer became aware of the offence. In any subsequent proceedings it is a defence to prove that the notification procedure was not complied with.

Rights of Entry and Inspection (ss.56-57)

In order to carry out their duties under the Act, authorised officers of a local authority are allowed access to land (which includes premises) and vessels at any reasonable time; they may also carry out any necessary measurements and tests and remove samples for analysis. This section does not apply to private dwellings except in relation to work required to effect compliance with a smoke control order.

The local authority may apply to a Magistrate (Sheriff in Scotland) for a warrant to enter (if necessary by force) in the following circumstances:

- if refused entry despite seven days notice having been given;
- the land/vessel is unoccupied or the occupier absent;
- there is an emergency;
- to apply for admission would defeat the object of the exercise.

Power of Local Authority to Obtain Information (s.58)

The local authority may serve a notice specifying what information it requires and by when in relation to Parts IV and V of the Act (Control of Certain Forms of Air Pollution and Information about Air Pollution). Non-compliance with such a notice is an offence, as is furnishing false information.

Inquiries (s.59)

The Secretary of State may cause an inquiry to be held in connection with any part of the *Clean Air Act* or for preventing or dealing with air pollution.

Schedules

The Act has the following Schedules appended to it:

- **Schedule 1:** Coming into Operation of Smoke Control Orders;
- **Schedule 2:** Smoke Control Orders: Expenditure on Old Private Dwellings;
- **Schedule 3:** Provisions having effect until repeal of *Alkali etc. Works Regulation Act 1906;*
- **Schedule 4:** Consequential Amendments;
- **Schedule 5:** General Transitional Provisions and Savings;
- **Schedule 6:** Repeals.

2.15 SULPHUR CONTENT OF LIQUID FUELS

The *Sulphur Content of Liquid Fuels (England and Wales) Regulations 2000* (SI 1460) and similar Regulations for Scotland (SSI 169), which came into force on 27 June 2000 (Scotland: 30 June), implement EU Directive 1999/32/EC on the sulphur content of certain liquid fuels – see 2.4.5a. These Regulations were made under the *European Communities Act 1972,* replacing the *Marketing of Gas Oil (Sulphur Content) Regulations 1994* which were made under the *Clean Air Act 1993.*

From 1 July 2000 it became an offence to use gas oil (including marine gas oil) with a sulphur content exceeding 0.2% by mass, reducing to 0.1% by mass on 1 January 2008.

On 1 January 2003, it will be an offence to use heavy fuel oil with a sulphur content exceeding 1% by mass; this regulation does not apply to operators of "new" large combustion plant (i.e. coming into operation after 1 July 1987) covered by an authorisation under the EPA or permit under the PPC Act, which contains conditions requiring the plant to meet emission limits for SO_2 which are at least as strict as those in the 1988 Large Combustion Plant Directive (see 2.4.5b).

Operators of pre 1987 combustion plant who do not require an EPA authorisation or PPC permit (those below 20 MW) may choose to comply with the 2003 limit or will need to apply for a "sulphur content of liquid fuels permit" from their local authority (Scotland: SEPA). As well as full details of the applicant, address of the plant and fuel used, the application should give details of the condition to be included in the permit which will satisfy the Regulations – i.e. ensure emissions of SO_2 do not exceed 1,700 mg/Nm³; where the combustion plant is used for combustion in a refinery, the monthly average of all SO_2 emissions from all over the plant (excluding those from new large combustion plant) shall not exceed 1,700 mg/Nm³. Fees for such applications are set in accordance with s.8 of the EPA. A permit may be transferred to another person, with the person to whom the permit is transferred notifying the local authority (SEPA) within 21 days of the date of the transfer. A permit may be surrendered by notifying the local authority (SEPA) which granted the permit.

The Secretary of State (Scottish Ministers) is responsible for ensuring that heavy fuel oil and gas oil is sampled on a regular basis to ensure compliance with the limits.

2.16 HEALTH AND SAFETY AT WORK ETC ACT 1974

The main purpose of this Act is to provide a comprehensive and integrated legal and administrative system for securing the health, safety and welfare of persons at work and for protecting other persons against risk to health or safety arising from the activities of persons at work. To this end all the various inspectorates and agencies involved in these matters were brought together in the Health and Safety Executive (established 1 January 1975) under the Health and Safety Commission which had been set up on 1 October 1974. The HSC is a public office responsible to the Secretary of State for the Environment, Transport and the Regions for the working of the HSW Act; the HSC can propose new or revised legislation, and is responsible for the day to day enforcement of health and safety legislation.

In Northern Ireland, the corresponding legislation is the *Health and Safety at Work (Northern Ireland) Order 1978.*

2.16.1 The Control of Major Accident Hazards Regulations 1999 (COMAH Regulations) (SI 743)

These Regulations, which came into force on 1 April 1999, implement the EU's 1996 Directive on the control of major accident hazards involving dangerous substances (Seveso

II) - see this chapter, 2.4.5d. They apply in England, Scotland and Wales and replace 1984 Regulations which implemented a 1982 Directive. The Regulations are enforced by the Environment Agency and the HSE in England and Wales and by the Scottish Environment Protection Agency and the HSE in Scotland (the competent authorities). Similar 2000 Regulations (SR 93, effective 1 May) apply in Northern Ireland replacing 1985 Regulations; the Environment and Heritage Service and the HSE for Northern Ireland are the competent authorities.

The Regulations apply to establishments which keep (or transport) listed dangerous substances in quantities exceeding thresholds (either individually or aggregated) set in the Regulations; thus they apply mainly to the chemical and petrochemical industries and to those which produce or use substances with flammable, toxic or explosive properties, and those which are dangerous for the environment; explosives and chemicals on nuclear sites are included but hazards created by ionising radiation are not. They do not apply to military installations, certain activities of the extractive industries or to waste landfill sites.

Operators of companies covered by the Regulations are placed under a general duty to take all necessary measures to prevent major accidents and to limit their consequences to persons and the environment, and to report any major accidents to the competent authority. They must prepare a "Major Accident Prevention Policy" which should demonstrate that an adequate safety management system is in place. The enforcing authority should be sent details ("notification") of the name and address of the operator, the address of the site concerned and who is in charge, and details and amounts of dangerous substances held at the site; significant increases in the quantities held or in the nature or physical form of the substances held should be notified to the authority. Site operators holding larger amounts of hazardous substances (top tier sites) must provide the competent authority with a safety report for approval. This should demonstrate that the company's operational, and indeed emergency, procedures are of sufficiently high standard and adequate to prevent accidents and damage both inside and outside plants; the report should include major accident scenarios and safety management systems.

The Regulations also require the operator to prepare an "on-site emergency plan" (which should include details of site remediation and clean up following an accident); the local authority for the area in which the establishment is situated is required to prepare an "off-site emergency plan". Both plans must be reviewed and tested at intervals of not more than three years. The company must also notify all those living in the locality of the fact that there is a hazardous site in the area, and advise what action should be taken in the event of an accident; information and safety reports relating to the establishment are available on public registers held by the competent authorities, subject to issues of commercial confidentiality and national security.

A charging scheme has been introduced to recover the costs of examination of top-tier sites' safety reports, inspection of major accident hazards at top and lower tier sites, enforcement of the Regulations and investigation of major accidents.

The HSE has published two guidance documents relating to the Regulations: *Preparing Safety Reports* (HSG 190, August 1999) which gives practical and comprehensive guidance to site operators on the preparing of safety reports; *Emergency Planning for Major Accidents* (HSG 191, August 1999) is aimed at those involved both in planning for a major accident at top-tier sites and those who may have to respond to them, including the operator who prepares the on-site emergency plan. The Environment Agency has also published (August 1999) interim draft guidelines relating to the environmental risk assessments aspects of safety reports.

Separate Regulations - the *Planning (Hazardous Substances) Regulations 1992* - require the storage of certain hazardous substances above a "controlled quantity" to be covered by a consent from the Hazardous Substances Authority (usually the local authority) - see also chapter 1, 1.23. These Regulations have been amended by the *Planning (Control of Major-Accident Hazards) Regulations 1999* (SI 981; Scotland: SSI 179, 2000; NI: SR 101, 2000) to implement the requirements of the Directive that land-use policies must take major hazard sites into account.

2.16.2 The Control of Substances Hazardous to Health Regulations 1999 (COSHH Regulations) (SI 437)

These Regulations, covering England, Scotland and Wales, came into force on 25 March 1999; they replace and consolidate 1994 Regulations (SI 3246) which came into force in January 1995 and subsequent amendments. (The 1994 Regulations replaced the original 1988 regulations which came into force in October 1989). An Approved Code of Practice (also updated at the same time as the Regulations) provides guidance on the application of the Regulations. Similar 2000 Regulations (SR 120, effective 1 June) apply in Northern Ireland; they replace 1995 (SR 60) and 1999 (SR 36) Regulations.

The Regulations apply to all "very toxic, toxic, harmful, corrosive or irritant" substances (defined in the *Chemicals (Hazard Information and Packaging for Supply) Regulations 1994* - SI 3247, as amended) and to all places of work; they provide a legal framework for controlling people's exposure to such substances. Hazardous substances may include gases, vapours, liquids, fumes, dusts and solids; they can be components of a mixture of materials including micro-organisms. COSHH also covers substances which have chronic or delayed effects such as those which are carcinogenic, mutagenic or teratogenic. The Regulations also apply to the use of pesticides, for which two codes of practice have been drawn up by the HSE (see chapter 5, pesticides), to the use of biological agents and to offshore oil and gas installations. Asbestos, lead, materials producing ionising radiations and inhalable dust below ground in coalmines are excluded as they are covered by separate legislation.

The Regulations require

- an assessment of the risk to health of employees arising from their work and what precautions are needed; this assessment must be regularly reviewed, particularly if it is suspected that the assessment is no longer valid or there has been a significant change in the work to which the assessment relates;

- the introduction of appropriate measures to prevent or control the risk;

- that control measures are used and equipment is properly maintained and procedures observed;

- monitoring the exposure of workers to hazardous substances; in general monitoring should be carried out every 12 months and more frequently for certain processes involving the use of local exhaust ventilation plant (see Schedule 4 to the Regulations); personal exposure monitoring records should be retained for 40 years and general monitoring records for at least 5;

- health surveillance of employees exposed, or likely to be exposed, to hazardous substances, with records being retained for at least 40 years;

- informing, instructing and training employees about the risks and the precautions to be taken, and providing them with results of monitoring and health surveillance;

- compliance with maximum exposure limits listed in HSE publication EH40, *Occupational Exposure Limits.*

Maximum Exposure Limits (MELs) are set for substances for which it is impossible to determine a "no adverse effect level" and must, therefore, not be exceeded. Occupational Exposure Standards (OESs) are set for those substances for which there is a clear "no adverse effect level", the standard representing a limit at which exposure may be harmful; exposure at a level below the standard is generally considered to be safe. HSE publication EH 40, Occupational Exposure Limits, which is published annually gives advice on short and long term exposure limits in the workplace, listing both control limits, recommended exposure limits and maximum exposure limits. The HSE uses these control limits in determining whether, in its opinion, the requirements of the relevant legislation are being observed. Failure to comply with control limits or, where practicable, to reduce exposure still further, may result in enforcement action. Recommended exposure limits are considered to represent good practice and realistic criteria. The Inspectorates use these as part of their criteria for assessing compliance with the HSW Act and other relevant statutory provisions.

The Regulations are enforced by HM Factory Inspectorate and any breaches prosecuted under the HSW Act.

The Health and Safety Commission has published (1995, revised 1997) three Approved Codes of Practice (in a single volume) relating to the 1994 Regulations, as amended; the first code is a general one which includes the full text of the 1994 Regulations; the other two codes cover the control of carcinogenic substances and control of biological agents.

2.16.3 Control of Asbestos Regulations

(a) The Control of Asbestos in the Air Regulations 1990 (SI 556)

These Regulations, effective 5 April 1990, apply to England, Scotland and Wales, and are made under the *Health and Safety at Work Act.* They implement the air pollution aspects of the EU Directive on the Prevention and Reduction of Environmental Pollution by Asbestos (87/217/EEC) which came into force on 31 December 1988.

All scheduled asbestos works involving the "use of asbestos" are required to meet an emission limit of 0.1 mg m^{-3}. The "use of asbestos" is defined as the production of raw asbestos from ore, and the manufacturing and industrial finishing of a range of products using raw asbestos.

To comply with the Directive the Regulations impose the emission limit on amosite and crocidolite although the import, supply and use of these substances for use at work is banned in the UK by virtue of the *Asbestos (Prohibitions) Regulations 1992.* The Regulations require asbestos emissions to be monitored at intervals of not less than six months; operators are required to prevent significant environmental pollution from the working of products containing asbestos or from the demolition of buildings, structures and installations containing asbestos.

(b) Control of Asbestos at Work Regulations 1987 (SI 2115)

These Regulations cover occupational exposure to asbestos; they came into force in March 1988 and implemented a 1983 Directive (83/477/EEC). 1988 Regulations (SR 74) apply in Northern Ireland. They impose duties on employers, similar to those contained in the COSHH Regulations (see above), for the protection of employees who may be exposed to asbestos at work. 1992 amendment Regulations implementing EU Directives 91/382/EEC and 90/394/EEC (the Carcinogens Directive) came into force on 1 January 1993 and require employers to

- review assessments made under the Regulations at regular intervals;

- prepare a plan of work where the activity concerned entails the removal of asbestos from plant, buildings or other sources;

- put greater emphasis on preventing exposure to asbestos as a carcinogen by using alternative non- or less dangerous substances;

- ensure that only essential workers enter the affected area if there is an unforeseen escape or concentrations are likely to exceed limits.

1998 Amendment Regulations (SI 3235), which came into force on 1 February 1999 (N. Ireland, SR 98, 2000), extend the Regulations to ensure better protection for those employees likely to come into contact with asbestos in their normal work (e.g. plumbers and electricians); they provide for improved training, maintenance and testing of respiratory equipment and impose more specific duties on employers to assess risk of exposure to asbestos; the action level at which employers must ensure extra safeguards to protect employees is also reduced.

Guidance Note EH 10 from the Health and Safety Executive details exposure limits and the measurement of airborne dust concentrations.

The Commission is to review the focus of the 1983 Directive with a view to strengthening the protection of workers involved in the removal of asbestos and maintenance and repair workers.

2.16.4 The Control of Lead at Work Regulations 1998 (SI 543)

These Regulations replace 1980 Regulations and revoke various pieces of legislation dating back to 1907 which placed employment prohibitions on women and young people working with lead.

The Regulations (and similar in Northern Ireland, SR 281) require employers, who have the duty under the *Management of Health and Safety at Work Regulations 1992*, to assess risks from exposure to lead in the workplace and to take steps to prevent or adequately control such exposure. If the employer concludes from the assessment that the exposure of employees to lead is likely to be "significant", specific controls must be introduced; these include issuing protective clothing, monitoring of air and medical surveillance.

2.16.5 The Genetically Modified Organisms (Contained Use) Regulations 1992 (SI 3217)

These Regulations (amended 1998 - SI 1548), made under the *Health and Safety at Work Act 1974*, came into force on 1 February 1993; The *Genetically Modified Organisms (Northern Ireland) Order 1991* amended by 1994 (SR 143) and 1999 (SR 14) Regulations contain similar provisions. Further 1993 Regulations (SI 15; NI, 1994, SR 145) relate to environmental risk assessment for genetically modified plants and animals. The Deliberate Release of GMOs is covered by Regulations under the *Environmental Protection Act 1990* - see 2.17 below.

The Regulations implement EU Directive 90/219/EEC which requires the setting up of a notification, consent and emergency system to protect human health and the environment. "Contained Use" refers to any work with GMOs which takes place in conditions which are intended to prevent any escape of the organisms into the environment. This Directive was amended in October 1998 by Directive 98/81/EC and must be implemented by

Member States by June 2000. The 1998 Directive aims to streamline administrative arrangements, specify minimum containment and control measures for each risk class and introduces the possibility of exemptions for safe GMOs.

The *Contained Use Regulations 1992* establish a consent procedure for work involving GMOs, as well as provisions for both the human health and environmental protection aspects of such activity. The main requirements on persons working with GMOs are to

- notify the HSE of an intention to carry out the work and, in certain cases, to await consent;
- classify operations and the organisms used according to a prescribed scheme;
- carry out a risk assessment;
- adopt controls, including suitable containment measures;
- draw up emergency plans and to notify the HSE of accidents involving GMOs.

Other provisions relate to the disclosure to the public of information given to HSE and the placing, subject to safeguards, of certain information relating to consents on a public register.

The HSE has issued proposals for amending Regulations to implement the 1998 Directive in England. These Regulations, which it was intended should come into force during 2000 will provide for:

- risk assessment in respect of human health and safety, and environmental protection of all contained use activities involving GMOs;
- the establishment of genetic modification safety committees to advise on risk assessments;
- classification of all activities involving genetically modified micro-organisms (GMMs) into one of four classes corresponding to the four containment levels; and notification procedures related to these classifications;
- notification to the competent authority of individual activities of classes 2, 3 and 4 involving GMMs;
- formal consent to be obtained from the authorities before starting activities of classes 3 and 4;
- inclusion of information from notifications on a public register, with provision for confidentiality of commercially sensitive information and personal data.

Legislation governing the environmental aspects of control over GMOs became the responsibility of the Scottish Parliament and the National Assembly for Wales from 1 July 1999.

2.17 ENVIRONMENTAL PROTECTION ACT 1990, PART VI

Genetically Modified Organisms (ss.106-127)

This part of the EPA aims to prevent or minimise damage to the environment resulting from the escape or release (i.e. deliberate release) from human control of GMOs. (The contained use - i.e. any work in conditions intended to prevent any escape - is dealt with under Regulations made under the *Health and Safety at Work Act 1974* - see above). This part of the Act also applies to Northern Ireland.

The Act defines "organism" as any "acellular, unicellular or multicellular entity (in any form) other than humans or human embryos; and ... any article or substance consisting of or including biological matter". "Genetically modified" means "if any of the genes or other genetic material in the organism have been modified by means of an artificial technique ... or are inherited or otherwise derived, through any number of replications, from genes or other genetic material which were so modified".

The Act places certain duties on persons proposing to import, acquire, keep or release or market GMOs. These include the need to carry out a risk assessment of any potential damage to the environment as a result of the activity; notifying the Secretary of State of the intention to carry out the activity and in most instances applying for a consent; this may include conditions and other limits or restrictions on the activities permitted. Implicit in all consents is a requirement to use BATNEEC to control organisms and prevent damage to the environment; all reasonable steps should be taken to remain informed about any damage which the activity might have caused and to notify the Secretary of State if the risk appears more serious than was first apparent; if it appears that despite the use of BATNEEC for keeping the GMOs under control, damage might occur, then the activity should be ceased.

Other requirements of this part of the Act relate to enforcement and prohibition notices, offences and fees and charges, and are similar to those in Part I of the EPA.

The *Genetically Modified Organisms (Deliberate Release) Regulations 1992* (SI 3280), as amended by 1995 Regulations (SI 304) came into force on 1 February 1993 and implement EU Directive 90/220/EEC on the Release of Genetically Modified Organisms into the Environment. The Regulations also implement the requirements of the EPA relating to Secretary of State consents and a charging scheme, risk assessments and make certain information publicly available subject to various exclusions on the grounds of confidentiality. Similar provisions for Northern Ireland are contained in the *Genetically Modified Organisms (Northern Ireland) Order 1991*, amended by 1994 Regulations.

A proposal to amend Directive 90/220/EEC was published in February 1998, with Environment Ministers reaching political agreement on it in June 1999. COM(98) 85 (as amended by COM(99) 139) requires marketing consents to be renewed every ten years and mandatory monitoring for environmental impact of products containing GMOs, with renewal of authorisation dependent on monitoring results. Other amendments relate to harmonisation of risk assessment and classification of risks, labelling and streamlining of administrative procedures, with a simplified authorisation procedure for certain categories of release

(defined in an Annex to the Directive). Authorisation authorities will also be required to consult the public on applications for consents.

REGULATION OF AGRICULTURAL POLLUTION

2.18 GENERAL

A number of agricultural practices contribute to air pollution or cause a nuisance. Among the main problems are odour, smoke nuisance and water pollution. Controls on agricultural practices causing pollution are included explicitly, or by implication, in a number of statutes and codes of good practice. Most of these have been covered in other sections of the *Pollution Handbook*, and include the following:

- *Clean Air Act 1993, Part I*: s.2 prohibits the emission of dark smoke from industrial or trade premises; this includes land being used for commercial agriculture or horticulture (this chapter, 2.14.1).

- *Clean Air Act 1993, Part III*: farms falling within a smoke control area must comply with ss.18-29 of the Act which prohibit the emission of smoke from any building or chimney and require the use only of authorised fuels (this chapter, 2.14.3).

- *Clean Air (Emission of Dark Smoke) (Exemption) Regulations 1969*: these permit the burning, in certain circumstances, of various farm wastes; these include the burning of animal or poultry carcases and pesticide containers (this chapter, 2.14.3).

- *Pollution Prevention and Control Regulations (England and Wales) 2000* (& similar in Scotland): operators of new (brought into operation on or after 31 October 1999) intensive farming installations require a Permit covering their activities; existing installations will be required to apply for a Permit between 1.11.06 and 31.01.07. The Regulations apply to facilities with 40,000 places for poultry, 2,000 for production pigs and 750 places for sows (chapter 1, 1.13.1)

- *Environmental Protection Act 1990, Part I*: this requires the farming industry to obtain an authorisation from their local authority (Scotland - SEPA) for carrying on any of the following processes: waste oil burners; straw or poultry litter combustion processes between 0.4 and 3 MW net rated thermal input; animal carcase incineration under 1 tonne an hour (incinerators under 50 kg/hour do not require authorisation); treatment and processing of animal or vegetable matter including fur breeding, animal feed composting and composting, including production of compost for mushrooms (subject to extensive exceptions) (this chapter, 2.12.2).

- *Environmental Protection Act 1990, Part II*: the disposal of certain organic wastes to land requires a waste management licence from the waste regulation authority (Environment Agency or SEPA) - see chapter 4, 4.19.3.

- *Environmental Protection Act 1990, Part III:* this enables local authorities and individuals to take action against statutory nuisance; statutory nuisances include smoke, odour, noise, accumulations or deposits and animals kept in such a way as to be prejudicial to health or a nuisance (see chapter 1, 1.16.1).

- *Highways (Amendment) Act 1986:* it is an offence to light a fire, permit or direct one to be lit, the smoke from which injures, interrupts or endangers anyone using a highway. This provision could also be used for bonfire smoke.

- *The Sludge (Use in Agriculture) Regulations 1989* (SI 1263) (as amended and Code of Practice dated 1996) control the spreading of sewage sludge on agricultural land, and restrict the planting, grazing and harvesting of some crops following application. The main aim of the controls is to prevent the accumulation of hazardous concentrations of heavy metals in soil and to prevent bacteriological contamination of crops; the Code of Practice recommends maximum concentrations for contaminants to limit risks to crops and animals, utilisation practices on the farm and monitoring requirements for soils receiving sludge. Similar Regulations came into force in N. Ireland in July 1990.

- *Code of Practice for the Safe Use of Pesticides on Farms and Holdings 1998.* This deals, among other things, with the disposal of waste pesticides and containers and aerial application of pesticides (see chapter 5).

- The control of water pollution from agricultural practices, in particular the use of nitrates and pesticides is covered in chapter 5.

It should be noted that implementation of the EU Framework Directive on Waste (chapter 4, 4.6) is likely to require further statutory controls on agricultural and farm wastes.

2.19 CODES OF PRACTICE

2.19.1 England and Wales

A *Code of Good Agricultural Practice for the Protection of Air* was published in 1992, and a revised version in 1998. It covers England and Wales and summarises the various pieces of legislation which farmers should be aware of; it gives practical guidance on reducing the problem of odours from housed livestock systems, slurry and manure storage, production of compost for mushrooms and land spreading of livestock wastes. There is also guidance on minimising the need to burn waste and other materials and alternative uses for straw. The Code describes ways of reducing emissions of ammonia and of the greenhouse gases. It does not cover noise nuisance (action for which can be taken under Part III of the *Environmental Protection Act 1990* (see chapter 1, 1.16.1); nor does it cover pesticide use for which there are separate codes of practice (see chapter 5).

The Code, which was prepared by the Ministry of Agriculture, Fisheries and Foods and the Welsh Office Agriculture Department, has no legal status; adherence to the Code is not a defence in a legal action.

A revised version of the 1993 *Code of Good Agricultural Practice for the Protection of Soil* was published in 1998. Like the Code covering the protection of the air. It summarises the legislative controls farmers should be aware of and suggests ways of preventing soil erosion and the loss of organic matter. The code gives a reminder that wastes and pesticides should not be applied in such quantities that they are likely to accumulate in the soil. It also provides advice on protecting soil from contamination and acidification.

2.19.2 Scotland

In Scotland there is a single Code of Practice covering the prevention of air, soil and water pollution. *The Code of Good Practice on the Prevention of Environmental Pollution from Agricultural Activity*, published in 1997, replaced a similar 1992 code. Those parts of the Code covering water pollution have statutory backing under s.5(1) of the *Control of Pollution Act 1974,* as amended by the *Water Act 1989* (see chapter 5).

The Code summarises all the various pieces of legislation in Scotland of relevance to the control of agricultural pollution. It provides advice and information on principles of land application and storage of livestock wastes, their management and disposal; silos and silage effluent; other organic wastes often disposed of to land; agricultural fuel oil and waste oil; waste treatment technology; sheep dip (use and disposal); pesticides; disposal of animal carcases; nitrates; straw and stubble burning and muirburn (a means of managing the vegetation of upland grazings); control of odours and ammonia emissions; disposal of waste products and litter; soil protection.

The various pollution problems caused by incorrect - or inadvisable - treatment and disposal practices are summarised, together with the advantages and disadvantages of various recommended good practices and action necessary to comply with legislation.

2.19.3 Northern Ireland

The 1994 codes for the protection of air, water and soil for Northern Ireland are similar to those for the rest of the UK.

2.20 STRAW AND STUBBLE BURNING

Section 152 of the *Environmental Protection Act 1990,* Part VIII enables Regulations to be made prohibiting or restricting the burning of crop residues on agricultural land and for exemptions relating to specified areas, specified crop residues, or in specified circumstances. The Regulations may impose requirements to be complied with before or after burning, and also make contravention of any Regulations an offence which on conviction is subject to a fine. Straw and stubble burning in England and Wales was previously controlled through local authority bye-laws; these were all repealed with effect from 2 April 1992.

2.20.1 The Crop Residues (Burning) Regulations 1993 (SI 1366)

These Regulations came into effect on 29 June 1993 and extend to England and Wales only and revoke earlier 1991 Regulations. The burning of cereal straw and stubble, and the residues of field beans and peas harvested dry and oilseed rape is banned. They may, however, be burnt in the following circumstances:

- for education and research purposes;
- in compliance with a notice served under the *Plant Health (Great Britain) Order 1993* (e.g. to eliminate pests);
- to dispose of broken bales and the remains of straw stacks.

The burning of linseed residues is currently exempted from the ban, but may subsequently be included in the light of the availability and practicability of alternative methods of disposal and the level of public complaint.

Any burning for education and research, in compliance with a plant health order or of linseed residues must be carried out in compliance with the conditions contained in Schedule 2 of the Regulations; these are:

a) No burning at weekends, bank holidays, or from one hour before sunset until the following sunrise.

b) No more than an area of ten hectares of straw and stubble and 20 hectares of other crop residues may be burnt in a single operation. Additional guidance from MAFF states that if sufficient fire-fighting equipment and manpower are available and fire-break requirements are observed, two or more burning operations may be undertaken simultaneously, so long as they are at least 150 metres apart.

c) No burning within certain distances of various "vulnerable" objects; these are:

- 15 metres for straw and stubble burn and 5 metres for other residues: tree trunks (including coppices or scrubland); fence belonging to another property; telegraph or telephone poles; electricity pole, pylon or substation.

- 50 metres for straw and stubble burn and 15 metres for other residues: residential buildings; thatched roofs; building, structure, fixed plant or machinery which could be set alight by heat from a fire; scheduled monument which could be set alight; hay or straw stack; accumulation of combustible material (other than crop residues) removed in making of fire-break; mature standing crop; woodland or land managed as a nature reserve; above ground gas or oil installation.

- 100 metres for burning of any residue: motorways, dual carriageways; A roads; and railway lines.

d) The area to be burnt must be completely surrounded by a fire-break. This must be 10 metres wide for cereal straw and stubble and 5 metres wide for other crop residues. Precautions should be taken to ensure that the fire will not cross the fire-break.

e) At least two adults who are familiar with the Regulations must be present during burning, one of whom must be in control of the operation and must be experienced in burning of crop residues.

f) At least one hour's notice (but not more than 24 hours' notice) must be given to the following: local environmental health department; occupiers of all premises adjacent to the area to be burned; air traffic control of any aerodrome within 800 metres.

g) At least 1000 litres of water must be available on the burning site, together with equipment to dispense the water in a spray or jet at a rate of 100 litres per minute; there must be five implements suitable for fire beating available and all vehicles used in connection with burning must be equipped with fire extinguishers.

h) Ash remaining from cereal straw and stubble burning should normally be incorporated into the soil within 24 hours of burning; if windy conditions mean that incorporating the ash might cause a nuisance, it should be incorporated as soon as conditions allow.

The maximum fine for each breach of the Regulations is currently £5,000.

The burning of broken bales and straw stack remains is still permitted, as is the burning of other crop residues not specifically mentioned, e.g. herbage seeds, reeds, lavender, hop bines and potato haulms. The local environmental health department must be notified of any permitted burning.

The Regulations do not ban burning when winds exceed certain speeds. However, guidance notes issued by MAFF suggest farmers should not burn when winds exceed, or are forecast to exceed, force 3 (8-12 mph). Farmers are also advised to pay attention to wind direction in order to minimise nuisance and hazard.

Action for burning on agricultural or horticultural land may also be taken under s.2 of the *Clean Air Act 1993* (see section 2.14.1 above), or under the nuisance provisions of the *Environmental Protection Act* (see chapter 1, 1.16.1 above).

In Scotland, there are no specific regulations covering straw and stubble burning as only a small percentage of stubble is burnt. A voluntary Code of Practice (*Straw and Stubble Burning and Muirburn Practice*) has however been agreed between the Scottish NFU and the Scottish Office Agriculture and Fisheries Department. Additional guidance is contained in the 1997 *Code of Good Practice on Prevention of Environmental Pollution from Agricultural Activity*. The advice given is similar to that contained in the Regulations for England and Wales.

Under the "set aside" arrangements, the burning of "set aside" is prohibited.

REGULATION OF POLLUTION FROM ROAD VEHICLES

2.21 INTRODUCTION

In 1996 there were over 26 million vehicles using nearly 470,000 km of road in Great Britain. This is forecast to rise by between 52-82% by 2025. Cars account for 82% of all road traffic, light vans for 9%, HGVs for 7% and buses and motorcycles for 1% each. (*Road Traffic Statistics Great Britain*, The Stationery Office, 1997). In its Green Paper on the Impact of Transport on the Environment (see also earlier this chapter 2.4.6) published in 1992, the European Commission predicted a probable growth in private cars in the European Union (EU) of 45% between 1987-2010 (i.e. from 115 million to a total of 167 million). Goods traffic is expected to increase by 42% between 1990-2010; total vehicle kilometres are predicted to grow 25% throughout the same period.

Road transport is an integral feature of modern life, moving people and goods for industry, commerce and pleasure; however, it is also a major source of a number of important air pollutants, including nitrogen oxides, hydrocarbons, carbon monoxide, particulate matter and carbon dioxide. The contribution from road traffic to total emissions of each of these pollutants in 1996 was as follows (1995 figures in brackets):

Hydrocarbons	29% (30%)
Nitrogen oxides	47% (46%)
Carbon monoxide	71% (75%)
Black smoke	58% (50%)
Particles (PM_{10})	25% (26%)
Carbon dioxide	20% (20%)

(*Source:* DETR Digest of Environmental Protection Statistics, No. 19, 1997 & No. 20, 1998)

As at the beginning of 1998, unleaded petrol accounted for 75% of the retail petrol market (DTI *Energy Statistics*, 1998). Levels of lead in the air resulting from petrol engined vehicles have halved since 1987 following the reduction in the permissible amount of lead in petrol from 0.40 g/l to 0.15 g/l; lead from this source is, however, still by far the most significant source of lead in the air, accounting for 73%, followed by lead/zinc/copper processes (9%) (EPAQS, 1998). Leaded petrol was withdrawn from general sale from 1 January 2000. In some areas noise from road transport is also a significant problem and there are various controls limiting noise emissions from vehicles (see chapter 3).

Early legislation in both the UK and EU limiting vehicle emissions was often based on model standards developed by the UN Economic Commission for Europe (which includes both EU and non-EU countries); the UNECE has no enforcement powers. A series of European Directives over the last 25 years has set progressively tighter emission standards for all road vehicles. However these gains have been more than offset by the rapid growth in the total volume of road traffic. Emissions from road transport therefore remain one of Europe's most pressing air pollution problems. Within the EU, this issue is being addressed through the Auto/Oil Programme (see below 2.22.1).

In the UK, attainment of the air quality objectives in the National Air Quality Strategy (this chapter, 2.7) will require a reduction in traffic related pollution. The emission of pollutants - as well as standards emanating from the EU - from road vehicles are governed by the *Road Vehicles (Construction and Use) Regulations* and the *Motor Vehicles (Type Approval) (Great Britain) Regulations* made under the *Road Traffic Act 1988*. Similar regulations made under the *Road Traffic (Northern Ireland) Order 1981* apply in Northern Ireland. The *Transport Act 1982* also specifies requirements for the manufacture of vehicles; Regulations made under the *Clean Air Act 1993* impose requirements as to the composition, content and marketing of fuel used in motor vehicles - see section 2.14.4.

In July 1998, the Government published a White Paper setting out its strategy for developing an integrated transport policy which aims to both improve public transport and cut road congestion and traffic generated pollution; *A New Deal for Transport* outlines the Government's policies for developing better and more integrated public transport systems, for more environmentally acceptable cars and car use, for more efficient and environmentally sustainable freight transport, and for the integration of transport and land-use planning policies. Similar documents for Scotland (*Travel Choices for Scotland*) and Wales (*Transporting Wales into the Future*) have also been published.

2.22 THE EUROPEAN UNION AND VEHICLE POLLUTION CONTROL

2.22.1 The Auto/Oil Programme

In 1992, the European Commission initiated a tripartite research programme with the European oil and motor industries. The aim of the programme was to identify technical measures to help achieve health-based air quality targets at least cost to society. The Auto/Oil programme was intended to consider not just motor and oil industry solutions but also the contributions of traffic management, public transport, new technologies and vehicle maintenance programmes.

Based on the results of the research, the Commission published proposals in June 1996 aimed at reducing emissions from road transport by up to 70% by the year 2010. Published as a Communication (COM(96) 248) "on a future strategy for the control of atmospheric emissions from road transport", the proposals take into account EU air quality targets, technological advances and improvements in fuel quality; the Communication also discusses the practicalities of measures such as fiscal incentives, traffic management and encouraging urban public transport as a means of reducing overall emissions. A number of Directives arising out of the Auto/Oil Programme have now been formally adopted; these are summarised below at 2.22.2, 3, 5 and 8.

2.22.2 Light Duty Vehicles

Light duty vehicles are cars and vans under 3.5 tonnes. As mentioned above a number of important EU Directives (see Appendix 6.2) and UNECE standards controlling vehicle emissions have been adopted: the first EU Directive (70/220/EEC) relating to measures to be taken against air pollution from positive ignition engines continues to be the basis for current Directives and proposals and has thus been amended and adapted a number of times; it applies to vehicles with no more than six seating positions and a maximum permissible mass of not more than 2500 kg. Directive 83/351/EEC enforces UNECE regulation ECE R15-04. This series of Directives relating to the UNECE Regulations laid down increasingly tight emission standards for CO and HC, and later NOx. All new cars in the UK, including diesel cars, have met the 83/351/EEC standards since April 1991.

The 1988 Directive (88/76) known as the "Luxembourg Agreement", partially agreed in 1985, proposed three classes of engine size: more than 2 litres, 1.4 to 2 litres, and less than 1.4 litres. New limits for CO, HC and NOx were proposed for new vehicles to be produced in the late 1980s/early 1990s. Agreement was reached immediately for the two larger classes; stricter limits for small (less than 1.4 litre) cars had to be agreed in two stages because of opposition from small car manufacturers. The stricter (2nd stage) limits were agreed in June 1989 (Directive 89/458/EEC) and were in line with US and Japanese standards. This Directive which applied to both petrol and diesel vehicles was largely superseded by the Consolidated Directive (91/441/EEC) - see below.

A 1988 Directive (88/436/EEC), on particulate emissions from diesel cars, agreed in December 1987, is also an amendment to the original 1970 Directive on vehicle emissions. It acknowledges health-related concerns and bases controls on the mass of soot emitted, rather than on some subjective judgement of smoke opacity, which is easier to measure and enforce. The standard is set by measuring the mass of emissions, rather than the opacity of smoke emitted. The standards, which applied from 1990, are 1.1g/test for new engine types and 1.4g/test for all new vehicles. However this did little more than enforce existing technology, and a second stage of stricter emission limits was proposed. The introduction dates for indirect injection diesel cars under 2 litres was April 1991 and for direct injection diesel cars under 2 litres April 1997.

Table 2.12: 91/441/EEC

	Emission limit (g/km)		
	CO	HC+NOx	Particulates
Type approval	2.72	0.97	0.14
Conformity of production	3.16	1.13	0.18

In June 1991 further, stricter, limits (Table 2.12) were agreed. This Directive (91/441/EEC - the Consolidated Directive) implemented new stricter limits for all passenger cars (except direct injection diesel vehicles) with no more than six seats, and under 2500 kg. It also contained an improved driving cycle with a high speed element as the basis for tests. Emission limits are expressed in grams per kilometre instead of grams per test (i.e. the amount of emissions allowable per km averaged over the whole test cycle). The new standards were mandatory and applied to all new cars from 31 December 1992, and to new models from 1 July 1992.

From 1 July 1994 the above limits also applied to new model light duty direct injection diesel vehicles and to new models from 31 December 1994.

To meet the standards, new petrol driven cars registered after 1 January 1993 had to be fitted with three-way catalytic converters; these fit into the car exhaust and act by converting CO, HC and NOx into CO_2, water and nitrogen. Diesel engined vehicles will require "state of the art" technology. These requirements were implemented through an amendment to the Type Approval Regulations (see 2.23.3 below). Research by the former Warren Spring Laboratory (an agency of the Department of Trade and Industry) showed that a vehicle fitted with a catalytic converter which is in good condition will reduce emissions of carbon monoxide, hydrocarbons and nitrogen oxides by 90% each. However fuel consumption increases by between 3-9% and emissions of carbon dioxide by between 9-23%. It should be noted, however, that catalytic converters do not become effective until the car engine has warmed up.

The Directive also contains provisions for the introduction of tax incentives to promote the introduction of cleaner vehicles. Hydrocarbons - or volatile organic compounds (VOCs) - which evaporate from the fuel tank and fuel system are limited to less than 2g/test; this will require the fitting of "carbon canisters" (a fuel vapour collection system). Carbon monoxide emissions are limited to 3.5-4.5% by volume at idling.

In 1994 a further Directive (94/12/EC) amending the original 1970 Directive on vehicle emission limits was agreed. Different limits are set for petrol and diesel engined vehicles and for the first time no distinction is made between standards for type approval and conformity of production (Table 2.13).

The new limits were mandatory from 1 January 1996 for new model vehicles and from 1 January 1997 for new

Table 2.13: 94/12/EC

	Emission limit (g/km)		
	CO	HC+NOx	Particulates
Petrol engines	2.2	0.5	
Diesel engines			
- indirect injection	1.0	0.7	0.08
- direct injection	1.0	0.9	0.10
DI from 1.10.99	1.0	0.7	0.08

registrations. The Directive has been implemented through a 1995 amendment (SI 2210) to the 1986 Construction and Use Regulations.

As with the 1991 Directive it was permissible to offer fiscal incentives to encourage manufacturers to meet the new standards before the deadline. Any such schemes had to be approved by the Commission prior to introduction and meet a number of criteria, including compatibility with the functioning of the internal market and be non-discriminatory.

Table 2.14: 98/69/EC

Petrol fuelled vehicles to meet following limits (g/km) by		
	2000	2005
CO	2.3	1.0
HC	0.20	0.10
NOx	0.15	0.08
Diesel fuelled vehicles to meet following limits (g/km) by		
	2000	2005
CO	0.64	0.50
HC/NOx	0.56	0.30
NOx	0.50	0.25
Particles	0.05	0.025

The latest emission limits (Table 2.14) for passenger vehicles (up to 2,500 kg) are contained in Directive 98/69/EC which originated from the Auto/Oil Programme, and was formally adopted in September 1998; this Directive also covers light commercial vehicles. The 2000 and 2005 compliance dates are those for new model types, with compliance by new cars a year later in each case. Petrol-engined vehicles with electronically controlled catalytic converters will also be required to carry an onboard diagnostic system from 2000 and diesel engined vehicles from 2005 (OBSs show if vehicle emissions are above permissible levels). Tax incentives will be permissible for vehicles already meeting the 2005 standards from 2000.

Further proposals from the Commission were due by 31 December 1999 for implementation after 2005.

2.22.3 Light Commercial Vehicles

A further amendment to Directive 70/220/EEC (Directive 93/59) adopted by Environment Ministers in June 1993 set emission limits for light commercial vehicles; these were as

strict as those for private vehicles, with vehicles being categorised according to their reference mass, i.e. the mass of the unladen vehicle in running order, as follows:

- Category I: commercial vehicles with reference mass up to 1250 kg and vans/cars designed to carry up to nine people; limits for these vehicles are the same as those for light duty vehicles as set in the 1991 Consolidated Directive (see above);
- Category II: commercial vehicles with reference mass between 1250-1700 kg;
- Category III: commercial vehicles with reference mass between 1701-3500 kg.

The new emission controls for type approvals came into force on 1 October 1993 and applied to new vehicles from 1 October 1994. Petrol engined vehicles need three-way catalytic converters to meet the exhaust limits and carbon canisters to control evaporative hydrocarbon emissions; diesel engined vehicles need engine modifications or two-way catalysts.

In October 1996 the Council of Ministers formally adopted a Directive - 96/69/EC (Table 2.15) - tightening emission limits further to bring them into line with those of Directive 94/12/EC. For Category I the limits applied to new models from 1 January 1997 and to new vehicles from 1 October 1997; for Categories II and III the respective dates were 1 January 1998 and 1 October 1998. Member States may use tax incentives as a means of encouraging the introduction of vehicles meeting the new emission limits before the mandatory dates.

These Directives have been implemented by amendments to the Construction and Use and Type Approval Regulations (see below, 2.23.2 and 2.23.3).

The most recent limits for light commercial vehicles are contained in Directive 98/69 (see above and Table 2.14, which also covers passenger vehicles.

2.22.4 Motorcycles and Mopeds

Directive 97/24/EC, introduced limits for CO and HC and NOx emissions from motorcycles, mopeds, tricycles and quadricycles, which the Commission is now proposing to tighten. In a proposal for a Directive published in June 2000, the Commission sets out reductions to be met by 1

Table 2.15: 96/69/EC

	CO		HC+NOx		Particulates
	P*	D*	P	D**	D**
Category I	2.2	1.0	0.5	0.9/0.7	0.10/0.08
Category II	4.0	1.25	0.6	1.3/1.0	0.14/0.12
Category III	5.0	1.5	0.7	1.6/1.2	0.20/0.17

Emission limit (g/km)

* P = petrol; D = diesel
** the first limit value applies to direct injection vehicles until 30.9.99

January 2003 for new model types and for new vehicles a year later; a second stage of reductions is to be brought forward before the end of 2002 for implementation from 1 January 2006, and will also cover mopeds.

2.22.5 Heavy Duty Vehicles

This applies to lorries, buses etc over 3.5 tonnes. A 1972 Directive (72/306/EEC) set limits on smoke emissions from large diesels (excluding tractors and public works vehicles) using visibility criteria. Limits for diesel-engined tractors are covered by Directive 77/537/EEC. Limits for gaseous pollutants emitted from heavy duty vehicles were set in Directive 88/77, subsequently amended through the adoption in October 1991 of Directive 91/542/EEC, agreed in October 1991 which tightens standards in two steps. It also introduces a strict, mass-based, standard for particulate emissions. Dates for compliance with the first step ("EURO 1") reductions were 1 July 1992 (new models) and 1 October 1993 (all new vehicles). Dates for introduction of the second step ("EURO 2") have now been agreed by Environment Ministers (Directive 96/1/EC) - see below; these limits match the very stringent US 1994 diesel standards. The agreed emission limits for heavy duty diesels, and dates for implementation, are as set out in Table 2.17.

These limits required an improvement in the quality of diesel fuel which emits sulphur as particulate sulphates. In 1993, a Directive was adopted reducing the sulphur content of diesel fuel to 0.2% by weight from 1 October 1994 and to 0.05% by weight from 1 October 1996. The Directive also required Member States to ensure that diesel fuels with the lower sulphur limit became available from 1 October 1994 to enable compliance with the tighter emission standards. In the UK the Directives are implemented through amendments to the *Type Approval*

Regulations and Construction and Use Regulations (see 2.23.2 & 2.23.3 below).

In December 1999, Directive 99/96/EC was adopted; it was proposed under the Auto/Oil I programme, and is also an amendment to Directive 88/77/EEC. As well as heavy duty diesel vehicles, it covers those fuelled by natural gas and liquefied petroleum gas (LPG). The new emission limits apply to new vehicle and engine types from 1 October 2000 and a year later to new engines and vehicles, with further cuts in emission limits to be met by 1 October 2005 (Table 2.18). A further reduction in NOx emissions to 2.0 g/kWh has been agreed for 2008 subject to the Commission confirming before the end of 2002 that it is technically feasible. Tax incentives will be allowed to encourage early compliance with emission limits. In addition all new vehicles will be required to carry onboard diagnostic systems from 1 October 2005.

The limit values to be applied (see Table 2.18) depend on the test cycle used: ESC and ELR test cycles for conventional diesel engines, including those fitted with electronic fuel injection equipment, exhaust gas recirculation and/or oxidation catalysts; ESC, ELR and ETC test cycles for diesel engines fitted with advance emission control systems, including de-NOX catalysts and/or particulate traps, and also gas engines.

2.22.6 Non-Road Mobile Machinery

In December 1997 Environment Ministers adopted Directive 97/68 relating to emissions of gaseous and particulate pollutants from non-road mobile machinery. This Directive applies to agricultural and forestry equipment, snow ploughs, fork lift trucks, mobile cranes and construction equipment. Stage I limits (Table 2.19) were phased in between 30 September 1998 to 31 March 1999 and Stage II limits between December 2000 and 31 December 2003.

Table 2.16 Proposed Limits for Motorcycles

	CO	HC	NOx
		Emission limit (g/km)	
Motorcycles – current limits			
Two-stroke	8.0	4.0	0.1
Four-stroke	13.0	3.0	0.3
Proposed new limits to be met by 2003			
Motorcycles	5.5	1.2	0.3
Tricycles & quadricycles			
- gasoline	7.0	1.5	0.4
- diesel	2.0	1.0	0.65

Table 2.17: 96/1/EC

	CO	HC	NOx	Particulates
		Emission limit (g/kWh)		
Euro I type approval	4.5	1.1	8.0	0.36*
Euro I conformity of production	4.9	1.23	9.0	0.4*
Euro II, TA & COP	4.0	1.1	7.0	0.15**

* for engines of 85 kW or less, a coefficient of 1.7 is applied to the limit value for particulate emissions.
** until 30 September 1997 (new models) and from 1 October 1996 to 30 September 1998 for existing models the limit was 0.25g/kWh.

In May 2000, Directive 2000/25/EC on action to be taken against the emission of gaseous and particulate pollutants by engines intended to power agricultural or forestry tractors was adopted. Emission limits are similar to those for other non-road mobile machinery covered by Directive 97/68/EC - see Table 2.19 below.

2.22.7 Reducing Carbon Dioxide Emissions from Cars

In June 1996 Environment Ministers endorsed the Commission's proposal for A *Community strategy to reduce carbon dioxide emissions from passenger cars and improve fuel economy* - Communication COM(95) 689. This forms part of the overall strategy to stabilise emissions of carbon dioxide at 1990 levels by the year 2000 - see this chapter 2.4.2. The main elements of the strategy are:

- agreement of auto industry to reach a specific CO_2 emission target for cars within an agreed timeframe - the Commission suggested a 33% reduction (186g/km to 120 g/km) in the average of CO_2 emissions of new cars sold in the EU by 2005 compared with 1990; the European Car Manufacturers Association (ACEA) has now agreed that average emissions should be reduced to 140 g/km by 2008 and to review in 2003 the possibility of meeting a target of 120 g/km by 2010. In

1999, Japanese and South Korean car manufacturers agreed to meet the target of 140g/km by 2009.

- monitoring CO_2 emissions: in June 2000 the European Parliament and Council of Ministers reached agreement on a Decision (1753/2000) establishing a system for monitoring CO_2 emissions from new passenger cars; it outlines the data that Member States will need to forward to the Commission to enable it to monitor and report on progress being made by manufacturers to meet target reductions;

- promotion of fuel efficient passenger cars and fuel economy labelling; Directive 1999/94/EC will require new passenger cars to carry a label on fuel consumption and CO_2 emissions and for information on fuel economy to be available at the point of sale.

- research and development programmes to improve the performance of cars;

- promotion of alternative modes of transport.

2.22.8 Fuel Quality

Directive 85/210/EEC, set a maximum of 0.15 grammes per litre of lead in petrol, and limited benzene to 5% by volume; it also required that unleaded petrol was to be made available in Member States by 1989, new model cars

Table 2.18: 99/96/EC

Limit values for engines tested on ESC and ELR test cycles (g/kWh, except smoke)			
	2000	2005	2008
Mass of CO	2.1	1.5	
Mass of HC	0.66	0.46	
Mass of NOx	5.0	3.5	2.0
Mass of Particulates	0.10*	0.02	
Smoke (m⁻¹)	0.8	0.5	
(*Derogation to 1.10.05 - 0.13 for engines with swept vol < 0.7dm³ per cylinder and rated power > 3,000 min⁻¹)			
Limit values for engines tested on ESC, ELR & ETC test cycles (g/kWh)			
	2000	2005	2008
Mass of CO	5.45	4.0	
Mass of NMHC	0.78	0.55	
Mass of methane	1.6*	1.1	
Mass of NOx	5.0	3.5	2.0
Mass of Particulates	0.16**	0.03	
(*for natural gas engines only; **Derogation to 1.10.05 - 0.21 for engines with swept volume < 0.7 dm³ per cylinder and rated power of > 3,000 min⁻¹ (diesel engines only))			

Table 2.19: 97/68

			Emission limit (g/kWh)		
Net Power P (kW)	Stage	CO	HC	NOx	Particulates
130 ≤ P <560	I	5.0	1.3	9.2	0.54
	II	3.5	1.0	6.0	0.2
75 ≤ P <130	I	5.0	1.3	9.2	0.70
	II	5.0	1.0	6.0	0.3
37 ≤ P <75	I	6.5	1.3	9.2	0.85
	II	5.0	1.3	7.0	0.4
18 ≤ P <37	II	5.5	1.5	8.0	0.8

designed to run on it from 1989, and all new cars to run on unleaded petrol from 1990. An amendment to this Directive (87/416/EEC) permitted Member States to ban the sale of regular grade leaded petrol with six months notice.

Directive 93/12/EEC limits the sulphur content of all gas oils (except aviation kerosene) to 0.2% by weight as from 1 October 1994, with a further reduction in the sulphur content of diesel fuel to 0.05% by weight as from 1 October 1996. The Directive also required Member States to ensure that diesel fuel with a sulphur content of 0.05% or less became available from 1 October 1995, thus enabling compliance with EU Directive 91/542/EEC on emissions from heavy duty vehicles (see 2.22.5). (As part of its strategy to combat acidification (see 2.4.5a), Directive 99/32 adopted on 26 April 1999 amends Directive 93/12/EC to reduce the sulphur content of gas oil to 0.1% by weight from 1 January 2008.)

In September 1998, a Directive relating to the quality of petrol and diesel fuels and amending Directive 93/12/EEC, was formally adopted. This Directive, 98/70/EC, arises out of the Auto/Oil Programme, and includes the following provisions:

- A ban on the marketing of leaded petrol from 1 January 2000; five year derogation for those Member States where this timetable may result in "severe socio-economic problems or would not lead to overall environmental or health benefits".

- Reducing the amount of benzene in petrol from 5% to 1% by volume by 2000, and olefins to 18%; aromatics to be limited to 42% by volume and sulphur to 150 mg/kg (with a three year derogation for those Member States where this would cause "severe socio-economic problems"). For diesel, polycyclic aromatic hydrocarbons are to be limited to 11% by volume and sulphur to 350 mg/kg. Sulphur in petrol must be reduced to 50 mg/kg from 2005 (to be phased in for diesel) and a limit of 35% aromatics. The summertime (June - August) Reid Vapour pressure is limited to 70 kPa; distillation evap/ted at 100C is limited to 46 v/v and at 150C to 75% v/v.

- From 2000 Member States can give tax incentives for fuels already meeting the 2005 limits.

In July 2000, the Environment Commissioner issued a consultation paper seeking views on reducing the level of sulphur in fuels to 30 ppm or less.

Directive 98/70/EC has been implemented in the UK through the Motor Fuel (Composition and Content) Regulations, made under the Clean Air Act 1993, Part IV - see this chapter, 2.14.4.

2.22.9 Petrol Storage and Distribution

In December 1994, Ministers formally adopted a Directive (94/63/EC) on controlling VOC emissions resulting from the storage of petrol and its distribution from terminals to service stations ("Stage I" controls). The Directive, which came into force on 31 December 1995, also covers the loading of petrol on to rail or new oil tanker lorries and inland waterways vessels. The Directive aims to reduce emissions from these sources by 90% over ten years through the use of technical measures such as vapour recovery, painting storage tanks with reflectance paint and bottom loading of tankers. Design and operating standards for installations and equipment have been set so as to reduce vapour losses to below a "target reference value" of annual throughput.

New storage installations, the loading and unloading of new road or rail tankers at new terminals or new petrol stations (i.e. not authorised or operated before 31 December 1995) had to comply with the new standards by 31 December 1995. Existing storage installations with an annual throughput of more than 50,000 tonnes, loading and unloading of rail tankers and barges at terminals with an annual throughput of more than 150,000 tonnes have a further three years to meet the Directive, as does the loading and unloading at petrol stations with an annual throughput of more than 1,000 m³; where the annual throughput exceeds 25,000 tonnes at existing storage installations or terminals loading and unloading road and rail tankers and petrol stations with an annual throughput of more than 500 m³, the compliance date is 31 December 2001; remaining installations, terminals and petrol stations have a further three years. Where vapour emissions at storage installations, terminals or petrol stations could cause adverse health or environmental effects, stricter requirements may be imposed.

Small service stations (below 1,000 m³ annual throughput) have been given longer to meet the new standards; small rural service stations (100-500 m³ annual throughput) have a limited derogation from controls where VOC emissions are likely to pose an insignificant threat to the environment; all service stations below 100 m³ annual throughput have been given an absolute derogation.

Implementation of the Directive in the UK has been effected through an amendment to the Environmental Protection (Prescribed Processes and Substances) Regulations 1991 - see below 2.23.4.

2.22.10 Roadworthiness Testing

The EU Roadworthiness Directive (77/143/EEC) applies to goods vehicles (including trailers and semi-trailers) over 3.5 tonnes gross vehicle weight, vehicles with more than eight passenger seats, taxis and ambulances. It was extended by Directive 88/449/EEC to apply to other goods vehicles with effect from 1 January 1993 in those Member States which already have testing schemes for such vehicles, and 1 January 1995 in other Member States. The Directive lays down the periodicity of testing and the items to be checked, including exhaust emissions. There is no need for an item to be checked if there is no in-use requirement in the Member State concerned. If, for example, a Member State does not require a vehicle to carry a fire extinguisher, the Directive does not force that item to be checked.

In addition, a Directive (91/328/EEC) agreed in June 1991 introduced common roadworthiness tests for private cars from 1998; it identifies the items to be checked and applies to all vehicles registered from 1994. The first test will be obligatory after four years and subsequently every two years.

Directive 92/55/EEC specifies the emission standards to be achieved by 1 January 1997. All vehicles fitted with a catalytic converter for which there is no manufacturer's standard must meet a carbon monoxide emission of 0.5% when the vehicle is running slowly and 0.3% when running at 2000 rpm. Where a manufacturer's standard is specified, this should not be exceeded when the car is running slowly and is again limited to 0.3% at 2000 rpm.

For cars without a catalytic converter for which no manufacturer's standard is given the limits to be met by 1 January 1994 were 4.5% for cars first used prior to 1986 and 3.5% for cars used after that date. A tolerance of + 0.5% will be allowed where a manufacturer's standard is specified. (See also vehicle testing, below.)

A visual inspection to ensure that the exhaust system is leak-free must also be carried out and applicable vehicles must be inspected to ensure the presence of an emission control system. The Directive also specifies emission standards for diesel engines, which will be measured according to opacity.

A further Directive - 93/116 - amends a 1980 Directive on fuel consumption; it sets out a new procedure for establishing carbon dioxide emissions, which are to be recorded in a document retained by the vehicle's owner.

In March 1998, the Commission published proposals for a draft Directive (COM(98) 117) on the roadside inspection of roadworthiness of commercial vehicles.

2.23 UK REGULATIONS

2.23.1 Composition of Fuels

The composition of motor fuel is governed by the *Motor Fuel (Composition and Content) Regulations 1999* (see section 2.14.4).

2.23.2 Construction and Use

The main objectives of Construction and Use Regulations are to ensure vehicles are manufactured to high standards, and to ensure such standards are maintained while vehicles are in-use; they also implement EU Directives on emission limits and roadworthiness testing.

(a) Use of Unleaded Petrol

The Road Vehicles (Construction and Use) (Amendment No. 6) Regulations 1988, Motor Vehicles (Type Approval) (Great Britain) (Amendment) Regulations 1988 and *Motor Vehicles (Type Approval for Goods Vehicles) (Great Britain) (Amendment) Regulations 1988* which came into force on 1 October 1988 require that all new vehicles shall be

capable of running on unleaded petrol in the 1990s. Implementation dates were 1 October 1989 for new type approvals and 1 October 1990 for existing model types. Special arrangements cover the small number of models that would need major engineering changes to comply.

(b) Compliance with Emission Standards

Under Regulation 61(5) of the *Road Vehicles (Construction and Use) Regulations 1986* (SI 1078) it is an offence to use a vehicle if it is emitting "smoke, visible vapour, grit, sparks, ashes, cinders or oily substances" in such a way as is likely to cause "damage to any property or injury or danger to any person".

These Regulations have been amended a number of times. The *Road Vehicles (Construction and Use) (Amendment No. 2) Regulations 1990* which came into force in June 1990 give effect to the various EU Directives on gaseous and particulate emissions mentioned above. The Regulations also require vehicle users to keep engines in tune and any emission control equipment, such as catalysts, working efficiently. 1992 Amendment Regulations implement the emission limits contained in Directives 91/441/EEC and 91/542/EEC relating to cars and heavy duty vehicles, respectively. 1993 and 1997 amendment regulations implement 93/59/EC and 96/69/EC respectively on light commercial vehicles. 1995 amendments implement EU Directive 94/12/EC and introduce new in-service emissions requirements. A further 1997 amendment requires drivers to switch off their vehicle's engine when stationary to prevent exhaust emissions (as well as noise).

The *Vehicle Excise Duty (Reduced Pollution) Regulations 1998*, effective 1 January 1999, enable HGVs and buses meeting particulate standards in EU Directive 99/96/EC to qualify for a Reduced Pollution Certificate, renewable annually when the vehicle undergoes its roadworthiness test, and thus a reduction in vehicle excise duty of up to £500. 1998 Type Approval Regulations prescribe requirements for reduced pollution devices.

(c) Vehicle Testing

The Road Vehicles (Construction and Use) (Amendment) (No. 5) Regulations 1995 (SI 2210) tightened in-service emission requirements for cars and light goods vehicles with effect from 25 September 1995. Petrol engined vehicles first used before 1 August 1975 are tested visually and checks on vehicles first used after this date are by metered test; diesel engined vehicles first used before 1 August 1979 are tested visually and those first used after that date by metered smoke test. The standards which are enforced through Type Approval Regulations and checked at the annual MOT (roadworthiness check for HGVs) and at roadside checks are:

- for petrol fuelled cars and other vehicles first used on or after 1 August 1975 and before 1 August 1986, CO should not exceed 4.5% of the total exhaust emissions by volume and HC 0.12% vol;

- for petrol fuelled cars and other vehicles first used on or after 1 August 1986 and before 1 August 1992 (1994 - other vehicles), CO should not exceed 3.5% of the total exhaust emissions by volume and HC 0.12% vol;

- diesel fuelled passenger cars and light commercial vehicles (< 3,500 kg) first used before 1 August 1979 - visual assessment;

- all other diesel fuelled vehicles - maximum smoke value (absorption coefficient measured under free acceleration) - 3.0 per metre (turbocharged engines); 2.5 per metre (naturally aspirated engines).

As from 22 April 1996, the latter standards also applied to London taxis; London taxis are tested annually at the Public Carriage Office and have to meet requirements which are equal to those of the MOT.

From 1 January 1996 the following standards (amended by 1996 Amendment Regulations) applied to certain other newer vehicles with advanced emissions control systems (e.g. catalytic converters):

- petrol-engined cars first used on or after 1 August 1992 and other petrol fuelled vehicles first used on or after 1 August 1994 listed in Department of Transport (now DETR) publication *In-service Exhaust Emission Standards for Road Vehicles* (this is regularly updated) will be required to meet emission limits specified by the manufacturer of the particular model;

- petrol fuelled cars first used on or after 1 August 1992 and before 1 August 1994 and other petrol fuelled vehicles first used on or after 1 August 1994, for which no model specific information is given in the DETR publication, CO not to exceed 3.5% vol and HC 0.12% vol;

- petrol fuelled cars first used from 1 August 1995 (1998 amendment Regulations; was 1 August 1994), but for which no model specific information is given in the DETR publication, CO not to exceed 0.5% vol under normal idling conditions and volume of CO and HC not to exceed 0.3% and 0.02% respectively with engine running between 2500-3000 rpm.

Since 1 August 1997, vehicles with more than five seats (plus the driver) or vans or other vehicles of 3.5 tonnes or less, first used from 1 August 1994 have also been required to meet the standards for vehicles with advanced emission control systems.

For all vehicles the Regulations require that "no excessive smoke" (dense blue or clearly visible black smoke) should be emitted from the exhaust after 5 seconds at idling.

Vehicle owners have 14 days in which to have the necessary repairs carried out and the vehicle rechecked, or face prosecution with a possible fine. Owners who have neglected to maintain their vehicles are prosecuted and face a fine as well as the cost of putting their vehicle right.

2.23.3 Type Approval

Before a new vehicle model is introduced on to the market it must be tested by the Type Approval Authority to ensure it complies with relevant EU Directives. All new vehicles produced must then meet Conformity of Production limits. These are set at 15-30% above type approval limits, depending on the pollutant.

Passenger cars, including three wheeled cars, first used on or after 1 August 1978 (and not manufactured before 1 October 1977) are subject to the *Motor Vehicles (Type Approval) (Great Britain) Regulations 1984* as amended. Goods vehicles are subject to the *Motor Vehicles (Type Approval for Goods Vehicles) (Great Britain) Regulations 1982*, as amended. The main effect of *Type Approval Regulations* is the enforcement of construction requirements and of construction requirements necessitated by EU and other legislation - e.g. to enable compliance with emission limits. Specimen vehicles are tested by the Department of the Environment, Transport and the Regions to ensure compliance with the international standards referred to in Construction and Use Regulations. No routine testing of new vehicles for this purpose is carried out under the Regulations.

2.23.4 Petrol Storage and Distribution

EU Directive 94/63/EC "on controlling VOC emissions resulting from the storage of petrol and its distribution from terminals to service stations" has been implemented through an amendment to the *Environmental Protection (Prescribed Processes and Substances) Regulations 1991;* under the 1996 Amendment Regulations (SI 2678), which came into effect on 1 December 1996, certain petrol stations are prescribed for air pollution control as Part B processes under the *Environmental Protection Act 1990,* as are those storage terminals not prescribed for IPC (see also this chapter, 2.12.2). Guidance from the DETR (AQ 6(97)) suggests that "petrol" includes all leaded, unleaded and lead replacement gasoline but excludes diesel motor fuel, kerosene and aviation fuels.

Existing installations (i.e. in operation or for which planning permission had been received before the end of 1995) require an authorisation, depending on annual throughput, by the end of 1998, 2001 or 2004. New service stations with an annual throughput of between 100-500 m³ in rural areas of Northern Scotland (where vapour emissions are unlikely to have an adverse environmental or health effect) do not require an authorisation.

2.23.5 Road Traffic Reduction Acts

The *Road Traffic Reduction Act 1997* was brought into force in England and Wales on 10 March 2000 and in Scotland on 21 April 2000. The Act puts local traffic authorities under a duty to prepare a report assessing local traffic levels and forecast growth; it should specify targets for reducing local traffic levels or for reducing the rate of growth - these can be different for the different areas within an authority (e.g. specific to congested areas or rural areas) and how these are to be achieved. The report must also contain any other information or proposals relating to levels of local traffic or which the Secretary of State may specify in guidance. The Act enables the Secretary of State to issue guidance relating to preparation of the report and on those who should be consulted during its preparation. All reports on traffic levels should be sent to the Secretary of State and published. Provisional traffic reduction plans to 2005 were due in July 1999, with the first report on traffic levels due in July 2000.

The *Road Traffic Reduction (National Targets) Act 1998* requires the Secretary of State and the devolved administrations for Scotland and Wales to prepare and publish reports which include targets for road traffic reduction in England, Scotland and Wales, aimed at reducing the adverse environmental, social and economic impacts of road traffic. If it is considered that traffic reduction targets are not the most appropriate way for reducing the adverse impacts of traffic, including congestion and pollution, the report should explain why and outline alternative measures or targets and their expected impact on traffic reduction. A report, covering England only, published in early 2000, proposes that targets aimed at reducing the adverse impacts of traffic, rather than actual traffic reduction targets, should be set.

Neither of the above Acts extend to Northern Ireland.

2.23.6 The Road Traffic Regulation Act 1984

This Act enables a local authority to make a traffic regulation order for preserving or improving the amenities of an area through which a road runs. The *Environment Act 1995* amends the Act to ensure that such an order could be made for the purpose of meeting statutory requirements in respect of air quality - see this chapter 2.7.

2.23.7 Road Traffic (Vehicle Emissions) (Fixed Penalty) Regulations 1997 (SI 3058)

These Regulations apply in England, Scotland and Wales and were brought into force on 26 December 1997. The Regulations have only applied in the areas of the following local authorities: Birmingham, Bristol, Canterbury, Glasgow and Westminster City Councils, Middlesbrough Borough Council and the City and County of Swansea. The Regulations enable authorised officers of a local authority (who have also received training in· roadside emissions testing) to test that emissions from a road vehicle comply with regulation 61 of the *Road Vehicles (Construction and Use) Regulations 1986* (as amended), i.e. that they comply with MOT standards. Note, the help of a uniformed police officer will be needed as only they have the right to stop vehicles on the road. The Regulations apply to all vehicle classes, including heavy goods vehicles, public service

vehicles, light goods vehicles, taxis and private vehicles. If the vehicle fails the emission test, the local authority officer may issue a fixed penalty notice for £60, increasing to £90 if not paid within 28 days. Drivers have a right to request a court hearing rather than pay the fixed penalty notice.

The Regulations also enable authorised officers of the local authority to issue a fixed penalty notice to drivers who leave their engines running unnecessarily, for example

* while waiting to pick up someone at a railway station;
* while waiting to pick up children from school;
* while waiting for a passenger to run an errand;
* on a coach to power the ventilation, heating or air conditioning system (except while actually picking up or dropping off passengers).

These would all be offences under s.98 of the Construction and Use Regulations which requires drivers to switch of their vehicle's engine when stationary to prevent noise emissions; a 1997 amendment to the Regulations extends s.98 to cover exhaust emissions. In this instance the fixed penalty is £20, rising to £40 if not paid within 28 days.

Following review,· the DETR has issued a consultation document (June 2000) for England and Wales proposing to extend the Regulations to enable their use in those local authorities which have declared an Air Quality Management Area. It is also proposed that motorists failing an emissions test would be entitled to have half the fixed penalty waived if the fault is rectified within two weeks (and corroborated through another emissions test) or it can be proved that the vehicle had passed an approved emissions test within the previous three months; if the fault was rectified within two weeks and the vehicle had passed an approved emissions test within the preceding three months, then the whole penalty would be waived. New Regulations will be made under s.87 of the *Environment Act 1995* but are unlikely to be available for use before April 2001.

2.23.8 Measurement of Smoke Emissions from Diesel Engined Vehicles

The UK and EU standards for smoke emissions from diesel engined vehicles are based on visual observations of light obscuration. In 1963 the British Standards Institution used a panel of observers to grade vehicle emissions which were measured by smoke meter measurements of light obscuration. The purpose of the test was to define a British Standard which would deal with the problem of the visual appearance of the smoke emissions; the possible implications for health and the environment were not at that time taken into account. The standard established as BS AU 141 and amended to BS AU 141a was made legally binding in the UK *Construction and Use Regulations*. Subsequently an EU Directive, 72/306, based on regulations developed by the United Nations Economic Commission for Europe, was also adopted; the standard

102   Vehicle Emissions – UK Regulations

was however based on measurement of smoke made by a different smoke meter to that used in the UK. Agreement was reached that BS AU 141a was a satisfactory alternative to the standard of Directive 72/306. These standards apply to new vehicles as constructed. While subsequent performance on the road is subject to legal control governing smoke emission, roadside measurement checks used in other countries such as ECE regulation 24 have been considered unsatisfactory or impracticable for use in the UK.

Since 1 January 1993 (although suspended for technical reasons until 1 February 1994) smoke density from light-duty diesel engined vehicles has been tested by meter while the engine is run at its maximum governed speed.

2.23.9 Steam Road Vehicles

Steam road vehicles - such as traction engines and steamrollers - used on the public highway are not liable to statutory nuisance action under the *Environmental Protection Act 1990*. They are however, subject to the *Road Vehicles (Construction and Use) Regulations*.

2.24 PLANNING POLICY GUIDANCE

Planning Policy Guidance Notes are advice from the Secretary of State to local authorities and others on policies and the operation of the planning system. PPG 13, *Transport*, looks at the needs of all road users (including pedestrians and cyclists), and the way in which land use planning and transport planning can be integrated to make optimum use of the transport system thus reducing the need to use the car, and indeed the length of journeys. A revised draft is now under consideration; it proposes that planners should require developers to include a green transport plan with their planning application; the guidance proposes more attention be given to the need to ensure developments are not dependent on travel by car for access, and to providing alternative modes of travel, such as bus services. The draft also includes guidance on the maximum number of parking spaces to be allowed per square metre of the floorspace of the development.

Draft guidance for Scotland was published in June 1996 (*National Planning Policy Guidance: Transport and Planning*).

2.25 AIRCRAFT EMISSIONS

Relatively few complaints relating to air pollution at airports are recorded and research so far shows that compared with other domestic, transport and industrial sources, aircraft make a negligible overall contribution to air pollution. However, because pollutants are mainly emitted at high altitudes, where they take longer to disperse, their contribution to global problems (such as ozone depletion and the greenhouse effect) are more serious. This is an area which is now coming under increasing investigation; tighter emission controls in other areas and environmental pressures are likely to have an effect on air traffic movements in the future. In the UK studies are being carried out around various airports to establish levels of pollution.

Fuel combustion in aircraft engines is relatively efficient and jet exhausts are now virtually smoke free. Current jet engines do however produce significant quantities of nitrogen oxides which react with sunlight to form ozone, a greenhouse gas. Other emissions of note from aircraft include carbon monoxide, hydrocarbons, nitrogen dioxide, water, sulphur dioxide and carbon dioxide; a 1999 report from the Intergovernmental Panel on Climate Change (IPCC) says about 2% of man-made carbon dioxide can be attributed to aircraft emissions and it suggests that this figure will rise to 4% by 2050. Improvements in fuel efficiency and aircraft design are however unlikely to offset the effect of aircraft on climate due to the forecast increase in air traffic of between 2-4% by 2050.

In Sweden, the Government has already decided to impose a tax on nitrogen oxide and hydrocarbon emissions from its domestic airlines. Regulations defining emission limits for smoke and exhaust gases from air traffic have been in force in Switzerland since 1985. In December 1997, the European Commission published a proposal for a Directive on the limitation of oxides of nitrogen from civil subsonic aeroplanes - COM(97) 629. Although aircraft are thought to be responsible for only about 3% of manmade NOx, they are the only source in the upper troposphere and lower stratosphere and thus they have a disproportionate effect on ozone formation.

The Directive would apply to aeroplanes fitted with engines of which the date of manufacture of the first production model is after 31 December 1999, or the individual engine manufactured after 31 December 2007. Member States would only be able to add to their Register aeroplanes fitted with engines complying with NOx emission levels meeting the ICAO's Committee on Aviation Environmental Protection's recommendation in December 1995. This, taken together with the ICAO's 1991 Agreement, would require individual aircraft to meet standards which reduced their NOx emissions by 33% compared to the 1986 ICAO Agreement. It is hoped that the draft will be adopted to enable its provisions to come into effect from 31 December 1999.

RADIATION

2.26 INTRODUCTION

Radiation of natural origin has always been present in our environment, and always will be. Natural radioactive materials are present in the earth, in the buildings we inhabit, in the food and water we consume, and in the air we breathe. Even our bodies contain natural radioactivity. Radiation of artificial origin has been used since the beginning of the century. There is no difference between the effects of radiation whether it is emitted from natural or from artificial radioactive materials. Natural radiation accounts for most of the public's exposure (about 86% of

Pollution Handbook 2001

the total). Most of the exposure from artificial radiation is due to medical uses (about 14% of the total).

2.27 NATURAL SOURCES OF RADIATION

(a) Cosmic Rays

A part of natural radiation comes from the sun and outer space in the form of cosmic rays. The atmosphere acts as a partial shield against these rays, but those that reach the earth's surface easily penetrate buildings. About 10% of our exposure comes from this source.

(b) Radiation from the Ground and Building Materials

Another part of natural radiation comes from the earth. Soils and rocks contain radioactive materials such as uranium and potassium-40, a radioactive form of the element potassium. Most building materials are extracted from the earth, so these are also somewhat radioactive. About 13% of our exposure comes from this source, principally from building materials, but with a small contribution directly from the ground itself. The level of exposure therefore varies mainly according to the type of building materials used in the construction of houses. Exposures in granite buildings, for instance, are generally higher than those in brick buildings. The overall variation in exposure is as large as the average exposure to radiation of artificial origin.

(c) Internal Exposure

Potassium-40 and other natural radioactive materials (from the ground or produced by cosmic rays in the atmosphere) are present in our diet and thus cause some radiation exposure inside our bodies. About 12% of our exposure arises from these radioactive materials, there being some variation depending on the individual's build and bodily processes.

(d) Radon

Naturally-occurring uranium, present in certain rocks, such as granite, and building materials, produces a gas called radon; it is a colourless, odourless and almost chemically inert gas. A similar gas (thoron) is produced from naturally-occurring thorium, which is also present in rocks and building materials. Together radon and thoron contribute about 50% of total exposure. In the open air, radon is diluted to very low levels and poses no danger. However, it can also seep upwards and become trapped in houses where it can build up to dangerously high concentrations.

The level of exposure received mainly depends on the type of rock underneath homes and how well ventilated they are. When radon is breathed in, it is mainly people's lungs that are exposed to radiation. Radon is thought to be the second most important cause of lung cancer after smoking; the NRPB estimate that 5% of lung cancer deaths in the UK can be attributed to radon.

2.28 ARTIFICIAL SOURCES OF RADIATION

(a) Medical Procedures

Radiation is used in a wide range of diagnostic procedures, as in chest and dental x-rays. Radiation is also used for treatment purposes, for example, in killing off cancerous cells. Actual exposure in any year depends on how many examinations an individual is subjected to, and the type of examination, but an average figure would be 14%.

(b) Fallout

Most tests of nuclear weapons now take place underground. But in the 1950s and early 1960s many tests took place in the atmosphere. Fallout is the term used to describe the radioactive particles that are released and which eventually drop to earth from the atmosphere. This radioactivity can add to the radiation from the ground. It can also be breathed in, and eaten when taken up in food. In the UK, exposure due to fallout from weapons tests is now less than one-tenth of the highest level experienced, which occurred in the mid 1960s.

Some of the radioactivity released by the Chernobyl accident in 1986 was deposited on the UK, the deposition being heaviest in the areas where it was raining at the time that the radioactive cloud passed overhead. Some of this radioactivity was taken up in foodstuffs. In the first year after the Chernobyl accident the total exposure of a typical individual in the UK was increased by about one per cent. Some people might have received increases of up to 40%, depending upon where they lived and what they ate.

Fallout from weapons tests and Chernobyl now contributes about 0.2% of our exposure on average. There are some variations in this average due, for example, to differences in rainfall between areas.

(c) Discharges from the Nuclear Industry

These occur routinely from nuclear power stations and plant that manufacture or reprocess the fuel. On average less than 0.1% (one-thousandth) of total radiation exposure is due to such discharges. Some people will get higher exposures than this if they live near nuclear installations. In some cases, these higher exposures are due to the concentration of radioactivity in locally produced foodstuffs such as shellfish. In the mid-1980s the most exposed individuals were getting up to·one-third of their total exposure from the nuclear industry, but by the late 1980s this had fallen to about one-tenth.

(d) Occupational Exposure

This covers workers who deal with radiation in the nuclear power industry, medicine, dentistry, research laboratories and general industry. There are also underground miners and aircrew who are exposed to increased levels of natural radiation. Miners in non-coal mines receive the highest average exposures of all workers. They typically get more than ten times the exposure of a worker in a nuclear power station. Overall, all these workers receive an average additional exposure amounting to nearly 50% of typical total exposure. Averaged out over the whole population, working with radiation contributes about 0.3% of the total population exposure.

(e) Miscellaneous Sources

This covers enhanced cosmic radiation exposure of aeroplane passengers, release of radioactive material through coal burning (mainly in power stations), and consumer products containing small amounts of radioactivity for various purposes (e.g. smoke alarms, and radioluminous watches and clocks). These combined sources are responsible for less than 0.1% of exposure.

2.29 EFFECTS OF RADIATION

If the exposure of the whole body to radiation is very high, death may occur within a matter of weeks. In this context "very high" means about 2000 times higher than a typical annual total exposure. Even if death does not occur, high exposures may soon lead to other effects such as reddening of the skin, cataracts and sterility. These same doses of radiation are given to individual organs in radiotherapy to kill cancer cells and prolong patients' lives.

If the radiation exposure is lower, or is received over a long period of time, immediate effects will not occur, but there may be risks that the exposure will lead to cancer later in life or to hereditary defects in future generations. A small increase in cancers has been observed in a number of population groups exposed to relatively high exposures. For instance, for the survivors of the Hiroshima and Nagasaki bombs, the cancer death rate is about 10% higher than that expected in a similar Japanese population.

For the purposes of controlling exposures it is assumed that the cancer risk increases in proportion to the exposure, even at very low levels of radiation. This is a cautious assumption, and deliberately so. It ignores the possibilities that very low levels of radiation may be incapable of causing damage or that the body may be able to repair any damage caused by low exposures. For the average person, radiation poses a very small risk and most of that risk is due to natural radiation.

2.30 RECOMMENDATIONS ON RADIATION EXPOSURE LIMITS

The basic assumptions about the risks from radiation exposure given in the previous section have led the International Commission on Radiological Protection (ICRP) to state three key recommendations for radiation protection. ICRP is the principle standard setting body for radiation protection and many countries throughout the world, including the UK, have adopted their recommendations. Their three key recommendations formulated in 1990 are:

a) *Justification:* no practice involving exposures to radiation should be adopted unless it produces sufficient benefit to the exposed individuals or to society to offset the radiation detriment it causes.

b) *Optimisation:* radiation doses and risks should be kept as low as reasonably achievable, economic and social factors being taken into account; constraints on risk or dose should be used to provide upper bounds to the optimisation process.

c) *Limits:* the exposure of individuals should be subject to dose or risk limits above which the radiation risk would be unacceptable.

All of these recommendations apply to all sources of radiation, except that exposure to normal levels of natural radiation and exposure due to medical practices are not subject to exposure limits, and thus only the first two recommendations should be applied. For example, public exposure due to both routine discharges of radioactivity to the environment and solid radioactive waste disposal is constrained by the application of all three principles. It should be noted that it is not sufficient merely to comply with the limits placed on exposure. The second principle ensures that efforts will be made to keep exposures well below these limits.

Nothing can sensibly be done about normal levels of exposure from natural radiation. But human activities can result in increased exposure to natural radiation. Examples of this include flying at high altitude resulting in elevated exposure to cosmic rays, and living in a house where there is a high concentration of radon. Where control of such exposures is feasible, it is given full consideration. This is the case with the relatively high levels of radon exposure which occur in some parts of the UK. Government-funded surveys are being carried out to identify buildings with high radon concentrations.

The National Radiological Protection Board has set an "action level" of 200 Bq m^{-3} average annual concentration above which it recommends measures to exclude radon from houses. Current estimates are that more than 1 in 100 homes in Cornwall, Devon, Somerset, Northamptonshire and Derbyshire are above this recommended action level - 80% of England's radon-affected homes are in these counties; the remaining 20% are in Avon, Cumbria, Dorset, Gloucestershire, Leicestershire, Lincolnshire, Northumberland, North Yorkshire, Nottinghamshire, Oxfordshire, Shropshire, Staffordshire and Wiltshire. Under the Government's radon measurement programme, all homes in England with a greater than 5% probability of radon levels above the action level have been offered a Government-funded radon test. DETR has also published (2000) a "Good Practice Guide" for use by local authorities in encouraging and assisting householders to take remedial action to reduce levels of radon in the home.

In new buildings seepage can be prevented by the use of suspended concrete floors. In existing buildings, such measures may involve improved underfloor ventilation by the installation of a fan and sealing of the floor to prevent the upward flow of radon gas. Home improvement grants are available towards the cost of carrying out remedial work, although these are strictly means-tested. With regard to new buildings in radon-affected areas, *BR211 Radon: guidance on protective measures for new dwellings*, (effective from 14 February 2000, published by the Building Research Establishment) provides technical guidance on measures to be taken as well as details of areas where they may be necessary. This guidance is also referred to in Approved Document C to the *Building Regulations 2000* (SI 2531).

The National Radiological Protection Board carries out scientific research on radiation hazards and advises the Government on whether or not recommendations made by bodies such as the ICRP should be applied in the UK. It provides information and advice about radiation protection to UK government departments and other interested parties.

2.31 REGULATORY CONTROLS

In the UK several government departments have responsibility for protecting the public from radiation exposure. No significant amount of radioactive waste can be discharged without a specific authorisation from the Environment Agency or the Scottish Environment Protection Agency (as appropriate). Discharges from major nuclear sites in England also require authorisation from the Minister of Agriculture, Fisheries and Food. The Secretaries of State for Scotland and Wales grant authorisations within their respective countries. The Department of the Environment is the regulatory body for Northern Ireland. Authorisations specify discharge limits, and inspectors check that the conditions of the authorisations are adhered to. Unless the level of discharge is extremely small, this includes a requirement to monitor the local environment (see chapter 4).

2.31.1 Ionising Radiations Regulations 1999 (SI 3232)

Responsibility for the control of radiation hazards at work falls on the Health and Safety Commission supported by the Health and Safety Executive which employs inspectors to enforce the *Ionising Radiations Regulations 1999* (made under the *Health and Safety at Work Act 1974*); these Regulations came into force on 1 January 2000 replacing and consolidating 1985 and 1993 Regulations. The 1999 Regulations reflect EU Directive 96/29 "laying down the basic safety standards for the protection of the health of workers and the general public against dangers arising from ionising radiation".

The Regulations (which cover England, Scotland and Wales) provide protection for the workforce from ionising radiations, including the handling and storage of radioactive waste; exposure to radiation must be kept as low as reasonably practicable, whether the source is artificial (e.g. nuclear reactor) or naturally occurring (e.g.

radon). A schedule to the Regulations sets out the annual dose limits which should not be exceeded for both occupational exposure and exposure of the general public. The Regulations require continuous monitoring to be carried out and designation as "classified persons" and records kept of any employee likely to receive an effective dose in excess of 6mSv per year; employers must make an assessment of the potential radiation hazard in the event of a possible accidental release or other accident. Radiation employers conducting certain types of work, including the use of electrical equipment intended to produce x-rays for various purposes, must obtain prior authorisation from the HSE; 28 days notice must be given to the HSE of any work with ionising radiation to be carried out for the first time and an assessment of its risk must be made to ensure that suitable protective measures are in place to restrict exposure of employees and other persons.

2.31.2 Public Information for Radiation Emergencies Regulations 1992 (SI 2997)

These Regulations which came into force on 1 January 1993 implement Euratom Directive 89/68. Members of the public within an area from which it is reasonable to foresee the possibility of a radiation emergency should receive certain information, such as what to do in the event of an accident. The company carrying out the work is required to prepare this information and ensure its dissemination. In addition, county and regional councils must prepare and keep up to date arrangements which ensure that members of the public actually affected by a radiation emergency receive prompt and appropriate information. This information should cover facts of the emergency and advice on health protection measures.

These Regulations will be revoked following the finalisation and bringing into force of new Regulations - *The Radiation (Emergency Preparedness and Public Information) Regulations* (REPPIR Regulations), on which the HSE consulted in 1999. These Regulations will implement those articles of Euratom Directive 96/29 covering emergency planning and information to the public in the event of an accident or an emergency at a major radiation site.

The REPPIR Regulations apply to all employers, including carriers, who work with ionising radiation involving specified quantities of radionuclides; all those covered by the Regulations have a duty to identify hazards and evaluate risks for all (big and small) radiation accidents, to prevent accidents occurring and to limit the consequences if they do occur; this hazard assessment, which should be reviewed at least every three years, should be sent to the HSE.

Operators at those premises where it is reasonably foreseeable that a radiation emergency may occur have to prepare an emergency plan; this should aim to restrict exposure and should take account of steps taken to prevent and limit the consequences of potential emergencies (as identified in the hazard assessment). In drawing up the plan the operator should consult those working on the site, the HSE, emergency services, the local authority and the health authority, and any other appropriate persons. Local authorities covering those operators required to prepare an emergency plan, have themselves to prepare an off-site emergency plan; this has the same aim as the operator's emergency plan and should be drawn up in consultation with the HSE, the operator - who must ensure the local authority has access to adequate information to enable it to draw up the plan - the emergency services, health authorities and members of the public.

Carriers, too, must prepare an emergency plan if it is reasonably foreseeable that an emergency might occur during transport of radionuclides, and should consult the HSE and the Radioactive Materials Transport Division; as it is intended that the plan should be generic - i.e. could be used on any route - the carrier should consult representatives of the local authorities, health authorities and emergency services.

The Regulations make provision for local authorities to charge for preparation of the off-site emergency plan, and for the review and testing of emergency plans. Operators and carriers should have in place adequate systems to ensure that emergency plans are implemented as soon as possible after an accident. Operators and carriers should advise the HSE of the dose level at which certain personnel may receive emergency exposure (e.g. in putting an emergency plan into effect); such personnel should be identified and given appropriate information, training, equipment and medical surveillance.

Copies of hazard assessments and emergency plans should be made available to the public, subject to exclusions reasons of industrial, commercial or personal confidentiality, public security or national defence. These REPPIR Regulations are consistent with the relevant sections of the *Control of Major Accident Hazards Regulations 1999* dealing with emergency plans etc - see 2.16.1.

CONTROL OF PROCESS ODOURS

2.32 INTRODUCTION

Complaints to local authorities about odour constitute a significant proportion of total complaints received. For the year 1996/97, the Chartered Institute of Environmental Health reports that there were 15,264 (1995/96: over 19,000) complaints of smell from industrial processes in England and Wales. A further 7,378 (1995/96: 9,005) complaints concerned agricultural practices, including slurry spreading and storage, and the keeping of livestock. Animal by-product plants are a serious source of odour pollution, particularly for people living near them. These plants process animal waste from abattoirs, other animal

and meat processing and rendering plants etc, into products such as tallow, bonemeal and animal feedstuffs. The handling, storage and cooking of the raw waste material can give rise to particularly difficult odour control problems.

2.33 PROCESS ODOUR COMPOSITION

It is usual to describe the odour by the nature of the process causing it but process odours, especially where animal or vegetable matter is heated, are often complex mixtures in air of many substances present at very low concentrations. These substances may be individually malodorous and will occur with large numbers of other compounds including hydrocarbons which cause little or no odour response. Recent years have seen the development of techniques for the sampling and analysis of such mixtures containing perhaps only parts per million (ppm) or even parts per billion (ppb) quantities in air.

Analysis of the process odour is likely to involve pre-concentration on an adsorbent and then separation on a gas chromatographic column, followed by identification of the separated components. The most positive and comprehensive method of identification is a combined gas chromatograph-mass spectrometer linked to a computer-based data system. If part of the flow of separated components is delivered to an "odour port", then the odour, if any, of each component can be described.

2.34 ODOUR PROPERTIES AND EFFECTS

Most complaints about odour relate to annoyance about smells caused by emissions from a factory or farm reducing enjoyment of homes and gardens or making working conditions unpleasant. It is now appreciated that annoyance is the combined result of a number of odour properties.

Odour intensity is the strength of the perceived odour sensation and depends in a complex way on the concentration of the odorous substances present. It can be measured by comparison with reference samples but often an alternative measure of odour strength, the dilution to threshold value, is determined.

Odour character is the property that enables one to distinguish between different odours and it is said that an odour with a distinct recognisable character tends to be more annoying.

The acceptability - or "hedonic tone" - of an odour is an important factor in judging whether or not it is offensive or a nuisance. Not only the nature of the odour is taken into account (whether it is pleasant or unpleasant), but also its intensity, time and duration of release. It should also be borne in mind that a normally "pleasant" odour becomes less acceptable when exposed to it frequently; for example, a "pleasant" odour from a fragrance factory may be unacceptable if persistent in a residential area.

2.35 REGULATORY CONTROLS

2.35.1 Odour as a Statutory Nuisance

Prior to the *Environmental Protection Act 1990,* nuisance from odour was controlled through the nuisance provisions of the *Public Health Act 1936* (ss. 91-100). In order for an odour to constitute a statutory nuisance it had to be either prejudicial to health or a nuisance. The Act provided a defence of Best Practicable Means which allowed a defendant to prove that the accumulation or deposit was necessary for the effective carrying out of business, and that the BPM was used to prevent the odour being prejudicial to health or a nuisance to the neighbourhood.

Local authorities had a duty to carry out periodic inspections of their areas in order to detect any matters needing to be dealt with under the statutory nuisance and offensive trades provisions, and if satisfied that a statutory nuisance existed could serve a notice requiring steps to be taken to abate the nuisance. The notice could be enforced by order in a Magistrates' Court. If a nuisance had occurred on the premises in the past and was felt likely to recur, the local authority could serve a prohibition notice under section 1 of the *Public Health (Recurring Nuisances) Act 1969.*

Under the *Environmental Protection Act 1990* those sections of the *Public Health Act 1936* dealing with statutory nuisance were repealed, together with the whole of the *Public Health (Recurring Nuisances) Act 1969.* The "offensive trades" provisions of the PHA 1936 were repealed in 1995. Statutory nuisance legislation is now covered by Part III of the EPA (see chapter 1, 1.16.1).

2.35.2 Environmental Protection Act 1990

Many of the main sources of odour complaint - e.g. animal and plant treatment processes - will, however, be prescribed processes under Part I of the EPA; as such they must have an authorisation from their local authority (from 1.4.96, SEPA in Scotland - *Environment Act 1995)* who are responsible for air pollution control under the Act. Although prescribed processes which release a prescribed substance in "trivial" amounts do not need an authorisation, where this results in an offensive smell outside the premises, then an authorisation will be required (see chapter 2, 2.12.2).

2.36 SENSORY MEASUREMENTS (OLFACTOMETRY)

In recent years, increasing use has been made of odour strength measurements, determined as dilution to threshold values. Samples of the odorous air are diluted with odour-free air until the observers (panellists) cannot detect any odour. The dilution to threshold value might be taken as the dilution required to obtain a negative response from 50% of the panellists. Various forms of olfactometer have been developed for presenting a continuously diluted sample to the panellists ("dynamic dilution").

Odour strength measurements have a number of practical uses. Measurements in the ambient air can be used to locate odour sources and to study their distribution in the community. The different operations in a factory can be investigated to determine which contribute most to the total odour emission rate with a view to possible process changes. Where abatement equipment has been installed, measurements of odour strength on inlet and outlet samples show the efficiency of odour removal. A knowledge of the dilution to threshold value together with the volume flow rate can also be used to estimate the maximum distance over which the process emission is likely to cause complaints, and hence to indicate the removal efficiency required from abatement equipment.

2.37 GENERAL CONTROL METHODS

There are various ways in which the nuisance caused by process odours can be minimised or eliminated. Here we outline some of the principles involved in various odour abatement techniques; there is however a large amount of published information on process odour control and this section therefore provides an overview on the subject.

(a) Process and Plant Changes

This is taken to mean not only changes in operating parameters but also improved facilities and procedures for the storage and handling of raw materials, products and waste; better buildings may encourage good housekeeping and should confine the process air so that it does not escape to the surrounding community before any treatment required. Plant in the open may require special attention to eliminate potential leakage points by better maintenance or re-design. Where biodegradable material is being stored in the open in heaps or lagoons or spread on the land, the practices involved may need to be reviewed.

(b) Dilution by the Atmosphere

Dilution in air, so that the concentration of the malodorous compounds in the process emission are reduced below their detection thresholds is, in principle, another method of avoiding local complaints. This may be achieved by siting a new plant well away from housing etc but future housing developments may nullify the initial benefit of an isolated site. Alternatively, sufficient atmospheric dilution may sometimes be achieved by discharging the untreated process gases through a stack of suitable height. Of course, the variability of meteorological conditions is such that stack dispersion alone is not a totally dependable method for avoiding all complaints.

The first step is to calculate the required stack height in the absence of any abatement equipment; the calculation will be complicated by the presence of other buildings and local topography. In practice, this height could well prove excessive (either visually or in cost terms) and then the target efficiency for abatement equipment must be calculated so that discharge at an acceptable height is only required as the final stage of odour control.

(c) Odour Modification

This involves the addition of other chemicals which modify a person's response to the process odour because of changes in the perceived odour intensity (counteraction) or the perceived odour quality (masking). They are well known for indoor applications where they are dispersed as aerosol sprays, or evaporated from wick or gel-type dispensers. For process odour control, the odour modifier may be sprayed into stack emissions; if incorporated into the process, the modifier must be capable of withstanding the process conditions. The selection of odour modifiers and the dispensing rate would seem to be critical and the modifier should never prevent the perception of toxic or harmful substances.

2.38 ODOUR TREATMENT

It is often necessary to treat the process gases before discharge by one or more abatement techniques. Such techniques include thermal or catalytic incineration, absorption in chemical reagent solutions, adsorption on carbon and biological oxidation. All are considered to offer 90-99% efficiency although the use of recycling and clean technologies are likely to become increasingly important methods of solving odour problems. (*Odour Measurement and Control - an Update*, AEA Technology, NETCEN, 1994)

(a) Incineration

Effective odour control can usually be achieved by raising the process emission to a sufficiently high temperature for an appropriate length of time; this oxidises the malodorous compounds present to carbon dioxide and water, plus the small amounts of the oxides of sulphur and nitrogen which have little odour. The design of thermal afterburners has been the subject of extensive study and it is now better appreciated that odour destruction requires considerable temperatures, typically 650-800 degrees Centigrade, good mixing (in, say, 0.3-0.5 s) to ensure that all the process gases reach the required temperature and then adequate time to allow completion of the oxidation reactions (say, 0.1-0.3 s). Specific temperatures and residence times have been designated by some statutory bodies, e.g. some US States require animal rendering emissions to be incinerated at 650 degrees Centigrade for at least 0.3 seconds.

A major disadvantage when treating large volumes (often containing little combustible material) can be the cost of fuel; three approaches have been adopted to lower operating costs: heat recovery, the use of an existing boiler

(or kiln), or the incorporation of a catalyst. In practice, feeding the malodorous air stream to an existing boiler, even when the required temperature is apparently achieved, may be unsatisfactory because of poor mixing, insufficient residence time, corrosion etc.

Catalytic incineration may provide effective odour control at 350-400 degrees Centigrade, thereby saving perhaps 40-60% on fuel costs compared with thermal incineration but partly offset by higher capital and catalyst replacement costs. Catalytic incineration is unsuitable for process emissions containing catalyst poisons which cannot be economically removed or where the catalyst surface is liable to become blocked with particulates or polymeric material.

(b) Absorption in Reagent Solutions

Transfer of the malodorous compounds from the process air stream to the liquid phase is often the best method for treating large air flows using, for example, an absorption tower. Water is the usual liquid but commonly a chemical reagent is added to increase the transfer efficiency and the capacity of the liquid phase. The complexity of many process emissions such as those arising from the heat treatment of animal or vegetable matter, means that in practice a number of separate absorption stages with different reagents may be required. The specification of suitable chemical reagents for each particular application can be a problem.

(c) Adsorption on Activated Carbon

The principle involved is the removal of the malodorous compounds by adsorption on the carbon as the air being treated passes through the carbon bed. The use of activated carbon for solvent recovery is well known and is also the basis of many indoor systems, e.g. to treat domestic and restaurant odours. In treating process odours, activated carbon may be the primary abatement method, or placed after other abatement equipment to improve overall efficiency.

(d) Biological Treatment

Biological towers are similar in principle to packed absorbers except that odour removal is achieved by the use of micro-organisms grown on an inert packing rather than by chemical reagent solutions sprayed over the packing. The biological tower may be started up with a mixture of activated sewage sludge and nutrient solutions. An alternative form of biological treatment is where the odorous air is passed through a bed of soil, peat or compost. The mechanism of odour removal is believed to involve the dissolution of the odorants and oxygen in water followed by their reaction under the influence of enzymes, generated by, or forming part of, the micro-organisms.

Neighbourhood Noise

Noise as a Statutory Nuisance

Entertainment

Road Traffic Noise

Aircraft Noise

Rail Noise

Occupational Noise

GENERAL NEIGHBOURHOOD NOISE

3.1 INTRODUCTION

In its widest sense, neighbourhood noise might be defined as any unwanted sound in the vicinity of the home or its locality. That definition might embrace industrial noise, noise from transport, as well as noise from domestic premises, which is the biggest source of noise nuisance and complaints. During 1997/98 there were 212,327 separate complaints about noise made to environmental health departments in England and Wales (1996/97: 242,181); this figure breaks down into 148,006 relating to noise from domestic premises; 47,516 from industrial and commercial premises; 3,835 complaints about noise from equipment in the street; 8,232 about construction noise; and 4,738 complaints about noise from vehicles (Chartered Institute of Environmental Health, Environmental Health Report 1997/98). In Scotland, environmental health departments received 7,929 complaints in 1996/97, with noise from industrial and commercial premises providing the biggest source of complaint, followed by domestic premises (DETR, *Digest of Environmental Statistics*, No. 20, published 1998).

The noise which affects people in the home varies according to the situation, and accepted habits and customs. Country dwellers expect to be far freer of industrial and traffic noise than city dwellers; they will accept some agricultural machinery noise although devices such as bird scarers (particularly when situated close to houses and left to operate throughout the night) can be obtrusive. However, country dwellers may also be affected by noisy, large-scale operations such as quarrying and open-cast mining. Usually, the noise implications of such developments are considered at the planning stage and conditions governing noise levels and methods of operation are attached to the planning consent.

In towns, traffic noise is usually inescapable, and to an extent it is tolerated as inevitable. Noise generated by long-established industrial or commercial operations will similarly be tolerated by long standing residents in the vicinity, although problems can arise when houses or flats change hands: newcomers are usually more sensitive to the noise and more likely to find it stressful. On the other hand, newcomers can change the character of an area and the types and levels of noise in it - for example when there is an influx of students. Most people now have domestic appliances of one sort or another, sophisticated audio systems or do-it-yourself tools; all of these can cause a nuisance if used at unsocial hours or at high volume; problems may also arise or be exacerbated by inadequate sound insulation. In some instances action under statutory nuisance legislation may be necessary; in others changes in furnishings - e.g. wall to wall carpeting - can lessen the effect to some extent. Part E of Schedule 1 of the *Building Regulations 2000* specifies that floors and walls between

new built houses and flats and buildings where there is a material change of use (e.g. flat conversions) should have reasonable resistance to airborne and impact sound. *Approved Document E - Resistance to the Passage of Sound* describes ways of meeting the requirements, with examples of widely used "satisfactory" constructions and test results. Similar Regulations, the *Building Standards (Scotland) Regulations 1990*, apply in Scotland; Part H to the Regulations deals with resistance to transmission of sound. In addition BS 8233: 1999 Code of Practice – Sound Insulation in Buildings, aimed at building designers and constructors, provides guidance on controlling noise in and around buildings, taking account of current legislation and other official guidance. It also gives guidance on providing the most appropriate sound insulation for the intended use of the building.

Legislative controls on noise pollution are of more recent origin than controls on other forms of pollution. Prior to the *Noise Abatement Act 1960* noise was largely dealt with locally as a nuisance and under local bye-laws. Under the 1960 Act, noise became a statutory nuisance for the purposes of the *Public Health Act 1936,* thus enabling local authorities to take action for noise nuisance, under a procedure not unlike current procedures for statutory nuisance.

The 1960 Act also introduced a complaints procedure whereby private individuals could take action: the Act required that three or more people, each of whom occupied land or premises affected by the noise nuisance, could complain direct to a magistrate. The "three neighbour rule" was to deter malicious and frivolous complaints. However this rule was not carried forward to either the *Control of Pollution Act 1974* or the *Environmental Protection Act 1990;* under both of these only one person need be affected for action to be initiated for statutory nuisance.

The 1960 Act was repealed by the *Control of Pollution Act 1974*, Part III. As well as dealing with statutory noise nuisance, it introduced provisions relating to noise from construction sites, street noise, the setting up of noise abatement zones and on drawing up codes of practice on specific noise problems (e.g. burglar alarms). The sections dealing with statutory noise nuisance have been repealed and re-enacted in the *Environmental Protection Act 1990;* in England and Wales this change took effect on 1 January 1991 and in Scotland on 1 April 1996 (see chapter 1, 1.16). The *Noise and Statutory Nuisance Act 1993* provides local authorities in England, Scotland and Wales with powers to control noise nuisance emitted from vehicles, machinery or equipment in the street - see below 3.8.1. The *Noise Act 1996* enables local authorities in England, Wales and Northern Ireland to make night-time noise nuisance a criminal offence and provides powers to confiscate noise-making equipment - see 3.9.2 below.

Later sections of this chapter cover the controls available to deal with noise from neighbours, entertainment noise, industrial and construction site noise, transport and occupational noise.

3.2 THE EUROPEAN UNION AND NOISE POLLUTION

3.2.1 Fifth Action Programme (1993-2000)

The Commission's Fifth Action Programme on the Environment, Towards Sustainability - (see also Appendix 6) proposes a number of measures aimed at reducing people's exposure to night-time noise. The Commission's targets are that

- exposure to more than 65 dB(A) should be phased out and at no time should 85 dB(A) be exceeded;

- those exposed to levels of between 65-55 dB(A), and those currently exposed to less than 55 dB(A), should not suffer any increase.

To achieve these levels the Commission proposes noise abatement programmes; standardisation of noise measurement and rating (see 3.2.2 below); Directives further reducing noise from transportation; measures related to infrastructure and planning (e.g. better zoning around airports, industrial areas, main roads and railways).

3.2.2 Assessment and Management of Environmental Noise

In July 2000, the Commission published a proposal for a Directive relating to the Assessment and Management of Environmental Noise (COM(2000) 468. This follows its 1996 Green Paper on Noise Policy (COM(96) 540) which recognised that current measures for reducing people's exposure to unacceptable levels of noise - particularly traffic noise - were not enough. While acknowledging that noise is essentially a local issue, the Commission suggested that there were a number of areas where a Community-wide approach was needed and it is on these areas that the proposed Directive concentrates. Environmental noise is defined as "the sound generated by human activity (road traffic, railways, air transport, industry, recreation and construction) and perceived in the domestic environment (e.g. in and near the home, in public parks, in schools)". It does not cover noise produced by animals, by nature or by neighbours. The timetable for the Directive, which is summarised below, envisages it entering into force by 1 January 2002 and being transposed into national legislation by 1 July 2003:

- L_{den} and L_{night}* to be used as indicators in EU noise policy, in new legislation on noise mapping, acoustical planning or noise zoning and in any revision to existing legislation; L_{den} is the day-evening-night level in decibels and is an indicator for "annoyance"*; L_{night} is the "overall night-time noise indicator", a reduction in which would reduce sleep disturbance. Annex II to the Directive sets out assessment methods for both indicators;

- Noise maps – using common indicators and assessment methods - covering large agglomerations (above 250,000 inhabitants), major roads, railways and airports to be prepared and approved within three

years of the Directive entering into force (i.e. by 1.1.05); to be repeated five years later when mapping will be extended to agglomerations between 100,000 and 250,000 inhabitants; maps should include data on noise levels, number of citizens affected and to what extent;

- within one year of the deadline for noise maps, action plans to be prepared for the mapped areas, to be repeated every five years, to include measures for protecting the relatively quiet areas and for reducing noise in noisier areas;

- noise maps are to be published within two months of approval by the competent authority, and the public to be consulted during the preparation of action plans; action plans are also to be published within two months of approval;

- Member States to be responsible for forwarding noise maps and action plans to the Commission who will set up a data bank of information on noise maps and publish a summary report every five years;

- No later than 31 December 2007, the Commission to submit to the Parliament and the Council a report summarising the effects of the Directive and if appropriate, propose environmental noise quality objectives, and strategies for implementing them.

* "Annoyance" is the scientific expression for non-specific disturbance by noise. When associated with dose-effect relations, L_{den} and L_{night} are both indicators that are able to predict the average response of a population that is subject to long-term noise exposure. [Thus they] are suitable for planning purposes and for an integral approach for a residential area, a city and larger areas. The value of noise indicators can be determined either by measurement or by computation. *Extracted from The Noise Policy of the European Union, Year 2 (1999-2000).*

3.2.3 Directives Limiting Noise from Transport and Equipment

As in other areas of environmental policy, the European Union (EU) has adopted a number of Directives aimed at reducing noise in the environment, which the UK must implement. These include maximum permitted noise levels for motor vehicles (cars, trucks, buses, motorcycles and agricultural tractors) - see 3.15 below, and subsonic jet aircraft - see 3.17 below. A Directive relating to noise exposure at work was implemented in 1990 through Regulations under the *Health and Safety at Work Act 1974* (see 3.21.1 below).

A number of Directives establish maximum noise levels for different types of machinery and equipment, including construction machinery and lawn mowers. The aim is to reduce the noise level of individual machines and thus bring about an overall reduction in neighbourhood noise.

In May 2000 the European Parliament and Council for Ministers formally adopted Directive 2000/14/EC relating to the noise emission in the environment by equipment for use outdoors.

As well as introducing consistent noise emission requirements and noise labelling for some equipment, the Directive also aims to reduce overall noise exposure to and nuisance from outdoor equipment. The Directive covers 57 types of equipment, of which 22 are subject to noise limits, ranging from concrete breakers, dumpers and excavators, to lawn mowers, hedge trimmers and leaf blowers. Manufacturers must guarantee that the noise level of a product conforms to the specific level for that category of equipment, and for a label confirming this to be affixed to it. For equipment for which a limit has not been set, there is a requirement for it to be labelled with its sound output. The Directive came into force on 3 July 2000 and will be transposed into UK legislation by 3 July 2001; on 3 January 2002, the noise limits of the new Directive become mandatory and all the earlier Directives will be repealed; a second stage of tighter limits take effect on 3 January 2006.

A list of Directives and other EU measures relating to noise is at Appendix 6.3. Brief details of the institutions of the EU and of the legislative process are given in Appendix 6.

3.3 WORLD HEALTH ORGANISATION

The World Health Organisation suggests that during the daytime to protect the majority of people from being "moderately annoyed" outdoor sound levels should not exceed 50 dB LAeq, and that to protect the majority of people from being "seriously annoyed" it should not exceed 55 dB LAeq. WHO recommends an indoor (bedroom) guideline value for undisturbed sleep of 30 dB LAeq for continuous noise and 45 dB LAmax for single sound events. (*Guidelines for Community Noise*, WHO, 2000).

3.4 IMPLEMENTATION AND ENFORCEMENT AUTHORITIES

Much of the responsibility for practical action to prevent or abate noise rests with local authorities and in particular environmental health departments under the general direction of central government departments.

At central government level, responsibility for noise control is shared among a number of departments. The Department of the Environment, Transport and the Regions is responsible for the control of noise from fixed sources, the use of planning control to prevent noise problems, and general noise nuisance questions; it also deals with legislation and policy on road traffic noise and noise from civil aircraft. Occupational noise is the responsibility of the Health and Safety Commission and its operational arm, the Health and Safety Executive.

The police, while having no specific powers to deal with noise nuisance, provide some support to environmental health officers and other officials in carrying out their duties; they also have powers to noise-test road vehicles.

Guidance drawn up by the Chartered Institute of Environmental Health and the Association of Chief Police Officers - *Good practice guidance for police and local authority cooperation* - was published by the CIEH in February 1997. This provides guidance on what is considered as a minimum standard of cooperation between the police and LAs when dealing with noise complaints. It sets out the roles and responsibilities of each and gives examples of effective local liaison arrangements. It suggests that both local authorities and the police in each area should draw up an agreement covering liaison which includes:

- their respective responsibilities and powers relating to noise;

- their respective response criteria - LAs in dealing with out of hours complaints, and the police on dealing with complaints received in the control room;

- resources available - LAs in dealing with out of hours complaints and extra resources which could be made available; support which police can provide where risk of threat or assault;

- the circumstances in which the LA would require police assistance, with the police providing contact points for requesting assistance;

- the chain of command and level at which the police and the LA should make contact.

The CIEH has also published (1997) *Noise Management Guidance for Local Authorities*. As well as providing guidance on noise control policies, this guidance aims to encourage consistency in the way local authorities deliver noise control services, while still enabling them to respond to local circumstances and needs.

Greater London Authority

The *Greater London Authority Act 1999* requires the Mayor to produce a noise strategy for London. The "London Ambient Noise Strategy" should include information about ambient noise levels related to road and rail traffic, aircraft and water transport in London and their impact on people living and working there. It should include an assessment of the impact on ambient noise levels of the other Strategies which the Mayor is required to prepare and a summary of the action proposed or taken to reduce ambient noise levels. In preparing or revising the Strategy, the Mayor is required to consult the Environment Agency. Consultation on the first Strategy is expected in May 2001.

3.5 PLANNING CONTROLS

Effective use of planning controls and related guidance will go a long way towards preventing many noise-related nuisances arising in the first place. Before any development can take place, planning permission under the *Town and Country Planning Act 1990* (Scotland - 1997 Act) must be obtained. In some cases an environmental impact assessment may be required (see also chapter 1, 1.22-1.24). In either case noise will be one of the criteria to be considered.

The *Town and Country Planning General Development Order 1988* permits the use of a specific site for an activity (e.g. clay pigeon shooting, helicopter landing site) for up to 28 days a year without the need for planning permission. There is no limit as to the amount of shootings or number of take-offs and landings in any one day.

3.5.1 Planning Policy Guidance

Planning Policy Guidance: Planning and Noise (PPG 24, 1994) replaced the 1973 *Planning and Noise Circular* (10/73); it builds on the principles established in the earlier circular and suggests new mechanisms and guidelines for local authorities to adopt. General principles of how noise should be taken into account in the planning process are suggested, including the need for special attention to be given to proposed developments which could affect "quiet enjoyment" of areas of outstanding natural beauty, national parks etc. Examples of planning conditions are given and the various statutory and other noise controls listed. The PPG deals with noise from road traffic; aircraft; railways; industrial and commercial developments; construction and waste disposal sites; sporting, entertainment and recreational activities; and mixed noise sources. An Appendix to the PPG lists four categories of noise exposure for the assessment of new residential developments near a noise source. The categories are:

- A: noise need not be considered as a determining factor in granting planning permission, although the noise level at the high end of the category should not be regarded as a desirable level;

- B: noise should be taken into account when determining planning applications and, where appropriate, conditions imposed to ensure an adequate level of protection against noise;

- C: planning permission should not normally be granted. Where it is considered permission should be given, for example because there are no alternative quieter sites available, conditions should be imposed to ensure a commensurate level of protection against noise;

- D: planning permission should normally be refused.

For each of these categories the PPG recommends limits for both day (0700-2300) and night (2300-0700) time exposure for new dwellings which it is planned to develop near one of the following existing noise sources - road traffic, rail traffic, air traffic, or mixed source.

In Scotland, SODD Circular 10.1999, *Planning and Noise,* and Planning Advice Note (PAN) 56 (2000) provide guidance on how planners should deal with noise in considering plans for new developments and the issues to be taken into account. The PAN introduces the use of noise exposure categories, outlines ways of mitigating the adverse impacts of noise and provides specific guidance on noisy and noise sensitive developments.

3.4.2 British Standard 4142

BS 4142, which was last revised in 1997, describes a "Method for Rating Industrial Noise Affecting Mixed Residential and Industrial Areas" and is thus of particular use when considering planning applications. It can be used to determine the likelihood of a complaint from an industrial source under normal operating conditions using a mixture of calculations and measurements, including measurement of background noise levels. It can be used to assess noise levels from both existing and new or modified premises in the vicinity of existing housing. BS 4142 has no legal status as it has not been approved under s.71 of COPA.

REGULATORY CONTROLS - NOISE NUISANCE

The principal legislative controls on excessive noise in and around the neighbourhood are:

- the *Environmental Protection Act 1990, Part III* which deals with noise as a statutory nuisance;

- the *Control of Pollution Act 1974, Part III* covers construction site noise and certain noise in the street;

- the *Noise and Statutory Nuisance Act 1993* which as well as amending the EPA and COPA also covers noise emitted from vehicles or equipment on the street, and burglar alarms.

- the *Noise Act 1996* makes certain night-time noise a criminal offence and provides powers to confiscate noise-making equipment.

3.6 GENERAL NOISE NUISANCE

Anyone living in the United Kingdom has a legal right to be protected against noise nuisance. Nuisance itself may be defined as "an unlawful interference with a person's use or enjoyment of land or of some right over, or in connection with it". Nuisance at law is a tort, i.e. a civil wrong, for which courts can provide a remedy, usually damages. In any action for noise nuisance the key factors are the need for an aggrieved person to establish that his occupation of land or property is affected by noise, and that each case will be considered on its merit.

General noise nuisance may be dealt with under ss.79-81 of the *Environmental Protection Act 1990* (as amended), which empowers local authorities to deal with noise from fixed premises: factories, shops, discos and dwellings. Individuals may take action under s.82 (see chapter 1, 1.16.1). Excessive noise from council dwellings can often be dealt with as a breach of tenancy agreement where this includes a clause restricting noise, and the tenants taken to court. The *Housing Act 1996* also enables both private and council landlords to evict tenants for anti-social behaviour - e.g. for causing a nuisance.

Minor noise nuisance is often restricted by local authority bye-laws, which the local authority enforces (although an individual may also prosecute). Bye-laws can be used to control such noise sources as: noisy conduct at night; noisy street trading; noisy animals; loud music; radios, television and other audio equipment; seaside pleasure boats; model aircraft; fireworks. Other regulations cover the use of loudspeakers and chimes.

Independent mediation services can also be an effective means of solving neighbour noise disputes where a statutory noise nuisance has not been established; in many cases mediation can be a quicker and more cost-effective way of tackling a range of neighbour nuisance disputes at an early stage and thus avoiding formal action. Independent or community based mediation services are now available in many local authorities, or contact Mediation UK, tel: 0117 904 6661.

It should be reiterated that mediation is not a substitute for formal action where a statutory nuisance has been established: in such instances an abatement notice must be issued.

Scotland

In addition to the *Environmental Protection Act 1990*, action can also be taken under the *Civic Government (Scotland) Act 1982* which covers many aspects of minor (or neighbourhood noise).

Northern Ireland

The control of noise and noise nuisance is regulated under the *Pollution Control and Local Government (Northern Ireland) Order 1978* and the *Noise Act 1996*.

The 1978 Order enables a noise abatement notice to be served placing a prohibition or restriction on the noise and for an appeal to be lodged against such a notice within 21 days; for noise caused in the course of trade or business, it is a defence to prove that the best practicable means have been used to prevent the noise; the Order also covers construction site noise and the establishing of noise abatement zones and codes of practice.

3.6.1 Environmental Protection Act 1990, Part III

This part of the Act deals with statutory nuisance (including noise) in England, Wales and Scotland. Section 79 of the EPA places a duty on local authorities to require its area to be inspected from time to time to detect whether a statutory nuisance exists; this includes "noise emitted from premises so as to be prejudicial to health or a nuisance". Premises include land and vessels (except those powered by "steam reciprocating machinery") and noise includes vibration. Noise from aircraft other than from model aircraft is excluded. Similar powers to investigate noise in the street are provided through an amendment to s.79 of the EPA in the *Noise and Statutory Nuisance Act 1993* (see below, 3.8.1).

Local authorities must also take such steps as are reasonably practicable to investigate any complaints of statutory nuisance in their area. Where the local authority is satisfied that a statutory nuisance exists, or is likely to occur or recur, it must serve an abatement notice requiring

• the abatement of the nuisance or prohibiting or restricting its occurrence or recurrence; and/or

• the carrying out of such works or other action necessary to abate the nuisance.

Individuals may also take action against statutory nuisance. Information about this, together with details of local authority powers with regard to statutory nuisance are covered in chapter 1, 1.16.1.

3.7 CONTROL OF POLLUTION ACT 1974, PART III

This part of COPA is specifically concerned with the control of noise pollution. Sections 57-59, which covered local authorities' duty to inspect, noise abatement notices and individuals' rights to take action in respect of a noise nuisance were repealed on 1 April 1996. On that date the statutory nuisance provisions of the EPA were extended to Scotland through implementation of s.107 and Sch. 17 of the *Environment Act 1995*.

In Northern Ireland, the *Pollution Control and Local Government (Northern Ireland) Order 1978* covers the same areas as the remaining sections of Part III of COPA.

3.7.1 Construction Sites (ss.60-61)

Construction activities are inherently noisy and often take place in areas which are normally quiet. During 1997/98, environmental health officers in England and Wales received 8,232 complaints (1996/97: 8065) relating to construction noise (CIEH Environmental Health Report 1997/98). In Scotland 885 complaints were received in 1996/97 (*Digest of Environmental Statistics*, No. 20, 1998).

Section 60 gives local authorities the power to serve a notice imposing requirements as to the way in which construction works are to be carried out.

British Standard 5228, *Noise Control on Construction and Open Sites*, provides guidance to enable compliance with s.60 and is applicable throughout the UK. It is in five parts, with Part 1 (1997) being a code of practice for basic information and procedures for noise and vibration control; Part 2 (1997) provides a guide to noise and vibration control legislation for construction and demolition including road construction and maintenance; Part 3 (1997) is a code of practice applicable to surface coal extraction by opencast methods; Part 4 (1992) is a code of practice for noise and vibration control applicable to piling operations; and Part 5 (1997) is a code of practice applicable to surface mineral extraction (except coal) sites. The earlier codes of practice which formed part of BS 5228 were approved under s.71 of COPA and approval is to be sought for the revised codes.

Neither COPA nor the related codes of practice set down specific limits for construction site noise, on the basis that the local authority knows its own locality best and would have a better idea of suitable noise limits. The person served with the notice may appeal within 21 days to the Magistrates' Court (Sheriff in Scotland; N. Ireland - Court of Summary Jurisdiction) and is guilty of an offence under the Act if, without reasonable excuse, any requirement of the notice is contravened.

Under s.61, the person intending to carry out works may apply in advance for a consent as to the methods by which the works are to be carried out.

If a local authority does not give consent to a building contractor/developer's own scheme of noise control, the contractor has a right of appeal to the court. Once a consent has been given, the contractor is effectively immune from action on noise grounds taken by the local authority so long as the terms of the consent are complied with.

The activities covered by these sections of the Act are:

a) the erection, construction, alteration, repair or maintenance of buildings, structures or roads;

b) breaking up, opening or boring under any road or adjacent land in connection with the construction, inspection, maintenance or removal of works;

c) demolition or dredging work; and

d) (whether or not also comprised in paras a, b, or c) any work of engineering construction.

Individual occupiers of premises (England, Scotland and Wales) may apply to a Magistrates' Court (Sheriff in Scotland) for an order under s.82 of the *Environmental Protection Act 1990,* on the grounds that the noise from the site nevertheless amounts to a statutory nuisance.

Construction work undertaken by statutory operators (i.e. on behalf of the government) is usually regarded as "emergency" and therefore exempt from COPA.

3.7.2 Noise in Streets (s.62)

Sub-section 62(1) bans the use of a loudspeaker in a street (Scotland - road) between the hours of 9.00 pm and 8.00 am. A loudspeaker includes a megaphone or other amplifying instrument. Under the *Noise and Statutory Nuisance Act 1993* (NASNA), the Secretary of State may vary these times but not so as to permit the use of loudspeakers between these times; additionally, local authorities may adopt powers enabling them to grant a Consent for a loudspeaker to be used later than 9.00 pm but not for advertising or electioneering purposes (see below, 3.8.2).

Under COPA, it is an offence to use loudspeakers in the street at any hour for advertising any entertainment, trade or business. Sub-section 62(2) exempts the emergency services (fire, police, ambulance) as well as the water authorities and local authorities in certain circumstances. Also exempt are loudspeakers on ground being used by pleasure fairs, and loudspeakers which form part of a public telephone system.

Vehicles which sell perishable foodstuffs (such as ice-cream) are exempted from this section, but may only use loudspeakers between noon and 7.00 pm; again, the loudspeaker must be operated in such a way as not to give reasonable cause for annoyance to persons in the vicinity. These times may be varied by local authority Consent

under the *Noise and Statutory Nuisance Act 1993* - see below, 3.8.2.

This section of COPA has also been successfully used to prosecute motorists with in-car stereo systems played at excessively loud levels.

In 1996/97 local authorities in England and Wales received 3,407 complaints under this section of COPA (CIEH Environmental Health Report 1996/97). In Scotland 114 complaints were received in 1996/97 (*Digest of Environmental Statistics*, No. 20, 1998).

3.7.3 Noise Abatement Zones (ss.63-67)

A local authority may designate all or part of its area as a noise abatement zone (NAZ); the purpose of a NAZ is the long-term control of noise from fixed premises in order to prevent any further increases in existing levels of neighbourhood or community noise levels, and to achieve reduction of those levels wherever possible.

An order setting up a NAZ was subject to the confirmation of the Secretary of State, until that provision was repealed by the *Local Government Planning and Land Act 1980.* However, a local authority should still take account of any objections made about the establishment of a NAZ by people within the affected area.

Following the implementation of a noise abatement zone order, the local authority measures noise levels from those types of premises (specified in the order) within the zone (s.64). These are recorded in a register kept by the local authority for the purpose and open to public inspection. Details of methods of measurement and maintenance of the register are given in the *Control of Noise (Measurement and Registers) Regulations 1976.*

Once the noise level has been registered, it may not be exceeded except with the local authority's consent (s.65). Over a period of time, the local authority may seek to achieve a reduction in the initially registered levels of noise by serving a reduction notice under s.66 of the Act, but only if it is satisfied that a reduction is practicable at a reasonable cost and would afford a public benefit. Section 67 empowers the local authority to determine the acceptance level of noise for a proposed new building, which when constructed will be subject to a noise abatement order. Section 68 allows the Secretary of State to make regulations for the reduction of noise caused by plant or machinery, whether or not in a noise abatement zone and s.69 gives the local authority default powers in the case of failure to comply with a noise abatement or noise reduction notice. There is a right of appeal (s.70) to the Magistrates' Court for three months from the date on which a Noise Reduction Notice is served. It is a defence to prove that the best practicable means were used to prevent or counteract the effects of the noise.

While the main benefit of a noise abatement zone is in controlling community noise, and reducing it where possible, without having to prove that the noise amounts to nuisance, it nevertheless remains a little used method of control; this may be because the procedures required by the Regulations for setting up a NAZ are considered cumbersome in practice. In 1990 the Government's Noise Review Working Party (The Batho Report) recommended that the noise testing procedures be simplified to make it easier to set up a NAZ. A 1993 report from the Building Research Establishment confirmed this view but felt a more extensive appraisal was needed. To date there has been no further action.

3.7.4 Codes of Practice (s.71)

This section gives the Secretary of State powers to prepare and approve, and issue codes of practice for minimising noise, or to approve such codes issued by non-government bodies, such as the Code of Practice on the control of noise on construction and demolition sites. This Code (BS 5228) was prepared by the British Standards Institution and originally approved by the Secretary of State in 1975, but has since been revised - see 3.7.1 above.

The Department of Environment (now DETR) has itself issued three codes, all in 1982 (with similar codes in Northern Ireland issued under the 1978 Order):

- Noise from ice cream chimes, etc (limits the use of chimes to between 12 noon and 7.00 pm).
- Noise from burglar intruder alarms (see also below, 3.8.3).
- Noise from model aircraft.

Such codes, although having statutory recognition, do not have the force of regulations, and infringement does not constitute an offence. Non-compliance, however, will usually be taken into account in any proceedings for noise nuisance.

Other Codes

There are a number of other draft and finalised codes of practice which have been prepared by various interest groups which have not received approval under s.71, although some have been submitted for such approval. These codes can, however, be used as guidance in determining what constitutes good practice. Such codes include:

- *Noise from Organised Off-Road Motor Cycle Sport*: prepared by the Noise Council in association with various other bodies (1994);
- *Clay Target Shooting: Guidance on the Management and Control of Noise* (draft): CIEH, Clay Pigeon Shooting Association and the British Shooting Sports Council, 1997; this guidance is intended for use by both those organising shoots or involved in their management, as well as local authorities. It provides practical guidance on the ways in which noise from such shoots can be controlled to minimise or prevent intrusion. A recommended method for noise measurement and subsequent rating, produced by the Building Research Establishment, is also given. Following finalisation it is planned to seek Secretary of

State approval of the Guidance as an Approved Code of Practice under COPA.

- *Bird Scarers* (National Farmers Union, 1992; 1997 - code being amended prior to submitting to DETR for approval under COPA): provides advice on siting and use of all types of bird scarers, including audible scarers.
- *Water Skiing and Noise* (British Water Ski Federation, 1996): provides guidance for clubs on avoiding significant impact from noise on surrounding community for both existing and new sites. Method for assessing noise from sites, advice on course layout, hours of operation, screening etc also provided.
- *Environmental Noise Control at Concerts* (Noise Council, 1994): it provides assistance for those planning concerts, for licensing authorities and for local authorities enforcing nuisance legislation. It includes music noise levels for both indoor and outdoor events and single as well as multiple events.
- *Guide to Health, Safety and Welfare at Pop Concerts and Similar Events* (HSE, Home Office, Scottish Office, 1993): this includes guidance on noise levels, covering the risks to health and safety (including noise) both to those at the concerts and to those living near the concert venue.
- *Short Oval Circuit Motor Racing* (NSCA's National Noise Committee, 1996): this covers stock car, hot rod, banger racing and similar events; it aims to help local authorities and organisers to minimise the noise impact of such events on nearby premises; it also outlines legal controls. This code has been submitted to DETR for approval under s.71 of COPA.
- *Noise from Pubs and Clubs* (draft issued for consultation by Institute of Acoustics, November 1999): provides guidance on control of noise affecting noise sensitive premises from the public and private use of pubs, clubs, hotels, discos, restaurants, cafés, community and village halls etc; noises covered include public address systems, children's play areas and from people in general, but not noise at live sporting events.

3.7.5 Best Practicable Means (s.72)

The law recognises that there is a limit to what a person may reasonably be required to do or to spend to reduce noise, and also that there may be technical limits on what can be done. The intention is to ensure that, while a firm can be asked to take all reasonable action to control noise, it cannot be faced with disproportionately expensive requirements for remedial action.

It is, therefore, a defence in any summary proceedings relating to noise caused by a trade or business to prove that the Best Practicable Means (BPM) have been used to prevent or counteract the effect of noise. Part III of COPA defines BPM as "reasonably practicable, having regard among other things to local conditions and circumstances, to the current state of technical knowledge and to the financial implications". Means includes "the design, installation, maintenance and manner and periods of operation of plant and machinery, and the design, construction and maintenance of buildings and acoustic structures".

3.7.6 Other Sections

Section 73 deals with the interpretation of some of the terms used in Part III of COPA, and s.74 with penalties for offences under Part III.

3.8 NOISE AND STATUTORY NUISANCE ACT 1993

This Act which, apart from the burglar alarm provisions, came into force on 5 January 1994, covers England, Scotland and Wales. It amends ss.79-82 of the *Environmental Protection Act 1990* to make noise in a street (Scotland - road) a statutory nuisance. Section 62 of COPA dealing with the hours in which loudspeakers may be used is also amended and provision is made for regulating burglar alarms. The Act is enforced by local authorities; the procedure for taking statutory nuisance action and the appeals procedure are outlined in chapter 1, 1.16.1 and 1.16.2.

Department of the Environment, Transport and the Regions Circular (Environment Circular 9/97, WO Circular 42/97) provides guidance to local authorities on implementation of the Act and their duties; it also explains the operational role of the police.

3.8.1 Statutory Nuisance - Noise in Street (ss.2-5)

An additional subsection is added to s.79 of the *Environmental Protection Act 1990* so as to make noise emitted from or caused by a vehicle, machinery or equipment in a street (Scotland - road) a statutory nuisance. This could include, for example, noisy car repairs, car alarms, car radios and parked refrigerator vehicles - in 1997/98 there were 3,835 complaints to local authorities in England and Wales under these sections of the Act (CIEH Environmental Health Report, 1997-98); in Scotland there were 53 complaints in 1996/97 (*Digest of Environmental Statistics*, No. 20, 1998). Traffic noise, noise by military forces or from political or other campaigning demonstrations (but not noise or disturbance as result of picketing) is excluded. Having satisfied itself that a statutory nuisance exists or is likely to occur or recur, the local authority must serve an abatement notice; the procedure for this is set out in chapter 1, 1.16.1.

The *Noise and Statutory Nuisance Act 1993* does, however, amend the EPA procedure for serving an abatement notice in respect of a nuisance from or caused by a vehicle, machinery or equipment (VME) on the street; if possible the notice should be served on the person responsible, but if the VME is unattended then the notice may be affixed directly to the VME. The enforcing officer

should then spend one hour endeavouring to trace the person responsible for the VME to serve a copy of the notice on them; where the person is found additional time should be allowed before the notice takes effect to enable them to abate the nuisance; if the person cannot be found the enforcing officer may then take the necessary steps to abate the nuisance.

Authorised persons are empowered to gain entry to a vehicle in order to carry out the terms of an abatement notice (e.g. to turn off an alarm); before doing so the police should be notified; the vehicle should be left as secure as before entry or, if this is not possible, should be immobilised or removed to a secure place and the police notified of where it has been taken.

So far as excessively loud car stereos are concerned, an alternative to nuisance action could be use of s.97 of the *Road Vehicles (Construction and Use) Regulations 1986* (SI 1078); this says that "no motor vehicle shall be used on a road in such manner as to cause any excessive noise which could have been avoided" by the use of reasonable care.

3.8.2 Loudspeakers (ss.7-8)

Section 7 of the Act gives the Secretary of State powers to further restrict the hours in which loudspeakers may be used (8.00 am - 9.00 pm) in a street (Scotland - road) under s.62 of COPA (see above, 3.7.2).

Under s.8 local authorities may adopt powers enabling them to grant a Consent for a loudspeaker to be used outside the hours of 9.00 pm and 8.00 am (except for advertising or electioneering). Schedule 2 to the Act sets out the procedure for granting a Consent: anybody wanting to use a loudspeaker at a different time must apply for a Consent specifying the purpose, date, location and duration of use. The local authority must deal with the application within 21 days and may attach any conditions it feels appropriate to the Consent. A charge may be made and the local authority may require details of the Consent to be published in a local newspaper.

3.8.3 Audible Intruder Alarms (s.9)

This section and Schedule 3 of NASNA have not yet been brought into force. They enable a local authority, following consultation with its chief police officer, to resolve that s.9 and Schedule 3 of the Act should apply in its area. The local authority would then be able to impose certain obligations on owners of burglar alarms, including

- audible intruder alarms would need to comply with the requirements of *The Audible Intruder Alarms Regulations* (draft issued Autumn 1995). Audible intruder alarms must be fitted with a device which automatically stops the alarm 20 minutes after it first sounds;

- the local authority to be informed of its installation within 48 hours;

- the police to be notified of names, addresses and telephone numbers of keyholders and the local authority advised at which police station this information is held;

- if the alarm is still sounding after one hour and is "giving reasonable cause for annoyance", the local authority would be empowered to gain entry to the premises to turn off the alarm. If unable to gain entry with the help of a keyholder, the local authority may apply to a magistrate for a warrant to enter by force, having left a notice to this effect at the premises. A police officer should be present if the premises are to be entered by force. The premises should be left secure with a notice saying what has been done. The local authority may recover any reasonable expenses incurred in gaining entry to premises.

The 1982 Code of Practice on Noise from Audible Intruder Alarms (approved under s.71 of COPA) gives guidance on minimising nuisance from faulty alarms. It suggests that alarms should be fitted with a 20 minute cut-out device and that keyholders of properties with alarms should be notified to the police.

It should be noted that in London the *London Local Authorities Act 1991* empowers local authorities to prosecute owners or occupiers of buildings whose audible intruder alarms contravene specified requirements or cause annoyance to people in the vicinity. Burglar alarms must be fitted with a 20 minute cut-out device and owners/occupiers of buildings with intruder alarms must notify their local council that an alarm has been fitted and give the police names and addresses of keyholders. They must also notify the council at which police station this information is held. The Act empowers local authority officers, accompanied by a police officer, to enter a building to deactivate an alarm.

3.8.4 Recovery of Expenses (s.10)

This section of the Act applies in England and Wales only. Its effect is to add two additional sections (81A and 81B) to the *Environmental Protection Act 1990* enabling local authorities to recover expenses incurred in abating a nuisance by placing a charge on the property - see chapter 1, 1.16.1.

3.9 NOISE ACT 1996

This Act, covering England, Wales and Northern Ireland, was introduced into Parliament as a Private Members Bill in February 1996 and received the Royal Assent on 18 July 1996. It deals with noise nuisance - in particular night-time noise - from domestic premises. Sections 2-9 relating to the procedure for dealing with night-time noise nuisance are adoptive - i.e. the local authority must resolve to implement these sections for application in its area; alternatively, the Secretary of State may, by order, require a local authority to implement ss.2-9. Section 10 and the Schedule to the Act - confiscation of noise-making equipment - apply to all local authorities.

The Government gave an undertaking that it would review ss.2-9 (both their implementation in practice and the number of local authorities adopting them) within two years of these sections being brought into force (i.e. by 23 July 1999). A review team was established towards the end of 1999 and details of their findings are awaited.

Department of the Environment, Transport and the Regions Circular (Environment Circular 8/97, WO Circular 41/97) published July 1997, provides guidance for local authorities on how they should carry out their duties under the Act.

The *Civic Government (Scotland) Act 1982* provides the police in Scotland with powers to abate noise nuisance from, among other things, musical instruments and sound-producing devices; see this chapter 3.11.7.

3.9.1 Night-time Noise Nuisance (ss.2-9)

These sections of the Act were brought into force on 23 July 1997, and could be used from 23 October 1997.

A local authority wishing to adopt these sections of the Act must pass a resolution stating from when the offence is to apply in its area - this should not be less than three months from the date of the resolution. It must publish a notice in a local newspaper on two consecutive weeks ending at least two months before the commencement date. The notice should state that a resolution has been passed, give the commencement date and summarise the effect of the resolution. An order from the Secretary of State requiring implementation of these sections must also allow three months from the date of the order before they are brought into force.

Section 2(6) defines night as 11.00 pm to 7.00 am the following morning. Local authorities have a duty to take reasonable steps to investigate a complaint from an individual about noise being emitted from another dwelling during night hours. Section 2(7) enables a local authority to investigate a complaint about night-time noise from a dwelling outside its area, whether or not these sections of the Act apply in that area. Section 11 defines dwelling as any building or part of a building used or intended to be used as a dwelling, or any garden, yard, outhouse or other appurtenance belonging to or enjoyed with the dwelling.

If it is thought that the noise exceeds, or might exceed, the permitted level as measured within the complainant's dwelling then a warning notice may be served on the person appearing to be responsible for the noise. (Note - it is not a requirement of the Act that the noise should be measured; for instance, there may be circumstances when it is obvious that the noise exceeds the permitted level.)

It should be noted that there may be circumstances that while the noise does not exceed the night-time permitted level, the investigating officer considers that it does constitute a statutory nuisance under s.80 of the *Environmental Protection Act 1990;* in such cases an abatement notice must be served - see chapter 1, 1.16.1a.

If a warning notice is to be served, it should state (s.3(1)) that

- in the opinion of the local authority officer, noise is

being emitted during night hours and that the noise exceeds, or might exceed, the permitted level;

- any person responsible for the noise being emitted during the time specified in the notice (beginning 10 minutes after service of the notice until 7.00 am) may be guilty of an offence.

If it is not possible to identify the person responsible for the noise then the notice should be left at the offending dwelling. The notice should state the time at which it was served or left.

The "permitted level" of noise has been set by the Secretary of State in Directions made under s.5; this is 35 dB(A) where the background level does not exceed 25 dB(A) and 10 dB(A) above the background level where this exceeds 25 dB(A); the noise level should be measured over a period of not less than one minute and no more than five. Secretary of State Approval under s.6 of the Act for measuring devices and specifying the manner and purpose for which such devices are to be used came into force on 23 July 1997.

An offence is committed (s.4) if the noise, when measured from inside the complainant's dwelling, continues to exceed the permitted level during the time specified in the warning notice; if convicted the offender will become liable to a fine not exceeding level 3 on the standard scale (currently £1,000). However the local authority authorised officer may, if he thinks that an offence has or is being committed, issue a fixed penalty notice (s.8), set at £100; the offender has 14 days to pay the penalty and in which case will not be prosecuted further. If the noise continues after the fixed penalty notice has been issued, then the local authority officer can prosecute the offender.

3.9.2 Seizure of Noise-making Equipment (s.10)

This section and the schedule to the Act apply where a warning notice has been served and the noise continues to exceed the permitted level; it was brought into force on 23 July 1997. (Section 10(7) clarifies that the powers of a local authority to abate a noise nuisance under s.81(3) of the *Environmental Protection Act 1990* include being able to seize and remove the noise-making equipment; this was brought into force on 19 September 1996 - see chapter 1, 1.16.1a.)

A local authority officer, or other authorised officer, may enter the offending dwelling and seize and remove - confiscate - any equipment which it is thought is or has been used to emit noise. If entry is refused, likely to be refused, or request for admission to the dwelling would defeat the object of the entry, the local authority authorised officer may obtain a warrant from a justice of the peace authorising entrance (s.10(4)). The authorised officer may take with him such other people or equipment as is necessary (s.10(5)). Prosecution for obstructing confiscation may result in a maximum fine of £1,000.

The seized equipment may be retained for 28 days or, if court proceedings are instigated, until the case has been dealt with or discontinued. If no court proceedings are begun, then the equipment should be returned to any person who appears to be the owner, or who makes a claim for the equipment within six months of the expiry of the 28 day period. The local authority should take reasonable steps to advise a potential claimant of their right to do so. If no claim is made within six months the local authority may dispose of the equipment.

Equipment seized at the time that a fixed penalty notice has been served under s.8 of the Act may not be retained if the fixed penalty is paid within the allowed period (14 days).

The court may make a forfeiture order if it convicts someone of a noise offence and is satisfied that the seized equipment was actually used for that offence; such an order can be made as the sole means of punishment for the offence. An offender loses all right to the equipment forfeited.

Where equipment has been forfeited, a claimant (other than the offender) may apply to the court within six months of the date of the forfeiture order, if the court is satisfied that

- the claimant had not given the offender permission to use the equipment; or
- did not know, or had no reason to suspect, that the equipment would be used in committing an offence.

If the court is satisfied that the claimant is the owner of the forfeited equipment it will make an order requiring the local authority to deliver the equipment to that person. Local authorities also have a duty to take reasonable steps to bring to the attention of any person entitled to claim the forfeited equipment their right to do so. If the equipment has not been claimed on the expiry of six months from the date of the forfeiture order, the local authority may dispose of it.

Regulations will provide for the retention and safekeeping of any equipment seized and the charges which the local authority may recover. The local authority will be able to keep any equipment until all charges have been paid; a person claiming seized or forfeited equipment will not be liable for charges if the local authority is satisfied that the person did not know and had no reason to suspect that their equipment was likely to be used to commit an offence.

ENTERTAINMENT NOISE

3.10 INTRODUCTION

All public places for music and dancing etc require a licence from the local authority under the *Local Government (Miscellaneous) Provisions Act 1982*. In addition, private events which provide music or dancing or other entertainment and are held for profit or gain require a licence under the *Private Places of Entertainment*

(*Licensing*) Act 1967. In both instances, it is open to the local authority to impose noise limits as a condition of the licence. The nuisance provisions of the *Environmental Protection Act 1990* may also be used in respect of entertainment noise.

Responsibility for enforcement of licence conditions lies with local authorities; infringement, or absence, of a licence may result in a maximum fine of £20,000 and/or imprisonment under the *Entertainment (Increased Penalties) Act 1990* (this does not apply in N. Ireland). If convicted, the *Criminal Justices Act 1988 (Confiscation Orders) Order 1990* empowers Magistrates to confiscate proceeds of an event where these exceed £10,000.

It should, of course, be noted that most of the undermentioned legislation can of course be applied to other types of entertainment such as concerts (both classical and contemporary music).

The Criminal Justice and Public Order Act 1994 enables the police to confiscate sound equipment from illegal raves or gatherings where the music is "wholly or predominantly characterised by ... repetitive beats".

3.11 CONTROL OF NOISY PARTIES

Although complaints do arise from private parties, these can usually be dealt with under statutory nuisance legislation (see below and chapter 1, 1.16.1), the main problems arise from "pay parties". These are often large events with music and dancing, attracting anything between 100 and several thousand people and sometimes lasting several days. An entrance fee is normally charged, thus bringing them within the legislation mentioned above.

In its report to the Government in 1990 (The "Batho Report"), the Noise Review Working Party drew attention to the increasing number of noisy parties (particularly large-scale parties), and the difficulties facing local authorities in controlling them. In response to a recommendation from the Working Party, the Home Office and Department of Environment published in 1992 a *Joint Guidance Note on the Control of Noisy Parties*. This outlines the main powers available to local authorities in England and Wales for dealing with noisy parties and provides advice and guidance on how the legislation can be interpreted. The Guidance Note also outlines the role of the police and how they can help local authority officers in dealing with noisy parties.

3.11.1 Statutory Nuisance Legislation

Action for noise nuisance from both the smaller private parties and pay parties can be taken under Part III of the *Environmental Protection Act 1990*. Under s.80 of the EPA, an abatement notice can be served requiring abatement of the nuisance; the notice can be served on anyone involved with the organisation of the party, e.g. host, disc jockey, sound engineer; the notice can be addressed to the occupier of the premises or indeed simply affixed to the premises. An abatement notice can also be served in anticipation of a nuisance - in such cases the notice could prohibit the delivery of audio equipment to the party site or require its removal. Contravention of an abatement notice is an offence.

The EPA provides local authorities with powers under s.80(3) to take whatever action is necessary to abate a nuisance themselves. This might include confiscating the offending noise-making equipment, a power clarified under s.10(7) of the *Noise Act 1996* (see above, 3.9.2). Schedule 2 of the Act provides powers of entry to the premises, although where these are mainly or wholly used for residential purposes 24 hours' notice should be given or where entry is likely to be refused, a warrant obtained.

Section 43 of the *Powers of Criminal Courts Act 1973* also enables local authorities in England and Wales to seek a deprivation order from the court for the permanent confiscation of noise making equipment following a prosecution.

For further details regarding procedures under nuisance legislation, see chapter 1, 1.16.1.

3.11.2 Public Entertainment Licensing

Under the *Local Government (Miscellaneous Provisions) Act 1982* and the *London Government Act 1963*, local authorities have powers to license all places used for public music and dancing etc. The DOE/HO Guidance suggests that case law would indicate that the legislation would also apply to all parties where there is an admission charge and music and dancing. It should be noted that in London the legislation covers both indoor and outdoor events, but outside Greater London it applies to indoor events only.

Before applying the legislation to outdoor musical events held on private land, local authorities outside London must adopt the relevant provisions of the legislation. Outside London, local authorities, in granting a licence, may only attach conditions and other restrictions aimed at preventing unreasonable noise disturbance to people nearby, to ensure the safety of performers and those attending, to ensure access for emergency vehicles and to ensure adequate sanitation. Licences for events held indoors or outside in Greater London may include whatever conditions are considered reasonable in the circumstances.

Contravention of a licence, or absence of a licence, is an offence, the penalties for which are outlined above (3.10).

3.11.3 Private Parties for Gain

These include all "private" events for which an admission or other charge has been made and the event can be regarded as having been promoted for private gain. Such events are controlled by the *Private Places of Entertainment (Licensing) Act 1967* and contain similar powers for local authorities to those outlined in the section above. Before using these powers, it is necessary for local authorities to adopt the whole of the Act.

3.11.4 Private Parties Not for Gain

The main way of controlling these is through statutory nuisance legislation - Part III of the *Environmental Protection Act 1990* - see above and chapter 1, 1.16.1. The *Noise Act 1996* (England, Wales and Northern Ireland) sets a limit on the level of noise which can be made between 11.00 pm and 7.00 am from a dwelling; disobeying a warning notice is a criminal offence - see above 3.9.1.

3.11.5 High Court Injunctions

Section 222 of the *Local Government Act 1972* empowers a local authority to seek a High Court injunction to prevent a party from taking place where it is felt that this is the only way of stopping a potential nuisance and thus promoting or protecting the interests of local inhabitants. In seeking an injunction, the Court will need to be convinced that action under other legislation (e.g. nuisance legislation) will be ineffective.

Section 81(5) of the EPA enables a local authority to seek an injunction for abating a nuisance in those instances where it is felt that taking action for contravention of an abatement notice would be ineffective.

Contravention of the terms of an injunction may lead to imprisonment or an unlimited fine.

3.11.6 Codes of Practice

A code of practice on *Environmental Noise Control at Concerts* (Noise Council, 1994) provides guidance for those planning concerts, for licensing authorities and for local authorities enforcing nuisance legislation. It includes music noise levels for both indoor and outdoor events and single as well as multiple events.

3.11.7 Scotland

Section 54 of the *Civic Government (Scotland) Act 1982* empowers uniformed police officers to request that noise from, for example, sound-producing devices be reduced if it is giving any other person "reasonable cause for annoyance". If the request is ignored then the police may confiscate the offending equipment as evidence for any prosecution. This section of the Act also covers annoyance caused by singing, playing musical instruments, televisions, radios etc. Loudspeakers used by the emergency services are exempt.

The Licensing (Scotland) Act 1976 enables the Licensing Board to include conditions limiting noise.

INDUSTRIAL AND CONSTRUCTION SITE NOISE

3.12 INTRODUCTION

In 1997/98 there were 47,516 complaints about noise from industrial and commercial (including leisure) premises in England and Wales, and 8,232 complaints about noise

from demolition and construction works (CIEH Environmental Health Report 1997/98). In Scotland there were 3,634 complaints about noise from industrial and commercial premises in 1996/97 (1992/3: 2,515), and 885 complaints (1992/3: 401) about noise from roadworks etc (DETR *Digest of Environmental Statistics, No. 20, 1998*).

The use of the planning system in controlling noise has already been summarised - see this chapter 3.5.

3.13 REGULATORY CONTROLS

3.13.1 Control of Pollution Act 1974

Sections 60-61 cover noise from construction sites and enable local authorities to impose requirements, including noise limits on the way in which work is carried out. British Standard 5228, *Noise Control on Construction and Open Sites*, provides guidance to enable compliance with s.60 - see 3.7.1 above.

Under ss.63-67 of COPA a local authority may by order designate all or part of its area a noise abatement zone; premises classified under the order - usually industrial premises - may not exceed their registered noise level (details of which are kept in a public register) - see 3.7.3 above. It is a defence to prove that the best practicable means have been used to counteract the effects of noise caused in the course of trade or business from premises in a NAZ.

3.13.2 Environmental Protection Act 1990

Statutory Nuisance

Action against noise (including vibration) from industrial or trade premises may be taken using Part III of the EPA. It is a defence to prove that the best practicable means were used to prevent or counteract the effects of the nuisance. See chapter 1, 1.16.1.

Waste Management Licensing

The EU's Waste Framework Directive (see chapter 4, 4.6) requires waste disposal processes to be regulated to ensure that they do not cause noise nuisance; relevant conditions are included in waste management licences. This, however, does not preclude action under statutory nuisance legislation.

The Environment Agency is currently finalising Internal Guidance for the Regulation of Noise at Waste Management Facilities; this includes guidance on appropriate noise limits in relation to the location of the facility. Conditions will be included in waste management licences to ensure the adverse noise impacts of waste management activities – including noise from vehicle movements, equipment on site etc – are minimised. Where the site is close to a sensitive location (such as residential housing), it is suggested that noise from sites should be kept below 10 dB above background levels. At all sites, except landfills, the Agency proposes that operators should draw up noise action plans where noise levels exceed 5 dB above background; if levels exceed 10 dB above background, enforcement action will be considered. See also chapter 4, 4.19.3(k).

3.13.3 Integrated Pollution Prevention and Control Regulations

The *Pollution Prevention and Control (England and Wales) Regulations 2000* came into force on 1 August 2000, with similar Regulations for Scotland coming into force on 28 September 2000. They implement a 1996 EU Directive which includes noise and vibration among the pollutants which operators of processes covered by the Directive are required to control - see chapter 1, 1.12 and 1.13.1. The Directive defines pollution from noise and vibration as that "which may be harmful to human health or the quality of the environment, result in damage to material property or impair or interfere with amenities and other legitimate uses of the environment". The Best Available Techniques must be used to control noise sources.

ROAD TRAFFIC NOISE

3.14 INTRODUCTION

A 1991 survey by the Building Research Establishment showed that while a higher percentage of those who heard it objected to noise from neighbours, road traffic noise was heard by considerably more people. (*Digest of Environmental Protection and Water Statistics, No. 16,* DOE, 1994)

Road traffic noise has two main components: the mechanical noise associated with the engine and transmission system of the vehicle, and the "rolling noise" of the vehicle - this latter is due to factors such as the frictional contact between the tyres and the road and the aerodynamic noise caused by the passage of the vehicle through the air. The noise levels caused by traffic on a road are dependent on the number of vehicles using the road, their speed and the proportion of heavy vehicles. Heavy vehicles are of course much noisier than cars and hence have a greater influence on overall traffic noise levels.

Other factors affecting traffic noise levels are road surface and the immediate topography of the street. Rough road surfaces cause more noise than smooth ones; asphalt surfaces, and in particular porous asphalt, tend to generate less noise than other conventional surfaces; nearby high walls or buildings also reflect noise causing an increase in the overall level. Noise from smoothly flowing traffic is less than noise from an interrupted flow because changes in engine speed and the use of low gears, necessary at traffic lights, junctions and hills, produce more noise than a steady cruising speed.

3.15 REGULATORY CONTROLS

3.15.1 Motor Vehicles

Maximum noise limits from the engines and exhausts of motor vehicles when new and in use are set out in regulations made under the *Road Traffic Act 1972; the Road Vehicles (Construction & Use) Regulations 1986* (SI 1078) (and amendments), and the *Motor Vehicle (Type Approval) (Great Britain) Regulations. Type Approval Regulations* set requirements to meet noise limits in EU Directives. The latest Directive, 92/97/EEC, adopted in 1992 has reduced the limits set in a 1984 Directive (84/424/EEC) by between 2-5 dB(A) - see Table 3.1 below. The new limits applied to new model vehicles, cars, dual purpose vehicles and light goods vehicles with petrol engines from 1 October 1995 and to all new vehicles from 1 October 1996. Subject to the agreement of the European Commission, Member States were permitted to offer tax incentives until October 1996 for all vehicles meeting the new limits before the deadline. Directive 92/97/EEC has been implemented in the UK through amendments to the type approval and construction and use regulations which came into force on 1 October 1996 (see also chapter 2, 2.23.2). These regulations also implement Noise Directive 96/20/EC which makes certain changes to the method of noise level testing set out in the 1992 Directive.

The Commission is expected to make proposals for further reductions in noise emissions in the near future.

Table 3.1: Maximum Noise Limits for Road Vehicles

Vehicle	dB(A)
Goods vehicles over 3.5 tonnes	
- over 150 kW engine power	80
- 75-150 kW engine power	78
- below 75 kW engine power	77
Goods vehicles below 3.5 tonnes	
- goods vehicles 2-3.5 tonnes	77
goods vehicles below 2 tonnes	76
Buses	
- with over 9 seats, over 3.5 tonnes GVW and over 150 kW engine power	80
- with over 9 seats, over 3.5 tonnes GVW but below 150 kW engine power	78
Cars	74

The Road Vehicles (Construction and Use) Regulations 1986 also make it an offence to use a motor vehicle in such a way as to cause excessive noise; the Regulations do not cover off-road uses, such as motorcycle scrambling. Maximum permitted levels for vehicles in use on the road are generally 3 dB(A) higher than the construction noise limits specified in Regulations, because of differences in measurement. Higher limits apply to older vehicles. Similar Regulations apply in Northern Ireland.

In addition the Regulations specify that motor horns may not be sounded in a restricted road between 11.30 pm and 7.00 am and not at all when a vehicle is stationary unless there is danger to another moving vehicle. Private vehicles must not be fitted with a gong, bell, siren or two-tone horn. For vehicles first used on or after 1 August 1973, no other multi-tone horns are permitted.

Car alarms are also covered by the Regulations; all car alarms fitted to vehicles must have a five minute cut-out device; if the alarm continues to sound then the police may prosecute the vehicle's owner (reg.37(7) & (8)).

3.15.2 Motorcycles

The first Directive to limit motorcycle noise was adopted in 1978 (78/1015/EEC) and set optional limits of between 86 dB(A) for motorcycles over 500 cc and 78 dB(A) for those less than 80 cc; these limits were reduced in two stages by Directive 87/56/EEC to 80 dB(A) for motorcycles over 175 cc, 77 dB(A) for those between 80-175 cc and 75 dB(A) for those under 80 cc. The 1978 Directive and its amendment have been repealed following implementation of Directive 97/24 which was adopted in mid-1997. This Directive, which also covers 2 and 3 wheel mopeds and tricycles, had to be complied with by 18 December 1998 and the limits observed by 17 June 1999 - see Table 3.2.

Table 3.2: Motorcycle Noise Limits

Vehicle	dB(A)
Motorcycles	
- < 80 cc	75
- 80 - 175 cc	77
- > 175 cc	80
Tricycles	80
Two Wheel Mopeds	
- up to 25 km/h	66
- > 25 km/h	71
Three Wheel Mopeds	76

A 1989 Directive (89/235 EEC) laid down standards for replacement exhausts and silencers and prohibited the marketing and use of those that did not meet the required standards from October 1990. Implementation was optional. The Commission is however expected to bring forward proposals for a Directive which would make implementation obligatory and require all replacement exhausts to meet EU standards.

In the UK, the construction and use requirements of the Directives are implemented through the *Road Vehicles (Construction and Use) Regulations 1986* and subsequent amendments (see also chapter 2, 2.23.2). So far as noise from motorcycles is concerned, the Regulations require silencers to be maintained in good and efficient working order; the silencer should not be altered so as to increase the noise made by the escape of exhaust gases. A silencer which forms part of the exhaust system of a motorcycle first used on or after 1 January 1985 shall be either the original one, or one that meets the relevant British Standard (and is so marked), or is of a make and type

specified by the manufacturer. Older motorcycles (used after 1 April 1970) must be able to meet noise standards specified in the Regulations.

Regulations made under *the Motor Cycle Act 1987* (SI 2370), the *Motor Cycle Silencer Regulations 1995*, effective 1 August 1996, make it an offence to sell, supply, offer to supply, or have available for supply, exhaust systems and silencers that are not marked BS AU 193/T2, BS AU 193a: 1990/T2 or BS AU 193a: 1990/T3. The Regulations (which also apply to mopeds and scooters) do not apply to silencers and exhausts to be used by off-road motorcycles but must be clearly marked "Not for Road Use"; nor do they apply to motorcycles first used before 1 January 1985 and the silencer is marked "Pre 1985 MC only".

The Motorcycles (Sound Level Measurement Certificates) (Amendment) Regulations 1989 ensure that a certificate may only be issued when the relevant standards are met.

3.15.3 Other Controls

A number of other legislative measures are of importance for controlling and abating noise pollution from road traffic.

The Road Traffic Regulation Act 1984 gives local authorities powers to make a traffic regulation order for preserving or improving the amenities of an area through which a road runs.

Part I of the Land Compensation Act 1973 provides for compensation in cases where property values can be shown to have fallen as a direct result of increased noise levels (and other specific factors). Part II, enables householders to claim a grant from their local authority to provide noise insulation if:

a) their property is within 300 metres of a new road or substantially improved roads and they experience increased noise levels as a result; and

b) the noise level reaches or exceeds 68 dB(A) $L_{10(18\ hour)}$ with at least 1 dB(A) resulting from the increase in traffic.

The Noise Insulation Regulations 1975 (and amendments - the latest dated 1988). These are made under Part II of the *Land Compensation Act 1973* and apply in England and Wales. They provide for grants to cover the costs of insulation. Grants are available for secondary glazing of eligible rooms of dwellings where it is estimated that maximum noise levels during the 15 years after the road opening will be at least 68 dB(a) $L_{10(18\ hour)}$, with a contribution of at least 1 dB(A) from traffic using the new road. However grants are not available to householders affected by increased traffic along existing roads resulting from re-routing or traffic management schemes, or from a general increase in traffic flow.

Similar legislation - the *Land Compensation (Scotland) Act 1973* and Regulations made under it, the *Noise Insulation (Scotland) Regulations 1985* - applies in Scotland.

AIRCRAFT NOISE
3.16 INTRODUCTION

In common with other forms of transport, air travel has an environmental impact, and is increasing rapidly. In the UK we have two of the world's busiest international airports: in 1995 there were over 420,000 take-offs and landings at Heathrow and 193,000 at Gatwick; over 55 million people used Heathrow in 1996 and 24 million used Gatwick (*Digest of Environmental Statistics*, No. 20, 1998).

The most obvious environmental threat from aircraft is noise - ranging from the regular rumble of large jets to the buzz of microlights and other light aircraft. A 1991 survey by the Building Research Establishment found that the number of people reporting hearing aircraft noise was second only to those hearing noise from road traffic, with 76% of those hearing noise from aircraft being disturbed by the noise periodically (*Digest of Environmental Protection and Water Statistics*, No. 16, DOE, 1994). In 1996/97, local authorities in England and Wales received 1,956 complaints about aircraft noise (CIEH Environmental Health Report, 1996/97). The impact of emissions to atmosphere from aircraft is briefly summarised in chapter 2, 2.25.

The noise generated by an aircraft is related to air velocity. Thus any fast moving components - propellers, compressor blades - as well as jet exhaust gases, will be efficient generators of noise.

Aircraft noise comprises a broadband background noise with the periodic components of rotating machinery noise superimposed on it. In newer aircraft with high by-pass ratio turbo-fan engines, these components operate at much lower speeds and are significantly quieter as a result.

Different aircraft produce different noise problems; for instance, jets produce more periodic component noise on landing than on take-off, when the broadband exhaust noise predominates; noise from the hull on landing tends to predominate in quiet-engined aircraft.

Jets currently in service are Chapter 2 and Chapter 3 aircraft - the term comes from the relevant annex of the Chicago Convention of 1944 – with Chapter 3 aircraft being the less noisy. Chapter 2 aircraft include the BAe 1-11, DC9 and Boeing 737-200. Chapter 3 aircraft include the Boeing 747, 757 and 767, DC10 and airbus. (Chapter 1 aircraft which are, on the whole, no longer in use include the DC8 and VC10.)

Noise standards are drawn up by the International Civil Aviation Organisation (ICAO) - a UN body - and by the European Civil Aviation Conference, whose members are drawn from throughout Europe, including the European Community. Their standards are then incorporated into European and national legislation. ICAO is also responsible for developing operating procedures, for example to minimise take-off and landing noise. It also carries out research and is currently looking at air quality around airports and emissions at high altitude.

3.17 THE EUROPEAN UNION AND AIRCRAFT NOISE

The European Union's first Directive on aeroplane noise (80/51/EEC) prevented the addition of any further non-noise certificated aeroplanes (i.e. Chapter 1 aircraft) to the civil registers of Member States, and required the removal of any such aeroplanes by 31 December 1986. A small number of exemptions enabled some of these aeroplanes to continue flying until 31 December 1988. An amendment to this Directive (83/206/EEC) prevented non-noise certificated aircraft registered outside the EU from landing within it from 1 January 1988 (with some exemptions until 31 December 1989). A 1989 Directive (89/629/EEC) limited noise from subsonic aircraft and permitted only Chapter 3 aircraft able to meet the tighter limits to be added to Registers. A further Directive (92/14/EEC) limiting aircraft noise was agreed in March 1992, and amendments, 98/20/EC and 1999/28/EC, adopted in March 1998 and April 1999 respectively. These ban all aircraft unable to meet Chapter 3 standards or Chapter 2 standards and are less than 25 years old, from operating into the EU after 1 April 1995; from 1 April 2002, all Chapter 2 aircraft will be banned. Various exemptions to the Directive cover such matters as extensions to an aircraft's life and aircraft from developing countries. This Directive is in line with a timetable agreed by the European Civil Aviation Conference in June 1991.

All the above Directives have been implemented through *The Aeroplane Noise Regulations 1999* (SI 1452) which came into force on 27 May 1999 and 1999 Amendment Regulations (SI 2253) which came into force on 16 August 1999.

EU Regulation 925/99, adopted in April 1999, bans the addition to Member States' registers from May 2000 of aircraft meeting the Chapter 3 standards through the use of "hushkits"; those fitted with hushkits and on registers prior to this date are allowed to continue operating until 1 April 2002; at that date all such aircraft, including those registered outside the EU will be banned from taking off or landing within the EU, unless they began operating in the EU after 1 April 1995. The implementation of this Regulation is, however, the subject of dispute between the EU member states and the USA which considers the Regulation discriminatory as it has a considerable number of aircraft fitted with hushkits.

3.18 REGULATORY CONTROLS

The Department of the Environment, Transport and the Regions (DETR) is responsible for policy on the control of aircraft noise. Section 78 of the *Civil Aviation Act 1982* gives the Secretary of State wide powers to enforce noise standards on aircraft, apply operational controls and restrictions and give directions to owners of designated airports in relation to operational requirements and noise insulation grant schemes. The policy is concerned with containing and effectively reducing aircraft noise by restrictions on aircraft movements, control of flight paths and use of certain operational procedures.

3.18.1 Civil Aviation Act 1982

While powers to control environmental noise are contained in Part III of the *Environmental Protection Act 1990,* s.79(6) specifically excludes noise from aircraft (other than model aircraft) from these controls which are designed to deal with noise from fixed rather than moving sources.

The principal legislation covering aircraft operations is the *Civil Aviation Act 1982.* This contains three main powers aimed at aircraft noise control at particular airports. Section 76 does, however, exclude the properly controlled flight of aircraft from action in respect of trespass or nuisance provided that rules and regulations such as the *Rules of the Air and Air Traffic Control Regulations* have been observed.

In July 2000, the DETR issued proposals, covering England, Scotland and Wales, for amending the *Civil Aviation Act*; these are summarised in the text below. It is also proposed to introduce two new powers:

- *non-designated (see s.78 below) aerodromes, possibly subject to a threshold defined by annual aircraft movements, to establish and enforce noise control arrangements, including noise amelioration schemes* – controls could include specifying "noise preferential routes" within the vicinity of the airport; specifying take-off and landing procedures; restrictions on periods within which all or certain aircraft can land or take off. It is also proposed that noise amelioration schemes (NASs) be treated as agreements between aerodromes and airport users, with aerodromes being given powers to impose sanctions for infringements of NASs and other noise control arrangements. Sanctions could include fines or suspending an operator.

- *the Secretary of State to be given power to designate aerodromes (not already designated for s.78) and thus give him power to direct an aerodrome to prepare a noise amelioration scheme* – this would cover matters such as landing and take off procedures, directions to pilots, while of course ensuring that safety was not compromised. The aerodrome would have to consult locally, including all those local authorities affected by its activities and the lead planning authority. The aerodrome will also have to consult and agree the NAS with the local authority named in the designating order. Where an aerodrome has been required to draw up a NAS, local authorities will be given power to compel the aerodrome to implement it; consideration is being given to extending this power to cover NASs drawn up voluntarily by non-designated aerodromes. It is proposed that disputes about a NAS be resolved through independent arbitration. The consultation document proposes that NASs be reviewed every 5-7 years, with the aerodrome and designated local authority reconfirming their agreement with the NAS and any amendments to it.

Implementation of the above proposals, and those outlined in the text below, will await time being made available in the parliamentary timetable.

Environmental Considerations (ss.5 & 6)

In licensing or relicensing an aerodrome, the Civil Aviation Authority is primarily concerned with safety issues, although under s.5 the Secretary of State can require it to take account of environmental issues, such as noise and atmospheric pollution. It is now proposed that this section be repealed as noise is to be dealt with under the new powers outlined above.

Section 6 enables the Secretary of State to give directions to the CAA on a number of issues, including taking action to prevent or deal with noise, vibration, pollution or other disturbance attributable to aircraft used for civil aviation.

Requirement to provide Consultation Facilities (s.35)

Where the Secretary of State designates an airport under this power, the airport management is required to establish suitable consultation facilities with users, nearby local authorities, and local representative organisations. Forty-seven airports have been designated under s.35, covering all the national and regional airports and some of the general aviation airfields. The DETR consultation paper asks for views as to whether the current consultation arrangements are satisfactory or whether there is a need to provide for a dispute resolution procedure.

Direct Responsibility for Designated Airports (ss.78 & 79)

Section 80 enables the Secretary of State to designate an aerodrome for the purposes of ss. 78 and 79. Heathrow, Gatwick and Stansted are designated for both sections.

The Secretary of State is directly responsible for noise abatement measures for aircraft landing and taking off (including during the night) at airports designated for the purposes of s.78; he can by notice require aircraft operators to adopt procedures limiting noise and vibration. In so doing, restrictions can be placed on the numbers or types of particular aircraft using the airport at specified times (see below for current restrictions on day and night time use).

Section 79 enables the Secretary of State to make noise insulation grant schemes for airports designated for the purposes of s.79.

It is proposed to expand and clarify s.78 to enable the Secretary of State to

- place constraints on how often aircraft (or a particular type of aircraft) can take off or land in any 24 hour period or between specified periods (e.g. through use of noise quota);
- subject to safety considerations, to direct that a particular runway be used for take-offs and/or landings;
- stipulate the range of fines to be levied by the courts, or explicitly enable the designated aerodromes to levy surcharges for aircraft operators violating a s.78 notice.

Daytime Noise Limits

Daytime noise limits were first introduced at Heathrow in 1959, at Gatwick in 1968 and at Stansted in 1993, and cover the period 0700-2300. The current limit is 97 dB(A). The airport companies are responsible for monitoring compliance with noise limits with breaches of the limit subject to financial penalty - currently £500 if the limit is exceeded by 3dB(A) or less, £1,000 if it is exceeded by more than 3dB(A).

The Government is now proposing (DETR, February 1998) to reduce the daytime noise limit to be complied with by all aircraft, except Concorde, to 94 dB(A). Aircraft exempted under the provisions of the EU Directive 92/14 until 31 March 2002 (e.g. on grounds of economic hardship or those registered in developing countries) will also be exempt from the new daytime limit.

Night-time Noise Limits and Flight Restrictions

Night flights have been restricted at Heathrow since 1962, at Gatwick since 1971 and at Stansted since 1978, and cover the period 2300-0700. Revised restrictions covering the period until the end of the summer season 2004 came into effect on 31 October 1999 and are set out in the document *Night Restrictions at Heathrow, Gatwick and Stansted: Revised restrictions with effect from 31 October 1999.*

The current limit is 89 dB(A). In addition, the noisiest aircraft (i.e. those with a QC of 8 or 16 - see below) may not, except in limited circumstances, be scheduled to take-off during the night-time period; arrivals during this period will count against the noise quota. The airport companies are responsible for monitoring compliance, with the same financial penalties applying as for daytime exceedances of the limit.

Further restrictions, in the form of quotas covering the period 2330-0600 have also been in force since October 1993. Aircraft are categorised into three bands - NN/A, NN/B and NN/C - with NN/A representing the noisiest aircraft which are not normally allowed to operate between 2330 and 0600. Each airport is allocated a total number of flight movements covering the B and C bands which should not be exceeded. A night noise limit of 89 dB(A) applies and any exceedance results in a reduction in the airport's quota.

In addition, all aircraft have been assigned a quota count (QC) of units for both take off and landing and each of the airports allocated an annual number of quota points for night (i.e. between 2330 and 0600) movements which should not be exceeded - the noisier the aircraft, the more points are deducted from the airport's allocation. Quota Counts range from 0.5 for aircraft with a certificated noise performance of less than 90 EPNdB (79 dB(A)) to QC 8 for those between 99-101 EPNdB (88 dB(A) or more) and QC 16 for those above 101.9 EPNdB. From the summer season 2002, aircraft classified as QC 4 are to be banned from take-off or landing during the period 2330-0600 (QC 8 and QC 16 aircraft are already banned). Certain jet aircraft and propeller aircraft with a certificated noise performance under 87 EPNdB are exempt from quota restrictions.

The quota are divided between summer and winter seasons, with airports allowed to carry forward up to 10% of the quota to the next season or to use 10% of the next season's quota to deal with any overrun. Any exceedance of the quota over 10% results in a loss of quota double the exceedance.

3.18.2 Rules of the Air and Air Traffic Control Regulations

These cover general rules as to flight: usually, aircraft or helicopters may not fly over any congested area of a town or settlement below the height of 1,500 feet above the highest fixed object and within 2,000 feet of it, or at such height as would not permit the aircraft to glide clear of the area in the event of a failure of a power unit. Landing and take-off routes are prescribed by air traffic control procedures and these usually include a requirement as to the rate of height gain or loss and turning on track with the intention of minimising noise over built up areas. Aircraft are prohibited from flying within 500 feet of persons, vessels, vehicles or structures. The Regulations, which include Northern Ireland, are enforced by the Civil Aviation Authority.

International airports often have formal "minimum noise" routes, which are to be observed as far as possible.

3.18.3 Noise Certification

Relevant standards, drawn up by the International Civil Aviation Organisation, are enacted in the UK, and domestic regulations tightened as the ICAO standards are revised. *Air Navigation (Noise Certification) Orders* prohibit non-certificated aircraft from taking off or landing in the UK and implement the latest international recommendations in respect of the control of aircraft noise at source.

Noise standards have also been introduced for light propeller driven aircraft, helicopters and microlights; in 1984 the British Microlight Association drew up a voluntary code of practice which gives advice on minimising the noise impact of microlights.

3.18.4 Helicopters

While the provisions of the *Civil Aviation Act 1982* apply to helicopters, their ability to land almost anywhere can be a particular source of noise nuisance in residential areas; currently very little can be done to alleviate the problem, except by use of planning controls (see below, 3.18.6).

3.18.5 Military Aircraft

In most cases legal liability in respect of nuisance by military aircraft is excluded by statute. Military airfields usually have their own schemes to limit disturbance, including sound insulation and compensation schemes.

3.18.6 Planning Controls

New airport developments are subject to planning permission under the *Town and Country Planning Act 1990*. However, airports which have established use operate without planning controls and increasing use does not require planning permission. Permanent helicopter landing sites require planning permission, although temporary use of land for up to 28 days per year is permitted under the General Development Order 1988. In this instance, there is no limit to the number of take-offs and landings in one day.

Private Aerodromes

Where private aerodromes are established by individuals and companies, normal planning procedures will apply except on those vested in or controlled by the British Airports Authority. Planning permission may include conditions to secure the abatement of noise and local authority bye-laws may also be used to restrict operations so as to limit or mitigate the effect of noise. The operating authority of the aerodrome may also make such bye-laws.

Compensation is payable in certain circumstances where there is a new runway or if there have been major changes to an existing runway/other features at the airport. Compensation will be paid where the value of an interest in land is depreciated by more than £50 as a result of noise and other physical factors. Compensation will only be payable where the authority responsible for the public works involved can claim statutory immunity from an action for nuisance in respect of the work.

3.18.7 Supersonic Aircraft

There are no noise regulations covering the operation of supersonic aircraft, such as Concorde, characterised by their sonic boom. Briefly, the sonic boom is a shock wave system produced by an aircraft flying at a speed faster than the local speed of sound. At a certain point the shock wave causes a sudden rise in atmospheric pressure followed by a gradual fall to below normal pressure before a sudden rise back to normal. The double sound of the sonic boom occurs when these pressure fluctuations occur at more than about 100 milliseconds apart. An aircraft in supersonic flight can trail a sonic boom audible over more than 50 km on either side of its ground track depending upon altitude and size of aircraft. Apart from Concorde, all supersonic aircraft in this country are military.

3.19 MONITORING AIRCRAFT NOISE

Since September 1990 the Department of Transport (now DETR) has used "equivalent continuous sound level" (L_{Aeq}) to measure the extent and intensity of noise disturbance around airports for the daytime period (0700-2300). This can be defined as the sound level of a steady sound having the same energy as a fluctuating sound over a specified measuring period (Batho Report, 1990).

RAIL NOISE

3.20 NOISE INSULATION

The introduction of high speed trains has created special noise patterns, especially when trains cross bridges or other structures which amplify the noise. Development of the high speed rail link from London to the Channel Tunnel is causing particular concern in South East England.

Under the *Noise Insulation (Railways and Other Guided Transport Systems) Regulations 1996* (SI 428), an authority constructing a new railway (or other guided transport system) or additional track has a duty to provide insulation or a grant towards the cost of insulation for homes affected by the noise. Only residential buildings within 300 metres of the works for the new, altered or extended system are eligible for grant or insulation. The Regulations also include discretionary powers to provide grants for homes affected by altered lines or the noise of construction work. The level at which insulation should be provided or a grant paid towards its cost is 68 dB $L_{Aeq\ 18h}$ during the day (0600-midnight) and 63 dB $L_{Aeq\ 6h}$ at night (midnight-0600). 1998 Amendment Regulations (SI 1701) amend the 1996 Regulations to include procedures for predicting noise from Eurostar trains. Noise levels should be calculated using Calculation of Railway Noise 1995 (as amended, and available from The Stationery Office), and based on expected normal traffic flows within a 15 year period.

OCCUPATIONAL NOISE

It is estimated that about one million people in the UK are working in conditions that may damage their hearing unless precautions are taken. People typically at risk are shipbuilders and steel workers using pneumatic hammers; workers engaged in riveting or drop forging; workers in canning and bottling plants; and those who operate wood-working machinery.

3.21 HEALTH AND SAFETY AT WORK ETC ACT 1974

Occupational noise is controlled under statute by the *Health and Safety at Work Act 1974*. Part I provides a comprehensive and integrated system of law to deal with the health, safety and welfare of persons at work and the health and safety of the public as they may be affected by work activities, including protection from occupational noise exposure.

3.21.1 Noise at Work Regulations 1989 (SI 1790)

In 1986 the European Union adopted a Directive on the protection of workers from the risks related to exposure to noise at work (86/188/EEC) which had to be implemented in 1990. This has been done through the above Regulations which came into effect on 1 January 1990. The Regulations apply to all workers in Great Britain covered by the HSW Act, except the crews of sea-going ships and aircraft or hovercraft moving under their own power. Enforcement of the Regulations is mainly the responsibility of the Health and Safety Executive, and of local authorities. Similar 1990 Regulations apply in Northern Ireland; they are enforced by district councils, the Department for Economic Development and the Department of Agriculture for Northern Ireland.

The Regulations impose a duty on employers to assess and, where necessary, measure noise levels to identify workers to which its specific provisions apply. Three action levels are defined:

- *First Action Level* - a daily personal noise exposure (LEP,d) of 85 dB(A);
- *Second Action Level* - a daily personal noise exposure (LEP,d) of 90 dB(A);
- *Peak Action Level* - a peak sound pressure of 200 pascals (140 dB re 20 uPa).

LEP,d should be regarded as total exposure to noise throughout the day, taking account of the average noise level in the working area and the time spent in it, but not taking account of any reduction through the use of ear protectors. Peak pressure is the highest pressure reached by the sound wave.

Noise exposures are generally to be reduced to the lowest level reasonably practicable, taking account of technical progress and the availability of measures to control the noise, in particular at source.

Where average daily personal noise exposures reach or exceed 85 dB(A), personal ear protectors are to be made available to those employees who ask for them. At average daily personal noise exposures of 90 dB(A) and above, or where the peak sound pressure level exceeds 200 pascals, employers must ensure that personal ear protectors are used. At these levels the employee has a duty to use ear protectors; at all action levels the employee must use any other protective equipment supplied and report any defects to the employer. Areas where noise exposures exceed these levels must be marked with signs, and access to them restricted.

The Regulations require a noise assessment to be carried out where it is likely that employees will be exposed to noise at or above the First or Peak Action Level. The assessment must identify all employees likely to be exposed to the noise levels and provide sufficient information to enable appropriate action to be taken; employers must implement technical or organisational measures to reduce exposures as far as reasonably practicable. Assessments must be reviewed if significant changes are made to either the equipment or nature of the work. Records of assessments or noise measurements must be kept and employees given access to them.

The Regulations also place a duty on manufacturers, designers, importers and suppliers to supply adequate noise data with all new articles, such as tools and machinery, whenever their normal use at work is likely to result in daily noise exposures of 85 dB(A) or above.

The HSE has published detailed Guidance Notes for employers on implementation of the Regulations. The Guidance Notes also contain advice on the provision of information to employees covering health and safety, maintenance of ear protectors and provision of training and instruction programmes for employees in order to minimise the risk of damage to hearing.

People may qualify for industrial injuries benefit on the grounds of deafness, but since it is very difficult to decide whether deafness was incurred at work or elsewhere, the definition of what is accepted as occupational deafness is extremely restricted.

The 1986 Directive did not cover workers in either the air or maritime transport industries; in late 1992 the Commission published a draft Directive on Physical Agents at Work which, as well as extending protection to these sectors, introduces further requirements for monitoring workers' exposure to noise hazards; it requires information and training for workers, medical screening and measures to ensure that equipment and practices do not expose workers to excessive risks. Following adoption, this Directive will replace the 1986 Directive. (The Directive also covers protection from mechanical vibration, electromagnetic fields and optical radiation.)

LOW FREQUENCY NOISE
3.22 A BRIEF OVERVIEW

A low frequency noise is very often characterised by a hum or rumble and may be confused with tinnitus. These sounds often have no obvious source though in some areas a number of people may complain about the same unidentified "noise". While many of these noises remain unidentified, sources of LFN can include ventilation and air conditioning systems in large buildings; domestic boilers; diesel powered transport, such as ships, locomotives and lorries; and even the vibration of high rise buildings in the wind. These can cause complaints for two reasons:

a) primary noise (low frequency or infrasonic) radiated from source and entering houses either through their structure or through open windows;

b) secondary noise, e.g. rattling windows and doors. This either causes disturbance in itself or wakes people up, whereupon they become conscious of the low frequency pulsation.

Although there is no convenient measurement unit to describe it, low frequency sound may be defined as having a frequency below 150 Hz. Low frequency sound has a long wavelength which radiates in a spherical manner, rather like the ripples caused by a stone being dropped into a pond. In this way it can cover a vast area.

It can be particularly difficult to track down the source of LFN and assess its magnitude - ordinary sound level meters may not be able to detect it on the decibel scale as its decibel level is often lower than background noise. Practical methods of control are technically difficult and often prohibitive in cost. Sound proofing in buildings is usually impracticable as the design - particularly of modern buildings - may enhance the effect. Enclosing the noise source is a better option and will provide a more comprehensive solution. This too is often difficult and expensive as it involves enclosing the source in a combination of massive structures to reduce sound transmission. LFN from machinery can sometimes be reduced by the use of vibration absorbing mountings.

In order to apply controls in a scientific manner, a standard measurement unit has to be established which describes the noise in a single number (such as is given by the A weighting curve when defining higher frequency noise.) The International Standards Organisation is studying a curve which approximates to the hearing threshold (the f weighting) and falls off by 12 dB per octave towards the low frequencies. However, as this curve tolerates very high sound pressures between 2 Hz and 4 Hz, it is also proposed to introduce another curve (N) which falls off at 6 dB per octave. Once these curves and their tolerances have been defined by the ISO each country will be free to prescribe its own limits for low frequency sound.

EFFECTS OF NOISE

3.23 WHO GUIDELINES

Noise can cause annoyance, interfere with communication and sleep, cause fatigue, reduce efficiency and damage hearing. The World Health Organisation has recently (2000) recommended a guideline level of 30 dB LA_{eq} for undisturbed sleep; it recommends that to prevent people from becoming "moderately annoyed" during the daytime outdoor sound levels should not exceed 50 dB LA_{eq}. (*Guidelines for Community Noise*, WHO, 2000)

Physiological effects of exposure to noise include constriction of blood vessels, tightening of muscles, increased heart rate and blood pressure and changes in stomach and abdomen movement. Although hearing sensitivity varies and the effects of exposure are therefore personal, exposure to constant or very loud noise – either occupational or leisure-associated - can cause temporary or permanent damage to hearing.

So far as low frequency noise is concerned, it is not clear at what level it may be physically damaging; however, the unpleasant symptoms it can induce are sufficient to cause disruption and significant social and economic penalties to sufferers.

MEASUREMENT OF NOISE

3.24 DEFINITIONS

The simple definition of noise as "sound which is undesired by the recipient" (Wilson Committee on the Problem of Noise, Cmnd 2056, 1963) requires that three conditions obtain - there must be a sound source, a transmission path, and a receiver who would have some adverse subjective reaction to the sound. It is this area of subjectivity which creates the major difficulty in the measurement and assessment of noise sources. There is no (nor is it likely there ever will be) equipment available which can measure "noise", but there are a wide range of instruments which measure sound levels and there are more sophisticated derivatives capable of carrying out statistical evaluations of total noise climates. Thus it is relatively easy, given suitable equipment, to measure sound but it is much more difficult to allow for the subjective reaction to noise, which varies widely within an exposed population.

3.24.1 The Decibel

The logarithmic scale on which sound levels are measured is called the decibel (dB). The fundamental unit is the Bel and this is the logarithm of the ratio of the intensity of the given sound and the reference level; 1 Bel equals 10 dB or a factor of 10 in intensity - a change of 10 dB roughly corresponds to a doubling or halving of the loudness of a sound, i.e. a sound of 80 dB sounds about twice as loud as one of 70 dB. 0 dB is the threshold of hearing and 140 dB the threshold of pain.

3.24.2 Effective Perceived Noise Level

EPNdB and PNdB are used to measure aircraft noise with 3 EPNdB representing a doubling of noise energy. The quietest aircraft currently generate less than 90 EPNdB (about 75 dB(A)). It includes corrections for the duration and tonal quality of aircraft noise which are dependent on the rotational frequency of propellers or fans. The measure is used internationally for noise certification of aircraft.

3.24.3 Frequency

Another physical parameter which it is often necessary to measure is the frequency of the sound. The ear has a nominal range of between 20 hertz (Hz) (formerly called cycles per second) and 20 kHz (20,000 Hz), although at very high levels sound outside this range may be sensed. This sensitivity obtains only for the young, healthy, adult ear; as one gets older, the upper limit is reduced progressively perhaps to around 10 kHz. Because the ear does not respond equally to sound of different frequencies, being most sensitive around the 1,000 Hz region and least sensitive at very low frequencies, a measurement of sound without a frequency "weighting" would not indicate the likely response which the auditory mechanism might have to that sound.

In order that a sound level meter may approximate the response of the human ear, certain standardised filter networks are built into instruments and the most commonly utilised network is termed the "A" weighting. Measurements made when this circuit is switched on are referred to as dB(A) - decibels on the A weighted scale. Other weightings are occasionally used, of which the most important is the "D" network used for certain (approximate) aircraft noise measurements.

Waste - General

The EU and Waste Management

Waste Management - Regulatory Controls

Control of Special Waste

Producer Responsibility

Contaminated Land

Litter

Radioactive Waste

WASTE - GENERAL

The need to protect the environment for current and future generations - i.e. to ensure that development is sustainable (see chapter 1, 1.3) - also impinges on the way in which waste is managed. A considerable amount of "waste" can in fact be recovered, re-used or recycled, thus reducing the amount of non-renewable resources needed for making the products - and their packaging - that have become an essential part of most people's lives. Poorly managed waste and waste disposal sites can adversely affect the environment by contaminating the air, soil or water; they can also pose a danger to human health.

Section 44A of the *Environmental Protection Act 1990* (s.92 of the *Environment Act 1995*) requires the Secretary of State to prepare a National Waste Strategy for England and Wales, and details the matters to be dealt with in the Strategy. Following extensive consultation, the *Waste Strategy 2000* (covering England and Wales) was published in May 2000. As well as emphasising the importance of reducing the amount of waste produced and of recycling, the waste that is produced, must be dealt with in a manner which causes minimum harm to the environment. Similar obligations to prepare a National Waste Strategy are placed on SEPA by s.44B of the EPA (Scotland's waste strategy was published in December 1999) and on the Department of the Environment (NI) by Article 19 of the *Waste and Contaminated Land (Northern Ireland) Order 1997;* for more details, see later this chapter 4.19.4.

The term "waste" is used to cover anything from the contents of the household dustbin to high level radioactive waste and clinical and other hazardous waste from hospitals, factories and other industrial premises.

This chapter covers legislation relating to the disposal of controlled and special waste from industry, commerce and households, the disposal of radioactive waste, as well as legislation on contaminated land and litter. The disposal of ship-generated waste is summarised in chapter 5, 5.27.

4.1 EARLY CONTROLS

Until 1972, when public concern about the dumping of toxic waste in the Midlands resulted in the *Deposit of Poisonous Wastes Act*, there had been no specific legislation in the UK dealing with the management of wastes on land, although local authorities had for many years had powers to control waste in the interests of public health. The *Deposit of Poisonous Wastes Act 1972* had made it an offence to deposit on land any poisonous, noxious or polluting waste in a manner likely to create an environmental hazard. The Act also required that the waste disposal authority or water authority be given prior notification of the composition, quantity and destination of the waste. The Act was repealed in 1981 and replaced by the *Control of Pollution (Special Waste) Regulations*

1980 made under s.17 of the *Control of Pollution Act 1974.* These Regulations were themselves revoked in September 1996 following implementation of the *Special Waste Regulations 1996* on 1 September 1996 (see this chapter 4.19.6).

The *Public Health Act 1936* had given local authorities powers to remove house and trade refuse and to require removal of any accumulation of noxious matter. It also placed a duty on them to inspect their areas "for accumulation or deposit which is prejudicial to health or a nuisance", with powers to serve abatement notices and to prosecute offenders. The *Town and Country Planning Act 1947* included a requirement for waste disposal sites to have planning permission. Part I of the *Control of Pollution Act 1974,* which was the principal legislation governing the collection and disposal of waste, has now been replaced by Part II of the *Environmental Protection Act 1990.* The main objective of this part of COPA was to ensure that licensed activities did not cause pollution of water, danger to public health or detriment to local amenities.

4.2 DEFINITIONS OF WASTE

4.2.1 Controlled Waste Regulations 1992 (SI 588)

Section 75 of the *Environmental Protection Act 1990* (EPA) and the *Controlled Waste Regulations 1992* defined waste as including

a) any substance which constitutes a scrap material or an effluent or other unwanted surplus substance arising from the application of any process; and

b) any substance or article which requires to be disposed of as being broken, worn out, contaminated or otherwise spoiled.

However, following implementation of the 1991 European Union (EU) Framework Directive on waste (91/156/EEC), s.75 of the EPA is to be amended by the *Environment Act 1995* (Sch. 22, para 88) to reflect the new definition:

"Waste means any substance or object in the categories set out in Schedule 2B to this Act [i.e. EPA] which the holder discards or intends or is required to discard;..."

Schedule 2B to the EPA (*Env. Act 1995,* Sch. 22, para 95) reproduces Annex I to the 1991 Directive - see Table 4.1. "Holder" is defined as the producer of the waste or the person who is in possession of it; and the "producer" is anyone whose activities produce waste or anyone who carries out pre-processing, mixing or other operations resulting in a change in the nature or composition of this waste.

Table 4.1: EU Framework Directive on Waste: Substances or Objects which are Waste when Discarded etc.

Annex I to Directive 91/156; Schedule 2B to *Environmental Protection Act 1990*

1. Production or consumption residues not otherwise specified below.

2. Off-specification products.

3. Products whose date for appropriate use has expired.

4. Materials spilled, lost or having undergone other mishap, including any materials, equipment, etc, contaminated as a result of the mishap.

5. Materials contaminated or soiled as a result of planned actions (e.g. residues from cleaning operations, packing materials, containers, etc).

6. Unusable parts (e.g. reject batteries, exhausted catalysts, etc).

7. Substances which no longer perform satisfactorily (e.g. contaminated acids, contaminated solvents, exhausted tempering salts, etc).

8. Residues of industrial processes (e.g. slags, still bottoms, etc).

9. Residues from pollution abatement processes (e.g. scrubber sludges, baghouse dusts, spent filters, etc).

10. Machining or finishing residues (e.g. lathe turnings, mill scales, etc).

11. Residues from raw materials extraction and processing (e.g. mining residues, oil field slops, etc).

12. Adulterated materials (e.g. oils contaminated with PCBs etc).

13. Any materials, substances or products whose use has been banned by law.

14. Products for which the holder has no further use (e.g. agricultural, household, office, commercial and shop discards, etc).

15. Contaminated materials, substances or products resulting from remedial action with respect to land.

16. Any materials, substances or products which are not contained in the above categories.

Department of the Environment (now Department of the Environment, Transport & the Regions) Guidance (Circular 11/94, SOED 10/94, WO 26/94) suggests the following be used as a starting point in deciding whether or not something is waste:

a) [has it been] discarded, disposed of or got rid of by the holder; or

b) [is it] intended to be discarded, disposed of or got rid of by the holder; or

c) [is it] required to be discarded, disposed of or got rid of by the holder.

A further consideration is whether "the substance or object [has] been discarded so that it is no longer part of the normal commercial cycle or chain of utility". Thus some items although eventually recycled will be treated as waste (discarded) because they need to be reprocessed before they can be brought back into re-use.

Waste subject to the provisions of COPA and the EPA is known as "controlled waste" and includes wastes arising from domestic, industrial and commercial premises, as well as "special waste" for which there are additional regulations (see this chapter 4.19.6). The types of waste to be treated under each of these classifications for the purposes of Part II of the EPA are defined in the *Controlled Waste Regulations 1992*, which took effect on 1 April 1992 and apply in England, Scotland and Wales:

- **Household waste** includes waste from: premises occupied by a charity; land belonging to domestic property, caravan or residential home, or a private garage for a car; private (domestic) premises; moored houseboat; camp sites; prisons and penal institutions; public meeting halls; royal palaces; litter collected under s.89 of the EPA. Local authorities may charge for the collection of certain types of household waste - see 4.19.5 below.

- **Industrial waste** includes waste from: commercial garages/maintenance premises (for vehicles, vessels, aircraft); laboratories and scientific research associations; workshops; dredging and tunnelling waste; clinical waste (other than from domestic property, residential home or houseboat); aircraft, vehicles, vessels not used for domestic purposes; leachate; poisonous or noxious waste from certain processes (e.g. dry cleaning, paint mixing/selling, pesticide sales); premises for breeding, boarding, stabling or exhibiting animals; waste oils, waste solvent, scrap metals (except from domestic premises); waste imports and waste from ships.

- **Commercial waste** includes waste from: offices; showrooms; hotels; private garages (more than 25 sq m); club/social premises; markets or fairs; courts, government departments, local and central government premises; corporate bodies; tents on land other than camp sites.

The *Waste Management Regulations 1994* (see below, 4.19.3) apply to disposal and recovery activities relating to "Directive Waste" - that is waste covered by the EU Framework Directive (91/156) (see below, 4.6).

It should be noted that waste from a mine or quarry and waste from premises used for agriculture are not "controlled waste" under the *Controlled Waste Regulations*, and thus do not require a waste management licence. However to comply with the Framework Directive it will be necessary to extend waste management controls to "non-natural" agricultural waste and to non-mineral mining and quarry waste; a consultation document covering the former was expected during summer 2000.

Clinical Waste

Clinical waste - also called, healthcare waste or healthcare risk waste - other than that from a private dwelling or residential home - is classified as industrial waste for legislative purposes. Handlers of clinical waste are also subject to the duty of care provisions of s.34 of the EPA: this places a duty on producers, handlers and disposers of waste to ensure it is disposed of safely and legally (see 4.19.2 below). Most clinical waste (except that from households) is also subject to the *Special Waste Regulations 1996* (see 4.19.6 below). The *Controlled Waste Regulations 1992* define clinical waste as

- any waste which consists wholly or partly of human or animal tissue, blood or other body fluids, excretions, drugs or other pharmaceutical products, swabs or dressings, or syringes, needles or other sharp instruments, being waste which unless rendered safe may prove hazardous to any person coming into contact with it; and

- any other waste arising from medical, nursing, dental, veterinary, pharmaceutical or similar practice, investigation, treatment, care, teaching or research, or the collection of blood for transfusion, being waste which may cause infection to any persons coming into contact with it.

The Health and Safety Commission has published (1999) guidance on the handling, storage, transport and disposal of clinical waste; *Safe Disposal of Clinical Waste* has been produced jointly with the Environment Agency and replaces the Department of the Environment's Waste Management Paper No. 25.

A Department of Environment Circular, 14/92, (WO 30/92; SOED 24/92) defines in detail wastes to be treated as "controlled waste". Further guidance is contained in DOE Circular 11/94 (WO 26/94; SOED 10/94) on waste management licensing and the Framework Directive on waste.

4.3 AMOUNTS OF WASTE GENERATED

Total waste arisings from all sources in the UK are currently estimated to be about 423 m. tonnes a year of which about 180 m. tonnes is controlled waste from domestic (26 m. tonnes), industrial (69 m. tonnes), construction and demolition (70 m. tonnes) and commercial (15 m. tonnes) sources. Other major sources of waste include agriculture (80 m. tonnes) and mining and quarrying (74 m. tonnes). Special waste arisings in the UK for 1993/4 are estimated at 2.07 m. tonnes (*Digest of Environmental Statistics*, No. 20, 1998). In England and Wales municipal waste arisings for 1997/98 totalled 27.2 m. tonnes (1995/96: 26 m. tonnes), 90% of which was from household sources. In both 1996/97 and 1997/98, 85% of municipal waste in England and Wales was disposed of to landfill; 14% of municipal waste (1996/97: 13%) had value recovered from it through recycling, composting or energy recovery. In 1997/98 approximately 2 million tonnes of household waste was collected for recycling or centralised composting (Municipal Waste Management 1996 & 1997/98, DETR, 2000).

In Scotland approximately 12 m. tonnes of controlled waste was sent to landfill in 1998; household waste accounted for 3.0 m. tonnes of this; commercial waste - 2.0 m. tonnes; industrial, construction and demolition waste - 7 m. tonnes. Ninety per cent of Scottish household waste is landfilled and 3.5% recycled or composted.

Scotland produces approximately 200,000 tonnes of special waste, most of which is disposed of in specialist facilities in England or Wales (National Waste Strategy, Scotland, SEPA, 1999).

The increasing amount of waste being generated is resulting in more awareness, both at EU and UK level, of the need for policies aimed at waste minimisation - i.e. reduction or prevention of waste at source, thus eliminating the need to treat and dispose of it. In 1996 the European Commission updated its 1989 *Community Strategy for Waste Management* which outlines its policy on waste prevention and minimisation - see below). The National Waste Strategies for England and Wales, Scotland, and Northern Ireland (see below, 4.19.4) must also include proposals for encouraging the prevention or reduction of waste production.

Although about half of our domestic waste could be recycled or re-used, there are still only a few appropriate schemes in the UK although more are likely to be established: section 49 of the EPA, which was brought into force on 1 August 1991, requires waste collection authorities to investigate and draw up plans for recycling schemes (see 4.19.5 below). The 1990 White Paper (*This Common Inheritance*) set a national target of 50% recovery of the recyclable content of domestic refuse by the year 2000 (i.e. about 25% of all household waste).

Clinical waste arisings from NHS Trusts are estimated at around 200,000 tonnes a year, with about the same amount being generated by private hospitals, GPs, dentists, nursing homes etc (MEL Research, 1998, for Environment Agency). HSC Guidance (*Safe Disposal of Clinical Waste, 1999*) provides guidelines on how the different types of clinical waste should be disposed of.

4.4 WASTE DISPOSAL: SOME OPTIONS

4.4.1 Landfill

Approximately 84% of municipal waste in England and Wales is disposed of to landfill (*Digest of Environmental Statistics, No. 20, 1998*). If not properly managed landfill sites can give rise to a variety of pollution problems, including leachate (a liquid formed when waste is broken down by bacteria which can cause contamination of groundwater); rodent infestation, production of potentially explosive levels of methane gas (65%), dangerous levels of carbon dioxide (35%), plus trace concentrations of a range of organic gases and vapours, are other problems associated with landfill sites.

Growing concern over the hazards posed by landfill gas has led to a number of government initiatives specifically aimed at minimising the risks to people and property from explosions; in July 1989, the Department of the Environment and the Welsh Office issued a circular (17/89) on the use of planning powers to control hazards posed by landfill gas. This followed the inclusion in the *Town and Country Planning General Development Order 1988* of a requirement for planning authorities to consult waste disposal authorities about any proposed development within 250 metres of land which has been used for waste disposal within the past 30 years. The DOE circular also suggests that particular attention be paid to proposals for new developments within 250 metres of existing developments and draws attention to existing powers which can be used to mitigate the hazards of landfill gas. It is suggested that some attention also be given to the problem of existing developments on or near landfill sites.

It should, however, also be noted that landfill gas can be harnessed as a valuable source of renewable energy, resulting in significant energy savings; in 1994 approximately 587 kt of landfill methane was extracted and flared or used for energy recovery; methane capture and use is now practised at over 150 landfill sites and in 1996 generated 136 MW of electricity.

Advice on the control of landfill gas is given in Waste Management Paper No. 27 (HMSO, 1991): this provides information on the production of landfill gas, and a summary, including key points for licensing officers, of the technical aspects of landfill gas; there is a discussion of the main factors responsible for the formation of landfill gas, advice on monitoring, information on the options available for its management and guidance on development on or near landfill sites.

WMP 26A (1994) provides guidance on assessing the completion of licensed landfill sites. In January 2000, the Environment Agency published draft guidance on monitoring leachate, groundwater and surface water at landfill sites. This is primarily aimed at licensing authorities to enable them to set appropriate monitoring conditions for health and environmental purposes; it will however also be of use to operators as it provides guidance on drawing up monitoring plans and programmes for meeting licence conditions.

Landfill Tax

As from October 1996 all waste deposited in landfill sites has been subject to a tax. Landfill operators licensed under the EPA or the *Pollution Control and Local Government Order (Northern Ireland) 1978 (or Waste Management and Contaminated Land (NI) Order 1997* once this is implemented) were required to register their liability for the tax by 31 August 1996. Landfill operators who also use their site for recycling, incineration or sorting waste may apply to have the relevant area designated a tax-free site.

The *Landfill Tax Regulations 1996* (SI 1527), as amended (1999, SI 3270) cover registration procedures, credits, accounting and environmental trusts. The *Landfill Tax (Qualifying Material) Order 1996* (SI 1528) defines the categories of waste which are subject to the lower rate of tax. The *Landfill Tax (Contaminated Land) Order 1996* (SI 1529) sets out the provisions for exempting waste generated as a result of cleaning up historically contaminated land; the Government is expected to amend this to ensure that waste produced as a result of cleaning up land subject to a Remediation Notice under Part IIA of the EPA is not exempt from landfill tax.

The tax is based on the weight of the waste to be deposited, thus applying the polluter pays principle; it also aims to promote a more sustainable approach to waste management by providing an incentive to dispose of less waste to landfill and to recover more value from waste, e.g. through recycling etc.

Active waste is taxed at £11 per tonne (from 1 April 2000, increasing by £1 per tonne per year to 1 April 2004), except for the following lower risk wastes where the tax is £2 per tonne:

- Naturally occurring rocks and soils, including clay, sand, gravel, sandstone, limestone, clean building or demolition stone, topsoil, peat, silt and dredgings.

- Ceramic or cemented materials: glass, ceramics (including bricks, tiles, clay ware, pottery, china, bricks & mortar), concrete. Refractories (bricks lining certain types of furnace).

- Processed or prepared mineral materials which have not been used or contaminated: moulding sands and clays, clay absorbents, manmade mineral fibres, silica, mica and abrasives.

- Furnace slags.

- Certain ash: bottom ash and fly ash from wood or coal combustion, including incineration.

- Low activity inorganic compounds: titanium dioxide, calcium carbonate, magnesium carbonate, magnesium oxide, aluminium hydroxide, magnesium hydroxide, calcium hydroxide and salt (if disposed of in a brine cavity), iron oxide, ferric hydroxide, aluminium oxide, zirconium dioxide.

- Gypsum and calcium sulphate-based plaster, if disposed of in a separate containment cell on a mixed landfill site, and on inactive-only sites.

Certain wastes are exempt from the tax; these include: dredgings arising from the maintenance of inland waterways and ports; naturally occurring minerals arising from mining and quarrying; burial of domestic pets at pet cemeteries; and waste resulting from remediation of historically contaminated land. From October 1999 inert waste used in the restoration of sites has also been exempt (Budget Statement, 17 March 1998). Leachate arising from landfill sites, which is then recirculated - for example being moved to another site for treatment) is also exempt (Customs & Excise ruling, 1999).

Landfill site operators may contribute funds to approved environmental bodies for spending on relevant environmental projects; they may then reclaim 90% of their contributions up to a maximum of 20% of their annual landfill tax payment. To qualify as "approved", environmental bodies must be non-profit distributing and independent of any local authority or site operator interest and they will need to enrol with ENTRUST, the regulatory body set up to oversee distribution of funds. Examples of projects falling within the scheme include: the restoration of closed landfill sites (or of damage caused by such sites) where liability was unclear or the person responsible has insufficient funds for clean up; provision, maintenance or improvement of a public park or amenity near a landfill site; funds could also be made available for research and development, education and dissemination of information on more sustainable waste management practices, including recycling practices and development of markets for recycled waste.

HM Customs and Excise has produced a series of information notes (1996) covering all aspects of the landfill tax and the way in which it is to be applied. The series includes: registration, tax liability, calculating the weight of waste, record keeping, environmental bodies, reviews and appeals, contaminated land.

The *Waste Management (Miscellaneous Provisions) Regulations 1997* (SI 351, effective 14 March 1997) make conviction for evading payment of landfill tax a "relevant offence" in relation to the definition of a "fit and proper" person under s.74 of the *Environmental Protection Act 1990*. Thus an offender risks being deemed unfit to hold a waste management licence. See also 4.19.8.

4.4.2 Incineration

Incineration is the burning of waste at high temperatures. This reduces the weight of the waste by about two-thirds and its volume by 90%. Uncontrolled burning of waste can give off poisonous chemicals such as hydrochloric acid, dioxins and furans and heavy metals. Hydrochloric acid contributes locally to acid rain and is given off by the burning of plastics. If organic matter and plastics are burnt at low temperatures, dioxins and furans may also be emitted. These are poisonous substances and it is therefore essential that incinerators operate at high temperatures in order to reduce such emissions to a minimum. Grit, chars and dust must also be controlled by special equipment. Heavy metals - such as cadmium, lead, arsenic and chromium - which originate in the waste will be collected in the dust filter; mercury, also a heavy metal, may however escape as a vapour. This is best controlled by reducing the source of mercury in waste (mainly batteries).

In the UK, around 10% of all waste is incinerated, and currently less than 2% of toxic waste. A growing shortage of suitable landfill sites may well lead to more waste being incinerated.

Incineration can be a valuable source of energy; a number of European cities have successful Combined Heat and Power (CHP) schemes generating heat and electricity using incinerators.

4.4.3 Recycling

The *National Waste Strategy* (for England and Wales), published in May 2000, sets a target of recovering 40% of municipal waste by 2005, and of recycling or composting 17% of household waste by 2003, rising to 25% by 2005 - see also 4.19.4. The *Environmental Protection Act 1990* (ss.49 & 52) requires waste collection authorities to draw up plans for recycling household and commercial waste and empowers waste disposal authorities to pay recycling credits as a result of waste collected for recycling by waste collection authorities (see this chapter 4.19.5).

Waste Policy Guidance: Preparing and Revising Local Authority Recycling Strategies and Recycling Plans (DETR, 1998) suggests ways in which local authorities can plan to achieve the target of recovering value from 40% of municipal waste by 2005. It also shows how waste disposal and collection authorities can together develop a coordinated approach to municipal waste management in their area, which integrates the various treatment and disposal options for municipal waste. DETR has also published (1999) guidance for local authorities on monitoring and evaluating their recycling, composting and recovery programmes; this outlines a single methodology for calculating recycling, composting and recovery rates and indicators for assessing a programme's performance.

An EU Directive on packaging waste adopted in 1994 also has as a prime purpose the recycling of such waste; this has been implemented in the UK through the *Producer Responsibility Obligations (Packaging Waste) Regulations 1997* which place certain obligations on producers to recover and recycle packaging waste - see this chapter 4.12 and 4.20.2.

4.5 WASTE MANAGEMENT PAPERS

This series of papers, prepared by the Department of Environment (now Department of the Environment, Transport and the Regions), provide technical guidance on all aspects of waste management, including legislative requirements and advice on treatment and safe disposal of waste. The papers were first issued following enactment of the *Control of Pollution Act 1974;* they are the responsibility of the Environment Agency, with some now being updated to take account of the *Environmental Protection Act 1990* and other technical developments. There are currently over 30 papers in the series - see Appendix 4.1.

THE EUROPEAN UNION AND WASTE MANAGEMENT

According to a 1987 report from the European Parliament, the Member States of the European Union (EU) together produce approximately 2,200 million tonnes of waste annually. Of this, 66% of household waste is landfilled, 33% incinerated and 7% composted. Over 60% of industrial waste and 95% of agricultural waste is re-used.

The European Union has adopted a number of Directives aimed at harmonising waste disposal policies throughout the EU and preventing the development of measures that might distort competition. Since October 1993, however, proposals for waste legislation have been based on environmental protection (Article 130S) rather than harmonisation (Article 100A).

In December 1996, European Environment Ministers adopted by Resolution an updated version of the 1989 *Community Strategy for Waste Management* (COM(96) 399). The hierarchy of principles of the 1989 Strategy was reaffirmed: i.e. that the prevention of waste should be the first priority, followed by recovery and then the safe disposal of waste. Implementation of the hierarchy would depend on choosing the best environmental solution having regard to economic and social costs (see also Table 4.2). The Strategy also highlights the important role of producers in preventing waste and discusses the use of economic instruments, regulation and voluntary agreements. The Strategy reaffirms that controls on waste shipments need to be properly enforced and that waste generated within the EU should be disposed of within it and in the nearest appropriate facility (the self-sufficiency and proximity principles).

Table 4.2: European Union Principles of Waste Management

Prevention: the following measures should be developed: promotion of clean technologies and products; reduction of the hazardousness of wastes, establishment of technical standards, and possibly EC-wide rules to limit the presence of certain dangerous substances in products, the promotion of re-use and recycling schemes, the appropriate use of economic instruments, eco-balances, eco-audit schemes, life-cycle analysis and actions on consumer information and education as well as the development of the eco-label system.

Recovery: where environmentally sound, preference should in general be given to the recovery of material over energy recovery operations. This reflects the greater effect on the prevention of waste produced by material recovery rather than by energy recovery.

Final disposal: particular care should be taken to avoid as much as possible incineration operations without energy recovery. Uncontrolled landfilling and contaminated land are two problems requiring special and strong actions at different levels.

Source: Executive Summary, Community Strategy for Waste Management, COM(96) 399, 30 July 1996.

The disposal of ship-generated waste is briefly covered in chapter 5, 5.27.

A list of EU measures relating to waste is at Appendix 6.4. Brief details of the institutions of the European Union, and of the legislative process are given in Appendix 6.

4.6 FRAMEWORK DIRECTIVE ON WASTE

Among the most important of the Directives adopted on waste is the 1975 "Framework" Directive 75/442/EEC which established general rules for waste management. This has been amended by a Directive adopted in 1991 (91/156/EEC) which had to be implemented by Member States by 1 April 1993. The Directive identifies 16 specific categories of waste, which is defined as "any substance or object ... which the holder discards or intends or is required to discard" (see 4.2.1 above). The Commission has drawn up a new list of materials to be treated as waste – Decision

2000/532 adopted on 3 May 2000 replaces the *European Waste Catalogue* (Decision, 94/3/EC, January 1994) and the Hazardous Waste list (Decision 94/904/EC, December 1994). The new list categorises waste by industry sector or process, and classifies materials as hazardous, non hazardous or potentially hazardous according to their physical, chemical and biological properties.

An important objective of the Directive is to ensure "that waste is recovered or disposed of without endangering human health and without using processes or methods which could harm the environment and in particular without

- risk to water, air, soil, plants or animals;

- causing nuisance through noise or odours; or

- adversely affecting the countryside or places of special interest".

Greater emphasis is placed on the prevention, reduction, re-use and recycling of waste, and on the use of waste as a source of energy. With the ultimate aim of the EU becoming self-sufficient in waste disposal, the Directive calls on Member States to establish a network of disposal facilities.

Member States are required to establish competent authorities who must draw up waste disposal plans in collaboration with other Member States and the Commission; the designated competent authorities are also to be responsible for issuing authorisations and waste management licences. Specified waste recovery operations and businesses which dispose of their waste on site do not require an authorisation but must be registered with the relevant authority; before permitting exemption from authorisation, Member States must have appropriate Regulations specifying the types of activity exempted, quantities of waste, disposal and recovery methods permitted and other conditions.

The Directive has been largely implemented through Part II of the *Environmental Protection Act 1990* and the *Waste Management Licensing Regulations 1994* - see later this chapter, 4.19.3. Department of Environment Circular 11/94 (WO 26/94; SOED 10/94) provides a detailed interpretation of the Directive's requirements and how these have been incorporated into national legislation.

4.7 INCINERATION

4.7.1 Municipal Waste Incinerators

Two Directives adopted in June 1989 require both new and existing municipal waste incinerators to meet much tighter emission standards. These Directives are to be repealed five years after the new incineration of waste Directive enters into force - see 4.7.3 below.

Municipal waste is defined as "domestic refuse as well as commercial or trade refuse and other waste which, because of its nature or its composition, is similar to domestic refuse". A municipal waste incinerator is defined as "any technical equipment used for the treatment of municipal waste by incineration, with or without recovery of the combustion heat generated but excluding plants used specifically for the incineration of sewage sludge, chemical, toxic and dangerous waste, medical waste from hospitals or other types of special waste, on land or at sea, even if these plants may burn municipal waste as well". This definition covers the whole site.

The Directive covering new plant (89/369/EEC) applies to all new municipal waste incinerators for which authorisation was granted after 30 November 1990. An objective of the Directive is to harmonise controls across the EU by setting standards which can be achieved with proven abatement technology and at a reasonable cost - i.e. Best Available Technique Not Entailing Excessive Cost (BATNEEC) (see chapter 1, 1.6). It sets emission limits which vary with the size of the plant, as well as operating and monitoring requirements. Requirements for meeting emission limits (see Table 4.3) are included in authorisations under Part I of the *Environmental Protection Act 1990* (see chapters 1 and 2).

The Directive specifies measuring and monitoring requirements for the various categories of incinerator: for incinerators with a capacity of one tonne per hour or more, there must be continuous measurement of dust, carbon monoxide, oxygen and hydrogen chloride. For these incinerators too, periodic monitoring for heavy metals, hydrofluoric acid and sulphur dioxide is required. There is also a general duty on Member States to specify maximum permissible periods during which emission limits may be breached due to "technically unavoidable stoppages", and to publish the results of emissions measurements. Other provisions of the Directive relate to emission limits in the case of technical stoppages, monitoring, and public access to information.

The Directive covering existing plant (89/429/EEC) required standards to be progressively improved to meet those set for new plant. Existing incinerators - i.e. those for which authorisation was granted before 30 November 1990 - with a capacity of six tonnes/hour or more had to meet the standards applicable for new plant by 1 December 1996, or close down.

A two-stage improvement programme was set for incinerators with a capacity of less than six tonnes/hour. Interim emission limits and operating standards had to be met by 1 December 1995, with full compliance with the standards set for new plant by 1 December 2000.

Both Directives are implemented in the UK through the *Municipal Waste Incineration Directions Order 1991* made under the *Environmental Protection Act*; this is reproduced as Appendix 2 to PG 5/4(95) – *General Waste Incineration Processes under 1 tonne/hour*. Incinerators with a capacity of 1 tonne an hour or more are currently subject to Integrated Pollution Control (see chapter 1, 1.14); those less than 1 tonne an hour are currently regulated for Local Air Pollution Control (see chapter 2, 2.12) - see also 4.22 below. Relevant incineration processes will transfer to control under IPPC in the second half of 2005; some will remain regulated for LAPC but under the IPPC Regulations – see chapter 1, 1.13.1.

In October 1998, the Commission adopted a proposal for a Directive on waste incineration (COM(98) 558). It was intended that this would replace the Directives on both new and existing municipal waste incinerators and cover the incineration of all wastes not covered by the 1994 Directive on hazardous waste incineration (including used oils, solvents, hospital wastes and tyres), municipal waste and other non-hazardous wastes. However, following a request by the European Parliament, this proposal, the hazardous waste incineration Directive and its proposed amendment were merged into a single proposal, agreement on which was reached in July 2000 - see 4.7.3 below. Both Directives on municipal waste incineration will be repealed five years after the new Directive enters into force.

Table 4.3: Emission Limits for New Municipal Waste Incinerators: Directive 89/369 EEC

Pollutant	Less than 1 tonne/h	1 tonne/h or more but less than 3 tonnes/h	3 tonnes/h or more
Total dust	200	100	30
Heavy metals			
- Pb + Cr + Cu + Mn	-	5	5
- Ni + As	-	1	1
- Cd and Hg	-	0.2	0.2
Hydrochloric acid (Hcl)	250	100	50
Hydrofluoric acid (HF)	-	4	2
Sulphur dioxide (SO_2)	-	300	300
Carbon monoxide (CO)	100	100	100
Organics (as total carbon)	20	20	20

Emission limits are in mg/Nm^3 as a function of the nominal capacity of the incineration plant. Combustion gases in combustion chambers must be kept after the last injection of combustion air at least 850 degrees C for two seconds in the presence of at least 6% oxygen. All measurements to be based on a standard gas condition of 101.3 kPa, 273 K (0 degrees C) 11% oxygen, or 9% carbon dioxide, dry gas.

4.7.2 Hazardous Waste Incineration

This Directive (94/67/EC) was formally adopted in December 1994; it came into force on 31 December 1994 and should have been transposed into national legislation by 31 December 1996. Decision 97/283/EC specifies a harmonised measurement method to determine the mass concentration of dioxins and furans in atmospheric emissions in accordance with Article 7(2) of the Directive. Municipal waste incinerators are excluded from the Directive as they are already covered by two 1989 Directives (see above); also excluded are combustible liquid waste burning plant; sewage sludge and small clinical waste incinerators (so long as their contents do not make the incinerator hazardous in terms of the Directive); crematoria; and incinerators for animal carcasses. Directive 94/67/EC is to be repealed five years after the new incineration of waste Directive enters into force - see 4.7.3 below.

The Directive specifies stricter standards for all incinerators of hazardous waste, including plant which burn such waste as a fuel in the industrial process. In aiming to minimise risks to human health and the environment, the Directive also has as an objective the adoption of an integrated approach to controlling emissions from incinerators to air, land and water.

A further aim is to raise the standards of hazardous waste management by introducing tighter standards, thus preventing the disposal of hazardous waste in older or less efficient incinerators. Specific standards are laid down for operating conditions and emissions (which were to be reviewed before the end of 2000) - see box below; there is a general requirement to use the best available technology.

New plant had to meet operating standards from 1 January 1997 and existing plant by 30 June 2000. Operators of existing incinerators who notified the Environment Agency (or SEPA) by 30 June 1997 of their intention to operate for no more than 20,000 hours over the next five years and then close do not have to upgrade. Other Articles of the Directive - such as licensing and public access to information - are compatible with the UK's Integrated Pollution Control requirements. An environmental impact assessment must be carried out before a licence can be granted.

This Directive has been implemented through the *Environmental Protection (Prescribed Processes and Substances) Amendment (Hazardous Waste Incineration) Regulations 1998* and through a statutory Direction to the Environment Agency and SEPA requiring them to include the Directive's obligations in conditions of authorisations - see 4.22 below.

4.7.3 Directive on Waste Incineration

COM(99) 330, published in July 1999 was a revised proposal merging COM(98) 558 on waste incineration (which was intended to replace the two Directives on municipal waste incinerators, 4.7.1 above), with the current hazardous waste incineration Directive (94/67); it also subsumes COM (97) 604 which proposed amending the HWI Directive to extend controls on emissions of heavy metals and dioxins to the aquatic environment. In July 2000 a final text was agreed by the Conciliation Committee, consisting of representatives of both the European Parliament and the Council of Ministers. It will enter into force on the day in which it is published in the Official Journal.

Table 4.4: EU Standards for Hazardous Waste Incineration

Daily average value (100% compliance), mg/m³		
Total dust	10	
Total organic carbon	10	
Hydrogen chloride	10	
Hydrogen fluoride	1	
Sulphur dioxide	50	
Half-hourly average value, mg/m³		
	100% and	**97% compliance**
Total dust	30	10
Total organic carbon	20	10
Hydrogen chloride	60	10
Hydrogen fluoride	4	2
Sulphur dioxide	200	50
Averages over sample period, minimum 30 mins, maximum 8 hours		
Hg	0.05 mg/m³ (total)	
Cd + Tl	0.05 mg/m³ (total)	
Sb+As+Pb+Cr+Co+Cu+Mn+Ni+V+Sn	0.5 mg/m³ (total)	

(new incinerators only; limits double for existing incinerators which must meet new standards within 42 months of Directive taking effect)

Dioxins and furans to be "reduced by the most progressive techniques"; from 1 January 1997 must not exceed 0.1 ng/m³ over min. 6 hrs, max. 8 hours sampling period.

Combustion gases in combustion chamber must be kept after the last injection of combustion air at least at 850 degrees C (or 1,100 degrees C for waste containing at least 1% halogenated organic substances) for 2 seconds in the presence of at least 6% oxygen or 3% when fed with liquid wastes.

The new Directive, which has as a main priority the minimisation of waste, will cover the incineration of both hazardous and non-hazardous wastes, requiring strict emission limits, based on best available techniques, similar to those currently in place for hazardous waste incinerators, as well as compliance with the IPPC Directive. Limit values have been set for hydrogen chloride, hydrogen fluoride, heavy metals, sulphur oxides, nitrogen oxides, dioxins and furans (Table 4.5), as well as discharges into water (Table 4.6) and leachate from residues; monitoring requirements for both hazardous waste and non-hazardous waste incinerators are specified. The Directive will also introduce strict requirements for the co-incineration of waste (i.e. the incineration of waste as an additional fuel in plants for energy generation) to ensure that operational standards are as high as for other plant. Operators of incineration plant will have a duty "to take all

necessary precautions concerning the delivery and reception of waste to prevent negative effects to the environment". They will require a permit from the competent authority which will include measures to ensure that

- the plant is operated in accordance with the Directive;
- heat generated during incineration is, as far as possible, recovered;
- residues are prevented, reduced or recycled as far as possible;
- the disposal of residues which cannot be prevented, reduced or recycled is carried out in conformity with Community legislation.

All waste waters discharged from an incineration plant will also require authorisation with strict conditions based on BAT, and operational controls parameters must be set for

Table 4.5: Air Emission Limit Values from Incinerators

(a) Daily average values (mg/m^3)

Total dust	10^a
Total organic carbon	10
Hydrogen chloride	10
Hydrogen fluoride	1
Sulphur dioxide	50

^{a} exemption may be authorised for existing plant until 1.1.08, provided permit foresees no exceedance of daily average of 20 mg/m^3

NO & NO$_2$ expressed as NO$_2$	
- existing plant with capacity exceeding 6 tonnes/hr, or new plant*b	200
- existing plant with capacity of 6 tonnes/hr or less*b	400

* Until 1.1.07, does not apply to plant incinerating hazardous waste only
b Exemptions for NOx emissions from existing plant may be authorised up to 1.1.08; exemptions are based on capacity of plant.

(b) Half-hourly average values (mg/m^3)

	100% compliance	97% compliance
Total dust	30	10
Total organic carbon	20	10
Hydrogen chloride	60	10
Hydrogen fluoride	4	2
Sulphur dioxide	200	50
NO & NO$_2$ expressed as NO$_2$		
- existing plant with capacity exceeding 3 tonnes/hr, or new plant*c	400	200

* Until 1.1.07, does not apply to plant incinerating hazardous waste only
c Exemptions may be authorised at existing plant with capacity between 6-16 tonnes per hour until 1.1.10 providing permit foresees no exceedance of 600 mg/m3 (100%) or 400 mg/m3 (97%)

(c) Average values over sample period, min. 30 mins, max. 8 hrs (mg/m3)

Hg	0.05	0.1*
Cd + Tl	0.05 (total)	0.1 (total)*
Sb+As+Pb+Cr+Co+Cu+Mn+Ni+V	0.5 (total)	1 (total)*

(*Until 1.1.07 average values for existing plant for which permit granted before 31.12.96 and which incinerate hazardous waste only.)

(d) Average values over sample period, min 6 hrs, max 8 hrs

Dioxins and furans	0.1 ng/m^3 (total)

(e) Carbon monoxide

Emission limit values not to be exceeded in combustion gas (excluding start up and shut down)
50 mg/m^3 as daily average value
150 mg/m^3 (95% of measurements) as 10 minute average value, or
100 mg/m^3 (all measurements) as half-hourly average values taken in any 24 hr period.

pH, temperature, flow and turbidity. The Directive requires instantaneous daily measurement for total suspended solids at the point of discharge, daily and monthly measurement of mercury, cadmium and thallium and daily measurements of the other heavy metals. For the first 12 months of operation of the incinerator, heavy metals, dioxins and furans must be measured every three months, and thereafter at least two measurements must be taken annually.

The following incineration plant are excluded from this Directive:

- vegetable waste from agriculture and forestry;
- vegetable waste from the food processing industry, so long as heat is recovered;
- the treatment of agriculture and forest residues (except where they may contain halogenic organic compounds or heavy metals as a result of treatment);
- animal carcase incinerators, including pet crematoria;
- waste resulting from the exploration of, or exploitation of, oil and gas resources from off-shore installations, and incinerated on board;
- cork waste;
- radioactive waste.

Also excluded are experimental plant used for research, development and testing to improve the incineration process and which treat less than 40 tonnes of waste a year.

Existing plant (i.e. in operation and complying with national legislation up to two years after the Directive enters into force) will need to comply with the Directive five years after it enters into force, when the 1989 MWI and 1994 hazardous waste incineration Directives will be repealed. New plant will have to comply within two years of the Directive's entry into force. Stationary and mobile plant used for the generation of energy must comply with the Directive four years after it enters into force.

4.8 HAZARDOUS WASTE

In 1975 and 1978, Directives were adopted on the disposal of waste oils (75/439/EEC), and on toxic and dangerous waste (78/319/EEC) respectively. The latter established a list of 27 substances which in certain circumstances might cause waste to be toxic and dangerous. This Directive, which was repealed upon implementation of the 1991 Directive in June 1995, also prohibited uncontrolled dumping and tipping and made provision for the labelling of packages containing waste; the licensing of storage, treatment and/or disposal establishments; control of the transport of wastes; and the planning by competent authorities within the Member States of a programme of disposals.

The Directive redefines "hazardous waste" and aims to achieve greater harmonisation in the management of hazardous waste. All wastes with characteristics which render them hazardous, e.g. corrosive, infectious or ecotoxic substances, are covered. Annexes to the Directive list the categories of waste to be covered, the various components which would make it hazardous; a third annex lists 15 characteristics of which one or more must be present for the waste to be hazardous. Domestic waste from domestic premises is exempt from this Directive.

The Directive prohibits the mixing of hazardous waste with other waste except where it is a necessary part of the disposal operation and places stricter controls on carriers of hazardous waste. Hazardous waste producers will be subject to periodic inspection and they and waste carriers must keep records of waste transactions for one and three years respectively; waste transfers must comply with the EU's 1993 Transfrontier Shipment of Waste Regulation which came into force in May 1994 - see below.

Commission Decision 2000/532, adopted on 3 May 2000, is a list of hazardous and non-hazardous waste pursuant to both the Framework Directive on Waste (see above) and to the Hazardous Waste Directive; it must be implemented by 1 January 2002 and replaces earlier Decisions 94/904/EC and 94/3/EC which established a list of hazardous waste and the European Waste Catalogue, respectively. In September 2000, the Commission published a proposal for a Decision – COM(2000) 546 – to add end-of-life vehicles to the List; further additions to the List are expected to be proposed and agreed late 2000/early 2001.

Compliance with the Directive in the UK is effected

Table 4.6: Emission Limit Values for Discharges of Waste Water from Cleaning of Exhaust Gases

Emission limit values expressed in mass concentrations of unfiltered samples		
Total suspended solids*	30 mg/l (95%)	45 mg/l (100%)
Mercury & its compounds	0.03 mg/l	
Cadmium & its compounds	0.05 mg/l	
Thallium & its compounds	0.05 mg/l	
Arsenic & its compounds	0.15 mg/l	
Lead & its compounds	0.2 mg/l	
Chromium & its compounds	0.5 mg/l	
Nickel & its compounds	0.5 mg/l	
Zinc & its compounds	1.5 mg/l	
Dioxins and furans	0.3 ng/l	

* Exemptions may be authorised until 1.1.08 for existing plant provided that permit foresees 80% of measured values do not exceed 30 mg/l and none exceed 45 mg/l

through the *Special Waste Regulations 1996* (see this chapter, 4.19.6) and similar 1998 Regulations in N. Ireland. Other requirements of the Directive, such as licensing and duty of care are already included in Part II of the *Environmental Protection Act 1990* covering England, Scotland and Wales and in N. Ireland by Part II of the *Waste and Contaminated Land (Northern Ireland) Order 1997*.

4.9 TRANSFRONTIER SHIPMENT OF WASTE

4.9.1 EU Regulation 259/93

A 1984 Directive on the Transfrontier Shipment of Hazardous Wastes (84/631/EEC), amended in 1986 (86/279/EEC), required pre-notification of transfrontier shipments of hazardous waste; they had to be sent only to facilities that could dispose of them without danger to human life or the environment, their passage documented, and exports of hazardous waste outside the European Union prohibited unless the receiving country had given its prior consent. The 1984 Directive has been replaced by Regulation 259/93 on the Supervision and Control of Shipments of Waste within, into and out of the EU, which came into force in May 1994. The earlier Directives were implemented in the UK by Regulations (1988) of the same name, these have now been repealed and replaced by 1994 Regulations. EU Regulations are binding in their entirety, taking precedence over national legislation and do not need transposing into national legislation; thus the 1994 UK Regulations cover such matters as designation and powers of competent authority, offences and penalties etc - see 4.25 below.

The EU's 1993 Regulation, while building on the terms of the 1984 Directive, tightens up the procedure for transfrontier shipments of waste; unlike the 1984 Regulation it covers all waste (as defined by the Framework Directive) and thus enabled the Community to ratify the 1989 Basel Convention on the Control of Transboundary Movements of Hazardous Wastes and their Disposal. A 1998 amendment to the Regulation incorporates the amendment to the Basel Convention listing the wastes banned for export under the Convention - see below.

The Regulation covers the movement of all wastes (i.e. not just hazardous waste) although there are various exemptions such as civil aviation waste, radioactive waste and waste covered by other EU legislation; different requirements apply depending on whether the shipment is between, into or outside (including transit through) Member States. There is a general requirement on Member States to ensure appropriate arrangements for dealing with movements of waste within Member States. The import of waste into, and export of waste out of, the EU for disposal except to EFTA countries which are a party to the Basel Convention, is banned. Shipments to African, Caribbean and Pacific countries covered by the Lomé Convention are also banned. Waste exported by an ACP country for reprocessing can be returned to that country following reprocessing.

In line with the EU's aim that States should become self-sufficient in waste disposal, all waste should be treated or disposed of in an appropriate facility nearest to where it was produced. An exception to this is where it would not be economically feasible to set up a facility for a particular type of waste because of the small amounts involved.

The Regulation includes detailed procedures for pre-notification, authorisation and documentation describing the waste and prior consent for transfrontier shipments. The person sending the waste (the notifier) is obliged to take it back if the person to whom it was sent (the consignee) is unable to deal with it appropriately; within 180 days of receiving the waste the consignee must send the notifier a certificate confirming that the waste has been dealt with in an environmentally sound manner. Multiple shipments of a similar nature may be covered by a single consignment document though the regulatory authority may require each shipment to be accompanied by specimen documentation. All shipments must be covered by financial guarantee in case the shipment has to be returned to the originator or sent elsewhere - this guarantee must be agreed with the waste regulation authority who will issue a certificate to this effect. This financial guarantee is in addition to any other insurance or financial guarantee covering the shipment and its disposal or recovery.

Waste for recovery or recycling is divided into three categories - red, amber and green - according to how hazardous it is; red wastes include PCBs, dioxins and asbestos; amber wastes include waste oils and petrol sludges, and green wastes include paper, glass, wood waste, waste from mining operations, textiles and rubber. For red and amber wastes intended for recovery or recycling the controls are the same as for shipments of waste for disposal with the added requirement that wastes on the red list must have the written consent of the authorities in the receiving country prior to shipment; amber wastes may be shipped within 30 days of the authorities in the receiving country acknowledging notification and no objections having been raised. Green wastes for recovery or recycling should be accompanied by basic information about the shipment, including a description and the quantities involved.

In January 1997 EU Environment Ministers adopted an Amendment to the 1993 Regulation (120/97/EC). This implements an amendment to the Basel Convention (see below): exports to non-OECD countries of hazardous waste for disposal have been banned with immediate effect; exports for recovery are banned from 1 January 1998. A further amendment to the Regulation (1420/99), adopted on 29 April 1999, extends the control procedures for red and amber wastes to certain exports of green wastes. The amendment covers exports of green wastes to non-OECD countries that have indicated they do not wish to receive some or all types of green wastes for recovery and also non-OECD countries that have not responded to

Commission communications regarding acceptance of green wastes for recovery.

A Department of Environment Circular 13/94 (revised by DOE letter 26.1.95; WO 44/94; SOED 21/94; NI WM 1/94) explains in detail the requirements of both the EU and UK Regulations (see 4.25 below).

The transfrontier shipment of radioactive waste is regulated by a European Atomic Energy Union Directive 92/3/Euratom, adopted in February 1992 - see this chapter 4.31.6. The shipment of radioactive wastes within the EU is regulated by Euratom Regulation 1493/93 of June 1993.

4.9.2 Basel Convention

The *Convention on the Control of Transboundary Movements of Hazardous Wastes and their Disposal*, prepared under the auspices of the UN Environment Programme, came into force on 5 May 1992. There are currently 132 parties to the Convention, including the European Community and the UK, which both ratified it in February 1994.

The Convention takes as a basic principle the need to reduce both the generation of hazardous wastes and their transboundary movement to a minimum. It says that all states have the right to ban the import of hazardous waste and there are extensive pre-notification requirements for all transfrontier movements of household and industrial wastes. The exporting state has a duty to ensure that all wastes, whether for recovery or disposal, can be dealt with in an environmentally sound manner; it also has a duty to arrange for the return of any wastes failing to go to an appropriate treatment or disposal plant. The Convention permits parties to it to agree bi-lateral arrangements for trade in hazardous waste and prohibits such arrangements with others. Hazardous wastes which are to be exported must be packaged, labelled and transported in accordance with recognised international standards.

In September 1995, parties to the Convention agreed an amendment to the Convention which will come into force 90 days after ratification by 65 Parties to the Convention. As at 20 October 1998, there had been 20 ratifications (including the European Community and the UK). The amendment provides for an immediate ban on exports of hazardous waste for disposal from OECD to non-OECD countries and a similar ban on exports for recovery or recycling from 1 January 1998, although such exports may be continued by agreement between an OECD and non-OECD country. Non-OECD countries that wish to continue importing hazardous waste for recycling or recovery must notify the Convention Secretariat of the types and quantities of waste they will accept, processes to be used and method of final disposal of the residues. Lists of hazardous and non-hazardous wastes covered by the ban to be annexed to the Convention were agreed by Parties to the Convention in February 1998. List A includes over 50 categories of waste defined as hazardous; List B covers those waste categories which the Basel Convention does not define as hazardous but which nevertheless may contain hazardous characteristics and thus be covered by the ban. A further list - List C - covers wastes "awaiting classification". This latter amendment to the Convention was implemented in the UK in November 1998 (Command Paper 4061).

A Protocol to the Convention signed in December 1999 establishes a liability and compensation system for damage for accidents resulting from the transfrontier shipment of waste; it applies primarily to hazardous wastes defined by the Convention and to other wastes notified to the Convention Secretariat which have been defined or are considered to be hazardous by the importing or exporting country. Compensation covers injuries, death and loss of income for individuals and environmental damage. Where liability cannot be established or the liable party is unable to pay, compensation will be paid from a Fund to be administered by the Convention Secretariat. The Protocol requires ratification by 20 countries before it can come into force.

4.10 DANGEROUS SUBSTANCES

Directives have been adopted on polychlorinated biphenyls (PCBs) and polychlorinated terphenyls (PCTs) - 96/59/EC which repeals a 1976 Directive (76/403/EEC); on wastes from the titanium dioxide industry (1978 and 1982); and on the use of sewage sludge in agriculture (1986, but now under review). This latter was implemented in the UK in September 1989 through the *Sludge (Use in Agriculture) Regulations* (amended 1990) - see chapter 2, 2.18.

The 1996 Directive on PCBs and PCTs, adopted in September 1996, aims to reduce risks to human health and the environment through stricter controls on their disposal; it includes requirements for inventories, labelling and treatment of all significant PCB holdings and tighter regulation of all treatment facilities. The Directive has been implemented through *The Environmental Protection (Disposal of Polychlorinated Biphenyls and other Dangerous Substances) (England and Wales) Regulations 2000* (SI 1043) and similar in Scotland (SSI 95) and Northern Ireland (SR 232). Both sets of Regulations were made under the *European Communities Act 1972* - see this chapter 4.24 and chapter 5, 5.23 regarding avoiding marine pollution in the disposal of PCBs.

A number of Directives dealing with the discharge of hazardous substances to water have been adopted and information about these is contained in chapter 5 on water pollution.

4.10.1 Batteries

A Directive (91/157/EEC) adopted in March 1991 aims to reduce the level of heavy metals in batteries and to ensure separate collection of both single use and rechargeable cells for recovery or disposal. In 1993 Member States had to begin drawing up an identification scheme for batteries and accumulators for separate collection, recycling and heavy metal content. The Directive has been implemented in part through 1994 Regulations in England, Scotland and

Wales (1995 Regulations in Northern Ireland. Further Regulations were expected before the end of 2000 - see this chapter, 4.23.

The Commission is expected to bring forward proposals for a further Directive which would set new collection and recycling targets for all types of batteries; it would also impose marketing restrictions on batteries containing more than the background level of mercury, phase-out batteries containing cadmium by 2008, and oblige Member States to set up schemes for collecting waste batteries separately from other household waste.

4.11 LANDFILL

In April 1999 Environment Ministers formally adopted Directive 99/31/EC on the landfill of waste; its aim is to reduce the amount of waste landfilled, to promote recycling and recovery, and to establish high standards of landfill practice across the EU, and through the harmonising of standards, to prevent the shipping of waste from one country to another.

The new Directive, which must be implemented by May 2001, requires Member States to have a strategy in place by July 2003 which will reduce the amount of biodegradable waste sent to landfill to 75% of the total generated in 1995 by 2006, 50% by 2009 and 35% by 2016. The final target will be reviewed in 2014. Member States (including the UK) who currently landfill a majority of waste have an extra four years to meet each target.

Three types of landfill site are defined - for hazardous waste, non-hazardous waste and inert waste - with the Directive also covering underground and mine storage, disposal at the place of production and sites used for the temporary storage of waste. All waste will need to be pretreated prior to landfilling unless this would have no environmental benefit or is not feasible (e.g. for inert wastes); co-disposal of hazardous and non-hazardous waste is also banned from 2004. The disposal of the following wastes to landfill will be banned: liquid waste; explosive, corrosive, oxidising or inflammable waste; infectious hospital waste; used whole and shredded tyres (two years and five years respectively after the Directive takes effect); and other waste not meeting certain criteria set out in an Annex to the Directive. Monitoring schemes to establish the amounts of waste being sent to landfill, and its biodegradable content, will need to be set up by 2001. Charges for landfilling must reflect the full costs of management of the site, as well as closure and aftercare for up to 30 years. A system of operating permits, many of the features of which are similar to the UK's current waste management licensing procedures, must be implemented. All sites will require licensing; existing sites not conforming to the Directive will need to do so by 2009 or close down.

Member States may exempt from the Directive landfills with a total capacity of less than 10,000 tonnes serving islands; also exempt are landfills serving isolated settlements - i.e. those with fewer than 500 inhabitants per municipality, and no more than 5 per sq. km, and more than 50 km from the nearest urban area with more than 250 inhabitants per sq. km.

The DETR published a consultation paper in October 1999 setting out various options for implementing the landfill Directive in England and Wales, with a follow up published in October 2000; among its proposals are:

* amendment of the *Pollution Prevention and Control (England & Wales) Regulations 2000* (see chapter 1, 1.13) to apply to all waste facilities; existing operational landfills which are not covered by the IPPC Directive will be required to apply for a PPC permit in a phased programme to be completed by end 2005 or during 2006; the Environment Agency will contact existing sites to tell them the period within which a PPC application must be made;

* new landfill sites (i.e. in operation on 16 July 2001) must comply with the Directive immediately (except those for whole used tyres – July 2003, and those for shredded used tyres – July 2006). (Landfill sites covered by the IPPC Directive coming into operation after 30 October 1999 also have to comply with that Directive.)

* existing landfill sites remaining in operation after 16 July 2001 will need to submit a "conditioning plan" to the Environment Agency by July 2002 outlining how they intend to upgrade to meet the requirements of the Directive; permits will include conditions setting out the works required which must be completed by July 2009;

* landfill sites which close before 16 July 2001 will, for the time being, remain subject to the surrender provisions of the *Waste Management Licensing Regulations 1994;*

* co-disposal of hazardous and non-hazardous waste to be banned at all sites from July 2004; such sites wishing to continue accepting hazardous waste after 16 July 2002 may apply for interim classification as a hazardous waste site; the site must however have ceased to accept hazardous waste by 15 July 2004 in order to revert to classification as a non-hazardous site or it will only be able to accept hazardous waste;

* landfilling of prohibited wastes (including liquid wastes and those which are explosive, corrosive, oxidising, highly flammable, hospital and other clinical wastes and whole used tyres and shredded used tyres) to be banned at hazardous waste sites from July 2002 and at existing sites from July 2009 at the latest;

* pre-treatment of wastes prior to landfilling at new sites from July 2001, at hazardous waste sites from July 2004 and at all other existing sites from July 2009.

4.12 PACKAGING WASTE

The Directive on Packaging and Packaging Waste (94/62/EC) was adopted in December 1994 and came into force on 31 December 1994. It applies to all waste packaging - household, commercial and industrial - and had to be implemented by 30 June 1996, when Directive 83/339/EEC (containers of liquids for human consumption) was repealed. Decision 97/129/EC established an identification system for packaging materials as required by the Directive; Decision 97/138/EC relates to the formats of databases on packaging and packing waste established under the Directive with the aim of making these compatible throughout the EU.

The EU produces about 50 m. tonnes of packaging waste annually, of which only about 18% is recycled. The Directive therefore places a strong emphasis on the prevention of packaging waste and on reducing the amount of packaging used (while safeguarding consumer safety and product quality); in promoting the use of recyclable and reusable materials and the use of packaging likely to have the least impact on the environment, an annex to the Directive lays down standards for manufacture, composition, etc to be complied with by the end of 1997. The composition by weight of lead, cadmium, hexavalent chromium and mercury in packaging and packaging waste must be reduced over five years.

A principle aim of the Directive is to harmonise the recovery and recycling targets to be achieved by Member States to ensure no barriers to trade and at the same time to achieve a high level of environmental protection. Within five years of coming into force a target of 50-65% recovery of packaging materials in waste should be met and a target of 25-45% recycled with a minimum of 15% of each material.

Also within five years of entering into force, the Directive requires all packaging to be labelled with its recyclable or recoverable content; Directives outlining marking and identification systems are currently being prepared. Member States must set up suitable systems for the collection of packaging and packaging waste and its recycling or reuse and should ensure that consumers have adequate information regarding the marking of packaging, the benefits of reusable packaging and about return systems.

Member States may use economic instruments as a means of achieving the Directive's objectives but only "in accordance with the principles governing Community policy on the environment, such as the polluter pays principle, and with full respect for obligations stemming from the Treaty".

The Directive has been implemented in England, Scotland and Wales through the *Producer Responsibility Obligations (Packaging Waste) Regulations 1997* (SI 648) which came into force on 6 March 1997, with similar Regulations for Northern Ireland coming into force on 1 June 1999 (SR 115); and the Packaging (Essential *Requirements) Regulations 1998* (SI 1165) which apply throughout the UK - see this chapter 4.20.2.

In 1996, the Commission issued a proposal for a draft Directive on marking of packaging and on the establishment of a conformity assessment procedure for packaging (COM(96) 191); only packaging meeting the 1994 Directive would be able to use the approved symbols - one for reusable packaging and one for recyclable packaging - with all other symbols being prohibited; manufacturers would be required to prepare a statement of compliance with the 1994 Directive to be available for inspection by national authorities.

The Commission is currently discussing proposals for a Directive setting recycling and recovery targets to be met by June 2006. Among the options being considered are a minimum recycling target for all packaging and specific targets for different types of packaging.

4.13 WASTE ELECTRICAL AND ELECTRONIC EQUIPMENT

In June 2000, the Commission published proposals for two Directives relating to waste electrical and electronic equipment, COM (2000) 347. The first Directive will require manufacturers to recover and recycle electrical and electronic equipment, thus reducing the amount sent for final disposal to landfill or incineration without processing. It will cover household appliances from toasters and toys to washing machines and audio-visual equipment. Equipment used for professional purposes is also covered. Member States would be required to provide convenient facilities for householders to return old electrical equipment free of charge and retailers would be required to take back such equipment free of charge. Five years after the Directive enters into force producers will be required to finance the waste processing, recovery and disposal of WEEE.

The second Directive aims to prevent the production of hazardous waste by banning or restricting the use of various heavy metals and brominated flame retardants in all electrical and electronic equipment placed on the market after 1 January 2008.

IMPLEMENTATION AND ENFORCEMENT AUTHORITIES
4.14 ENVIRONMENT AGENCY

As from 1 April 1996 the Environment Agency took over responsibility for waste regulation from the local authority waste regulation authorities. As well as ensuring high standards of waste management and implementing the National Waste Strategy, the Environment Agency's responsibilities include

- issuing waste management licences and enforcement of licences and any conditions attached to them; surrender of licences (4.19.3 below);
- compliance with the 1991 duty of care regulations (4.19.2 below);
- registration of waste carriers and brokers (4.22.1 & 2 below).

The Agency is also responsible for those areas of contaminated land designated as "special sites" because of the nature of contamination - see below 4.28.3.

Details of the Environment Agency's objectives and other responsibilities are given in chapter 1, 1.7.1.

4.15 SCOTTISH ENVIRONMENT PROTECTION AGENCY

As from 1 April 1996, SEPA also took over responsibility for the regulation of waste, including those areas of contaminated land designated as "special sites".

Details of SEPA's objectives and other responsibilities are given in chapter 1, 1.7.2.

4.16 NORTHERN IRELAND

Under the *Pollution Control and Local Government (NI) Order 1978* district and borough councils in Northern Ireland have a duty to arrange for the collection and disposal of controlled waste; they are also currently responsible for licensing private waste disposal facilities, and for drawing up ten year waste disposal plans for their area.

New legislation - the *Waste and Contaminated Land (Northern Ireland) Order 1997* (WCLO) - received Royal Assent on 26 November 1997; it came into operation in March 1998 and is currently being implemented; the WCLO introduces controls on waste management and contaminated land similar to those operating in the rest of the United Kingdom. A statutory waste strategy was published in April 2000 (see 4.19.4) and new waste licensing regulations are expected in 2001. The legislation is enforced by the Waste Management and Contaminated Land Inspectorate of the Environment and Heritage Service, an agency of the Northern Ireland Department of the Environment.

4.17 LOCAL AUTHORITIES

The *Environment Act 1995*, s.57, adds a new Part IIA to the *Environmental Protection Act 1990* on contaminated land. Local authorities have a duty to inspect their land from time to time to identify whether any of it is contaminated and to ensure its suitable remediation - see later this chapter, 4.28.3.

Local authorities - acting as principal litter authorities - have a statutory duty to keep road, land, open highways etc free of litter and refuse; see later this chapter, 4.29.

District Councils in Northern Ireland have similar duties to those in the rest of the United Kingdom.

4.17.1 Waste Disposal Authorities

Waste disposal authorities - county or district councils or unitary authorities as appropriate - are responsible for arranging for the disposal of all controlled waste in their area collected by the waste collection authority.

Under the *Environmental Protection Act*, local authorities in England and Wales had either to privatise their disposal operations, set up a joint operation with the private sector or set up local authority waste disposal companies (LAWDCs) as "arms length companies" to be run as commercial undertakings; waste disposal operations are subject to competitive tendering.

4.17.2 Waste Collection Authorities

Waste collection is the responsibility of district, metropolitan or city councils, or of the appropriate unitary authority. Waste collection authorities have a duty to arrange for the collection of household and, if requested, commercial waste. WCAs are also responsible for drawing up and implementing recycling plans. Many local authorities have privatised their collection facilities.

WASTE ON LAND: REGULATORY CONTROLS

4.18 PLANNING CONTROLS AND ENVIRONMENTAL ASSESSMENT

As is the case with any use of land (apart from agricultural or defence activities) planning permission under the *Town and Country Planning Act 1990 (Town and Country Planning (Scotland) Act 1972)*, or exemption from its requirements, must be obtained. Application for planning permission, together with a copy of the environmental assessment where necessary (see chapter 1, 1.22 and 1.24) is made to the district council and this must be advertised locally. A public inquiry may be held if sufficient objections are received, if the developer appeals against a refusal or if the Secretary of State "calls in" the application. Where the local authority is the developer it must pass a resolution in council to give itself planning permission whereupon the normal requirements to advertise and receive objections still apply and the Secretary of State may still call in the application for a public inquiry if so minded.

Where a site was in use for waste disposal in July 1948, planning permission need not be sought as it is deemed to have an established use for that purpose. However if the nature of the operations on the site changes - e.g. if an incinerator is to be built where only landfill operations have been carried out - new planning permission must be obtained.

Planning permission, if and when granted, will usually contain conditions on the use of the site such as the limits of the area involved in the operations and, where relevant, the provisions to be made for the restoration of the land after operations have ceased. For land which may already be contaminated, the planning permission may be granted subject to conditions relating to the remedial action required. Specific details as to how a site should be operated will be included in the conditions attached to a waste management licence issued under the *Waste Management Licensing Regulations 1994* - see below 4.19.3.

Planning Policy Guidance Note on *Planning and Pollution Control* (PPG 23) outlines the responsibilities of planners and their relationship with statutory pollution control bodies and advises on avoiding duplication between planning and pollution control authorities.

PPG 10, *Planning and Waste Management, published in September 1999,* replaces the pollution and waste management sections of PPG 23; it provides a link between planning policy and the National Waste Strategy and will also help waste planning authorities to plan for future waste disposal facilities which will meet the requirements of the new EU Directive on landfill (see 4.11 above). Thus, PPG 10 outlines the implications of landfill for long term land use planning and summarises the responsibilities of local authorities as land use planning authorities, and the Environment Agency as the waste management licensing authority; wherever possible it is suggested that the two authorities should deal with applications simultaneously to avoid duplication. In drawing up their waste management plans, waste planning authorities should take account of the preferred waste hierarchy - reduce, reuse, recover, dispose - and consider waste minimisation schemes, recycling, composting and energy recovery. Also, while it is preferable for waste to be disposed of as near as possible to where it was created, it is recognised that sometimes it may be more environmentally appropriate to dispose of it in another region with spare capacity, rather than to develop a new waste facility close by – the best practicable environmental option should be the prime consideration; the PPG thus stresses the need for regional waste planning and close liaison with both regional authorities and the Environment Agency; regional technical advisory boards should be established to provide technical advice on regional planning strategies. PPG 10 also provides guidance on the type of issues to be taken into account when considering waste facilities; these range from increased traffic, noise, dust and odour to conservation and "visual intrusion".

The *Town and Country Planning (Development Plan) (England) Regulations 1999* (SI 3280) which came into force on 4 January 2000 require local planning authorities to have regard to the National Waste Strategy and to the land use planning requirements of the COMAH Directive when preparing structure plans; among the latter's requirements are to need to ensure "appropriate" distance between residential areas and hazardous installations; this would include hazardous waste facilities.

In Scotland, *National Planning Policy Guidance 10, Planning and Waste Management* (March 1996) reminds planning authorities of the need to take account of the Framework Directive on Waste (see above, 4.6) - i.e. that waste should be recovered, or disposed of in the nearest suitable facility, without risk to the environment or human health. Planners are urged to safeguard groundwater when developing plans for all new waste facilities and to consult SEPA at appropriate stages. Guidance is also given

on which decisions belong to planning and which to pollution control.

4.19 ENVIRONMENTAL PROTECTION ACT 1990, PART II

With the implementation of the *Waste Management Licensing Regulations 1994* in May 1994 Part I of the *Control of Pollution Act 1974* was finally replaced by Part II of the *Environmental Protection Act 1990* (EPA).

As noted above (4.16), the *Waste and Contaminated Land (Northern Ireland) Order 1997,* which is currently being implemented, introduces similar controls to those applying in the rest of the UK. Reference to the appropriate article of the Northern Ireland legislation is given throughout this chapter and is shown as follows: (NI: WCLO, Art.0).

The EPA builds on the system put in place by COPA with stricter licensing controls and other provisions aimed at ensuring waste handling, disposal and recovery operations do not harm the environment. Responsibility for waste rests on the person who produces it and everyone who handles it, right through to final disposal or reclamation. Only "fit and proper" persons may run waste sites and responsibility for a closed landfill site will continue until all risks of pollution or harm to human health and safety are past.

As well as reorganising local authority responsibilities for waste management, the EPA increased the former HM Inspectorate of Pollution's role in this area by giving it responsibility to oversee the activities of local waste regulation authorities. As from 1 April 1996, however, waste regulation became the responsibility of the Environment Agency in England and Wales and of the Scottish Environment Protection Agency (*Env. Act 1995,* ss.5(5) & 21(1)); thus, all references to a waste regulation authority in the EPA as amended are references to the Environment Agency or SEPA, as appropriate; in Northern Ireland the Waste and Contaminated Land Inspectorate of the Environment and Heritage Service (EHS) will take over responsibility for waste management licensing etc from the district councils following implementation of the relevant sections of the *Waste and Contaminated Land (Northern Ireland) Order 1997.*

Part II of the EPA, as amended by the *Environment Act 1995,* Sch. 22, paras 62-88, applies to the disposal of all "controlled waste"; this includes household, industrial and commercial waste as defined by the Controlled *Waste Regulations 1992* and the 1991 EU Framework Directive (see 4.6 above); it also covers "special waste" - i.e. waste that is difficult or dangerous to dispose of - for which special provisions are made.

This part of the EPA (NI, WCLO, Part II) also introduces a duty of care for producers and handlers of waste; the separation of local authority regulatory and disposal functions; and amends waste disposal planning requirements and licensing controls.

It should be noted that incinerators with a capacity of 1

tonne/hour or less are regulated by local authorities under Part I of the EPA 1990 (in Scotland by SEPA) - see chapter 2, 2.12. Larger incinerators - with a capacity of more than 1 tonne an hour, chemical recovery, and waste derived fuel manufacturing processes - are prescribed for Integrated Pollution Control under Part I of the EPA and thus the responsibility of the Environment Agency or SEPA (see chapter 1, 1.14). Other legislation of relevance to incinerators is given later in this chapter, see 4.22. It should be noted that certain waste activities will require an IPPC permit as a result of implementation of the EU Directive on Integrated Pollution Prevention and Control (see chapter 1, 1.12 and 1.13).

In Northern Ireland, incinerators are regulated by the EHS.

In this chapter of the *Pollution Handbook*, unless otherwise stated, the term "regulatory authority", means the Environment Agency, SEPA, or the Waste and Contaminated Land Inspectorate of the Environment and Heritage Service (EHS).

4.19.1 Prohibition on Unauthorised or Harmful Depositing, Treatment or Disposal of Waste (s.33) *(NI: WCLO, Art.4)*

Under this section

*   it is an offence to deposit, knowingly cause or permit the disposal of controlled waste on land without a waste management licence;

*   any waste to be deposited must be treated, kept or disposed of in accordance with the terms of the waste management licence, and

*   waste must be dealt with in such a way that it is unlikely to cause pollution or harm to human health.

This sub-section - 33(1) - of the Act does not apply to household waste which is treated, kept or disposed of within an area attached to a domestic property (and with the permission of the occupier). Under the *Controlled Waste Regulations 1992*, this exclusion does not extend to clinical waste, asbestos, or any mineral or synthetic oil or grease.

The latter sub-section was brought into force on 1 April 1992, and the first two on 1 April 1993 (E, W & S).

It is however, a defence to prove that an act (e.g. unauthorised deposit, treatment or disposal etc) in relation to the waste was done in an emergency and appropriate steps taken to minimise environmental pollution and harm to human health, and that full details of the act were given to the waste regulation authority as soon as practicable (*Env. Act 1995,* Sch. 22, para 64). It is also a defence for an employee to show that waste was deposited illegally under instructions or that there was no reason to believe anything was wrong.

Dumping of any waste (including special waste) or treating it without a licence may result in a maximum fine of £20,000 and/or six months in prison on summary conviction or an unlimited fine and/or two years in prison (five years if special waste is involved) on conviction on indictment.

4.19.2 Duty of Care etc as Respects Waste (s.34) *(NI: WCLO, Art.5)*

This section, aimed at curbing the illegal disposal of controlled waste, has been implemented through Regulations which came into force on 1 April 1992 (E, S & W). A legal duty of care is imposed on anyone - from producers, to carriers and disposers of waste - to ensure that

*   waste is not illegally disposed of or dealt with without a licence or in breach of a licence or in a way that causes pollution or harm;

*   waste does not escape from a person's control;

*   waste is transferred only to an "authorised person", such as a local authority, a registered carrier or a licensed disposer;

*   when the waste is transferred, it is accompanied by a full written description so that each person who has it knows enough to deal with it properly and thus avoids committing an offence under s.33 of the Act.

The duty does not apply to domestic householders in respect of their own domestic waste; nor does it apply to animal waste collected and transported under the *Animal By-Products Order 1992*. The duty does however apply to a householder who disposes of household waste from a neighbour's property and to builders disposing of rubble etc from a house in which they are working. The duty of care also applies to the Crown - i.e. government departments etc - and since 1 October 1995 has applied to scrap metal yards. Special waste is covered by the duty of care; such waste must of course also comply with the requirements of the *Special Waste Regulations 1996* - see 4.19.6 below.

Environmental Protection (Duty of Care) Regulations 1991 (SI 2839)

These Regulations cover England, Scotland and Wales and came into force in April 1992. They provide for a mandatory system of signed transfer notes and require all those subject to the duty of care to keep records of waste received and transferred. Information to be recorded on the transfer note must include a full description of the waste - its special features, hazardous substances, source, how it was produced etc. Other details to be recorded include quantity of waste (by weight if possible), whether/how containerised, names and addresses of those involved in the transfer, and place and date of transfer. In summary, sufficient information should be given to ensure that anybody coming into contact with the waste has enough detail to deal with it properly and in compliance with the duty of care.

A transfer note, together with the full description of the waste must accompany each consignment of waste.

Regular or multiple transfers of waste between the same people need not be individually documented provided that the details on the transfer note remain unchanged (amendment to EPA by s.33 of *Deregulation and Contracting Out Act 1994);* in the case of regular transfers, the transfer note should be renewed at least once a year. Records of all waste must be kept for at least two years.

Before transferring waste to a waste carrier it is important to check that a valid registration certificate is held; waste holders should assure themselves that their waste falls within the scope of the licence or exemption at the site to be used.

Where a waste regulation authority (i.e. Environment Agency or SEPA) wishes to assure itself that the duty of care is being complied with, or to follow up a suspected unlicensed dumping of waste, it may serve notice on a waste holder requesting copies of relevant documents within seven days.

A statutory code of practice (1991, updated 1996) giving practical guidance on how to discharge the duty of care has been drawn up by the Department of Environment (now DETR) and the Welsh Office, and a similar code for Scotland by the Scottish Development Department. This gives step by step advice on following the duty of care and what to do if it is suspected that the waste does not correspond to its description or is being handled incorrectly. The code also outlines the law with regard to the duty of care and the regulations on keeping records.

Breach of the code is not an offence (although breach of the duty of care is). It is however admissible in court as evidence in deciding if a breach of the duty has occurred. An offence under this section of the Act may result in a £5,000 fine on summary conviction, or an unlimited fine on conviction on indictment.

A joint circular from the Department of Environment (19/91), Welsh Office (63/91) and Scottish Office (25/91), gives advice on the operation of the duty of care. It complements the advice for producers and holders of waste given in the code of practice.

A draft of similar Regulations and a code of practice were due to be published for consultation in Northern Ireland in May 2000, with implementation planned for September 2000; as at the end of November, however, no draft was available (EHS website).

4.19.3 Waste Management Licences (ss.35-44) *(NI: WCLO, Arts.6-18)*

These sections of the EPA have been implemented through the *Waste Management Licensing Regulations 1994* which came into force on 1 May 1994. They replace and repeal ss.3-11 of the *Control of Pollution Act 1974* which covered site licensing, and under which almost anybody could get a site licence provided planning permission had been obtained for use of the land. Changes to procedures and the regulation of waste management licensing as a result of amendments to the EPA in Schedule 22 to the *Environment Act 1995* are reflected in the text below.

In Northern Ireland, Articles 6-18 of the *Waste and Contaminated Land (Northern Ireland) Order 1997* will have the same effect as ss.35-44 of the EPA as amended by the *Environment Act 1995.*

Fees and charges in relation to waste management licences are fixed in accordance with ss.41-43 of the *Environment Act 1995* (NI: WCLO, Art.15) - see 4.20.1 below.

The Waste Management Licensing Regulations 1994 (SI 1056)

The *Waste Management Licensing Regulations 1994* (WML Regulations) apply in England, Scotland and Wales. They came into force on 1 May 1994 and ensure compliance with the EU's Framework Directive on Waste 75/442, as amended by 91/156 (see 4.6 above). It was hoped to publish a consultation document outlining similar regulations for Northern Ireland during 2000, with the aim of bringing them into force in late 2001/early 2002.

The Regulations set out the procedure for obtaining a licence and also deal with revocations and suspensions of licences, appeals, public registers (EPA: ss.64-66; NI: WCLO, Art.34-36) and the definition of fit and proper persons (EPA: s.74; NI: WCLO, Art.3). The Regulations list the offences under which if a person has been convicted they would not be considered a fit and proper person to be a licence holder. They also introduce a system for the registration of waste brokers - see below 4.21.2.

1995 Amendment Regulations (SI 288) extend the licensing regulations to the scrap metal industry; 1996 Amendment Regulations (SI 634) and similar in Scotland (S.100) and 1997 Amendment Regulations (SI 2203) are largely concerned with amending the provisions relating to qualifications for fit and proper persons (see below, 4.19.8). 1997 Regulations - *the Waste Management (Miscellaneous Provisions) Regulations 1997* (SI 351) make evasion of landfill tax a "relevant offence" for the purposes of whether someone is "fit and proper" to hold a waste management licence (EPA, s.74; see 4.19.8 below). 1998 Amendment Regulations (SI 606) relate to registration of waste brokers and charging schemes for registration of scrap metal recovery and vehicle dismantling sites (see 4.21.2 below).

Much of the detailed procedure on compliance with the Regulations is contained in the EPA itself and in schedules attached to the Regulations, as amended by the *Environment Act 1995.*

A Department of the Environment Circular 11/94 (SOED 10/94; WO 26/94) gives guidance on the EU Framework Directive on Waste and its incorporation into UK legislation and also on implementation of the UK Regulations. Waste Management Paper No. 4, *The Licensing of Waste Facilities* (published 1994), provides guidance for the regulatory authorities on how they should carry out their licensing functions; under s.35(8) of the EPA, the regulatory authorities are under a duty to have regard to this guidance (or any other issued by the Secretary of State).

It should be noted that waste from a mine or quarry and waste from premises used for agriculture are not "controlled waste" under the *Controlled Waste Regulations*, and thus do not require a waste management licence. However to ensure compliance with the Framework Directive it will be necessary to extend waste management controls to "non-natural" agricultural waste and non-mineral mining and quarry waste; a consultation document concerning the former was expected during 2000.

(a) Requirement for a Licence

Under the EPA, the deposit, keeping, treatment or disposal of controlled waste (i.e. Directive Waste - see above, 4.2 and 4.6 - in or on land (including treatment or disposal in mobile plant) requires a waste management licence. There are various exemptions (see below). It should be noted that certain waste installations will fall within the scope of the IPPC Directive and will thus require a Permit under the *Pollution Prevention and Control Regulations 2000* - see chapter 1, 1.12 and 1.13.

The licence is issued by the waste regulation authority within which the waste disposal facility is situated (i.e. the appropriate office of the Environment Agency or SEPA). In the case of mobile plant, this will be the office in which the operator's principal place of business is located. The WML Regulations define mobile plant as incinerators which are exempt under Part I of the EPA (Section 5.1 of Schedule 1 of *Prescribed Processes & Substances Regulations 1991* - see Appendix 1.1) and "which are designed to be moved on roads or other land". The definition does not include any other kind of mobile plant.

Disposal licences granted under COPA were converted into waste management licences under s.77 of the EPA, valid until the expiry date of their COPA licence, and as such become subject to the EPA. Operators of such sites were automatically deemed "fit and proper" for the purpose of holding a licence under the Regulations - see also 4.19.8 below. Time-limited converted licences should then have been reviewed and a new licence issued before the expiry date; however in most cases this has not been done and thus the sites have effectively been operating illegally (i.e. without a licence) although the relevant subsistence fees and landfill tax have been paid. The situation has now been regularised through s.4 and sch. 2, para 5 of the *Pollution Prevention and Control Act 1999* which applies in England and Wales, and which amends s.77(2) of the EPA; under this time-limited licences that have expired, are deemed not to have expired and thus any action under the EPA (e.g. modification or transfer of licence, payment of fees, surrender of licence etc) validated.

(b) Exclusions from Licensing

Certain activities do not require a waste management licence where these are part of a process registered or authorised under other legislation. These are:

- recovery or disposal of waste from a process authorised for Integrated Pollution Control under Part I of the EPA;

- disposal of waste from incinerator authorised for control of air pollution under Part I of the EPA (see Appendix 1.1, section 5.1, Incineration);

- disposal of liquid waste under a consent for discharge to water (but not to a sewer) granted under Part III of the *Water Resources Act 1991;*

- recovery or disposal of waste where activity forms part of operation requiring licence under Part II of the Food and *Environment Protection Act 1985* (dumping at sea).

In July 1996 the Government announced that the following activities would also not require a waste management licence:

- operators of waste effluent treatment plant where disposal is subject to a discharge consent under Part III of the *Water Resources Act 1991* (Part II of COPA in Scotland), or a discharge consent under Part IV of the *Water Industry Act 1991;*

- discharges of effluent covered by the *Urban Waste Water Treatment (England & Wales) Regulations 1994* (1995 Regulations in Scotland and Northern Ireland) - see chapter 5, 5.18.

These exclusions, which do not have to be registered (see next section) also apply where the activity involves special waste; however a waste management licence will be required if the activity involves the final disposal of waste in or on land.

(c) Exemptions from licensing

Schedule 3 to the WML Regulations lists the activities for which a waste management licence will not normally be required - see Table 4.7.

Table 4.7: Exemptions from Waste Management Licensing

Recovery or reuse of waste: glass manufacture and production; scrap metal furnaces; scrap metal and waste motor vehicle dismantling; burning as fuel; packaging or containers; burning waste as fuel in a small appliance; burning waste oil as fuel in an engine; waste for the benefit of land; sludge and septic tank sludge on land; sewage and water treatment works; preparatory treatment of certain wastes; composting waste; construction and soil materials; manufacture of finished goods; use of waste; Diseases of Animals (Waste Food) Order 1973; storage of waste in a secure place; waste in secure containers; waste for construction; recovery of textiles; preparatory treatments of waste plant matter; recovery of silver; animal by-products.

Operations leading to recovery/reuse or disposal: crushing, grinding or size reduction of bricks, tiles or concrete; waterway dredging; recovery or disposal as part of the production process; baling, compacting or pulverising; storing returned goods.
Disposal of own waste at the place of production: disposal by incineration at the place of production; burning waste in the open; waste from railway sanitary conveniences or sinks; peatworking; railway ballasts; waste from prospecting.

Other deposits of waste: temporary storage of ships' garbage or tank washings; pet burial, storage of medicines, and medical, nursing or veterinary waste; storage of waste not at the place of production; storage of waste at the place of production.

It should be noted that an activity falling into one of the exempted categories will not necessarily be exempt and thus the Schedule to the Regulations (or in the case of scrap metal*, the 1995 Amendment Regulations, SI 288) should be consulted for details of any limitations or other requirements affecting the exemption. In most cases the exemptions do not apply to special waste and the person carrying on the exempt activity must have the permission of the occupier of the land or be entitled to use the land for the activity. (*Guidance published in 2000 from the Environment Agency and British Metals Federation describes which types of scrap metal should be considered as waste and therefore require either licensing or registering as being exempt – see bibliography.)

All establishments or undertakings (i.e. not private individuals) carrying on an exempted activity had to register with the appropriate registration authority (Environment Agency or SEPA) by 31 December 1994 (for smaller scrapyards the deadline was 1.10.95); non-registration is an offence. Registered sites are usually inspected by the Agency/SEPA once a year; exempted activities forming part of a process authorised by a local authority (England and Wales only) under Part I of the EPA will be registered with the local authority; exempted activities relating to other licensed operations should be registered with the appropriate licensing authority. The register, which is open to the public, will contain details of the establishment or undertaking, the exempt activity and where it takes place. Registration is valid indefinitely.

Amendments to the Schedule to encourage the recovery/recycling of wastes which are now special wastes under the *Special Waste Regulations 1996*, with exemptions for the following subject to appropriate conditions, are under consideration:

- storage of up to 23,000 litres of unused household paint;
- laundering of up to 250 tonnes of waste textiles contaminated with oil;
- storage, pending recovery, of up to 5 tonnes of nickel cadmium or nickel metal hydride batteries, and up to 10 tonnes of lead acid batteries;
- storage, pending recovery, of up to 23,000 litres of silver bearing waste from printing or photographic processing.

(d) Licence Applications

An application for a licence (EPA, s.36) may only be made if planning permission has been granted, or the land in question has an "established use" certificate (see 4.18 above). Applications must be made on a form provided by the appropriate Agency (*Env. Act 1995*, Sch. 22, para 68(2), brought into effect 1 April 1998); as well as general details of the site and of the operator, the application should include:

- details of the nature and quantities of wastes to be dealt with;

- details relating to the operation and management of the site;
- any other information required by the regulatory authority.

The licence application should demonstrate that the applicant is a "fit and proper" person (EPA, s.74 - 4.19.8 below), and should be accompanied by the appropriate fee (*Env. Act 1995*, s.41 - see 4.20.1 below).

(e) Consideration of Applications

The regulatory authority may refuse to deal with an application if the information which it requires to accompany the application has not been provided, or until the information is provided (s.36(1A), see *Env. Act 1995*, Sch. 22, para 68(2)). The regulatory authority has four months (or longer if mutually agreed) in which to consider the application - the four months beginning once all the information has been received (ss.36(9) & 36(9A) - *Env. Act*, Sch. 22, para 68(5)). If at the end of that time the regulatory authority has neither advised the applicant of acceptance of the application, nor that it intends to reject it, then the application is deemed to have been refused.

The regulatory authority may only reject a licence in order to prevent pollution of the environment, harm to human health or serious detriment to local amenities. A licence application may also be rejected if the regulatory authority is of the opinion that the applicant is not a fit and proper person or has insufficient financial resources to comply fully with licence conditions. The applicant has a right of appeal (s.43 - see (j) below, & *Env. Act 1995*, s.114) to the Secretary of State with regard to any refusal of licence.

If the regulatory authority plans to grant a licence it must first consult both the appropriate planning authority and the Health and Safety Executive. If any of the land falls within a Site of Special Scientific Interest, English Nature, Scottish Natural Heritage or the Countryside Council for Wales (as appropriate) should be consulted. All consultees have 28 days from the day on which the regulatory authority received the application in which to submit any comments (*Env. Act 1995*, Sch. 22, para 68(6)).

If granted, the licence will include conditions relating to types and quantities of waste covered by the licence, treatment methods, operation and management, hours of operation, record keeping and security provisions. The conditions will also cover standards to be achieved and measures to ensure site activities cause no pollution or other harm to the environment or human health. If necessary conditions to control noise impacts on the surrounding environment will also be included; the Environment Agency is currently finalising *Internal Guidance for the Regulation of Noise at Waste Management Facilities* (see chapter 3, 3.13.2). Licences must also ensure compliance with the 1991 Framework Directive on Waste, with the 1980 Groundwater Directive regarding direct discharges of specified substances (see chapter 5, 5.15.2(b)) and with any Directions from the Secretary of State including waste management papers.

Licence conditions will remain in force even after closure of the site and until a certificate of completion has been issued. In addition site operators will also be required to provide financial guarantees covering care of the site following its closure and until surrender of the licence is accepted – see also (h) below: surrender of site licence.

It is an offence to breach any of the conditions of a waste management licence. Summary conviction may result in a fine of £20,000 and/or six months in prison, or an unlimited fine and/or two years in prison on conviction on indictment.

Details of licence applications, and of any comments on the application, as well as full details (subject to certain exemptions) of all licences, conditions, etc must be kept by the regulatory authority on a register open to public inspection (see below, 4.19.7).

Licence conditions will normally be reviewed annually to ensure they remain appropriate to the activities carried out at the site. Unless otherwise revoked or surrendered, the waste management licence and any accompanying conditions apply to closed disposal sites, with operators retaining a duty of care for them.

The *Environment Act 1995,* Sch. 22, para 69 (brought into force on 1 April 1998), adds new s.36A to the EPA: if the regulatory authority plans to issue a licence which includes a condition requiring work which the applicant may not be entitled to do, it should notify all those with an interest in the land (e.g. the owner, lessee or occupier) who will be required to grant rights to the licence holder to carry out such works; the notice should set out the condition, the work required in connection with it, by when it has to be done and the date by which any representations must be received (the length of time allowed for such representations to be set in Regulations); the regulatory authority must take any such representations into account. A similar requirement is imposed by Article 9 of the *Waste and Contaminated Land (Northern Ireland) Order 1997.* The *Waste Management Licences (Consultation and Compensation) Regulations 1999* (SI 481), made under ss.35A, 36A & 37A (paras 67, 69 & 71 of *Env. Act* Sch. 22), came into force in England, Scotland and Wales on 1 April 1999. They specify a consultation period of three months in the case of a new licence and six weeks (see below) in the case of a variation. The Regulations also specify the circumstances under which compensation may be payable for loss or damage to those granting rights; a claim should be made within 12 months of the date in which entitlement to compensation arises or within six months of the licence holder exercising their rights.

(f) Variation of Licence

Section 37 of the EPA (NI: WCLO, Art.10) places a duty on the regulatory authority to take the necessary steps to ensure that licence conditions are being met and that licensed activities are not causing any pollution or harm to human health; if necessary the regulatory authority may by notice modify the licence conditions, stating when the modification is to be effected. Licence holders may also apply (with the appropriate fee) for licence conditions to be varied. However, if after two months (or longer as mutually agreed), the regulatory authority has neither approved nor rejected the application for modification, it must be assumed that it has been rejected. In all instances there is a right of appeal to the Secretary of State.

New s.37A (*Env. Act 1995*, Sch. 22, para 71, brought into force on 1 April 1998) (NI: WCLO, Art.11) requires the regulatory authority to consult anyone with an interest in the land where it proposes to vary a licence by adding a new condition requiring certain works which the site operator may not be entitled to do. In such instances the regulatory authority should serve a notice on the interested persons setting out the new condition and the work which might be required to meet it. The notice should specify the date by which any representations should be received (the period allowed for such representations to be set in Regulations); any representations received must be taken into account before finally issuing the licence variation.

(g) Revocation and Suspension of Licence

Where the regulatory authority has reason to believe that the licence holder has ceased to be a fit and proper person, that licence conditions are being breached or that the activities covered by the licence are, or are likely to, cause serious harm to human health or the environment, it may serve notice that it intends to suspend or partially revoke the licence (EPA: s.38; NI: WCLO, Art.12). In suspending, or partially suspending a licence, the regulatory authority may require the licence holder to take the necessary steps to deal with or avert the pollution; s.36A of the EPA (see above) - consulting those with an interest in the land - applies in this instance, though such consultation or notification may be postponed in an emergency (EPA s.38(9A-C), *Env. Act 1995*, Sch. 22, para 71(1)). If emergency remedial action is required, the regulatory authority may carry out the necessary work and recover the expenditure from the licence holder, or in the case of a surrendered licence from the former licence holder.

Notices suspending, or partially or totally revoking a licence, or modifying its conditions to prevent pollution or harm take immediate effect, whether or not an appeal has been lodged (see below). Failure to pay fees or charges also results in immediate revocation.

Where a licence has been suspended or revoked, and action required by the regulatory authority for remedying a situation has not been carried out, it may prosecute the licence holder, who on summary conviction may be liable to a maximum fine of £20,000 (and/or six months' imprisonment if special waste involved); on conviction on indictment, the offender becomes liable to imprisonment for up to two years (five years in relation to special waste) and/or an unlimited fine.

Copies of all enforcement notices and convictions will be put on the public register.

(h) Surrender of Site Licence

Section 39 of the EPA, as amended by the *Environment Act 1995* (Sch. 22, para 73), (NI: WCLO, Art.13), applies to all sites for which a waste management licence is required. An application to surrender a licence must be made on a form provided by the regulatory authority, together with any information and evidence required by them, and the appropriate fee.

Prior to making such an application, however, and despite the fact that the site is no longer in use, the site operator will need to maintain any pollution control systems and continue regular monitoring until the site has stabilised - this may take 30 years or more. Once this state has been reached, and in agreement with the regulatory authority, it is considered that the site no longer requires a pollution control system, a period of completion monitoring may be commenced to confirm the site's stability and safety. The period of completion monitoring will be decided by the regulatory authority - probably two years if regular monitoring data exists or five years in other instances.

Schedule 1 to the *Waste Management Licensing Regulations* specifies the information to be given on the application: this includes full details of the site location, licence number, activities carried out on the site and when and estimated quantities of each type of waste dealt with; details should also be given on landfill gas and leachate production and quality of surface water and groundwater; in the case of special wastes, plans should be included showing where the waste was deposited and information about possible contamination.

In considering whether to accept the surrender of a licence, the regulatory authority has a duty to inspect the site to determine whether the condition of the land is likely to cause pollution or harm to human health on the basis of deposits made during the lifetime of the licence. If the regulatory authority plans to accept an application for surrender, it must refer the proposal to the appropriate planning authority which has 28 days from the day on which the regulatory authority receives the application (*Env. Act 1995*, Sch. 22, para 73(3)) to make any comments, or longer if mutually agreed. Where the regulatory authority has neither accepted nor rejected an application for surrender within three months of its receipt (or longer if mutually agreed), then it is deemed to have been rejected. If the appropriate planning authority wishes the application to be rejected because it is of the opinion that there is a risk of pollution, then either it or the regulatory authority may refer the matter to the Secretary of State for determination. Surrender of a licence for a closed site will only be accepted after the site has been certified safe and a "certificate of completion" issued.

The requirements for surrendering waste management licences apply to all sites; Waste Management Paper 26A (1994) provides detailed guidance on the completion of waste management licences for landfill sites in view of their potential to cause more serious pollution. It outlines the requirements for monitoring completed landfill sites up

to and including applying to surrender the licence. Guidance note WMP 401, published in 1999 by the Environment Agency outlines the Agency's policy on licence surrender. Under s.35(8) of the EPA, the Agency/SEPA has a duty to take account of guidance, such as WMPs, issued by the Secretary of State.

Full details of applications to surrender a licence etc must be put on the public register kept by the regulatory authorities.

(i) Transfer of Licences

Where it is proposed to transfer a licence (EPA, s.40; NI: WCLO, Art.14), the current and proposed licence holders must make a joint application to the regulatory authority (on the form provided), together with the relevant fee (*Env. Act 1995*, Sch. 22, para 74). Schedule 2 to the WML Regulations specifies the information to be given on the application: this should include full details of the licence and information to demonstrate that the proposed licence holder is a fit and proper person (EPA, s.74, 4.19.8 below). If within two months (or longer as mutually agreed) from the date of receiving the transfer application, the regulatory authority has neither agreed to nor rejected the transfer, then it is deemed to have been refused. Again, full details will be put on the public register.

(j) Appeals

There is a right of appeal (EPA: s.43; NI: WCLO, Art.17) to the Secretary of State (NI: Planning Appeals Commission) against a decision of the regulatory authority in the following instances:

- an application for a licence or modification of licence conditions is rejected;
- disagreement about licence conditions;
- disagreement over modification of licence conditions;
- a licence is suspended;
- a licence is revoked because it is thought the licence holder is no longer a fit and proper person or the licensed activities may cause environmental pollution or harm to human health and subsequent requirements to remedy the situation have not been carried out;
- rejection of an application for surrender of a licence;
- rejection of an application to transfer a licence.

There is also a right of appeal under s.66 of the EPA (NI: WCLO, Art.36(5)) where the regulatory authority rejects a request for information to be kept off the public register on the grounds of commercial confidentiality.

The WML Regulations prescribe that appeals should be made in writing to the Secretary of State; section 114 (& Sch. 20) of the *Environment Act 1995* enables the Secretary of State to appoint someone else to handle the appeal on his behalf. As from 1 April 1996, the Secretary of State transferred his powers to take decisions on waste management licensing appeals to the Planning Inspectorate which is based in Bristol. The Secretary of State will determine only those appeals of "major importance" or where difficulties arise.

The written statement should include the reasons for the appeal, copies of relevant documents and a statement as to whether the appellant wishes the appeal to be determined by means of a hearing or by correspondence. Appeals relating to licences should be made within six months of the action precipitating the appeal; those relating to information for the public register should be made within 21 days of the regulatory authority's initial decision.

Details of the appeal etc should be copied to the regulatory authority who will put a copy on the public register. Copies of all appeal decisions will also be put on the public register.

NB. The *Waste Management Licensing Regulations 1994* also deal with the following:

- Registration of waste brokers and dealers (see 4.21.2).
- Public registers (ss.64-66 of the Act): see below, 4.19.7).
- Fit and Proper Person (s.74 of the Act: see below, 4.19.8).
- Implementation of certain parts of the EU Directive on protection of groundwater against pollution by certain dangerous substances - see also chapter 5, 5.15.2(b).

(k) Supervision of Licensed Activities

Section 42 of the EPA (as amended by the *Env. Act 1995*, Sch. 22, para 76) (NI: WCLO, Art.16) places a duty on regulatory authorities to ensure that licences and their conditions are being complied with and that authorised activities are not causing pollution, harm to human health or having a detrimental effect on local amenities.

If the regulatory authority is of the opinion that emergency work is needed to prevent pollution etc, it may carry out the work itself, recovering any expenditure from the licence holder or as the case may be the former holder of the licence.

Where the regulatory authority is of the opinion that a licence condition is not being complied with, or is likely not to be complied with, it should serve a notice on the licence holder stating this; the notice will detail the activities constituting the non-compliance or likely non-compliance, the remedial steps to be taken and the time within which those steps must be taken. Non-compliance with the notice may result in partial or total revocation of the licence or in its suspension; if it is felt that this would be an ineffectual remedy, the regulatory authority may take action in the High Court to secure compliance (EPA, s.42(6A), see *Env. Act 1995*, Sch. 22, para 76(7)). See also above, Revocation and Suspension of Licences and Appeals.

The Environment Agency is introducing a risk-based inspection scheme for waste sites which will determine their inspection frequency. "Operator and Pollution Risk Appraisal" (OPRA) enables a "score", to be reviewed quarterly, to be set for each site based on such aspects as the type of facility, number of enforcement notices, breaches of licence conditions etc. The appraisal looks at issues such as how well the site is managed and makes an assessment of the environmental risks associated with the particular site. The site's "score" will determine its minimum inspection frequency. The scheme will also (subject to consultation) be used to determine the annual subsistence charge paid by each operator, with poor performers who require more frequent inspections paying higher charges.

In June 2000 the Secretary of State issued statutory guidance on supervising operators' compliance with waste management licences and the frequency of site inspections; this replaces paras 2.30-2.37 of, and para B9 of Appendix B of, WMP 4 (*Licensing of Waste Management Facilities*) and paras 6.8-6-9 of WMP 4A (*Licensing of Metal Recycling Sites*). The guidance applies in England, Scotland and Wales.

4.19.4 National Waste Strategy (ss.44A-B)

These sections of the EPA, together with Schedule 2A, are added by the *Environment Act 1995*, s.92 and Schedule 12. (It should be noted that the requirement for waste regulation authorities to prepare waste disposal plans under s.50 of the EPA was revoked by the *Env. Act*, Sch. 22, para 78 with effect from 1 April 1996.)

Section 44A requires the Secretary of State for the Environment, Transport and the Regions to prepare a National Waste Strategy for England and Wales; s.44B places a similar obligation on the Scottish Environment Protection Agency as regards Scotland; in Northern Ireland, the Department of the Environment (Environment & Heritage Service) has a similar obligation under Article 19 and Schedule 3 of the *Waste and Contaminated Land (Northern Ireland) Order 1997*, which was brought into force on 1 December 1998. Preparation of the Strategies will implement Article 7 of the 1991 Framework Directive on Waste. The Strategies should include policies for meeting the following objectives:

- ensuring that waste is recovered or disposed of without endangering human health or using processes or methods which could harm the environment (including causing noise or odour nuisance).
- establishing an integrated and adequate network of waste disposal installations taking account of BATNEEC; the network should also aim to help the EU meet its objective of becoming self-sufficient in waste disposal, and that waste is disposed of in the nearest appropriate installation.
- encouraging the prevention or reduction of waste through the development of clean technologies, the technical development and marketing of products with

the least impact on the waste stream, and the development of techniques for the final disposal of dangerous substances in waste for recovery.

- encouraging recovery, reuse, reclamation, recycling etc and the use of waste as a source of energy.

The Strategy should also include details of the amounts of waste to be recovered or disposed of, general technical requirements and requirements for specific types of waste.

The Environment Agency must be consulted in the preparation or modification of the Strategy, together with representatives of local government and industry; others may be consulted as considered appropriate. SEPA and the DOE(NI) should consult similar bodies.

The Secretary of State may require the Environment Agency to advise on the policies to be included in the Strategy and to carry out an investigation and report on the amount and types of likely waste arisings, and the facilities which are or may be needed to deal with them. Before carrying out its investigation, the Agency should consult representatives of local planning authorities and of industry, and should report its findings to them. *Waste Management Planning - Principles and Practice*, (DOE, 1995), sets out good practice for the conduct and design of surveys to obtain key information on waste arisings and waste management facilities; the guidance suggests that surveys should be carried out every three years.

In Scotland, the Secretary of State may direct SEPA as to the policies to be included in the Strategy as well as requiring it to carry out an investigation with similar objectives to those for England and Wales.

England and Wales

In June 1998, the Government published a first consultation paper on its proposals for a National Waste Strategy for England and Wales. *Less Waste, More Value* highlighted the need to develop sustainable waste management practices based on reducing the amount of waste produced and encouraging more recycling and recovery of waste; waste which could not be recycled or recovered must be disposed of in such a way that it caused minimum harm to the environment. Following further consultation in July 1999, the National Waste Strategy (*The Waste Strategy 2000*) was published in May 2000. In emphasising waste reduction and the need to maximise recycling, the Strategy takes account of the following principles:

- an integrated approach to waste management
- a reduction in the quantity and hazard of waste arisings
- higher levels of re-use
- increased recycling and composting
- increased energy recovery
- further development of alternative recovery technologies
- increased public involvement in decision-making
- effective protection of human health and the environment.

It outlines how each sector - central and local government, regulatory authorities, community and voluntary groups, households and individuals - can contribute to achieving the aims of the Strategy, and the targets for reducing waste, which are:

- by 2005, to reduce the amount of industrial and commercial waste landfilled to 85% of its 1998 levels;
- to recover 40% of municipal waste by 2005, 45% by 2010 and 66% by 2015;
- to recycle or compost at least 17% of household waste by 2003, rising to 25% by 2005, 30% by 2010 and 33% by 2015.

Local authorities in England are to be set statutory performance standards for recycling for the year 2003 and will be required to draw up action plans for meeting them. Performance standards will be based on the actual recycling percentages achieved by waste disposal authorities in 1998/99:

- those which achieved less than 5%: 10% by 2003
- those which achieved between 5-15%: 10-30% by 2003
- those which achieved more than 15%: 33% by 2003

These standards will be prescribed under the *Local Government Act 1999* which enables the Secretary of State to set performance standards for any local authority service.

Other key measures in the Strategy include:

- Government departments are to be required to buy recycled products, starting with paper;
- a new Waste and Resources Action Programme to develop markets for recycled waste;
- tradable permits limiting the amount of waste local authorities can send to landfill sites;
- extending producers' responsibilities to recover their products (e.g. newspapers, junk mail);
- working with the National Waste Awareness initiative in continuing to raise public awareness on the need to reduce waste.

While the Strategy covers both England and Wales, the National Assembly for Wales has responsibility for its implementation in Wales and is preparing a programme aimed at meeting Wales' portion of the targets for reducing waste.

Section 353 of the *Greater London Authority Act 1999* requires the Mayor of London to prepare and publish a "Municipal Waste Management Strategy". This should contain proposals and policies for the recovery, treatment and disposal of municipal waste in Greater London; in preparing (or revising) the Strategy, the Mayor should have regard to recycling plans prepared by London local authorities and to the National Waste Strategy (ss.49 and 44A respectively of the EPA), as well as to any guidance or Directions from the Secretary of State. The Mayor is required to consult: the Environment Agency; waste disposal authorities in Greater London and any whose area adjoins Greater London; local authorities in whose area municipal waste is disposed of by WDAs in London; and other bodies concerned with waste minimisation, recovery, treatment or disposal of municipal waste which the Mayor considers it appropriate to consult. Waste disposal authorities and waste collection authorities in London must have regard to the Mayor's Waste Strategy.

Scotland

Scotland's National Waste Strategy was adopted by the Scottish Executive and published by SEPA in December 1999. It outlines programmes aimed at ensuring all those involved in waste planning and management put in place the policies needed to achieve sustainable waste management. It envisages a need for up to 11 new waste treatment facilities - including recycling, composting and energy to waste plant - to meet the EU targets for reducing the amount of biodegradable waste sent to landfill (see 4.11). To facilitate achievement of the Strategy's objectives and to encourage locally based waste management proposals, SEPA plans to establish eleven regional waste strategy groups.

Key measures for reducing waste and implementing sustainable waste management policies in Scotland include:

- local authorities to review and implement recycling plans by 2002;
- SEPA to ensure sufficient staff trained in waste minimisation to facilitate development of waste minimisation plans by industry;
- SEPA to give guidance on recycling targets for household waste;
- industrial waste arisings (excluding construction and demolition waste) to be reduced by 3-5% by 2005, 6-9% by 2010 and 10-12% by 2015;
- targets for recovery and recycling of construction and demolition waste, and other industrial waste, to be established by 2002;
- municipal waste arisings to be reduced by 1% per annum;
- establish an increase in market capacity for three key recycled materials of 50% by 2003.

Northern Ireland

Northern Ireland's Waste Management Strategy was published in March 2000 and includes as a key objective the need to reduce the amount of waste sent to landfill by two-thirds. Other key objectives are to make the best use of the waste that is generated; to minimise the risk of environmental damage or harm to human health; and to move towards re-use, recycling and recovery of waste, with landfill disposal as a last resort.

As well as a commitment to meeting the targets in the EU's landfill Directive, the Strategy sets provisional targets, which are to be reviewed in 2003, of

- the recovery – through recycling, composting or energy

recovery – of 25% of household waste by 2005, and 40% by 2010;
- recycling of 15% of household waste by 2005 and 25% by 2010;
- a reduction to 85% of 1998 levels in the landfill of commercial and industrial waste;
- reduction in household waste arisings to 1998 levels by 2005, followed by further 1% reduction every three years.

4.19.5 Collection, Disposal or Treatment of Controlled Waste

Collection of Controlled Waste (ss.45-48)

Most of these sections came into effect on 1 April 1992 (E, S & W). They detail the duties of waste collection authorities for collecting controlled waste, and the provision of bins for both household and commercial or industrial waste. Similar provisions for Northern Ireland are contained in Article 20 of the *Waste and Contaminated Land (Northern Ireland) Order 1997,* which came into effect on 6.10.99; the waste collection authority is the district council.

The WCA may charge for the collection of commercial and industrial waste, and under the *Controlled Waste Regulations 1992* (E, S & W), may charge for the collection of certain types of household waste or from those premises whose waste is classified as household waste (see 4.2.1 above). Examples of when a charge may be made include: garden waste; clinical waste from a domestic property; waste from camp sites or self-catering accommodation; waste from residential hostels, homes, educational establishments or premises forming part of a hospital or nursing home; asbestos; dead domestic pets; waste from halls used for public meetings; and waste from royal palaces.

Waste Management Plans (NI: WCLO, Art.23)

This Article was brought into force on 6 October 1999 through Commencement Order (SR 373). Each district council in Northern Ireland is required to carry out an investigation with a view to deciding what arrangements are needed for the purpose of treating, recovering or disposing of controlled waste within its area; the need to prevent or minimise environmental pollution and harm to health is a prime objective. In drawing up an appropriate plan the council should take account of the objectives and targets contained in the Waste Strategy (Art.19, and see 4.19.4 above). The Strategy also suggests that councils should cooperate regionally in producing their plans which, it says, "is essential to improving the environmental performance of waste management facilities ... and meeting recycling and recovery targets".

The plan should include information on types and quantities of waste to be disposed of; methods of disposal and treatment with costs and savings attributable to each method; quantities of waste which the district council expects to be disposed of or treated in its area, including waste to be brought into its area or taken out of it. Wherever possible priority should be given to recovering waste. In preparing the plan, the district council should consult the DOE(NI), any other district council which might be affected by its plans as well as others (e.g. local business or industry) who might have an interest in it. Before finalising the plan, the district council must publicise it locally to give the public an opportunity to comment on it. The draft must be sent to the DOE(NI) – the Strategy requires this to be done by January 2001 - as must a copy of the final version (by June 2001), and it should also be publicised locally. The district council should keep a copy of the plan, to which members of the public should have free access; a charge may be made for copies of the plan.

Section 50 of the EPA, which was repealed by the *Environment Act 1995* on 1 April 1996, contained similar provisions for England, Scotland and Wales. Locally based waste disposal plans have been replaced by a Waste Strategy for England and Wales and similar for Scotland - see ss.44A & 44B of the EPA, above.

Waste Recycling (s.49, s.52 and ss.55-56)

Under s.49 which was brought into force on 1 August 1991, waste collection authorities are required to draw up plans for recycling household and commercial waste. WCAs in England (except those in Greater London) and Wales should send a draft of the plan to the Secretary of State; section 361 of the *Greater London Authority Act 1999* amends the EPA to require local authorities in Greater London to submit their draft plan to the Mayor.

The plan should include details of the amounts and types of controlled waste it is expected to recycle, arrangements for dealing with it and costs. Following its finalisation, the waste collection authority must ensure that copies of the plan are available for public inspection and must also send a copy to the local waste disposal authority and to the regulatory authority.

Scottish councils are to be required to produce recycling plans as necessary, following the publication of guidance and of the Scottish Waste Strategy (This Common Inheritance: UK Annual Report, 1997).

Section 52 of the Act (which mainly applies in England only), introduces a system of "recycling credits"; where the WDA avoids disposal costs due to recycling initiatives by the WCA, it must pay the WCA a sum equivalent to that saved. Similarly, if the WDA retains waste for recycling, thus saving the WCA collection costs, the WCA must pay the WDA an equivalent sum. Both the WCA and WDA may pay a third party to recycle waste on their behalf (this latter point applies in Scotland and Wales also).

Article 24 of the *Waste and Contaminated Land (Northern Ireland) Order 1997* makes provision for the district council to pay another person in respect of waste collected by them for recycling; the payment should represent the council's net saving in not collecting and disposing of the waste itself.

Waste collection and disposal authorities may buy and sell waste for the purpose of recycling and make arrangements for the production of heat and electricity from waste (EPA: s.55; NI: WCLO, Art.26 - effective 6.10.99).

The Environmental Protection (Waste Recycling Payments) Regulations 1992 (SI 462)

These Regulations which cover Great Britain came into force on 1 April 1992. They specify how waste recycling credits are to be valued. However, they implement only that part of section 52 requiring the WDA to pay recycling credits to WCAs for savings as a result of waste recycled. WDAs are also encouraged to pay similar credits to other organisations for recycling but such payments are not mandatory. A Schedule to the Regulations provides figures (updated annually) for determining the net saving of expenditure in those areas where sufficient information is not available or could only be determined at disproportionate cost - for 2000/01 see the *Environmental Protection (Waste Recycling Payments) (Amendment) (England) Regulations 2000* (SI 831); similar Regulations apply in Scotland – SSI 185 which came into force on 7 July 2000.

Land Occupied by Disposal Authorities (Scotland) (s.54)

This section of the Act is revoked by the *Environment Act 1995.* Scottish district and island councils were responsible for both waste regulation and waste disposal though the functions had to be separated internally. This section of the Act detailed the additional provisions applying in Scotland with regard to the deposit of waste on land occupied by WDAs.

Acceptance of Waste (s.57-58) (NI: WCLO, Art.27)

These sections empower the Secretary of State (NI: DOE) to require holders of waste management licences (and in Scotland a WDA) to accept and keep/treat or dispose of controlled waste as directed by the Secretary of State.

Removal of Unlawfully Deposited Waste (s.59) (NI: WCLO, Art.28)

Waste regulation authorities and waste collection authorities may by notice require the removal or treatment within 21 days of waste deposited unlawfully on any land in their area. Failure to comply with the notice without adequate excuse is an offence. Where there is a danger of pollution or harm to health, the regulatory authority or WCA may arrange for removal of the waste and recover the costs from the occupier of the land.

The occupier of the land may appeal against the notice to the appropriate Magistrates' Court (Sheriff Court in Scotland; Court of Summary Jurisdiction in NI). The court may quash the notice if the occupier proves that the waste was not deposited by them or that it was deposited without their permission. In this instance, or where the occupier of the land is unknown, or to prevent pollution or harm to health, the regulatory authority or WCA may arrange for removal of the waste.

Interference with Waste and Waste Sites (s.60) (NI: WCLO, Art.29)

It is an offence for an unauthorised person to interfere with waste put out for collection or at a disposal site, unless consent has been obtained from the WCA, WDA or waste disposal company.

Closed Landfill Sites (s.61)

This section of the Act, which was never brought into force, was revoked on 1 April 2000 by the *Environment Act 1995* (commencement order no. 16). It would have applied to those sites for which the licence was surrendered prior to the *Waste Management Licensing Regulations* coming into force and to those sites for which surrender of the licence was accepted under the Regulations.

4.19.6 Special Waste and Non-Controlled Waste

Special Waste (s.62) (NI: WCLO, Art.30)

This section of the EPA (which came into force on 11 August 1995), as amended by the *Environment Act 1995* (Sch. 22, para 80) empowers the Secretary of State to make regulations for the treatment, keeping or disposal of particularly dangerous or difficult wastes. The relevant provision of the NI WCLO took effect on 17 September 1998. The regulations may impose, among other things, requirements on consignors and consignees relating to their handling of the waste, as well as provisions relating to record keeping and public registers and the penalty for contravening the regulations. Provision may also be made relating to the supervision by regulatory authorities of the activities authorised by the regulations or of the persons carrying out the activity, for the recovery of costs incurred by the regulatory authorities in carrying out their regulatory functions and for appeals in respect of their decisions.

It should be noted that all producers, handlers and disposers of special waste are subject to the duty of care provisions (EPA: s.34; NI: WCLO, Art.5).

Special Waste Regulations 1996 (SI 972)

These Regulations, which came into effect on 1 September 1996 (together with amending regulations - SI 2019 - which came into effect on 31 August 1996) apply in England, Scotland and Wales; further amendment Regulations (SI 251), and in Scotland (SI 257) came into force on 28 February 1997. The Regulations replace the *Control of Pollution (Special Waste) Regulations 1980* (SI 1709). The 1996 Regulations implement the 1991 EU Hazardous Waste Directive (91/689/EEC) and the EU List of Hazardous Waste (4.8 above). Similar Regulations, *The Special Waste Regulations (Northern Ireland) 1998* (SR 289), made under Article 30 of the WCLO, came into force

on 18 September 1998, replacing the 1981 Northern Ireland Regulations; they are enforced by the DOE(NI) - Environment and Heritage Service (EHS).

The Regulations apply to all movements of controlled waste (as defined by s.75 of EPA; Art.2 of WCLO) which is also special waste, including movements of waste to and from storage, treatment and recycling facilities and movements of waste to final disposal sites. The Regulations also apply to imports and exports of special waste between Great Britain and Northern Ireland or Gibraltar and special waste landed by ship. Household waste (including clinical waste and waste oil, but not asbestos, generated by households) is exempted but most non-domestic hospital and laboratory waste is not. Unless authorised by a waste management licence (or exempted from licensing) or an authorisation under Part I of the EPA, the mixing of different categories of special waste is prohibited as is the mixing of special and other waste.

Controlled waste is defined as special if it is on the EU's Hazardous Waste List and has one or more of the following hazardous characteristics:

> explosive; oxidising; highly flammable and flammable; irritant; harmful; toxic; carcinogenic; corrosive; infectious; teratogenic; mutagenic; substances and preparations which release toxic or very toxic gases; substances and preparations which after disposal can produce a hazardous characteristic; and ecotoxic.

In addition the Regulations define controlled waste which has any of the following characteristics above a certain threshold as special: highly flammable, irritant, harmful, toxic, corrosive and carcinogenic; medicinal products (as defined by the *Medicines Act 1968*, s.130) are also included in the definition of special waste; it should also be noted that some wastes not on the EU's list may be classified as special, particularly if they contain one or more hazardous characteristic. Examples of special wastes are: waste oils, photographic chemicals, acids, alkaline solutions, industrial solvents, fly ash, pesticides, batteries, prescription-only medicines, pharmaceutical compounds and wood preservatives.

The Regulations require the Environment Agency or SEPA ("the Agency"; in NI, the Environment & Heritage Service) to assign to each consignment or carrier's round of special waste a unique code which must be used on all documentation. (A carrier's round is defined as a journey made by a carrier during which more than one consignment of special waste is collected for transportation to the same consignee; each type of waste must be listed on a schedule to the consignment note; the round must be completed within 24 hours (although it is proposed to increase this to 72 hours). The Agency need not issue a code until the relevant fee has been paid and, in any event, fees must be paid within two months of requesting a code (fees in relation to special waste are set by the Agency/SEPA under the *Environment Act 1995).*

All movements of special waste (unless exempt, see next

paragraph) must be prenotified through completion of the relevant part of the standard consignment note to the office of the Agency in the area to which the special waste is being sent; this should be done at least three working days, but not more than one month, in advance of any movement of the waste. Repeat consignments of the same waste to the same destination can be notified at the time of the first consignment with no further notification being required for 12 months, although Part A of the consignment note should indicate that there are to be a number of consignments and estimate the quantities of waste to be involved in each; waste carriers collecting similar consignments of special waste from various premises to be transported to the same destination need only complete one prenotification which again will last for 12 months.

Certain types of special waste movements are exempt from prenotification, although the standard consignment note procedure still applies; these include:

- special waste movements (except by waste management businesses) within a company where the waste is to be stored prior to recovery or disposal;

- special waste products or materials being returned to their originator because they do not meet the required specifications;

- lead acid vehicle batteries.

Each consignment of special waste should be recorded on the consignment note which has five sections (Parts A to E) for completion at various stages in the procedure and of which there are five copies. Following completion of Parts A and B, the consignor should send one copy to the office of the Agency in whose area the waste is to be sent. The carrier should complete Part C of the remaining four copies, and the consignor Part D; the consignor should keep one copy, with the carrier having the remaining three copies. These three copies should accompany the waste during transportation and should be given to the consignee on delivery of the waste; he should complete the remainder of the consignment note (Part E), retain one copy, give one to the carrier and send the fifth copy to the local office of the Agency. A similar procedure is followed for the second and subsequent removals of repeat consignments or carrier's rounds (for which a schedule in quadruplet must also be prepared) of special waste, and for removals of ships' waste to reception facilities.

The consignor should normally send the (prenotification) copy of the consignment note to the relevant office of the Agency not more than one month, but not less than 72 hours, before removal of the consignment; the consignee should send a copy of the consignment note (or an explanation as to why the delivery has been refused - see also next para) to the relevant office of the Agency within one day of receipt of the special waste.

If for any reason the consignee does not accept the consignment, he should give his reasons on Part E of the consignment note and retain one copy; one copy should be sent to the local office of the Agency/EHS (within one day of receipt of the waste) and one copy given back to the carrier. If there is no consignment note, the consignee should send the Agency a written explanation of his reasons for refusing the waste. The receiving Agency should, within two weeks, send a copy of the consignment note (or explanation of refusal of consignment) to the office of the Agency from which the waste was transported.

Where a delivery has been refused, the carrier should also inform both the consignor and the Environment Agency (or SEPA/EHS) of the fact and get instructions from the consignor as to where the waste should be taken; the consignor should also inform the Agency of the action to be taken.

A fee of £15 (NI: £24), (or £10 for automotive lead-acid batteries), will apply to most consignments and carrier's rounds of special waste, to be paid when the Agency assigns a code to the consignment. No fee is payable for:

- second or subsequent carrier's rounds if the carrier is also the consignee for all rounds, only one consignment is collected from any consignor during the succession, the total weight collected in each round does not exceed 400 kg, or there is less than one week between collection of the first consignment and delivery of the last consignment in a round;

- the removal of a single consignment of special waste if it does not meet the specifications of the person to whom it was supplied;

- the removal of special waste from a ship in a harbour area to a conveyance for transportation outside the area, to reception facilities within the harbour area, or by pipeline to reception facilities outside the harbour area - such waste is also exempt from pre-notification though a consignment note must be completed and a code number obtained from the relevant agency.

Registers containing a copy of all consignment notes and where relevant a copy of the carrier's schedule must be kept by consignors, carriers and consignees. Data must be retained on the registers of consignors and carriers for three years. Consignees must retain all data on their registers until their waste management licence is revoked or surrendered; they should then send their register to the Agency (NI: local district council) for the site which should keep it for not less than three years. In addition details of all consignments of special waste are to be entered on a national database enabling both the Environment Agency and SEPA/EHS to have access to up-to-date information on all special waste movements.

Regulation 16 requires that full site records be kept of all deposits of special waste; this should include a site plan marked with a grid, or with overlays on which deposits are shown. Descriptions of deposits should accord with those on the register of consignment notes; where the waste is disposed of by pipeline or at the place of production, a full record of the quantity, composition and date of disposal should be kept. A written statement of quantity, composition and date of disposal should be prepared of any liquid waste discharged without containers into underground strata or disused workings. The Environment Agency is proposing an amendment to the Regulations which would enable site registers, in exceptional circumstances and with the consent of the Agency to be kept at a site other than that from which the waste was removed. All site records must be kept until a waste management licence is surrendered or revoked, when they should be sent to the Environment Agency (or SEPA, or in NI the local district council).

It is an offence not to comply with the Regulations; it is a defence to prove that non-compliance was due to an emergency or grave danger and that all steps were taken to minimise any threat to the public or the environment and that subsequent compliance took place as soon as reasonably practicable. Summary conviction renders the offender liable to a fine not exceeding level 5 on the standard scale; conviction on indictment may result in a fine and/or imprisonment for up to two years.

The Environment Agency, SEPA and DOE (NI), Environment and Heritage Service have produced a Technical Guidance Note on special wastes (1999); it provides guidance on the definition and classification of special wastes to establish whether or not they fall under the Regulations; it updates and expands Waste Management Paper 23 on special waste and replaces the 1996 Circulars.

The Transfrontier Shipment of Waste Regulations 1994 (see 4.25) are also of relevance to the control of special waste.

A number of amendments to the 1996 Regulations have been proposed (DETR, April 1998), including:

- movement of a consignment of special waste between islands, or between islands and the mainland will be defined as a single journey, although two or more carriers are usually involved, and thus attract only one fee; the consignment note will need to carry details of all carriers;
- in those cases where a consignment of waste has been refused and it is then to be taken to a place other than the original collection or delivery address specified on the consignment note, a new consignment note and fee will be required;
- the £10 fee which currently only applies to automotive lead-acid batteries will be extended to all lead-acid batteries.

The DETR, together with the National Assembly for Wales, Scottish Executive and Northern Ireland Assembly, is reviewing the Regulations with a view to evaluating their efficiency and effectiveness in meeting objectives for hazardous waste management. The review will also consider possible alternative regulatory options, while bearing in mind the need to comply with the Hazardous Waste Directive. The review will also look at the control and disposal of hazardous waste in relation to national

waste strategies, including promotion of the waste hierarchy, BPEO, the need to dispose of waste in the nearest appropriate facility, and the aims of sustainable development.

Non-Controlled Waste (s.63) (NI: WCLO, Art.31)

It is an offence to deposit or knowingly cause or permit the deposit of non-controlled waste which, if it were controlled, would be special waste. Such a deposit done in accordance with a condition of a waste management licence or other consent is not an offence. The penalty for an illegal deposit is the same as that for an illegal deposit of special waste - see above s.33 of EPA.

Waste Minimisation (s.63A)

This section was added by the *Waste Minimisation Act 1998,* which received Royal Assent in November 1998. It enables local authorities to include targets for reducing and recycling waste in waste contracts, to include strategies for minimising waste in waste plans and to promote schemes which encourage consumers to reuse or repair products, e.g. laundry services and household appliance repair services.

4.19.7 Public Registers (ss.64-66) *(NI: WCLO, Arts.34-36)*

These sections (as amended by the *Env. Act 1995,* Sch. 22, paras 82-83) have been implemented through the *Waste Management Licensing Regulations 1994.* Similar provision for public registers in Northern Ireland is made in Articles 34-36 of the *Waste and Contaminated Land (Northern Ireland) Order 1997.*

Waste regulation authorities must maintain public registers containing copies of applications for waste management licences and supporting documentation, as well as copies of the actual licences. In Northern Ireland the register will be maintained by the DOE(NI), with district councils having registers relating to the keeping, treatment and disposal of waste in their areas. The registers must also include details of variations of licence conditions and notices relating to breaches of licence conditions; revocations, suspensions and convictions; monitoring data and inspectors' site reports; appeals and other written representations etc; applications for surrender of a licence and completion certificates (issued once a closed landfill site has been declared safe). Information relating to the *Special Waste Regulations 1996* will also be put on the register. Registers should also show when a person authorised under s.108 of the *Environment Act 1995* (powers of entry) has exercised his powers, for what purpose, the information obtained and action taken. Written reports relating to articles or substances seized and rendered harmless (s.109(2)) should also be put on the register.

Exemption may be sought for exclusion of information from the register on the grounds of commercial confidentiality or national security (EPA, ss.65 & 66). In the latter case the Secretary of State may give directions as to the types of information to be excluded or types of information which he will determine whether or not should be excluded. A person may give notice to the Secretary of State that they wish certain information excluded on the grounds of national security; such information will then remain off the register until the Secretary of State has made his decision. The Agency should be advised that a request is being made to the Secretary of State for the exclusion of certain information on grounds of national security.

Where a request is made for information to be excluded on the grounds of commercial confidentiality, the Agency should consider the request within 14 days; if it does not the information automatically receives that classification. If the Agency does not agree that information is commercially confidential, the information should not be placed on the Register for 21 days, thus allowing time for an appeal to the Secretary of State; s.114 of the *Environment Act 1995* enables the Secretary of State to appoint someone to deal with the appeal on his behalf. The appeal statement should be in writing and should include copies of the material in dispute (see above - Appeals under *Waste Management Licensing Regulations 1994*). A further seven days should elapse following determination or withdrawal of the appeal before information is placed on the Register (*Env. Act 1995,* Sch. 22, para 83(1)).

Information excluded on the grounds of commercial confidentiality loses this classification after four years unless an application is made for classification to continue. Where information has been excluded, a statement to this effect will be included on the register; if the exclusion relates to the terms and conditions of the licence, a statement confirming, or otherwise, compliance with licence conditions will be included.

Waste collection authorities in England and Wales are also required to maintain public registers relating to the treatment, keeping or disposal of controlled waste in their area. The WRA has a duty to supply waste collection authorities with the relevant information to enable them to maintain their registers.

The registers are open to the public free of charge and copies of information available for a "reasonable charge". The Secretary of State may prescribe where such Registers are to be available (*Env. Act 1995,* Sch.22, para 82(5)).

Information relating to licences will be retained on the register for the duration of the licence plus twelve months. Rejected applications will be retained on the register for twelve months from the date of rejection. Monitoring data is retained for four years and for four years if superseded by new data.

Annual Reports (NI: WCLO, Art.37)

The DOE(NI) must prepare an annual report covering its regulatory responsibilities for waste management, including income and expenditure; reports should also include information relating to implementation of waste disposal and recycling plans and prosecutions. The report

should be published not later than six months after the end of the year to which it relates.

Section 67 of the EPA, which placed a similar duty on waste regulation authorities, was revoked on 1 April 1996 following implementation of the *Environment Act 1995.*

4.19.8 Fit and Proper Person (s.74) *(NI: WCLO, Art.3)*

Section 36 of the EPA (NI: WCLO, Art.8(4)) states that (subject to compliance with certain other conditions), a WRA cannot reject an application for a waste management licence if it is satisfied that the applicant is a fit and proper person. A person should not be treated as fit and proper (EPA, s.74, NI: WCLO, Art.3(3)) if they are not technically competent to manage the site concerned, do not have adequate financial resources (to manage the site in compliance with licence conditions) or have been convicted of a relevant offence (see reg.3 of WML Regulations); this includes an offence under various sections of the EPA, COPA and the *Transfrontier Shipment of Hazardous Waste Regulations 1994;* evasion of landfill tax is also a relevant offence (see this chapter 4.4.1).

A person will be considered as technically competent if they hold a certificate of competence at the appropriate level from the Waste Management Industry Training Board (WAMITAB); for instance, an applicant for a licence for a landfill site which receives biodegradable or special waste which requires substantial engineering works would need to have a certificate of technical competence in managing landfill sites at level four. Similar appropriate qualifications from another industry board may also be acceptable. For some smaller landfill sites and waste treatment operations, formal qualifications will not be a necessity; instead, before granting a WML, the regulatory authority will need to be satisfied that the site management has appropriate knowledge and understanding of the operations. Persons considered technically competent to handle waste which has subsequently become special as a result of the *Special Waste Regulations 1996* do not have to apply for a new certificate of competence (*Special Waste (Amendment) Regulations 1997*, SI 251).

The Waste Management Licensing Regulations 1994 (as amended in 1996 - SI 634 England & Wales; SI 100 in Scotland) prescribe that an existing manager (i.e. someone who has been manager of a relevant facility in the twelve months prior to 1 October 1996 and is registered with WAMITAB) will be exempt from the requirements and permitted to manage the same type of facility until 1 October 2001. People 55 and over on 1 October 1996 with at least five years relevant experience at a particular type of facility over the last ten years will be treated as technically competent until 1 October 2006. The management at sites where COPA licences have been converted into EPA licences will be deemed technically competent for that site only. 1997 Amendment Regulations (SI 2203) specify the type of certificate required to be considered technically competent for different types of treatment plant.

Section 74 of the EPA requires the management of the licensed activity to "be in the hands of a technically competent person". DOE (now DETR) guidance interprets this as being in the hands of one or more individuals who together make up the technical competence required for the site or sites and are in a position to ensure proper management of the site on a day to day basis.

To be considered a fit and proper person, the licence applicant must also demonstrate to the regulatory authority that adequate financial provision has been made to ensure that licence conditions, including post-closure monitoring and pollution control obligations, can be met. DOE guidance suggests that the regulatory authority should let the applicant have a draft copy of the licence to enable a suitable financial plan to be submitted.

The Waste Management Licensing Regulations (see above) list the various Acts under which, if an offence was committed, it would be considered relevant to the holding of a licence; these include legislation relating to waste disposal and transportation, *Public Health Acts*, certain sections of the EPA and of the *Water Resources Act 1991*.

Further guidance on what constitutes a fit and proper person is given in Waste Management Paper No. 4, *Licensing of Waste Facilities* (published 1994).

4.20 ENVIRONMENT ACT 1995

4.20.1 Fees and Charges for Licences

Section 41 of the EPA was repealed on 1 April 1996 following implementation of ss.41-43 of the *Environment Act 1995* which contain powers for the Environment Agency and SEPA to make charging schemes for environmental licences; such schemes have to be approved by the Secretary of State. In Northern Ireland, a charging scheme will be made under Article 15 of the *Waste and Contaminated Land (Northern Ireland) Order 1997.*

In common with other charging schemes for pollution control, the aim is to enable the Agencies to recover their costs for both assessing applications for licences (or alterations to them) and to fulfil their duty (EPA, s.42) to supervise licensed activities (e.g. inspections and monitoring). Charges are not intended to cover duties such as maintenance of public registers and enforcement activities. The level of charges and fees is reviewed annually.

The Waste Management Licensing (Fees and Charges) Scheme (originally made under the EPA) was first introduced on 1 May 1994 and covers:

a) application fee for waste management licence;

b) application fee for varying or modifying licence (where the request comes from the licence holder);

c) application fee to surrender a licence;

d) annual subsistence charge (for landfill sites this will be based on whether the site is active, or closed but no certificate of completion issued) - see also final para this section;

e) application fee to transfer a licence.

In those instances where the Agency (or SEPA) has a duty to consult the appropriate planning authority, the fee payable will include an amount to cover their costs. The subsistence charge will also include an amount to cover the costs of the planning authority if it is consulted because of concern that a licensed activity may, or is causing pollution.

The fee payable is based on the quantity and type of waste to be dealt with and on the activity to be carried out - i.e.

- treatment of controlled waste in or on land;
- keeping of controlled waste in or on land;
- disposal of controlled waste in or on land;
- disposal of controlled waste in or on land where disposal operations have ceased;
- treatment or disposal of controlled waste by mobile plant.
- sites authorised to take waste newly defined as "special" under the *Special Waste Regulations 1996.*

Where the application (or subsequent licence) is for the keeping and treatment of waste, only one charge will be payable and that will be the higher of the two. However, where the activity relates to either the keeping and disposal of waste or the treatment and disposal of waste, separate fees will be payable. An operator requiring both a site licence and a mobile plant licence will also have to pay two fees. However in certain circumstances where more than one site licence is held by the same person only one standard component is payable. Detailed schedules of the amounts which apply in each instance are appended to the Scheme document.

The Environment Agency is proposing to use its "Operator Pollution Risk Appraisal" scheme to determine annual subsistence charges; this assigns a "score" for a site based on operator performance and the environmental risk posed by the site; thus, poorly managed sites and those posing a greater risk are likely to pay higher charges reflecting the Agency's need to inspect the site more frequently.

4.20.2 Producer Responsibility Obligations (Packaging Waste) Regulations 1997 (SI 648), as amended

A 1994 European Union Directive on packaging waste aims to increase the use of reusable and recyclable packaging and sets targets to this end; the UK is required to recover a minimum 50% by weight of packaging material and to recycle a minimum of 25% by weight of the total waste flow by 2001 - see earlier this chapter 4.12.

Sections 93-95 of the *Environment Act 1995* (which came into force on 21 September 1995) relate to producer responsibility for packaging and packaging waste. The

Secretary of State may, after consultation with bodies likely to be affected, make Regulations imposing an obligation on producers to increase the reuse, recycling or recovery of products and materials (at a time when it becomes, or has become, waste). Regulations should only be introduced if they will result in significant economic and environmental benefit, when weighed against the cost of imposing producer responsibility; the Regulations should impose the minimum burden necessary on business to achieve the desired result. The Regulations may specify:

- the classes or descriptions of persons to whom the producer responsibility applies and of products or materials covered;

- targets to be met by weight, volume or other method;

- registration of persons subject to producer responsibility and of exemption schemes and associated requirements; the registers would be the responsibility of the Environment Agency and SEPA, and in Northern Ireland, the Environment and Heritage Service;

- fees, application for registration and appeals procedure, etc.

The *Producer Responsibility Obligations (Packaging Waste) Regulations 1997* (SI 648) came into force on 6 March 1997 and, together with 1999 amendment Regulations (SI 1361, effective 4 June and SI 3447, effective 14 December), apply in England, Wales and Scotland; Similar Regulations, SR 115 which came into force on 1 June 1999 and amendment Regulations, SR 496 which came into force on 14 December 1999 apply in Northern Ireland. Further amendment Regulations covering England and Wales were laid before Parliament on 21 November altering the obligations for recovery and recycling targets to be met by producers (see Table 2.8); the amendment Regulations were expected to come into force on 31 December 2000.

The Regulations apply to all businesses involved in the packaging chain (see Table 4.8) and which handle more than 50 tonnes of packaging material and/or packaging in a year, and with an annual turnover of £5 million or more; from 1 January 2000, businesses with an annual turnover of more than £2 million had to comply with the Regulations.

Businesses covered by the Regulations had to join a registered compliance scheme or register as an individual business with the Environment Agency or the Scottish Environment Protection Agency by 31 August 1997. Registration must be renewed each year by 7 April and a fee paid.

It should be noted that individual branches of a business should register in the country in which the branch is located.

The Agencies are required to monitor compliance with the Regulations and to maintain a public register containing details of individual businesses and schemes registered under the Regulations, together with details of their recovery and recycling obligations; from 1999 the register should also contain a statement confirming that evidence of compliance has been received.

Guidance on compliance with the Regulations has been issued by the Environment Agency and SEPA and the EHS.

Northern Ireland

The *Producer Responsibility Obligations (Packaging Waste) Regulations (Northern Ireland) 1999* (SR 115) came into force on 1 June 1999. These Regulations, as amended, mirror those in force in the rest of the UK. Producers must either join an approved compliance scheme or register as an individual. In either case, those covered by the Regulations had to register with the Environment and Heritage Service before 30 September 1999 (and in subsequent years, for renewals or new registrations by 1 April).

Compliance Schemes

A business may choose to become a member of a compliance scheme; such schemes will be responsible for meeting the aggregated targets of its members and will be required to provide data demonstrating compliance to the relevant Agency - the first date for compliance with targets was 31 December 1998. Scheme members are charged an annual fee of £460 and required to provide the scheme with packaging data. Registered compliance schemes are required to let the appropriate Agency have aggregated packaging data and a certificate of compliance with the Regulations by the end of January of the following year to which the data applies; by 30 June updated operational plans should be provided. Records and returns to the Agencies must be kept for at least four years.

A scheme which commits an offence under the Regulations, e.g. by knowingly submitting false data, will be de-registered by the appropriate Agency; individual members of the scheme then become liable for meeting their own recycling and recovery obligations.

Individual Business

Alternatively, a business may choose to take on the obligation of meeting the recovery and recycling targets on its own and must calculate its recovery and recycling obligation for meeting its targets by 31 December. Evidence of compliance must be submitted to the relevant Agency by 31 January of the following year. As a condition of registration, individual businesses with an annual turnover of more than £5 million must prepare an annual compliance plan by 30 June each year, to be updated annually.

An individual business who commits an offence under the Regulations, such as knowingly supplying false data to the appropriate Agency, is liable for prosecution; a fine not exceeding the statutory maximum (currently £5,000) may be levied on summary conviction or an unlimited fine on indictment.

Table 4.8: Producer Obligations

Recovery and Recycling Targets:	
2001	
56% recovery (of which at least half must be recovered through recycling) and 18% recycling by material	

Packaging Chain: % of recovery and recycling target to be met by each:	
- raw materials manufacturers	6%
- converters	9%
- packers/fillers	37%
- sellers	48%
- secondary provider	83%

4.20.3 Packaging (Essential Requirements) Regulations 1998 (SI 1165)

These came into force throughout the UK on 31 May 1998 and apply to all packaging manufactured after 31 December 1994. They specify the "essential requirements" to which all packaging must comply, including that

- it is the minimum necessary to meet safety and hygiene criteria for the product concerned;
- it can be re-used, recycled or recovered and will have minimal environmental impact if disposed of;
- it has been made with the minimum use of substances which become noxious or hazardous when incinerated or landfilled.
- limits for concentrations of lead, mercury, cadmium and hexavalent chromium of packaging or its components do not exceed 600 ppm after 30 June 1998, 250 ppm after 30 June 1999 and 100 ppm after 30 June 2001.

Technical documentation showing compliance with the Regulations must be kept for four years following the placing of the packaging on the market.

These Regulations are enforced by trading standards officers who can inspect compliance documentation and issue enforcement notices prohibiting the supply of packaging which it considers does not comply with the Regulations. An offence under the Regulations carries a maximum fine of £5,000, or unlimited on indictment.

4.20.4 Powers of Entry

Sections 108-109 of the *Environment Act 1995* empower "a person who appears suitable to an enforcing authority" to be authorised in writing to enter premises etc where they have reason to believe that an activity for which a licence is required is being, or has been, operated without a licence or where they believe there is a risk of serious pollution. Except in an emergency, a warrant should be obtained if entry has been or is likely to be refused and it is probable that force will be needed to gain entry. See also chapter 1, 1.15.2.

In Northern Ireland, Article 72 and Schedule 4 of the *Waste and Contaminated Land (Northern Ireland) Order 1997* provide similar powers for authorised persons.

4.21 CONTROL OF POLLUTION (AMENDMENT) ACT 1989

This Act deals with the registration of waste carriers and provides powers to control fly-tipping (illegal dumping of waste). The Act empowers the Secretary of State to make Regulations dealing with applications for registration, renewal, maintenance of registers and access to them, and appeal procedures etc.

The Act and Regulations under it are the responsibility of the Environment Agency in England and Wales and the Scottish Environment Protection Agency in Scotland.

In Northern Ireland, Articles 38-43 of the *Waste and Contaminated Land (Northern Ireland) Order 1997* (which came into force on 19 August 1999) cover the registration etc of waste carriers. The legislation is enforced by the Waste & Contaminated Land Inspectorate of the Environment and Heritage Service.

4.21.1 The Controlled Waste (Registration of Carriers and Seizure of Vehicles) Regulations 1991 (SI 1624), amended 1998 (SI 605)

These Regulations which implement the above Act apply in England, Scotland and Wales and came into force on 14 October 1991. Similar Regulations (SR 362) applied in Northern Ireland from 21 September 1999, with applications for registration required by 11 March 2000. The cost of registration is £120 and renewals £60.

From April 1992 (NI: 11 March 2000), it became an offence to transport controlled waste in the course of business or for profit unless registered with the regulation authority. Waste carriers - including producers of building and demolition waste (which includes waste arising from improvements, repairs or alterations) - are subject to s.33 (prohibition on unlicensed deposits of waste etc) and s.34 (duty of care) of the EPA (NI: WCLO, Arts.4 & 5).

Waste carriers, including those operating in Great Britain who do not have, or are not proposing to have, a place of business in Great Britain, must apply for registration from the office of the regulatory authority (i.e. Environment Agency or SEPA) appropriate to the location of their principal place of business; waste carriers should also register with it. Schedule 22, para 37(2), of the *Environment Act 1995* (brought into force on 1 April 1998) adds s.2(3A) to the *Control of Pollution (Amendment) Act 1989*; this empowers the regulatory authority to prescribe the application form and the information to be included (1998 amendment Regulations). An application to register should be made by all (including prospective) partners in the business. Persons wishing to register, or renew registration, as a carrier and as a broker (see below) can make a single application covering both.

There are a number of exemptions to registration; these include:

- charities and other voluntary organisations;

- waste regulation, disposal and collection authorities;
- ferry operators in respect of waste on a vehicle being carried on the ferry;
- ship operators carrying waste for disposal at sea under licence;
- persons authorised under the Animal By-Products Order 1992 (NI: 1993) to hold or deal with animal waste; (carriers whose sole business is carrying animal waste are not exempt).

The regulatory authority has two months (or longer, as agreed mutually) in which to consider the application. Registrations may only be refused if:

- the application procedure has not been complied with;

- the applicant or another relevant person has been convicted of a "prescribed offence" (e.g. contravening environmental pollution control legislation) and is, therefore, in the opinion of the waste regulation authority not suitable for registration as a waste carrier.

Registrations are valid for three years and apply throughout Great Britain. Transporting waste without a valid registration makes the offender liable to a maximum fine of £5,000.

The charging scheme for registration is made under s.41 of the *Environment Act 1995* (1998 amendment Regulations). The current charge for registration as either a carrier or broker is £114 and £78 for renewal; there is an additional charge of £25 if registering as a carrier and broker (see below).

The Code of Practice on the Duty of Care suggests that every vehicle used by a waste carrier should carry a numbered copy of the registration certificate (obtainable from the regulatory authority - photocopies are not valid). This will facilitate checking of registration details by, for example, the police or a waste producer.

The Regulations provide for appeal to the Secretary of State when an application for registration or renewal is refused, or registration revoked; in the latter two cases registrations remain valid until the appeal is determined. (In Northern Ireland appeals will be made to the Planning Appeals Commission, WCLO, Art.41). Any appeal must be made within 28 days (NI: 2 months). Section 114 of the *Environment Act 1995* enables the Secretary of State to appoint someone to handle the appeal on his behalf. On 1 April 1996 the Secretary of State transferred determination of registration appeals to the Planning Inspectorate (based in Bristol).

The Regulations - and a Circular published jointly by the Department of Environment (11/91), Welsh Office (34/91) and Scottish Office (18/91) - detail the action a regulatory authority can take if it has reasonable grounds to believe that controlled waste is being carried by an unregistered carrier or that a vehicle has been used for the illegal disposal of waste (fly-tipping). In the former instance, authorised officers of the regulatory authority and police constables have powers to stop vehicles and to request

production of the registration certificate. They can also take samples of the waste for analysis (NI: WCLO, Art.42).

Where the regulatory authority believes a vehicle has been used for fly-tipping, it must first try to obtain the name and address (through the DVLA) of any person who would be able to provide information as to who was using the vehicle at the time the offence was committed - for instance the vehicle might have been hired out to a third party. If this proves unsuccessful, or the regulatory authority has reasonable grounds for believing a particular vehicle has been used for an illegal deposit - and thus committed an offence under s.33 of the EPA - it can apply to a Justice of the Peace (E & W) or Sheriff (Scotland) (*Control of Pollution (Amendment) Act 1989*, s.6) for a warrant to seize the vehicle. In Northern Ireland, a warrant would be obtained from a Justice of the Peace under Art.43 of the WCLO. Note: any seizure of vehicle on a road should only be carried out by a uniformed police officer as only the police have powers to stop vehicles on public roads.

The Regulations provide for the return of vehicles and their contents subject to certain conditions, e.g. establishment of ownership and carrying out of such other requirements as may be ordered. The regulatory authority may sell or otherwise dispose of or destroy the vehicle and/or its contents only after efforts have been made to inform the owners and following a notice in a newspaper and after a prescribed period (*Env. Act 1995*, Sch. 22, para 37(4)); however the regulatory authority may arrange immediate disposal where the condition of the vehicle's contents so require.

Details of registrations, amendments, renewals, offences etc, will be filed on a register to be maintained by the regulatory authority; the registers will be open to public inspection free of charge.

4.21.2 Registration of Waste Brokers and Dealers

The European Union Framework Directive on Waste (91/156/EEC - see above 4.6) requires that, in addition to waste carriers, waste brokers and dealers - i.e. those who recover or dispose of waste on behalf of somebody else - should be registered; brokers may also apply to be carriers. This requirement has been implemented in Great Britain through the *Waste Management Licensing Regulations 1994* (Reg.18 & Sch.5), as amended by the *Waste Management Licensing (Amendment) Regulations 1998* (SI 606) which came into force on 1 April 1998. Brokers of controlled waste must use a form prescribed by the Environment Agency (or SEPA) in applying for registration or for registering exempt activities. The 1998 Regulations also amend the 1994 Regulations to require charges to be paid in accordance with a scheme made under section 41 of the *Environment Act 1995*. Charitable and voluntary organisations, and waste regulation, collection and disposal authorities are exempt from registering.

Waste brokers and dealers include:

- companies which buy and sell scrap metal and other recoverables either operating from a yard, or as middleman finding both buyer and seller and making all the necessary arrangements for the transaction;

- companies which arrange for the disposal of waste to an appropriate facility on behalf of either another company or waste producer;

- waste disposal operators, carriers etc who arrange for the disposal of waste not covered by their own operating licence.

4.22 INCINERATION: REGULATORY CONTROLS

4.22.1 Integrated Pollution Prevention and Control Regulations 2000

Regulations covering England and Wales (SI 1973) were brought into force on 1 August 2000, with similar Regulations for Scotland (SSI 323) taking effect on 28 September 2000. New incinerators were required to apply for a Permit from the Environment Agency, SEPA, or local authority, as appropriate before 1 January 2001 (Scotland: 1 April 2001). Existing incinerators are not due to transfer to control under the IPPC Regulations until 2005. See chapter 1, 1.13.

4.22.2 Environmental Protection Act 1990, Part I

Prior to implementation of the *Environmental Protection Act 1990,* many of the provisions of Part I of the *Control of Pollution Act 1974* - e.g. site licensing and preparation of waste disposal plans etc - applied to disposal of waste by incineration. Currently all incinerators with an aggregate works capacity of one tonne per hour or more are regulated by the Environment Agency or Scottish Environment Protection Agency for Integrated Pollution Control under Part I of the EPA. Incinerators with a capacity of less than one tonne per hour, but designed to burn at a rate of more than 50 kg/hour, are controlled for air pollution under Part I of the EPA by local authorities in England and Wales and by SEPA in Scotland; this includes most clinical waste incinerators and crematoria. Details of the regulatory controls are contained in chapters 1 and 2 respectively.

The Municipal Waste Incineration Directions 1991 made under s.7(2) of the EPA require the enforcing authorities to include in authorisations conditions complying with standards and emission limits in the two 1989 EU Directives on new and existing municipal waste incinerators (see 4.7.1). A copy of the 1991 Directions is appended to the air pollution control Process Guidance Note for general waste incineration processes (PG5/4(95)).

The EU's 1994 Hazardous Waste Incineration Directive has been implemented through the *Environmental Protection (Prescribed Processes and Substances) (Amendment) (Hazardous Waste Incineration) Regulations 1998* (SI 767);

these apply in England, Scotland and Wales and came into force on 13 April 1998. All hazardous waste incineration processes (including those currently prescribed for air pollution control only) are prescribed for IPC. Authorisations for incineration processes granted before 31 December 1996 had to be varied (or in the case of a Part B process, a new authorisation in place) by 30 June 2000, to ensure compliance with the Directive; authorisations granted after 31 December 1996 had to be varied as soon as possible or, in the case of a Part B process, a new authorisation applied for before 13 July 1998. *The Hazardous Waste Incineration Direction 1998,* dated 29 January 1998, requires the Agency to include conditions in compliance with the Directive in authorisations, or to issue variations as appropriate.

In Northern Ireland, similar regulations apply - the *Industrial Pollution Control (Prescribed Processes and Substances) (Amendment) Regulations 1999* (SR 26), which came into force on 22 February 1999.

4.22.3 Environmental Protection Act 1990, Part III

This part of the Act (Statutory Nuisances and Clean Air) can be used to control certain aspects of incineration not covered by the provisions of other Acts - for instance action in respect of recurring odorous and gaseous emissions which may be prejudicial to health or a nuisance (see chapter 1, 1.16.1).

4.22.4 Clean Air Act 1993

(a) Chimney Height

Local authorities must take grit, dust, and gas emissions into account when accepting plans for new chimneys serving furnaces of 100 lb/hr or more. Chimney height is broadly calculated in relation to the probable future sulphur content of the refuse and the hourly burning rate. Reference to the *Memorandum on Chimney Heights* provides a general guide, and particular attention should be given to the interrelationship of chimney heights, gas plume height, wind velocity and direction, the nature of the terrain and other industry in the area. (See also Appendix 2.5)

(b) Solids Emissions

Smoke emissions from incinerators must be no darker than Shade 2 on the Ringelmann Chart. In smoke control areas, unless special exemption has been made, it is an offence to emit smoke.

Section 5(5) of the *Clean Air Act 1993* makes it an offence not to use the Best Practicable Means for minimising the emission of grit and dust from a chimney. There are no specific limits on grit and dust emissions from incinerators - the *Grit and Dust Regulations 1971* do not apply. However, the DOE issued draft regulations in May 1977 which may be used as a Best Practicable Means guideline for local authorities. A table sets out prescribed maximum rates of emission in kilograms per hour related to the melting rate of the furnace in metric tons per hour. Gas conditions are standardised at 10% carbon dioxide, NTP, dry. The heat release figures are arrived at using, for convenience, a calorific value of 5,000 Btu/lb, but it should be borne in mind that raw refuse, even in a given location, often changes substantially in composition and moisture content.

(c) Sulphur Content of Fuel Oil

Section 31 of the *Clean Air Act 1993* empowers the Secretary of State for the Environment, Transport and the Regions to impose regulations limiting the sulphur content of fuel oil used in furnaces and engines. *The Marketing of Gas Oil (Sulphur Content) Regulations 1994,* came into which came into effect on 1 October 1994, now only apply in Northern Ireland. Among other things, these Regulations make it an offence to market gas oil with a sulphur content in excess of 0.2% by weight (see chapter 2, 2.14.4). Section 36 of the Act also empowers local authorities to require the owner of plant to provide information on emissions to atmosphere, subject to certain restrictions.

In England and Wales and in Scotland the sulphur content of liquid fuels is regulated under the *Sulphur Content of Liquid Fuels Regulations 2000* (E & W: SI 1460; S: SSI 169, which came into force in June 2000. From 1 July 2000 it became an offence to use gas oil with a sulphur content exceeding 0.2%. For more details of these Regulations, see chapter 2, 2.15.

4.23 BATTERIES AND ACCUMULATORS

European Union Directive 91/157/EEC requires Member States to set up schemes for the separate collection of spent batteries and accumulators containing specified amounts of lead, mercury or cadmium with a view to recycling or controlled disposal. A further Directive (93/72) deals with the marking system to be adhered to.

The *Batteries and Accumlators Containing Dangerous Subatances Regulations 1994 (SI 232)* apply in England, Scotland and Wales and were made under the *European Communities Act 1972*. Similar 1995 Regulations apply in Northern Ireland (SI 122). The Regulations:

- prohibit the sale of alkaline manganese batteries with more than 0.025% mercury by weight; button cells and batteries composed of button cells and alkaline manganese batteries containing 0.05% mercury by weight and intended for prolonged use under extreme conditions are exempted;

- require that appliances using batteries covered by the Directive must be designed to ensure that the batteries can be easily removed;

- introduce a marking system for batteries covered by the Directive to indicate separate collection and heavy metal content; this will not apply to those manufactured or imported into the EU before 1 August 1994; nor will it apply to those marketed in Great Britain on or before 31 December 1995.

The first two provisions came into force on 1 March 1994 and the third on 1 August 1994.

The Department of Trade and Industry has issued a consultation document (September 2000) proposing to amend the amend the Regulations covering England, Scotland and Wales as follows:

- from 18 December 2000, batteries and accumulators may not be marketed in Great Britain if they contain more than 0.0005% (5 ppm) by weight of mercury; for button cells or batteries containing button cells, the limit is 2% of mercury by weight;

- the potential fine on summary conviction is raised to level 5 on the standard scale (currently £5,000).

4.24 DISPOSAL OF PCBs AND OTHER DANGEROUS SUBSTANCES

The Environmental Protection (Disposal of Polychlorinated Biphenyls and other Dangerous Substances) Regulations 2000 were made under the *European Communities Act 1972* covering England and Wales came into force on 4 May 2000 (SI 1043). Similar Regulations (SI 95) came into force in Scotland on 8 May and in Northern Ireland (SR 232) on 7 August. They implement a 1996 EU Directive requiring the phasing out of PCBs. They also apply to polychlorinated terphenyls, monomethyl-dibromo-diphenyl methane, monomethyl-dichloro-diphenyl methane and monomethyl-tetrachloro-diphenyl methane.

Holders of PCB contaminated equipment with a total volume greater than 5 dm^3 (5 litres) or any other PCBs at a concentration greater than 0.005% (50 ppm) weight/weight had to register with the Environment Agency (SEPA or DOE, NI) by 31 July 2000 (NI: 31 October 2000). The holding of any substances to which the Regulations apply after these dates is prohibited unless registered.

Registered holders (subject to various exceptions) had to remove from use and dispose of properly all the substances covered by the Regulations by 31 December 2000 (NI: 31 March 2001). Those permitted to continue holding stocks of PCBs etc after these dates include:

- companies authorised to decontaminate or dispose of PCBs;
- laboratories using PCBs for analytical or research work;
- transformers with PCBs in oil at concentrations of 50-500 ppm (the transformer can continue to be used until the end of its useful life);
- companies specifically permitted to continue holding PCBs by the relevant Agency.

The Regulations required the Agencies to compile an inventory of the PCB contaminated equipment held at each registered location by 30 September 2000, to be updated annually. The inventory is to be publicly available.

4.25 TRANSFRONTIER SHIPMENT OF WASTE REGULATIONS 1994 (SI 1137)

In 1996 the UK imported 76,136 tonnes of hazardous waste for treatment and disposal and exported 12,072 tonnes (originating in E, W & NI). (*Digest of Environmental Statistics,* No. 20, 1998).

The above Regulations which came into effect in May 1994 were made under the *European Communities Act 1972* and replace the *Transfrontier Shipment of Hazardous Waste Regulations 1988* (N. Ireland 1989). They apply throughout the United Kingdom and amplify various parts of the EU Waste Shipments Regulation (259/93) to ensure its full implementation in the UK. (NB EU Regulations are binding in their entirety on Member States and thus do not require transposing into national legislation.) The main requirements of the EU Regulation, which covers the supervision and control of waste shipments between Member States and into and out of the European Union, are detailed earlier in this chapter - see 4.9 above. The Environment Agency, SEPA and local authorities in Northern Ireland are the competent authorities for imports and exports of waste, and the Environment Agency for transit shipments.

All shipments of waste will normally be covered by a contract between the notifier (person "who proposes to ship waste or have the waste shipped") and the consignee (person who is going to finally dispose or effect recovery of the waste). Under the UK Regulations, waste regulation authorities are designated as the competent authorities of dispatch and destination. It is proposed to amend the Regulations (DETR, Consultation, 29.9.00) to make the Environment & Heritage Service the competent authority for despatch and destination for Northern Ireland. They are thus responsible for ensuring documentation procedures (consignment notes and movement/tracking forms) are complied with and that the waste is handled in accordance with the documentation and with the EU Regulation. In addition the Regulations require competent authorities to raise objections to any shipments which do not conform to the *UK Management Plan for Exports and Imports of Waste* (see below). If the relevant UK competent authority has objections to a shipment, it may request HM Customs to detain the import or export at a port for up to three days; it is proposed to amend this Regulation to enable HM Customs itself to detain a shipment for up to three days.

The UK Regulations provide for the enforcing authority to issue a certificate confirming that the shipment is or will be covered by a financial guarantee or insurance.

To comply with the EU Regulation, the enforcing authority may serve a notice

- on the notifier requiring the return of a waste shipment to the UK,
- on the consignee to dispose of, or recover the waste, in an environmentally sound manner.

Copies of all consignment notes must be sent to the Secretary of State, with a statement saying whether the shipment received authorisation or not. A Department of Environment Circular 13/94, revised by letter dated 26.1.95 (WO 44/94; SOED 21/94; NI WM 1/94) advises that information given on consignment notes is environmental information for the purposes of the *Environmental Information Regulations 1992;* it will thus normally be accessible to the public, subject to various exemptions in those Regulations such as commercial confidentiality.

It is an offence to contravene either the EU or UK Regulations; summary conviction may lead to a maximum fine of £5,000 (£2,000 in N. Ireland); conviction on indictment may result in an unlimited fine and/or imprisonment for up to two years.

The Department of Environment Circular mentioned above provides detailed guidance on both the EU and UK Regulations, including full advice on the documentation procedures and other requirements.

4.26 UK MANAGEMENT PLAN FOR EXPORTS AND IMPORTS OF WASTE

This document, prepared in accordance with the Waste Framework Directive and the above UK Regulations, sets out Government policy with regard to imports and exports of waste. It is a statutory document and has been legally binding since 1 June 1996. The Plan also provides technical guidance and assessment criteria to enable decisions to be taken on proposed shipments. It does not apply to radioactive waste.

Under the Plan all exports of waste for final disposal are banned; exports of waste for recovery are permitted only to OECD countries but exports of hazardous waste for recovery to non-OECD countries are permitted only in very limited circumstances.

In line with the principle that all countries should aim for self-sufficiency in waste disposal, the UK has adopted a general policy of importing waste only for "genuine recovery operations" including energy recovery. Imports for disposal to landfill will only be permitted if it is considered that the exporting country does not have the necessary technical capacity and facilities to dispose of the waste in an environmentally sound way; imports for incineration from all countries will only be accepted in an emergency. Hazardous waste imports for high temperature incineration from Portugal and Eire are to be allowed indefinitely (because of the small amounts involved); imports from other EU countries were allowed until 31 May 1999, and imports of clinical waste from Eire permitted until the end of 1997.

A draft revised UK Plan was issued for consultation in May 2000; this updates the earlier Plan to incorporate amendments to the EU's Regulation on the Transfrontier Shipment of Waste and to the Basel Convention (see 4.9). It was expected to enter into force in November 2000, when the 1996 Plan would cease to have effect. The Plan applies to all shipments of waste covered by the EU Regulation to and from the United Kingdom; shipments between the UK and Gibraltar are not covered by the Plan as these are regarded as movements within the UK; the Plan does, however, apply to shipments between the UK and its Crown Dependencies and Overseas Territories. The Environment Agency, on behalf of the Secretary of State for the Environment, Transport and the Regions, is the UK competent authority of transit and thus responsible for all shipments passing through the UK, liaising as appropriate with other UK competent authorities.

The main elements are the Plan are as follows:

a) All exports of waste are banned with the exception of: those from Northern Ireland to Ireland as part of sub-regional waste management plans being drawn up under the N. Ireland Waste Strategy; shipments of waste for trial runs to EC and EFTA countries (which are also a party to the Basel Convention) are also allowed; "trial runs" are shipments of waste which would enable an importer to try out a waste management process before deciding whether to import the process itself.

b) Exports of hazardous waste for recovery are permitted to OECD countries, with the consent of the importing country; exports of non-hazardous waste to OECD countries are subject to normal commercial controls. Exports of hazardous waste for recovery to non-OECD countries are banned and those of non-hazardous waste must conform to control under the EU Regulation and Basel Convention.

c) Imports of waste for disposal are only permitted under very limited circumstances, for instance when a country does not have, and cannot reasonably be expected to have the technical capacity to dispose of the waste itself in an environmentally sound manner. Certain imports are permitted from Ireland into N. Ireland, so long as these accord with sub-regional waste management plans (where for instance these propose cross-border cooperation) and with the principle that waste should be disposed of in the nearest suitable facility.

d) Imports of hazardous waste for high temperature incineration are prohibited except in an emergency, or where the exporter is a member of the Basel Convention or has signed a bi-lateral agreement with the UK and/or EC and the Environment Agency is satisfied that there are no suitable facilities closer to the country in question. Such imports are currently permitted from Ireland and Portugal; the draft Management Plan suggests those from Portugal should continue to be permitted but that it is minded to phase out those from Ireland on a timescale that permits Ireland to develop its own high temperature incineration facility.

e) Imports of other waste for incineration are prohibited except from parties to the Basel Convention or where a bi-lateral agreement has been signed and the UK competent authorities are satisfied that no suitable facility exists closer to the country in question. Imports of waste for incineration at sea are also prohibited.

f) Imports of waste for recovery for use principally as a fuel or other means to generate energy or for recycling and recovery of materials are generally permitted.

CONTAMINATED LAND

4.27 INTRODUCTION

Land may become contaminated as a result of a variety of human activities, and the polluted soil present problems for centuries. The metal extraction industries are well known for causing soil contamination and mineral processing also frequently leads to contamination. Indeed, the toxic effects of spoil from Roman lead and silver mines are still visible in parts of North Wales while the more recent extraction of zinc in the Shipham area of Somerset resulted in high levels of cadmium in soil - and hence in home grown vegetables - in the area.

The depositing of wastes, both industrial and domestic, into landfill sites can in some instances result in contamination of ground or surface waters unless properly contained: as different materials decompose, they react together and form leachate, a noxious liquid. A more serious problem with landfill sites can be the build up of methane gas to potentially explosive levels, posing a danger to nearby housing.

The contamination of soil with toxic chemicals may have direct effects on human health if houses and gardens are built on the land in question. Particles of soil handled or ingested by adults or children may carry irritant or poisonous chemicals while the inhalation of such particles, or vapours from the pollutants, provide another absorption route. Vegetable gardens sited on polluted land may produce crops contaminated by the direct uptake of toxins or the deposition of contaminated particles on the growing plants.

Once a pollutant reaches the soil a number of things may happen to it. It may break down or be neutralised; it may be washed out by rain or, if volatile, evaporate; or it may remain in the soil, building up to high concentrations with successive additions. The fate of a pollutant and its concentration are determined by the balance between the rate of input and the rate of removal. Removal mechanisms are, in turn, determined by the chemical, physical and biological properties of the contaminant and of the soil medium, together with the presence and activity of soil organisms, the amount of rainfall and its composition, and the nature of any other materials subsequently deposited.

Pollutant breakdown, by various chemical and microbiological processes, can be an important removal mechanism. Phenols, for instance, can be destroyed by micro-organisms providing that they are not present at concentrations sufficient to inhibit or kill the organisms concerned. Certain herbicides are also decomposed microbiologically and their frequent use leads to the establishment of populations of soil flora particularly adept at breaking them down.

Materials not broken down by micro-organisms - and the breakdown products of those that are - may be leached out if they are soluble in water at the prevailing pH. The type of soil and its permeability affect the rate of leaching with higher rates observed in sandy soils with a low organic content. Leaching through clay soils, and those with large amounts of humus, is much slower as contaminants tend to be more tightly bound to soil particles. Leaching can be prevented by properly lining landfill sites and covering them to prevent rainwater penetration.

Where breakdown and/or leaching do not occur to any great extent, the accumulation of contaminants in the upper layers of the soil occurs and high levels may be reached if repeated or continuous additions of materials are made. This build-up may not be permanent, as subsequent changes in conditions may cause the remobilisation of some materials bound to soil particles under the original circumstances, but in most instances soil contaminated with persistent materials remains damaged indefinitely.

With regard to contamination from landfill sites, the buried biodegradable matter decomposes anaerobically, producing large quantities of carbon dioxide and methane. Depending on the geology of the area, these gases can seep underground or rise to the surface. Methane, as mentioned earlier, is potentially explosive and can cause fires; methane from landfill sites can either be vented to the atmosphere, collected and used as a fuel supply, or simply burned off.

The total restoration of contaminated land to an "unpolluted" state is rarely achievable and, in many cases, unnecessary. Instead, a remedial approach tailored to the intensity and extent of the contamination found and the intended end-use of the site is adopted. In some cases it may be necessary to zone the land for specified non-residential purposes, endorsing the title deeds to that effect. The use of lightly contaminated land for amenity purposes may be possible if the materials present are largely inorganic and a sealing sward of tolerant grasses can be planted to prevent both human contact with the soil and the windborne transport of polluted dust.

More heavily contaminated sites may only be usable for purposes such as car parks, warehouses and other industrial developments where a layer of tarmac or concrete would be laid on the surface, thereby sealing off the pollution. In certain instances, such as the occurrence of highly contaminated pockets in otherwise fairly clean sites, or small sites badly contaminated throughout, the polluted soil may be removed in its entirety to a licensed waste disposal site and replaced with cleaner material.

Chapter 8 of the Royal Commission on Environmental Pollution's 19th report, *Sustainable Use of Soil* (HMSO, 1996), looks at the industrial contamination of soil and also outlines a number of remediation processes, including:

- **solidification**, where a binder (e.g. cement) is used to enclose the contaminated soil in a solid form, reducing its solubility, mobility and toxicity; this method is suitable for dealing with heavy metals but not mercury or organic compounds.

- **physical**, where contaminants are isolated or concentrated, but not destroyed, e.g. by vapour extraction or soil washing.

- **chemical**, where reactants are used to destroy, immobilise, extract or neutralise contaminants.

- **thermal treatment** at 800-2,500 degrees C to destroy contaminants.

- **biological** methods to produce degradation of organic contaminants; to transform to less harmful or mobile forms; or convert to more mobile form to allow separation.

4.28 REGULATORY CONTROLS

4.28.1 Planning Controls

Prior to introduction of the new contaminated land regime, the main means of ensuring contaminated land was not used for any unsuitable purposes was through the planning system; thus controls or conditions, based on both current use and the proposed new use, were put on the land, or remedial work specified as part of the development permission.

PPG 23, *Planning Policy Guidance: Planning and Pollution Control* (June 1994) highlights the need to be aware of the previous use of land in considering development plans. Where contamination is suspected, the developer is responsible both for investigating the land to determine what remedial measures are necessary to ensure its safety and suitability for the purpose proposed, and for actual remediation. Further guidance from DETR will clarify the relationship between planning and Part IIA of the EPA, and give more advice on land contamination issues.

4.28.2 Environmental Protection Act 1990, Part II

Section 34 (effective 1 April 1992) places a duty of care on all those involved in dealing with waste from its generation to its disposal (see this chapter, 4.19.2). The duty of care extends to closed landfill sites where the site operator remains responsible for the site until it has been declared safe and a "certificate of completion" issued.

Section 61 of the Act, which was never implemented and was revoked on 1 April 2000 would have placed a duty on waste regulation authorities to identify and inspect closed landfill sites to ensure their condition was not likely to cause pollution of the environment or harm to human health. Section 143 of the EPA, which came into effect in England and Wales on 14 February 1992 and was also revoked on 1 April 2000 provided for the establishment by local authorities of public registers of contaminated land in their area.

4.28.3 Environmental Protection Act 1990, Part IIA

A consultation document, *Paying for our Past* (DOE, 1994), reviewing arrangements for dealing with contaminated land proposed a "suitable for use" approach - i.e. it should be "treated to deal with unacceptable actual or perceived threats to health, safety or the environment, taking account of the actual or intended use of the site"; and that where practical such land should be brought back into beneficial use. This would not preclude a developer or owner from carrying out more extensive remedial work, nor a regulatory body from requiring it. These proposals have been given effect through s.57 of the *Environment Act 1995*, which adds Part IIA (ss.78A-78YC) to the EPA and contains the legislative framework for identifying and dealing with contaminated land. These sections of the Act, together with Regulations and Statutory Guidance were brought into force in England on 1 April 2000 and in Scotland on 14 July 2000.

The Contaminated Land Regulations 2000

Regulations for England, - *The Contaminated Land (England) Regulations 2000* (SI 227), together with DETR Circular 2000/02 containing the Statutory Guidance came into force on 1 April 2000.

Similar Regulations and Statutory Guidance were brought into force in **Scotland** (SSI 178) on 14 July 2000. Planning Advice Note (PAN 33), published in October 2000 by the Scottish Executive provides advice on developing contaminated land.

The Regulations, which give effect to the relevant sections of the EPA, cover the following:

- Land required to be designated as special sites;
- Pollution of controlled waters (i.e. the circumstances in which controlled waters are adversely affected by land, which is thus designated a special site);
- Content of remediation notices, and persons to whom they should be copied;
- Compensation for rights of entry, etc.
- Grounds of appeal against a remediation notice; appeals to the Magistrates Court and to the Secretary of State.
- Registers.

The Guidance contains much of the detail of how the new regime will operate and covers:

- Definition of contaminated land (including definition of "significant harm" (s.78A(2) & (5) of the EPA);
- Identification of contaminated land and special sites (s.78B(1) & (2));
- Remediation of contaminated land (s.78E(5));
- Exclusion from, and apportionment of, liability for remediation (s.78F(6) & 7));
- The recovery of the costs of remediation (s.78P(2)).

The Agencies may issue Guidance to a local authority in respect of its functions in relation to a specific piece of contaminated land (EPA: s.78V; NI: WCLO, Art.67); the local authority is required to have regard to any such Guidance.

The Regulations and Guidance are described in more detail in the following text.

The Regulations do not cover harm, or pollution of controlled waters as a result of the radioactive properties of any substance (EPA: s.78YC; NI: WCLO, Art.71); a consultation document was published in February 1998 proposing a similar regulatory regime for such land - see this chapter 4.31.5.

Local authorities (district councils and unitary authorities) are the enforcing authority for contaminated land and the Environment Agency or Scottish Environment Protection Agency for any land designated a special site due to the nature of its contamination. The Agency also carries out technical research, and publishes scientific and technical advice.

Northern Ireland

Part III of the *Waste and Contaminated Land (Northern Ireland) Order 1997*, Articles 49-71, makes similar provision for dealing with contaminated land; district councils are the main enforcing authority, except for land designated as a "special site", which is the responsibility of the Waste & Contaminated Land Inspectorate (WCLI) of the Environment and Heritage Service, an agency of the DOE(NI). The WCLI is also responsible for preparing Guidance on relevant Articles of the Order in accordance with Article 69. Reference is made throughout the text to the relevant Articles of the Northern Ireland legislation, which has yet to be implemented.

(a) Identification of Contaminated land and Designation of Special Sites (ss.78A-78D) (NI: WCLO, Arts.50-52)

Local authorities have a duty to inspect their land to identify whether any is contaminated and whether any such land should be designated as a "special site" (see (f) below) because of the nature of the contamination. In identifying contaminated land, local authorities must act in accordance with Guidance from the Secretary of State. This requires them to "take a strategic approach to the identification of land which merits detailed individual inspection". Thus all local authorities are required to draw up a Contaminated Land Strategy which looks at those circumstances – such as evidence of past use of land, evidence that significant harm or pollution of controlled waters has or is being caused; records of contamination and remedial action that has already been taken; in developing its Strategy, which should be formally adopted and published by June 2001, the authority should consult the Environment Agency and other appropriate public bodies, English Nature, English Heritage and the Ministry of Agriculture, Fisheries and Food. Development of the Strategy will enable local authorities to ensure that resources are used efficiently and effectively and concentrated on identifying and investigating those sites most likely to be most seriously contaminated.

In Scotland local authorities are required to complete their initial strategies for identifying contaminated land by 14 October 2001, consulting as appropriate.

Section 78A(2) defines contaminated land as

"land which appears . . . to be in such a condition, by reason of substances in, on or under the land, that -

(a) significant harm is being caused or there is a significant possibility of such harm being caused; or

(b) pollution of controlled waters is being, or is likely to be, caused."

The Statutory Guidance defines what "harm" is to be regarded as "significant" to:

- **human beings:** death, disease, serious injury, genetic mutation, birth defects, or the impairment of reproductive functions. Disease is to be taken to mean an unhealthy condition of the body or some part thereof; this might include cancer, liver dysfunction or extensive skin ailments.

- **living organisms or ecological systems:** an irreversible or other substantial adverse change in the functioning of the habitat or site;

- **property (crops (inc. timber), produce grown domestically or on allotments for consumption, livestock, other owned animals, wild animals which are the subject of shooting or fishing rights, crops):** for crops, this means a substantial diminution in yield or loss of value due to death, disease or other physical damage; for domestic pets the benchmark is death, serious disease or serious physical damage; for food, when it is no longer fit for the purpose intended and fails to comply with food safety legislation;

- **property (buildings):** structural failure or substantial damage making them unfit for their intended purpose.

The Department of the Environment (now DETR) has produced a number of industry profiles detailing the likely types of contamination to be found, and the materials and processes which would have been used by the industry sector concerned.

It should be noted that while two or more sites if considered individually would not be considered to be contaminated, but if considered together would, then each site should be treated as being contaminated (s.78X(1)). Also if land adjoining or adjacent to the area of a local authority appears contaminated, it may act as though the land were within its boundary (s.78X(2)). (NI: WCLO, Arts.68(1) and 68(2) respectively.)

Following identification, the local authority should then by notice (s.78B) inform the appropriate agency, the owner of the land, the occupiers of any part of the land and any other appropriate person.

If the local authority considers that any of the land which it has identified as being contaminated warrants being designated a special site, it should seek the appropriate Agency's advice in making its decision (see (f) below). The local authority should also notify the relevant persons that it considers a site should be designated a special site. The Agency may also advise the local authority that it considers certain land should be designated as a special site; only local authorities have powers to designate land as being contaminated.

Following a decision to designate land as a special site, the local authority should notify the appropriate Agency and other relevant persons (as above). The decision then takes effect on the day after the expiration of 21 days of the notification, or the day after notification is received from the appropriate Agency that it agrees with the designation (whichever is the soonest). All the relevant persons should then be notified that the decision has taken effect.

However, if the appropriate Agency disagrees with the local authority over whether land should be designated a special site, it has 21 days from the date of notification of the decision to notify the local authority that it disagrees and to give a statement of its reasons for doing so. The matter is then referred by the local authority to the Secretary of State (NI: Planning Appeals Commission) for decision. The appropriate Agency should send the local authority a copy of its notification and statement. The local authority should also notify all relevant persons that a decision has been referred to the Secretary of State (or Planning Appeals Commission in NI); decisions to designate special sites do not take effect until the referral is determined and then take effect (as confirmed, revised, etc) the day after notice of determination has been sent to the relevant persons and to the local authority.

(b) Remediation Notices (ss.78E, F, G, H(1)-(4)) (NI: WCLO, Arts.53 & 70)

Following designation of land as being contaminated land or a special site, the enforcing authority should serve a Remediation Notice on the appropriate person(s) specifying what needs to be done and the period within which the various pieces of work should be done. The *Contaminated Land Regulations 2000* specify the contents of the Remediation Notice. The Notice should include the name and address of all the persons on whom the Notice is being served and the reason for serving it on them – i.e. why the enforcing authority considers them to be an "appropriate person"; it should also include details of the location and extent of the contaminated land in question and the substances by which it is contaminated; particulars of the significant harm or pollution of controlled waters resulting in the land being designated contaminated land.

The appropriate person so far as responsibility for remediation is concerned will normally be the person(s) who knowingly caused or permitted the presence of a substance in, on or under the land, thereby causing it to become contaminated. However if after inquiry the person who knowingly caused or permitted the contamination cannot be found, then the appropriate person is the person(s) who currently occupy or own the land. Where more than one person is required to carry out remediation work because of the presence of different substances, a Notice should be served on each person specifying what each needs to do. Where more than one person is to be responsible for cleaning up the same contamination, the Notice should specify the proportion of works and costs to be borne by each in accordance with Guidance from the Secretary of State.

Before serving the remediation notice, however, the enforcing authority should endeavour to consult the appropriate persons about the remediation to be done and, where necessary to consult any other person who might be required to give consent or grant rights (e.g. of access) for certain work to be done - where known, the name and address of all such persons should also be included on the Remediation Notice. Such rights or consent should be granted to the person on whom the remediation notice is served (s.78G). The person granting consent or rights may be entitled to compensation from the person on whom the remediation notice has been served. Regulation 6 and Schedule 2 (E; Sch.3 – Sc.) of the *Contaminated Land Regulations* outline the procedure for making such a claim and the way in which compensation is to be determined.

In specifying what it is reasonable to do by way of remediation, the enforcing authority must take into account the likely costs of the work and the seriousness of the harm, or pollution of controlled waters; the enforcing authorities should have regard to any Guidance from the Secretary of State as to what should be considered as "reasonable", the remediation to be done in any particular case and the standard to which land or waters should be remediated.

It should be noted that a Remediation Notice should not normally be served before the expiry of three months following service of the initial notice identifying the contaminated land (see (a) above) (s.78H); exceptions include when the enforcing authority considers that the condition of the land warrants it, there is imminent danger of serious harm, or of serious pollution to controlled waters.

The Remediation Notice should also note that it is an offence (EPA: s.78M; NI: WCLO, Art.59) not to comply

with the terms of a Remediation Notice without reasonable excuse and the penalties that non-compliance may incur - i.e. on summary conviction this may result in a fine not exceeding level 5 on the standard scale, plus an amount equal to one-tenth of level 5 for each day the offence continues following conviction. Where the offence relates to industrial, trade or business premises, a fine not exceeding £20,000 may be imposed, plus a further fine of one-tenth of £20,000 for each day the offence continues following conviction.

A Remediation Notice should not be served if contamination has arisen as a result of non-compliance with an IPC authorisation, or enforcement or prohibition notice served under Part I of the EPA (NI: *Industrial Pollution Control Order 1997*) or, as appropriate an installation regulated under the *Pollution Prevention and Control Regulations 2000*. In such circumstances, the appropriate Agency (as IPC/IPPC enforcing authorities) may with the written permission of the Secretary of State and of any other person whose land is affected, take remedial action and recover costs from the offender. Similarly where land becomes contaminated as a result of a breach of a waste management licence issued under Part II of the EPA (NI: Part II of WCLO), the offence should be dealt with under that Part of the Act (EPA: s.78YB (1)-(3); NI: WCLO, Art.70). Contamination due to unlawful waste deposits (e.g. fly-tipping) will normally be dealt with under s.59 of the EPA (see 4.19.5 above).

A remediation notice should not require any action which could impede or prevent a discharge permitted under a consent granted under Part III of the *Water Resources Act 1991* or Part II of the *Control of Pollution Act 1974* in Scotland (EPA: s.78YB (4)). In Northern Ireland Art.70(4) of the WCLO contains the same provisions in relation to the *Water Act (Northern Ireland) 1972* and the *Water and Sewerage Services (Northern Ireland) Order 1973*.

Finally, the Remediation Notice should also state that there is a right of appeal against it, grounds for appeal, and the time within which any appeal should be made, and that such Notices are suspended pending the determination or abandonment of an appeal - see (d) below.

The *Contaminated Land Regulations 2000* require local authorities to send copies of Remediation Notices which they serve to the Environment Agency/SEPA. The Environment Agency/SEPA should copy any Remediation Notices it serves to the local authority in which the contaminated land in question is situated.

(c) Remediation Declarations and Statements (s.78H(5)-(9)) (NI: WCLO, Art.56(5)-(9))

A remediation notice will not be served in the following circumstances (see also above):

(a) where it appears to the enforcing authority that there is nothing by way of remediation that could be specified in the notice taking into account such matters as cost, seriousness of harm or pollution, standard of remediation, what it is reasonable to do, etc;

in this instance the enforcing authority must publish a Remediation Declaration saying what it would have specified in a Remediation Notice if it could have, and its reasons for not doing so.

(b) if the appropriate person is already carrying out the necessary remediation work or it has been done or is planned;

(c) if it appears that the appropriate person on whom to serve the remediation notice is the enforcing authority itself;

(d) if the enforcing authority is to carry out the remediation work itself for various reasons - see below;

in the case of (b) above the person(s) carrying out the remediation should publish a Remediation Statement or in the case of (c) and (d) the enforcing authority. The Statement should say what is, has or is likely to be done and the timescale, and the names and addresses of all those involved in the remediation work.

If, however, the appropriate person in (b) above does not publish a Remediation Statement within a reasonable time after the date on which a Remediation Notice could have been served, then the enforcing authority may publish the Statement, recovering its costs from the appropriate person. The enforcing authority may also then serve a Remediation Notice.

(d) Appeals (s.78L) (NI: WCLO, Art.58)

A person on whom a Remediation Notice has been served may appeal within 21 days to the Magistrates Court/Sheriff (NI Court of Summary Jurisdiction) in the case of a notice served by a local authority; appeals against notices (relating to special sites) served by the Environment Agency/SEPA should be sent to the Secretary of State. (s.114 of the *Environment Act 1995* enables the Secretary of State to appoint someone to handle the appeal on his behalf. In Northern Ireland appeals in relation to special sites will be dealt with by the Planning Appeals Commission (Art.58).

The *Contaminated Land Regulations 2000* detail the grounds for appeal against a Remediation Notice which include:

- failure of the enforcing authority to have regard to, or act in accordance with any parts of the Statutory Guidance;
- that action to deal with the contaminated land should be dealt with under other legislation (e.g. breach of an environmental licence);
- a defect in the Remediation Notice (e.g. should have been addressed to another person (or persons); where addressed to more than one person, failed to specify what each should do by way of remediation, or to apportion liability or unreasonably apportioned liability);
- that the time allowed for remediation is insufficient to carry out the required works;

- that the enforcing authority in seeking to recover all or part of its costs, failed to take account of the hardship such action would cause or unreasonably determined that it would recover such costs;
- that the enforcing authority has failed to take account of action already been taken to deal with the contamination without service of a Remediation Notice.

In filing a Notice of Appeal at the Magistrates Court, the appellant should copy it to the enforcing authority and to any other person mentioned in the Remediation Notice or Notice of Appeal. A copy of the Remediation Notice and names and addresses of all those listed in the Notice of Appeal and Remediation Notice should also be filed and copied as before. Directions for the conduct of the appeal are notified to all concerned by the justices' clerk or the court. In Scotland appeals should be addressed to Scottish Ministers.

Where an appeal is made to the Secretary of State (in respect of a Remediation Notice concerning a special site), the appellant should state whether he wishes the appeal to be determined through written representations or a hearing. A copy of the Appeal Notice should be sent to the Environment Agency/SEPA and all those named in the Notice or in the Remediation Notice, together with a statement noting the names and addresses of all those concerned. The Secretary of State decides if the hearing should be held in private or take the form of a local inquiry. A person appointed to conduct a hearing will report his recommendations as to how the appeal should be determined to the Secretary of State unless he has been appointed under s.114 of the *Environment Act 1995*; this enables the Secretary of State to delegate his functions in respect of appeals to another person.

Where it is proposed to modify a Remediation Notice in a manner which would be less favourable to the appellant than the original Notice, a copy of the proposed modification should be sent to all those who received notification of the appeal, including the enforcing authority; all are permitted to make representations regarding the proposed modification if they so wish.

Remediation Notices do not take effect pending determination or abandonment of an appeal. The Magistrates Court (or Secretary of State, as appropriate) can refuse an appellant's request for an appeal to be abandoned where the appellant has been notified that it is proposed to modify the Remediation Notice. Appeals against a decision of the Magistrates Court are heard in the High Court (England).

(e) Powers of Enforcing Authority to carry out Remediation (s.78N & P) (NI: WCLO, Arts.60 & 61)

The enforcing authority may carry out the remediation work itself in the following circumstances:

- to prevent occurrence of serious harm, or serious

pollution of controlled waters, of which there is imminent danger;

- where the appropriate person has given written agreement that the enforcing authority should carry out the remediation work (at his/her expense);

- failure to comply with remediation notice;

- contamination has resulted from water from an abandoned mine or where the owner or occupier of land has not caused or knowingly permitted the presence of contaminating substances in on or under land which have subsequently contaminated other land;

- where the enforcing authority decides to carry out certain work itself but does not intend to recover all or part of the cost of remediation work;

- where, after reasonable inquiry, the appropriate person cannot be found to do the particular work.

Where the enforcing authority has carried out the remediation work itself, it may recover all or part of its costs, bearing in mind the degree of hardship this may cause to the person concerned and with regard to any Guidance from the Secretary of State. The enforcing authority should serve a Charging Notice on the person concerned detailing the amount of the charge and any interest payable. The charging notice should also be copied to anyone who might have an interest in the premises affected by the charge. The charge becomes a charge on the premises 21 days after the service of the notice or, if there is an appeal, following its determination. (Any appeal should be made within 21 days of its service.) Where the charge is a charge on the premises, the enforcing authority may by order recover the costs over a period of up to 30 years.

(f) Special Sites (s.78Q) (NI: WCLO, Art.62)

The Contaminated Land Regulations 2000 require contaminated land to be designated as a special site in the following circumstances:

- presence of waste acid tars in, on or under the land;
- land which has been used for purification (inc. refining of crude petroleum or oil extraction from petroleum, shale or other bituminous substance (except coal) , or for manufacture or processing of explosives;
- land within a nuclear site;
- land on which an IPC process or IPPC installation designated for control by the Agency (unconnected with a remediation process) has or is being carried out;
- land owned or occupied by or on behalf of: Secretary of State for Defence or other defence organisation which is being used for naval, military or air force purposes;
- land on which chemical weapons or biological weapons have been, or are being, manufactured, produced or disposed of, or land which has been designated under the *Atomic Weapons Establishment Act 1991.*

In all the above cases, the adjoining or adjacent land will also be designated a special site if it appears to have been contaminated as a result of an escape from the actual site.

Contaminated land will also be designated as a special site in the following circumstances:

- land which adversely affects controlled waters which are, or are intended to be used, for the supply of drinking water for human consumption, and which will need treatment before they can be regarded as wholesome under Part III of the *Water Industry Act 1991;*
- land which adversely affects controlled waters which results in those waters not meeting the relevant quality classifications under s.82 of the *Water Resources Act 1991* (see chapter 5, 5.15.2);
- land which is or is likely to pollute controlled waters due to the escape of specified dangerous substances and where the waters are contained in specified underground strata – listed in Schedule 1 to the Regulations.

If contaminated land is designated a special site after a remediation notice has been served, the appropriate Agency may adopt the Remediation Notice, notifying the local authority and any appropriate person of its decision to do so. If the local authority has already begun doing some remediation work, it may continue to do so and the appropriate Agency may inspect the land from time to time to review its condition.

Where the Agency considers that contaminated land no longer requires to be designated as a special site, it should notify both the Secretary of State and the local authority. In Northern Ireland, the WCLI will notify the district council. The land may subsequently be redesignated as a special site if its condition requires.

(g) Public Registers (s.78R-T) (NI: WCLO, Arts.63-65 & Sch.2)

Each enforcing authority will maintain a public register containing particulars relating to contaminated land and special sites for which it is the enforcing authority; local authority registers will also contain details relating to special sites in its area. The registers which may be in any form should be available for inspection by the public, with copies of documents available at a reasonable charge. *The Contaminated Land Regulations 2000* (E: Sch.3; Sc: Sch.4) specify that, as well as details of the location and extent of contaminated land, name and address of person(s) responsible for remediation, the registers should contain full details of the following:

- remediation notices and appeals against such notices;
- remediation statements and declarations; any other notifications given to the enforcing authority relating to work which has been done, or is claimed to have been done, as a result of a remediation notice;
- appeals against charging notices;
- notices relating to the designation of land as a special site, or withdrawal of that designation;

- convictions for offences under s.78M of the EPA;
- for local authorities - guidance issued by the Environment Agency under s.78V of the EPA; Agency registers should note the date of any such guidance issued;
- details of land which is contaminated as a result of
  - a breach of an IPC authorisation (Part I of EPA) or IPPC permit;
  - deposit of controlled waste (Part II of EPA);
  - discharge covered by a Consent under the *Water Resources Act 1991,*

  and which is therefore dealt with under the relevant legislation;   (the enforcing authority is precluded from serving a remediation notice - s.78YB in these circumstances.)

Information may be excluded from the registers on the grounds of national security or commercial confidentiality. In the former case, the enforcing authority should notify the Secretary of State of any information excluded on these grounds; or the person concerned may notify the Secretary of State direct of the information to be excluded on these grounds and notify the enforcing authority accordingly.

Where a person requests that information be treated as commercially confidential but the enforcing authority disagrees, 21 days should elapse before putting the information on the register. An appeal against the enforcing authority's decision may be made to the Secretary of State (NI Planning Appeals Commission) in which case the information in question will not be put on the register until seven days following determination or withdrawal of the appeal. Where either party requests a hearing, or the Secretary of State (NI Planning Appeals Commission) decides on a hearing, this must be held in private. Information remains commercially confidential for four years, but the person concerned may apply to the enforcing authority for this classification to be extended.

(h) Reports on the State of Contaminated Land (s.78U) (NI: WCLO, Art.66)

The Environment Agency, SEPA and the WCLI are required to prepare and publish from time to time reports on the state of contaminated land in their respective countries. They may request local authorities to provide information to enable them to prepare their reports.

4.28.4 Water Resources Act 1991

Anti-Pollution Works (s.161)

This section of the Act empowers the Agency to serve a "works notice" on any person who has "caused or knowingly permitted" a pollutant to enter controlled waters, including from contaminated land, requiring them to deal with the problem. If urgent action is needed the Agency is empowered to take remedial action to deal with the pollution and to recover the costs from the person responsible for the pollution. The *Control of Pollution Act*

1974, sections 46A-C, give the same powers to SEPA in Scotland. See chapter 5.

Guidance from the Agency (Policy and Guidance on the Use of Anti-Pollution Works Notices) suggests that in most cases of actual or potential pollution of controlled waters as a result of contamination, the problem will usually be dealt with under the contaminated land provisions of the EPA.

LITTER
4.29 ENVIRONMENTAL PROTECTION ACT 1990, PART IV

This introduces strict controls in England, Scotland and Wales to deal with litter. Prior to the Act, this was mainly regulated under the *Control of Pollution Act 1974* and in England and Wales under the *Litter Act 1983* and in Scotland under provisions contained in the *Local Government and Planning (Scotland) Act 1982;* all remain of relevance though certain sections are repealed as a result of the new legislation. In Northern Ireland the comparable legislation is the *Litter (Northern Ireland) Order 1994* which came into effect on 1 October 1994.

Responsibility for enforcement of the legislation lies with local authorities - principal litter authorities; they have a statutory duty (s.89) to keep open land and roads and highways under their control free of litter and refuse, and to ensure roads and highways are kept clean in accordance with the *Code of Practice on Litter and Refuse* (see below). The duty to keep land free of litter, which also applies to statutory undertakers, designated educational establishments and national parks to which the public have access, became effective on 1 April 1991. This duty was extended to statutory transport undertakers from 1 May 1991 and the 1999 revision of the code of practice states that Orders are to be brought forward extending the duty to Railtrack and the train operating companies - this will require tracks, sidings, embankments and stations to be kept clear of litter, and will also make water companies responsible for rubbish etc on river banks.

Section 90 of the Act, brought into force on 1 July 1991 through the *Litter Control Areas Order 1991* (SI 1325), as amended in 1997 by SI 633 (N. Ireland: *The Litter Control Areas Order (Northern Ireland) 1995,* effective 5 July 1995), enables local authorities to designate as Litter Control Areas the main categories of land to which the public is entitled or permitted to have access. These include

- land or buildings used as car parks;
- shopping centres of 100,000 sq. ft or more of retail space. This is primarily intended to cover "out-of-town" retail parks and not high street shopping centres;
- business parks, industrial estates etc with a floor space of 100,000 sq. ft or more;
- cinemas, theatres, bingo halls, etc, skating rinks,

amusement arcades, indoor and outdoor sports centres;
- inland beaches and seashores;
- aerodromes;
- marinas or similar boating facilities;
- land on which markets are held (other than on a highway or public road);
- camping and caravan sites;
- picnic areas on trunk roads;
- land to which the public has access and which is under the control of e.g. parish councils, NHS, police, national parks authorities, waste disposal authorities.

Land in such areas must be kept free of litter and refuse to the standards required by the designated zone into which the land falls (see below). Where standards are not met, members of the public may apply to the Magistrates' Court (Sheriff Court in Scotland) for a litter abatement order (s.91), having first given the offender five days notice of intention to do so. Failure to comply with a litter abatement order without adequate excuse may lead to further prosecution and a maximum fine of £2,500, plus a maximum daily fine of one-twentieth for each day the offence continues after conviction.

Principal Litter Authorities may serve a litter abatement notice (s.92) specifying a timescale within which the litter or refuse must be cleared up, or prohibiting the land in question from becoming defaced by litter or refuse. Offenders may appeal against the terms of the notice within 21 days to the Magistrates'/Sheriff Court. Again failure to comply with the notice without adequate excuse may result in prosecution and a fine.

In addition, ss.93 & 94 of the Act, also brought into force on 1 July 1991 through the *Street Litter Control Notices Order 1991,* as amended in 1997 by SI 632, empower local authorities to issue Street Litter Control Notices to various premises with a street frontage which may cause a litter problem. These include take-away food premises, service stations, cinemas, theatres and other recreational premises; banks and building societies with cash machines on an outside wall are also covered. Local authorities must give 21 days' notice of their intention to serve a Notice and must take into account any representations made. The Notice can specify the length of street covered, as well as cleansing practices such as the number of litter bins, frequency of emptying and street washing. Any appeal against the terms of a Notice must be made to the Magistrates'/Sheriff Court. Once again, failure to comply with the terms of a Notice may result in prosecution and a fine.

A further deterrent to dropping litter is provided by the *Litter (Fixed Penalty) Order 1996* (SI 3055); this replaces a 1991 Order and came into effect on 1 January 1997 (*NI: the Litter (Fixed Penalty) Order Northern Ireland 1998* (SR 166). This enables enforcement officers to issue a fixed penalty notice of £25 to anyone who drops litter. If it is not paid within 14 days, the offender is liable to prosecution, for which the maximum fine on conviction is £2,500.

Code of Practice on Litter and Refuse

The legislation is backed up by a statutory code of practice, originally published in 1991 and revised in 1999. It describes the extent of the duty placed on local authorities and others covered by the Act to keep their land clear of litter and refuse. Advice is given on standards of cleanliness to be achieved for particular zones, and the timescale within which a Grade A standard (see below) should be achieved for each zone (see below). For instance for Zone 1 areas, Grade A should be achieved immediately after cleaning and within six hours of falling to Grade B, within three hours of falling to Grade C and within one hour of falling to Grade D; Zone 5 (beaches) should be predominantly free of litter from May - September.

The standards of cleanliness are:

- *Grade A:* No litter or refuse;
- *Grade B:* Predominantly free of litter, apart from small items such as cigarette ends;
- *Grade C:* Widespread distribution of small items and larger items (such as beverage containers etc) and animal faeces;
- *Grade D:* Heavily littered.

Zones have been classified as follows:

1) Town centres, shopping areas, railway and bus stations, public car parks and other open public spaces;
2) High density residential areas, recreational areas, suburban car parks, railway and bus stations;
3) Low density residential areas, public parks and industrial estates;
4) All other areas;
5) Local authority beaches;
6) Motorways and other main routes;
7) Other roads;
8) Educational establishments;
9) Railway embankments (within 100 m of platform ends);
10) Railway embankments within urban areas (other than above);
11) Canal towpaths (paved) in urban areas.

RADIOACTIVE WASTE
4.30 INTRODUCTION

Radioactive materials are used in the generation of electricity, in industry - including the food processing industry - in medicine, research and defence. Their use results in gaseous, liquid and solid wastes which can be divided into three categories:

- *high level (or heat generating) waste (HLW):* this results from reprocessing of spent nuclear fuels; about 97% is recycled into new fuel;
- *intermediate level waste (ILW):* this includes scrap metal, sludge and residues from fuel storage ponds, plutonium contaminated materials and fuel cladding;

- *low level waste (LLW):* this includes paper towels, protective clothing, laboratory equipment and soils.

Strict safety standards have been set by the Government with which any disposal scheme for radioactive waste must comply. The National Radiological Protection Board advises the Government on radiological protection criteria to be applied to the disposal of all types of solid radioactive waste and in 1992, it published new objectives for its land-based disposal. This includes the following recommendations:

a) future generations should not be subjected to risks which would be considered unacceptable today, i.e. people alive at any time in the future should be given a level of protection at least equivalent to that accorded to members of the public alive now;

b) the radiological risk from one disposal facility to the most exposed group of people should not exceed a risk of serious health effects in the individuals or their descendants of 1 in 100,000 per year;

c) the radiological risks to members of the public should be as low as reasonably achievable (ALARA), economic and social factors being taken into account.

All high-level wastes must be stored for at least 50 years to allow them to cool. They are currently kept in liquid form in double-walled cooled stainless steel tanks enclosed in thick concrete walls at Sellafield in Cumbria and Dounreay in Scotland. In 1990 British Nuclear Fuels brought into operation a vitrification plant at Sellafield; HLW will be converted into glass blocks and sealed in stainless steel containers and stored for at least 90 years before eventual disposal.

Current research worldwide is looking at emplacement in deep geologic formations on land or beneath the seabed which must remain impermeable for tens of thousands of years.

In June 1998, the Government announced that Dounreay is to be closed in 2004 on scientific and economic grounds, and also because of safety concerns. Reprocessing of waste currently stored at the plant is expected to be completed by 2006; decommissioning and clean-up of the plant is expected to take 60 years to complete; however it could be another 300 years before the site returns to a "natural" state – i.e. is completely free of radioactivity (Report from UK Atomic Energy Authority, October 2000).

The volume of ILW produced annually is currently about 5,000 cubic metres and of LLW, 40,000 cubic metres. Very low level solid waste can be collected and deposited at local authority landfill sites, provided its activity is below authorised limits. Other low level waste of a higher activity may be buried in a "near surface facility", such as that owned by British Nuclear Fuels at Drigg; this comprises concrete lined trenches which will be capped and earthed over when full. BNFL estimate that Drigg should be able to accommodate all the UK's LLW until around 2050. Conditions attached to such authorisations limit the

intensity of radiation detectable at the surface of the site to specified limits. There are other conditions, one of which specifies the minimum depth at which the waste must be buried.

In 1982, the Government set up UK NIREX Ltd - the Nuclear Industry Radioactive Waste Executive - to implement Government strategy for disposal of LLW and ILW produced by the UK nuclear industry, and by users of radioactive materials in hospitals, industry, research and defence. In 1985, it was reconstituted as a company, UK Nirex Ltd, with the same remit. Following a period of public consultation and initial investigations of sites at Dounreay and Sellafield, Nirex chose the latter as its preferred site for the underground storage of ILW. However, in 1997, following a public inquiry, the Environment Secretary refused planning permission, mainly on scientific grounds, but also because he considered the proposal unacceptable for the Lake District National Park. Nirex will now need to consider alternative sites.

An independent committee - the Radioactive Waste Management Advisory Committee (RWMAC) - advises "the Secretaries of State for the Environment, Scotland and Wales on the technical and environmental implications of major issues concerning the development and implementation of an overall policy for all aspects of the management of civil radioactive waste, including research and development; and on any such matters referred to it by the Secretaries of State".

Sources and effects of both natural and artificial radiation are summarised in chapter 2, sections 2.27 and 2.28.

4.31 REGULATORY CONTROLS

Under the *Radioactive Substances Act 1993*, anybody wishing to keep or use radioactive materials requires to be registered by the Environment Agency in England and Wales, the Scottish Environment Protection Agency in Scotland and the Department of the Environment (Industrial Pollution and Radiochemicals Inspectorate) in Northern Ireland; the accumulation or disposal of radioactive waste also requires an authorisation from the same bodies.

4.31.1 Nuclear Installations

The Nuclear Installations Act 1965 requires that before a site can be used for a commercial nuclear installation, it must obtain a nuclear site licence. The *Nuclear Installations Regulations 1971* (SI 381) prescribe the types of installations and activities covered by the Act. HM Nuclear Installations Inspectorate (which is part of the Health and Safety Executive) is responsible for licensing and may attach specific conditions to licences to ensure appropriate standards are maintained. The NII continuously monitors sites for which it is responsible to ensure compliance with conditions and also ensures that emergency procedures are up to date and staff familiar with them. In setting conditions both the appropriate Agency and the Ministry of Agriculture, Fisheries and Food will be consulted. This

Act does not cover radioactive waste or discharges from nuclear sites, which are licensed separately under the *Radioactive Substances Act 1993*.

4.31.2 Ionising Radiation

The Ionising Radiations Regulations 1999 (SI 3232) (made under the *Health and Safety at Work Act 1974*) provide protection for the workforce from ionising radiations, including the handling and storage of radioactive waste. These Regulations came into force on 1 January 2000, replacing 1985 Regulations (see also chapter 2, 2.31.1).

4.31.3 Radioactive Substances Act 1993

The Radioactive Substances Act 1993 (RSA) which consolidates and replaces the 1960 Act came into force on 27 August 1993 and applies to the whole of the UK. It brings together under a single Act the provisions of the 1960 RSA (which is repealed), together with all the various amendments to it made under other Acts. Consolidating Acts, such as this, do not amend legislation but may make minor changes for the purposes of clarification or consistency of approach.

The Act controls the keeping and use of radioactive materials and the accumulation and disposal of radioactive wastes through authorisation and registration systems; it also provides for public access to information held by the enforcing authorities.

This Act applies to Crown premises, except those occupied for navy, army or air force purposes, visiting forces or the Secretary of State for Defence.

The Act is enforced, on behalf of the Secretary of State by the Environment Agency in England and Wales, the Scottish Environment Protection Agency in Scotland, and by the Department of the Environment in Northern Ireland. Sites in England which are also registered under the *Nuclear Installations Act* will be jointly controlled with the Minister of Agriculture, Fisheries and Food, and those in Northern Ireland with the Department of Agriculture for N. Ireland.

A number of amendments were made to the RSA by the *Environment Act 1995,* Schedule 22, paras 200-230; these are noted in the following text and most came into effect on 1 April 1996. The Government is considering what further amendments are needed to reflect Directive 96/29/EURATOM which lays down basic safety standards for the protection of health of workers and the general public arising from ionising radiation (see also chapter 2, 2.31.1). The Directive requires comprehensive systems for regulating the use, reuse or recycling of radioactive materials, much of which already happens in the UK through the RSA.

Registration for Users of Radioactive Materials (ss.6-12 & 19-20)

Anybody who keeps or uses radioactive materials, including mobile radioactive apparatus, must apply for registration under the RSA. The application must include details of the premises (or mobile apparatus), what they are used for, the materials being kept or used and likely quantities, and how the materials are to be used. The application must be accompanied by the appropriate fee (see below). A copy of the application, and the subsequent registration certificate, should be sent to all those local authorities in whose area the premises fall except where the Secretary of State has decided that national security could be compromised (s.25).

In granting a certificate of registration, the appropriate Agency may impose such conditions as it thinks fit; these may include alterations to the premises, requirements as to apparatus or equipment used or to be used, restrictions on selling or supplying radioactive materials from the premises. Sections 23-24 enable the Secretary of State (in the case of nuclear sites, with the Minister of Agriculture, Fisheries and Food) to direct the appropriate Agency as to how an application for registration is to be determined - see below. Copies of the certificate of registration should be prominently displayed so that all those with duties on the premises will see it (s.19).

Applications not dealt with within the prescribed determination period (or other period as agreed) should be deemed to have been refused. Section 12 of the Act enables the appropriate Agency to cancel or vary registrations and to notify the operator; the appropriate local authorities should also be advised that such action has been taken.

The appropriate Agency may, by notice, require an operator to retain records of operations for a specified period after ceasing those activities to which registration relates; where registration has been cancelled, authorisation revoked or activities ceased, the operator may by notice be required to give the appropriate Agency copies of relevant records (s.20).

Holders of licences under the *Nuclear Installations Act* do not require registration under s.7 although the appropriate Agency may direct that conditions in accordance with s.7 should be imposed on the licensee; premises which keep or use watches and clocks which are radioactive material do not require registration although their repair or manufacture using luminous materials does (s.8(4) & (5)).

It should be noted that any radioactive materials kept or used on premises for more than three months will be considered to be accumulated for subsequent disposal and thus require authorisation under s.14(4).

Authorisation of Disposal and Accumulation of Radioactive Waste (ss.13-18 & 19-20)

The disposal of any radioactive waste (including disposal from mobile radioactive apparatus) and accumulation of radioactive waste for subsequent disposal requires a certificate of authorisation.

Exceptions to the above are the accumulation and disposal of radioactive waste from clocks and watches, although its accumulation and disposal from premises using luminous materials to repair clocks and watches does (s.15). The disposal of radioactive waste from educational establishments and from hospitals is also exempt from authorisation - conditions and restrictions relating to disposal from such premises are set out, respectively, in the *Radioactive Substances (Schools etc) Exemption Order 1963* (SI 1832) and in the *Radioactive Substances (Hospitals) Exemption Order 1990* (SI 2512, amended 1995, SI 2395).

Applications for authorisations for the accumulation and disposal of radioactive waste will be determined by the appropriate Agency. Applications should be accompanied by the prescribed charge (see 4.31.4a below) - this will be refunded in full should the application be withdrawn within eight weeks of the regulator receiving it.

Section 16(3) - determination by the appropriate Minister of authorisations for disposal of radioactive waste from a nuclear site in England, Wales and N. Ireland - has been revoked by the *Environment Act 1995*, Sch. 22, para 205(3); in its place, s.16(4A) (Sch. 22, para 205(5)) requires the appropriate Agency to consult both the relevant Minister and the Health and Safety Executive prior to making a decision on whether to grant an authorisation and if minded to grant an authorisation on what terms and conditions etc; before granting an authorisation the appropriate Agency should forward a copy to the relevant Minister. Sections 23 and 24 of the Act enable the Secretary of State (and Minister of Agriculture, Fisheries and Food if a nuclear site - *Env. Act 1995, Sch. 22, para 211(2) and 212(2)*) to give directions to the appropriate Agency as to how a registration or authorisation is to be determined, or conditions to be imposed or to call in an application for his determination.

All applications (and subsequent authorisations), subject to the usual considerations of national security (s.25), should be copied to those local authorities within whose areas it is intended to accumulate or dispose of radioactive waste. In addition, before granting a disposal authorisation in respect of a nuclear site other local authorities public bodies and water bodies as is thought appropriate should be consulted.

Authorisations will set conditions for the operation of such plant, including discharge limits for radioactive waste and the manner in which it is to be disposed. The authorisation may permit the radioactive waste to be removed from the premises for disposal in a local authority disposal site; in such instances the local authority has a duty to accept the waste and to deal with it as specified in the authorisation. Authorisations will normally take effect not less than 28 days after a copy of it would have been received by the relevant local authorities.

A copy of the certificate of authorisation must be prominently displayed where all those with duties on the premises will see it (s.19). Failure to do so renders the offender liable to prosecution and a fine (s.33).

Applications (other than those relating to disposal of radioactive waste from a nuclear site - *Env. Act 1995, Sch. 22, para 205(7)*) not dealt with within the prescribed period (or such other period as has been agreed) are deemed to have been refused. Following notice, an authorisation may be varied or revoked and the relevant local authorities advised. However, before varying an authorisation relating to disposal of radioactive waste from a nuclear site, the appropriate Agency must follow the same consultation procedure as for an authorisation - see above: *Env. Act 1995, Sch. 22, para 206(1)*. Authorisations and their conditions will normally be reviewed every four years in case updating is needed in the light of new knowledge, experience or technology.

Enforcement and Prohibition Notices (ss.21-22)

The Environment Agency and SEPA may issue enforcement, prohibition and revocation notices where conditions of a registration or authorisation are being contravened, or where there is a risk of environmental harm. The notice will state the problem and action to be taken to remedy the situation and the timescale within which this should be done. If there is considered to be an imminent risk of pollution or harm to human health, the authorisation or registration may be withdrawn in whole or in part. A copy of any notice will be sent to the relevant local authority. Once the appropriate Agency is satisfied that any risk has been dealt with, it can withdraw the notice; the local authority should be advised that this has been done. A similar procedure applies to registrations issued by MAFF.

Secretary of State Powers (ss.23-25)

These sections have been dealt with above. They deal with the Secretary of State's powers to give the Agency and SEPA directions as to how various matters relating to registrations and authorisations are to be determined. Section 25 enables the Secretary of State to declare data confidential on grounds of national security.

Appeals (ss.26-27)

An operator may appeal to the Secretary of State (MAFF for nuclear sites) if an application for authorisation or registration has been refused, conditions are considered unreasonable or in respect of the terms of an enforcement, prohibition, variation or revocation notice. It should be noted that the terms of all notices issued take immediate effect, except for those relating to revocation of authorisation or registration which are dependent on the outcome of any appeal. There is no appeals procedure in respect of

- decisions imposed by direction of the Secretary of State (s.23);
- applications etc determined by the Secretary of State (s.24);
- in N. Ireland, prohibition or other enforcement notices issued under ss.21-22.

The Radioactive Substances (Appeals) Regulations 1990 require that any appeal be made to the Secretary of State within two months of the appropriate Agency's decision (28 days in the case of revocation); the appellant may specify a preference for the appeal to be decided by written representations or by a hearing. Section 27 enables the Secretary of State to refer an appeal (except where it relates to a decision or notice served by SEPA - *Env. Act 1995*, Sch. 22, para 215) to another person appointed by himself. In Scotland, where an appeal has been made in respect of a decision or notice of SEPA, the Secretary of State may appoint someone to handle the appeal on his behalf under s.114 of the *Environment Act 1995*.

Where the matter is to be decided through written representations, the appropriate Agency has 28 days to comment on the appellant's statement, and the appellant a further 17 days to respond to those comments. All public authorities who commented on the original application for a registration or authorisation may also comment on the appeal; both the appropriate Agency and the appellant have 14 days in which to comment on any such statements received.

Where the matter is to be dealt with in a hearing, the Secretary of State must give 28 days' notice of its date, time and place and must also publish details in a local newspaper. Public authorities who commented on the original application must be given 21 days' notice. The person conducting the hearing may decide if it should be held wholly or partly in public depending on whether matters of national security or commercial confidentiality are involved.

Powers of Secretary of State to deal with Accumulation and Disposal of Radioactive Waste (ss.29-30)

Section 29 empowers the Secretary of State to arrange for adequate facilities to be provided (by the state or another person) for the safe accumulation or disposal of radioactive waste, to consult with relevant local authorities and to charge for the site's use.

Under s.30 the appropriate Agency (*Env. Act 1995*, Sch. 22, para 217) may dispose of radioactive waste in certain circumstances; these include where premises are empty, the owner is insolvent or there is a risk that the waste may be disposed of unlawfully. Costs may be recovered from the owner or occupier of the premises.

Offences (ss.32-38)

It is an offence not to comply with the conditions of registration or authorisation, or with the terms of an enforcement or prohibition notice; summary conviction may result in a maximum fine of £20,000 or maximum six months imprisonment or both for each offence or an unlimited fine or maximum five years imprisonment or both on conviction on indictment.

Failure to display a copy of registration or authorisation is also an offence, punishable by fine; failure to retain or produce records as specified by the appropriate Agency is also punishable by fine and/or imprisonment.

It is also an offence to disclose information relating to a process unless the person giving it has agreed, disclosure is in accordance with a direction from the Secretary of State, or is in connection with legal proceedings. Summary conviction is subject to a fine not exceeding the statutory maximum and/or up to three months in prison; conviction on indictment is subject to an unlimited fine and/or a maximum two year prison sentence.

Public Access to Documents and Records (s.39)

The Environment Agency and SEPA are required to keep, and to make publicly available, copies of all applications, authorisations and registrations under the RSA, and other relevant documentation, including details of enforcement or prohibition notices, and records of any convictions. Information may be withheld on the grounds of commercial confidentiality or national security and a note to this effect put on the file. Local authorities who have been sent copies of registrations and authorisations etc are also required to make these publicly available.

The public should be allowed access to documents at all reasonable times and may be charged for copies of any documents.

4.31.4 Environment Act 1995

(a) Fees and Charging (ss.41-42)

Prior to implementation of these sections of the *Environment Act 1995*, charging schemes for premises regulated by the *Radioactive Substances Act 1993* and the *Nuclear Installations Act 1965* were made under s.43 of the RSA. This has been replaced by ss.41-42 of the *Environment Act* which contain powers for the Environment Agency and SEPA to make charging schemes for environmental licences and for their approval by the Secretary of State. Fees and charges are usually revised annually with new rates applying on 1 April each year.

The *Charging Scheme for Radioactive Substances Act Regulation* enables the enforcing agencies and MAFF to recover their costs in respect of the following (Scotland and N. Ireland have similar schemes):

- considering applications, issuing authorisations or registration certificates, including related inspection visits;

- ongoing costs related to authorisations and registrations, e.g. inspection, assessment, reviews, monitoring related to discharges (but not general environmental monitoring), enforcement controls and various administrative costs.

Operators are categorised into four bands for charging purposes:

- *Band 1:* British Nuclear Fuels Ltd Sellafield plant;

- *Band 2:* All nuclear sites licensed under the Nuclear Installations Act 1965 (except Sellafield), together with UK Atomic Energy Authority premises.

- *Band 3:* All other premises authorised under ss.13 or 14 of the RSA to dispose of or accumulate radioactive waste (e.g. hospital or university laboratories).

- *Band 4:* factories and other holders of minor radioactive sources, e.g. small hospitals, registered under s.7 of the RSA or s.10 in respect of mobile equipment.

Premises in Bands 1 and 2 are charged individually by MAFF and the enforcing agency on the basis of the actual regulatory time and costs incurred.

Premises in Bands 3 and 4 (all regulated by the appropriate Agency) pay an initial application fee and then an annual subsistence charge. For 1999/00 fee for an application or major variation for Band 3 premises was £1,600 per application, and for an intermediate variation £795; no charge was made for minor variations. The annual subsistence charge was £1,250, with a lower charge applying where the registration relates solely to the use of Technetium 99M and the registered holding does not exceed 10 Gbq (Band 3A) or where the registered holding does not exceed 20 MBq (Band 3B). For Band 4 premises, the fee for an application for registration or for a major variation was £575 per application with no charge being made for a minor variation. The annual subsistence charge in Band 4 applies only to those operators holding larger closed sources, any one of which exceeds 4 TBq, measuring, testing and investigative mobile equipment, and open sources kept at premises not subject to authorisation (Bands 4C-4F); the majority in Band 4 (A, B & G), with smaller open or closed sources, will not pay an annual charge since these sources do not require routine inspection. Charges in 2000/01 for nuclear sites increased 3.7% and for non-nuclear sites 4.0%.

Failure to pay fees and charges will constitute a breach of authorisation or registration and may result in revocation or other enforcement action. A full refund will often be made if an application is withdrawn within eight weeks of receipt.

(b) Powers of Entry (ss.108-110)

Provisions relating to right of entry to premises regulated under the *Radioactive Substances Act 1993* were formerly set out in s.31 of the RSA. This section of the Act was repealed by the *Environment Act 1995* on 1 April 1996.

The Environment Agency or SEPA or other authorised person must be given access to premises to which a registration or authorisation relates in order to carry out their duties under the Act and in emergency (or possible emergency) situations. Photographs and samples may be taken; the occupiers can be required to leave certain parts of the premises undisturbed and to give the Agency (or SEPA or other authorised person) such assistance as is needed. An offence under this section is subject to a fine. See also chapter 1, 1.15.2.

4.31.5 Remediation of Radioactively Contaminated Land

A DETR consultation document published in February 1998 proposes a similar regulatory regime to that for non-radioactively contaminated land, with regulations to be made under s.78YC of the *Environmental Protection Act 1990* (see 4.28.3 above).

The regulations would apply only to sites which are radioactively contaminated through an industrial process (i.e. not by, for example, naturally occurring radon). The Environment Agencies would be the lead enforcement agency. Where a site is contaminated by both radioactive and non-radioactive pollutants, the choice of enforcement authority would depend on which contamination posed the more serious risk. Guidance on risk assessment and when a site can be considered suitable for use will be prepared. The regulations would not apply to contaminated sites licensed under the *Nuclear Installations Act 1965*, as these remain licensed until all risk of radioactivity has gone.

4.31.6 Transfrontier Shipment of Radioactive Waste

The Transfrontier Shipment of Radioactive Waste Directive (92/3/Euratom) lays down standards for authorisation, information exchange and monitoring such transfers both between Member States and into and out of the European Union. A principle aim of the Directive is to protect the health of both citizens and workers from any dangers from ionising radiation.

The Directive has been implemented in the UK through the *Transfrontier Shipment of Radioactive Waste Regulations 1993* (SI 3031), which came into effect on 1 January 1994. The Regulations are enforced by the Environment Agency (and its counterparts in Scotland and Northern Ireland). All shipments require prior authorisation and notification of arrival at destination using EU standardised consignment documentation. The Regulations provide for prohibition of any shipments into the UK unless the holder (i.e. originator) guarantees to take back the waste if the shipment cannot be completed or if the authorisation is not complied with. There is a similar requirement on UK holders wishing to export waste. Shipments to African, Caribbean or Pacific states party to the Lomé Convention may not be authorised; shipments are also banned to third countries which it is considered are unable to deal with radioactive waste safely. Other provisions of the Regulations deal with appeals, offences and other procedural matters.

The shipment of radioactive *substances* within the EU is regulated by Euratom Regulation 1493/93 of June 1993; this deals with such things as documentation, information exchange etc.

The European Atomic Energy Community was founded in 1957 by the six founder members of the then European Economic Community - see Appendix 6.

Water Pollution

EU Controls

UK Regulatory Controls

Marine Pollution

Pesticides

WATER POLLUTION - GENERAL
5.1 LEGISLATIVE CONTROLS - 1388-1973

Legislation to control water pollution has been developed over a number of centuries. The earliest recorded legislation prohibiting the pollution of water dates from 1388 with an Act forbidding the dumping of animal remains, dung and garbage into rivers, ditches and streams because of the "great annoyance damage and peril of the inhabitants" - the penalty for non-compliance being death. *The Bill of Sewers* in 1531 laid a duty on persons responsible for sewers "to cleanse, and purge the trenches, sewers and ditches, in all places necessary" with a view to protecting public health.

However, it was not until the 19th century when the effects of increasing industrialisation and, as a consequence, the increasing concentration of the population in towns and cities and industrial areas, that more attention was paid to the problems of industrial pollution of water and the need to protect public health through the provision of proper sanitation. A series of Acts in 1847, known as the "Clauses Acts" variously provided a framework for legislative control of both industrial and domestic water pollution. The first *Public Health Act* in 1848 also aimed to improve sanitation by providing for a system of local management of water supply, sewerage etc which would be subject to overall national control; subsequent legislation between 1858 and 1875 amended and extended the provisions of the 1848 Act with the *Public Health Act 1875* remaining the primary piece of legislation in respect of sanitation facilities until the *Public Health Act 1936*.

The first statute specifically aimed at controlling water pollution was the *Salmon Fisheries Act 1861* which made it an offence to discharge sewage into salmon fishing waters; its main objective was however the protection of salmon and fishing interests, rather than protection of public health. This was followed by the *Rivers Pollution Prevention Act 1876* under which it became a criminal offence to pollute water. Part I of the Act dealt with pollution by solid matter, Part II with sewage pollution and Part III with pollution from manufacturing and mining. The Act provided for local authorities to take legal proceedings against offenders after having obtained permission from central government. The court could require the offender to abstain from committing the offence or order him to treat the discharge in a specific manner in future. The Act also included a defence of "best practicable and available means". Thus, if it could be shown that the best practicable and reasonably available means had been used to render harmless sewage or other polluting matter before discharging to water, no offence was committed.

In the years following the 1876 Act as the population became more urbanised, the use of waterborne sanitation became increasingly common. Simultaneously there was a corresponding rise in the demand for water for abstraction purposes both for domestic and industrial use.

Consequently it became necessary to create local bodies responsible for the management of the rivers which served the various towns and districts. Initially these authoritative bodies were created piecemeal, starting with the rivers serving the major urban and industrial areas, but by the 1930s they existed for most of the more important rivers. The *River Boards Act 1948* established river boards for the whole of England except the Thames and London area. They acquired functions relating to land drainage, fisheries and river pollution within defined catchment areas. The boards were superseded by 27 river authorities as a result of the *Water Resources Act 1963*.

Other Acts, such as the *Salmon and Freshwater Fisheries Act 1923*, the *Water Act 1945* and the *River Boards Act 1948* laid down various powers to prevent pollution of water but in the main the procedure outlined in the 1876 Act remained in use until 1951 when the *Rivers (Prevention of Pollution) Act* was passed. This repealed virtually the whole of the 1876 Act and established a procedure whereby anyone wishing to make a new discharge of sewage or trade effluent to a stream was required to seek the consent of the river board (subsequently the regional water authority).

The Public Health Acts of 1936 and 1961 and the *Public Health (Drainage of Trade Premises) Act 1937* made it an offence to discharge into public sewers any matter which by its nature or its temperature was likely to damage the sewer or the treatment process; in order to safeguard the condition of the water to which the treated mixed effluents would ultimately discharge, authorities were empowered to impose conditions on discharges of trade effluent. *The Clean Rivers (Estuaries and Tidal Waters) Act 1960* extended controls to all discharges commenced or altered after the prescribed date to most major estuaries.

The Rivers (Prevention of Pollution) Act 1961 strengthened controls by bringing within it the pre-1951 discharges for which specific consent had not been required by the earlier Act. *The Water Resources Act 1963* extended the control system to cover discharges to underground strata via wells, pipes or boreholes, and gave river authorities specific powers to take emergency measures in the event of pollution of the water.

The river authorities in England and Wales remained in existence until 1973 when the *Water Act* of that year replaced them with ten regional water authorities. Each Authority was made responsible for one or more of the major river systems (e.g. Thames, Severn Trent), including the management of the entire hydrological cycle within its area and the adjacent coastal waters. The responsibility included water conservation and supply, pollution control, sewerage, sewage treatment, the development and control of aquifers, land drainage, flood prevention, freshwater and sea fisheries, and the use of the water for amenity and recreation. As a result of privatisation, ownership of the water authorities was transferred to the private sector and a new regulatory framework instituted in 1989 (see 5.15 below).

5.2 CONTROL OF POLLUTION ACT 1974, PART II

Until the enactment of the *Water Act 1989* (see below), Part II of COPA contained much of the legislation covering water pollution control in England and Wales. It re-enacted and extended earlier controls in the *Rivers (Prevention of Pollution) Acts 1951* and 1961 and ss.72 & 76 of the *Water Resources Act 1963*.

This part of COPA is still the main legislation (although substantially added to and amended since 1974) controlling water pollution in Scotland (see 5.10 below and references to COPA throughout 5.15 below). Its main objectives are

a) to extend the control system to all inland waters, estuaries, tidal rivers, the sea within a three-mile limit (and in certain cases beyond) and specified underground waters;

b) to ensure that, subject to a few exceptions, the entry of poisonous, noxious or other polluting matter through casual or spontaneous acts, (e.g. dumping waste in a river) is totally prohibited;

c) to permit discharges of trade or sewage effluent providing that consent is obtained and that any conditions attached to that consent observed;

d) to enable water authorities to carry out operations to prevent the pollution of water or, where pollution has already occurred, to remedy its effects and to recover the costs of so doing from those responsible;

e) to expand and open procedures for the control of effluent discharges to public involvement, including provision for public advertisement, third party representations and, exceptionally, call-in by the Secretary of State and public enquiry.

5.3 WATER ACT 1989

This Act, which applied to England and Wales, paved the way for the sale of the utility functions of the existing water authorities to the private sector. The Act established the National Rivers Authority (NRA) - a statutory body - to take over the responsibilities of water authorities in England and Wales in relation to water pollution, water resource management, flood defence, fisheries, and in some areas navigation; the Act removed the regulatory functions of water authorities, and provided for terms of appointment and financial arrangements for new limited companies to provide water and sewerage services; provision was made for the division of the property, rights and liabilities of the water authorities between the successor water and sewerage companies and the NRA, and for the sale of the new companies; the Act also provided for the appointment of a Director General of Water Services responsible for the provision of water and sewerage services.

The Act also established a new statutory framework for the control of drinking water quality, river quality and

other standards, and required the NRA to take specific steps, such as controlling polluting discharges in order to attain objectives set by the Secretary of State for maintaining and improving river quality.

Most of the *Water Act* has now been repealed by, and re-enacted in, the *Water Industry Act 1991* and the *Water Resources Act 1991*. These Acts took effect on 1 December 1991 and apply in England and Wales only. The former Act deals with the functions of the water and sewerage undertakers, the Director General of Water Services and local authority responsibilities for water supplies. The latter Act covered the duties of the National Rivers Authority, which from 1 April 1996 became the responsibility of the Environment Agency - see 5.9 below. The main purpose of these two Acts, together with three others enacted at the same time, is to consolidate all the legislation covering water, which was previously spread over some 20 statutes.

5.4 RIVER QUALITY SURVEYS

Since 1958 surveys have been periodically carried out to establish the overall state of rivers, estuaries and canals in England and Wales. More recently, these surveys were carried out every five years (1980, 1985 and 1990), with similar surveys being carried out in Scotland.

Under a National Water Council scheme rivers and canals were classified as good (1A and 1B), fair (2), poor (3) and bad (4). Waters classified as good were suitable for potable supply abstractions, game and high class fisheries and had high amenity value; waters classified as fair were suitable for the same purposes although their quality was not so high. Poor quality waters were probably unable to support fish life and waters of bad quality were "grossly polluted and likely to cause a nuisance".

River and canal water quality is now surveyed every five years using the General Quality Assessments Scheme; this is not a statutory scheme. In England and Wales the Environment Agency is responsible for the scheme and in Scotland, SEPA. Chemical quality is assessed on the basis of concentrations of dissolved oxygen, biochemical oxygen demand (BOD) and ammonia. Stretches of rivers and canals are assigned one of six grades: A (very good), B (good), C (fairly good), D (fair), E (poor) and F (bad). In England and Wales 91.8% of rivers and canals were assessed as being in categories A-D in 1997/99. For Scotland the figure was 97.5% and for Northern Ireland 95.7%. (DETR press release, 21/9/00; ENDS, September 2000)

Biological quality is assessed on the basis of the number and diversity of tiny animals (macro-invertebrates) which live in or on the beds of rivers. In 1996, 93% of rivers and canals in England and Wales were of good or fair biological quality; in Northern Ireland all were assessed as being of good or fair biological quality *(Digest of Environmental Statistics, No. 20, 1998)*.

Surface waters in England and Wales are surveyed and

classified according to the *Surface Waters (River Ecosystem) (Classification) Regulations 1994* - see below 5.15.2a and Appendix 5.5.

THE EUROPEAN UNION AND WATER POLLUTION CONTROL

The reduction and control of water pollution and contamination has always been an important priority in the European Union's (EU) environmental programme. As with other areas of EU pollution control legislation, Directives emanating from the EU are having a growing influence on UK legislation. European Union controls on water pollution can be classified in three categories: discharge of dangerous substances (including wastes); quality objectives; and by sector or industry (to date only one industry - the titanium dioxide industry - has been covered). In September 2000 agreement was finally reached on a 1997 proposal for a Framework Directive on Water (see below 5.5); some of the earlier Directives will be repealed ten years after its formal adoption.

The European Commission's Fifth Action Programme, *Towards Sustainability*, (see also Appendix 6) builds on current EU policies aimed at securing sufficient water supplies and maintaining and improving quality. In particular, policies to 2000 have been aimed at:

* prevention of pollution of fresh and marine surface waters and groundwater;
* restoration of natural ground and surface waters to an ecologically sound condition;
* ensuring that water demand and water supply are brought into equilibrium on the basis of more rational use and management of water resources.

Also, in line with the basic principles of the Fifth Action Programme, the Commission has aimed to integrate water policy into other areas of Community policy.

Brief details of EU institutions and legislative processes are given in Appendix 6. Water-related Directives are listed in Appendix 6.5.

5.5 FRAMEWORK DIRECTIVE ON WATER POLICY

The proposal for a Directive establishing a Framework for Community Action in the field of Water Policy (COM(97) 49) was first published in March 1997, and finally adopted following agreement in the Conciliation Committee in September 2000. The overall purpose of the Directive is to establish a framework for the protection of surface fresh water, estuaries, coastal waters and groundwater in the Community; the objective is to prevent deterioration and protect and enhance the status of aquatic ecosystems; to promote sustainable water consumption; and to contribute to the provision of a supply of water in the qualities and quantities needed for sustainable use of resources. Among the Directive's main features are:

* Member States must take all necessary measures to ensure groundwater quality does not deteriorate and to prevent or limit the input of pollutants to groundwater. A further Directive defining measures to achieve good groundwater chemical status within 15 years is to be drafted within the next two years;
* discharges of hazardous substances must cease or be phased out within 20 years of their identification as a hazardous substance;
* by 2010 water pricing policies to reflect the need to encourage efficient use of water resources and attainment of environmental objectives of the Directive; costs should have regard to the polluter pays principle, though they would also be able to take account of regional geological conditions, as well as economic and social conditions.

The Directive defines guiding principles for the qualitative and quantitative protection of groundwater, adopting a more integrated approach to water policy and applying both the precautionary and polluter pays principles; in addition the economic development of a region must not be allowed to jeopardise the status of surface waters. Environmental quality objectives using Best Available Techniques (BAT) are to be set so as to ensure consistency with emission limits required by other legislation, e.g. the IPPC Directive and that on pollution caused by dangerous substances to water (76/464/EEC) - see 5.6 below.

Member States will be required to consult on, and designate river basin management areas and to set up arrangements for cooperation where use of water within a river basin has transboundary effects. Member States would then need to establish a river basin management plan within 10 years of the Directive coming into force which meets the objectives of the Directive and achieves good ground and surface water status within 15 years of the formal adoption of the Directive; for groundwater this would be on the basis of chemical and quantitative status and for surface water on the basis of ecological and chemical status - these are defined in an annex to the Directive together with monitoring and other requirements. Member States unable to meet the deadline would be able to apply for a derogation. Other requirements to be carried out for each river basin district by 31 December 2001 (and reviewed and updated every six years) include

* an analysis of the characteristics of each river basin;
* a review of the impact of human activity on the status of surface and groundwater for each river basin district; this should include estimates of point source pollution, diffuse source pollution, and of water abstractions, and an analysis of other anthropogenic influences on the status of water;
* an economic analysis of water use.

The Directive includes requirements for a register of those areas within each river basin district requiring special protection and monitoring programmes for such areas, as well as the establishment of monitoring of surface and ground water status. By 2010, Member States must ensure full cost recovery for all services provided for water use. Exemptions would be allowed to ensure the basic level of water use for households remained affordable, for climatic or geographical reasons or for certain infrastructure projects.

In February 2000, the Commission published a proposal for a Decision (COM(2000) 27) establishing a priority list of 32 hazardous substances to be included as an annex to the Framework Directive – see Appendix 5.1. Once agreed discharge limits and environmental quality standards will be set for the substances, which have been selected because of the risk posed to the aquatic environment and to human health. The Directive requires the Commission to review the list every six years.

Among the Directives (or drafts) to be repealed ten years after adoption of the framework Directive are:

- 75/440/EEC - surface water
- 78/659/EEC - freshwater fish
- 79/923/EEC - shellfish waters
- 80/68/EEC - protection of groundwater from dangerous substances
- COM(93) 680 - draft on ecological quality

5.6 DANGEROUS SUBSTANCES

Discharges to surface and other waters are covered by the Framework Directive on pollution caused by certain dangerous substances discharged into the aquatic environment (76/464/EEC), and subsequent "daughter" Directives. Discharges to groundwater are dealt with by Directive 80/68/EEC. There are also various Directives (76/769/EEC and amendments) which relate to the marketing and use of certain dangerous substances with the primary objective of reducing risks to human health as well as protecting the aquatic environment; these are implemented through Regulations under the *Environmental Protection Act 1990* - the *Environmental Protection (Control of Injurious Substances) Regulations*. See also chapter 4, 4.10, Directive on the disposal of polychlorinated biphenyls and polychlorinated terphenyls.

In August 2000 the Environment Agency published a consultation paper reviewing the procedure for the consenting of dangerous substances in discharges to surface waters under the *Water Resources Act 1991* – see 5.15.3(a).

5.6.1 Black List Substances

The Framework Directive (76/464/EEC) listed 129 substances considered to be so toxic, persistent or bio-accumulative in the environment that priority should be given to eliminating pollution by them. Included are substances such as organohalogens, organophosphorus, cadmium and mercury and their compounds. Control of these substances is to be achieved largely through the setting of limit values or environmental quality standards in

subsequent "Daughter" Directives, thus formally giving the substance List I - or Black List - categorisation. From the original list of 129 substances, Daughter Directives have now been adopted for discharges of mercury, cadmium, hexachlorocyclohexane (HCH) (which includes lindane), DDT, pentachlorophenol (PCP), carbon tetrachloride, the 'drins' group of pesticides (aldrin, endrin, dieldrin and isodrin), hexachlorobenzene (HCB), hexachlorobutadiene and chloroform. In 1990, a further Daughter Directive covering 1,2-dichloroethane, trichloroethylene, perchloroethylene and trichlorobenzene was adopted.

In all cases, the Directives provide for emission limits and quality objectives, and they encourage the use of best available technology in new plant.

The remaining substances from the priority list which have not yet been given formal List I status in a Daughter Directive are in the meantime treated as List II substances for regulatory purposes.

In the UK, the *Environmental Protection (Prescribed Processes and Substances) Regulations 1991* (as amended) list a number of Black List substances whose releases to water are prescribed for Integrated Pollution Control (see chapter 1 and Appendix 1.2). The same substances, together with carbon tetrachloride, are also prescribed substances under the *Trade Effluents (Prescribed Processes and Substances) Regulations 1989* (as amended; see later this chapter, 5.17.3). All processes producing these substances, sometimes referred to as Red List substances in the UK, must use BATNEEC (Best Available Techniques Not Entailing Excessive Costs) to control polluting releases - see chapter 1, 1.6. Discharge consents will also have to ensure that strict environmental quality standards are met. *The Surface Waters (Dangerous Substances) (Classification) Regulations 1989*, as amended, and similar in Scotland (see this chapter, 5.15.2a) implement the environmental quality standards laid down in the 1990 Directive.

A Department of Environment Circular (DOE 7/89) gives guidance on the implementation of the various Directives setting specific environmental quality standards and discharge limits. The Circular emphasises that the aim should be "minimisation of inputs of the most dangerous substances to the aquatic environment".

5.6.2 Grey List Substances

List II substances - the "Grey List" - on the 1976 Framework Directive covers those substances considered less harmful when discharged to water. Included here are metals, such as zinc, nickel, chromium, lead, arsenic and copper; various biocides and substances such as cyanide and ammonia. It also covers those substances awaiting formal List I categorisation. The EU Directive requires Member States to establish pollution reduction programmes and to provide environmental quality objectives and standards for List II substances. Department of Environment Circular 7/89 also includes environmental quality standards for all Grey List substances. Concentrations of Grey List substances in freshwater should not be at such a level that freshwater fish cannot be supported.

The *Surface Waters (Dangerous Substances) (Classification) Regulations 1997* (SI 2560) and 1998 (SI 389) set statutory quality objectives for a total of 21 List II substances (see 5.15.2a below).

5.6.3 Groundwater

In 1979, a Directive (80/68/EEC) on the protection of groundwater against pollution caused by dangerous substances was adopted, for compliance in December 1981. This Directive will be repealed ten years after adoption of the Framework Directive on water (see 5.5 above).

The Directive requires the prevention of the discharge of List I substances to groundwater, and investigation of List II substances prior to direct or indirect discharge. (The Lists I and II referred to in this Directive are not identical to those contained in the dangerous substances Directive; also, unlike the dangerous substances Directive, List I status is definitive and does not need confirmation in a Daughter Directive.)

The Commission has also published (July 1996) a proposal for an "action programme for integrated groundwater protection and management" (COM(96) 315); this emphasises the need for

- licensing systems and other instruments providing an appropriate system of national management of groundwater;

- measures to provide for preventive, comprehensive groundwater protection;

- general provisions for the safety of installations handling substances harmful to water;

- general provisions to promote agricultural practices consistent with groundwater protection.

Member States would be expected to draw up national programmes meeting the above objectives in the light of national, regional and local conditions and needs. Some elements of the Groundwater Action Plan have also been included in the Framework Directive - see above, 5.5.

Brief details of the National Rivers Authority *Policy and Practice for the Protection of Groundwater* (published 1992) are given below at 5.15.2b (*Water Resources Act 1991*, protection of groundwater).

The *Waste Management Licensing Regulations 1994* (see chapter 4, 4.19.3) require waste regulation authorities to review all landfill licences, and to vary or revoke conditions as appropriate to prevent pollution of groundwater by List I and List II substances. In Northern Ireland, the Directive is implemented in part by the *Pollution of Groundwater by Dangerous Substances Regulations (Northern Ireland) 1994*. 1998 Groundwater Regulations require disposal or tipping of controlled substances to be authorised and enable the Environment Agencies to issue notices

prohibiting activities to prevent the entry of List I substances to groundwater or its pollution by List II substances - see 5.15.2b.

5.7 QUALITY OBJECTIVES FOR WATER USED FOR PARTICULAR PURPOSES

A number of Directives define the acceptable quality of water for particular purposes and make provision for both achieving and monitoring the quality of the water. Directives have been adopted concerning the quality of surface water intended for the abstraction of drinking water, for bathing water, freshwater fish, shellfish and for water intended for human consumption.

Following agreement on the Framework Directive on water policy (see above, 5.5), the Directives on both surface and groundwater will be repealed and the proposed Directive on Ecological Quality withdrawn (and thus the Freshwater Fish and Shellfish Waters Directives will also be repealed).

5.7.1 Ecological Quality

The proposal for a Directive on the Ecological Quality of Surface Waters (COM(93) 680) was published in 1993; it was intended to complement other water Directives, including the urban waste water Directive and that on nitrate pollution (see below) as well as the Directive on Integrated Pollution Prevention and Control (see chapter 1, 1.12) by ensuring a harmonised approach to controlling pollution of surface waters and thus achieve high ecological quality. This proposal will be withdrawn as a result of adoption of the Framework Directive (see above 5.5).

5.7.2 Surface Water

A Directive (75/440/EEC) adopted in 1975 classified the quality of surface waters intended for the abstraction of drinking water, and specified the treatment and timetable necessary to bring such waters up to drinking water quality. A1 waters required simple filtration and disinfection; A2 required normal physical and chemical treatment, and disinfection; and A3 waters intensive physical and chemical treatment and disinfection. This Directive will be repealed ten years after adoption of the Framework Directive on water (see above 5.5).

This Directive was initially partly implemented in England and Wales through the *Surface Waters (Classification) Regulations 1989* (and similar 1990 Regulations in Scotland and Northern Ireland). The 1989 Regulations have been revoked and the Directive implemented through new Regulations, *The Surface Water (Abstraction for Drinking Water) (Classification) Regulations 1996* (see below, 5.15.2a).

5.7.3 Bathing Water

This Directive (76/160/EEC) was adopted in December 1975, with Member States being given until December 1985 to bring designated bathing waters up to the required quality. Bathing waters are defined as fresh or sea water (other than swimming pools) where bathing is "traditionally practised by a large number of bathers". An annex to the Directive sets out sampling frequencies, guideline and mandatory values, as well as analysis and inspection methods for a number of microbiological and physio-chemical parameters (see Appendix 5.2a).

Proposals for a new Directive (COM(94) 36), to replace the 1976 Directive, were published by the Commission in 1994, and a revised proposal (COM(97) 585 in November which took account of some of the amendments adopted by the European Parliament. In protecting bathers' health, the draft Directive required monitoring and measurement for contamination and pollution as indicated by 12 instead of the current 19 parameters; these are: escherichia coli, faecal streptococci, enteroviruses, bacteriophages, pH, colour, mineral oils, surface active substances reacting with methylene blue, phenols, transparency, dissolved oxygen and tarry residues and floating materials. All except enteroviruses would require sampling at a minimum frequency of every fortnight during the bathing season, with sampling for enteroviruses carried out monthly. However, as it has proved impossible to reach agreement on the draft Directive, new proposals are to be prepared.

In England and Wales, the Bathing Waters (Classification) Regulations 1991 (and comparable Regulations in Scotland) implement the current Directive - see this chapter, 5.15.2a. In Northern Ireland the Directive is implemented through the Quality of Bathing Waters Regulations (Northern Ireland) 1993. In 2000, 94% (1999 - 91%) of UK bathing waters met EU mandatory coliform bacteria standards (DETR press release, 4/12/00).

5.7.4 Freshwater Fish and Shellfish Waters

Directives adopted in 1978 and 1979 lay down quality requirements for freshwater fish (78/659/EEC) and shellfish waters (79/923/EEC), respectively. These Directives are to be replaced by the Framework Directive on Water - see above 5.5.

The freshwater fish Directive requires Member States to identify and designate fresh waters needing protection or improvement in order to support fish, requiring compliance with the Directive's standards by 1985; an annex to the Directive lists a number of physical and chemical parameters - some mandatory and some guidelines. Implementation of the Directive in England, Scotland and Wales has been through the Control of Pollution Act 1974 and in Northern Ireland by 1993 Statutory Order. New regulations are likely to be made under the Water Resources Act 1991 following the finalisation of statutory water quality objectives under ss.82-83 of that Act. In 1996, 93% of the total length of designated rivers in England and Wales complied with standards in the freshwater fish Directive (Scotland 98%; Northern Ireland 28%).

The shellfish waters Directive also requires Member States to designate shellfish waters and lays down water quality objectives aimed at ensuring that such waters "contribute to the high quality of shellfish products directly edible by man"; compliance with the Directive's standards was required by 1987. There are 93 designated waters in England and Wales and 33 in Scotland (including 11 proposed in February 2000). The Surface Waters (Shellfish) (Classification) Regulations 1997 prescribe a system for classifying the quality of controlled waters in order to support shellfish - see 5.15.2a below.

5.7.5 Water Intended for Human Consumption

The 1980 Directive (80/778) relating to the quality of water intended for human consumption - the drinking water Directive – is to be repealed on 25 December 2003 when standards set in its replacement Directive (98/83/EC) have to be met. The 1980 Directive set quality standards for some 60 substances (including some pesticides), as well as requirements for sampling frequency, measuring methods etc; three types of standard - Guide Levels (GL); Maximum Admissible Concentrations (MAC); and Minimum Required Concentrations (MRC) – were laid down in respect of organoleptic, physico-chemical and microbiological parameters, for substances undesirable in excessive amounts and for toxic substances.

Directive 98/83/EC concerning the quality of water intended for human consumption was formally adopted in November 1998. National legislation implementing it had to be in place by 25 December 2000 and most of the new standards met by 25 December 2003. (The standard for lead does not have to be met until 2013, and those for bromate and trihalomethanes until 2008.)

The 1998 Directive covers all water for domestic use (whether from tap, bottle or container) and water used by the food industry where this affects the final product and, thus consumers' health; it does not apply to water for agricultural purposes, natural mineral water or medicinal waters. An important objective of the Directive is to contribute towards achieving sustainable development by ensuring a sufficient supply of water of adequate quality, with Member States having a duty to ensure that drinking water is wholesome and clean.

The number of parameters is reduced from 67 to 53 (including 13 new parameters), retaining only those essential for the protection of water quality and health; these are divided into three groups: microbiological, chemical and indicator parameters and are to be reviewed at least every five years. Chemical parametric values have been based largely on WHO guidelines adopted in 1992, and include the following:

- **Arsenic:** 10 µg/l.
- **Nitrate concentrations:** 0.5 µg/l.
- **Total pesticides:** 0.5 µg/l, and 0.1 µg/l for individual pesticides.
- **PAHs:** 0.1 µg/l (0.01 µg/l for benzo(a)pyrene).
- **Benzene:** 1µg/l.
- **Chlorinated solvents:** trichloroethene and tetrachloroethene combined -10 µg/l.

- **Lead:** maximum permitted concentration to be reduced from 50 µg/l to 25 µg/l over five years and to 10 µg/l within 15 years; the lengthy period for compliance takes account of the costs involved in replacing lead pipes and fittings. (Plans for replacing lead pipes in homes must, however, be submitted to the Commission within five years.)
- **Bromate:** 25 µg/l to apply from 2003, reducing to 10 µg/l in 2008.
- **Trihalomethanes:** 150 µg/l from 2003, reducing to 100 µg/l in 2008.

Member States are free to set additional parameters in the light of local environmental conditions; enforcement authorities must inform consumers when water quality falls below standard, of any danger to health, and give advice on what to do; consumers must also be advised when action has been taken and water quality restored. As now, monitoring is required to check on water quality and assess that measures taken to ensure quality are operating correctly; monitoring is also required to verify the efficiency of disinfection treatment of water intended for human consumption and to ensure no contamination from disinfection by-products.

In England and Wales the 1980 Directive was implemented through the *Water Supply (Water Quality) Regulations 1989* (Scotland, 1990), as amended and the *Private Water Supplies Regulations 1991* (Scotland, 1992), and in Northern Ireland by 1994 Regulations - see 5.17.1c below.

The 1998 Directive is to be implemented in England and Wales through new *Water Supply (Water Quality) Regulations* which will consolidate and replace the 1989 Regulations, and through new *Private Water Supplies Regulations* – see 5.17.1.c below and introduction to this edition of the Pollution Handbook, and also Appendix 5.2b.

5.7.6 Urban Waste Water Treatment

A Directive (91/271/EEC) adopted in 1991 lays down minimum requirements for the treatment of municipal waste water and for the disposal of sludge. The Directive also aims to control the discharge of industrial waste waters which are of a similar nature to municipal waste water but which do not enter municipal waste water treatment plants before discharge. The release of treated or untreated sludge from treatment plants in fresh or seawater was banned from 31 December 1998.

Receiving waters are classified according to "sensitivity". In most cases secondary biological treatment prior to discharge will be required as a minimum, with tertiary treatment for waters which are, or are likely to become, eutrophic. Primary treatment - such as the settlement of suspended solids - may be considered sufficient for discharges from treatment processes serving less than 150,000 inhabitants into coastal waters less sensitive to pollution. Limit values for various industrial sector discharges to rivers, estuaries and coastal waters should be set in regulations.

Member States should have drawn up plans for implementation of the Directive by the end of 1993 with the aim of achieving the various deadlines for treatment standards. However, in England, Scotland and Wales designation of "sensitive" and "less sensitive" areas was not completed until 1994.

This Directive has been implemented in England and Wales through *The Urban Waste Water Treatment (England and Wales) Regulations 1994* and by similar Regulations in Scotland and Northern Ireland - see below 5.18. Discharges to controlled waters are currently regulated under IPC (chapter 1, 1.14) and consents issued under regulations made under the *Water Resources Act 1991* (see this chapter 5.15.3a).

5.7.7 Nitrate Pollution

Directive 91/676/EEC places restrictions on the use of natural and chemical fertilisers to reduce the risk of nitrate pollution of river, coastal and sea waters and ensure a level of no more than 50 mg/l of nitrates in fresh water sources used for abstraction purposes. Catchment areas in which nitrate levels exceed, or are likely to exceed, the requirements of the Directive at any time in the year will be designated vulnerable zones. In such areas, an annual limit of 210 kg/ha of organic manure will be mandatory, reducing to 170 kg/ha four years later. Designation of such zones should have been completed by the end of 1993; action programmes to control nitrate leaching should have been in place by December 1995 to begin no later than December 1998 to ensure annual limits on nitrogen fertilisers are complied with by the implementation date of December 1999; programmes must be reviewed every four years.

The Directive also requires the drawing up of codes of good agricultural practice which must, as a minimum, include

- details of periods when use of fertilisers would be inappropriate;
- guidelines on use of fertilisers on sloping, flooded, frozen or snow covered ground;
- guidelines on use of fertilisers near water courses;
- measures to prevent run-off and seepage into rivers of manure-containing liquids and other effluents;
- conditions for general use of fertilisers.

Finally the Directive requires monitoring programmes to be established and reports on implementation progress to be sent to the Commission every four years.

The Protection of Water Against Agricultural Nitrate Pollution (England and Wales) Regulations 1996 (SI 888), which came into force on 17 April 1996, designate 68 nitrate vulnerable zones (NVZs). There is also one NVZ in Scotland (SI 1564). A review of these zones had to be carried out before 19 December 1997, with further reviews every four years to revise or add to the list as necessary. In England, a consultation paper is to be issued regarding the designation of further zones, mainly in Eastern and Central England. In Scotland, the *Designation of Nitrate Vulnerable Zones (Scotland) Regulations 2000* (SI

96, effective 8 May 2000) amend SI 1654 and designate a further NVZ in Scotland. Further NVZs for Scotland are under consideration.

The Environment Agency is required to monitor the concentrations of nitrates in freshwaters at designated sampling stations and to review the eutrophic state of fresh surface waters, estuarial and coastal waters before 19 December 1997 and thereafter on a monthly basis over a period of a year every four years. Where previous monitoring has shown nitrate concentrations to be consistently below 25 mg/l, the dates for monitoring by the Environment Agency are 19 December 2001 and thereafter every eight years. The Regulations designate relevant sections of the *Code of Good Agricultural Practice for the Protection of Water* (see below 5.15.5d) as the code of good practice required by the Directive.

1998 Regulations which came into force on 19 December 1998 - *The Action Programme for Nitrate Vulnerable Zones (England and Wales) Regulations 1998* (SI 1202) and similar for Scotland (SI 171) and Northern Ireland (SR 1999, no. 156) - establish action programmes to control nitrate leaching. Measures in the programme to ensure nitrate limits were met by 19 December 1999 include:

- no chemical fertilisers to be applied between 1 September (15 September in the case of grassland) and 1 February;
- no more than 250 kg per hectare of organic manure per year to be applied to grassland; for other agricultural land no more than 210 kg per hectare per year to 19 December 2002, and then 170 kg per year;
- no applications of organic manure in the form of slurry, poultry manure or liquid digested sewage sludge to sandy or shallow soil between 1 September (1 August for other types of soil) and 1 November; sufficient storage capacity to be available when manure and slurry spreading is restricted;
- detailed records to be kept of fertiliser and manure use, which should be retained for 5 years.

These measures, which are enforced by the Environment Agency/SEPA, are mandatory unlike participation in the scheme establishing nitrate sensitive areas (NSAs) - see below 5.15.5c, *Water Resources Act 1991*, nitrate sensitive areas.

In Scotland the *Code of Good Practice on the Prevention of Environmental Pollution from Agricultural Activity*, implemented in 1992 with a revised edition published in 1997, also meets the requirements of the Directive. Those parts of the Code which relate to water pollution have statutory backing (see below 5.15.5d).

In Northern Ireland, the relevant Regulations are the *Protection of Water Against Agricultural Nitrate Pollution Regulations (Northern Ireland) 1996* (SR 217), as amended by 1999 Regulations (SR3); these latter include a Code of Good Agricultural Practice, and require a review and revision of the zones as soon as practicable and no later than 19 December 2001, and then at least every four years.

5.8 INTERNATIONAL CONVENTIONS

5.8.1 Protocol on Water and Health

This Protocol, drafted by the WHO Regional Office for Europe and the UN Economic Commission for Europe, was drawn up under the UNECE's 1992 Convention on the Protection and Use of Transboundary Watercourses and International Lakes. It was adopted in London in June 1999 and remained open for signature until 18 June 2000. It will enter into force 90 days after the 16th instrument of ratification has been filed.

The objective of the protocol is "the protection of human health and well-being ...through improving water management, including the protection of water ecosystems, and through preventing, controlling and reducing water-related disease". It applies to surface freshwater, groundwater, estuaries, coastal waters used for recreation or the production of fish and/or harvesting of shellfish, bathing waters, water in the course of abstraction, transport treatment or supply, and waste water throughout the course of collection, transport, treatment and discharge or reuse. Parties to the Protocol will take all appropriate measures to prevent, control and reduce water related disease within a framework of integrated water management, aimed at sustainable use of water resources. To this end parties to the Protocol will endeavour to provide access to drinking water and sanitation for everyone. Within two years of ratifying the Protocol, Parties to it should establish and publish national and/or local targets in such areas as quality of drinking water, bathing waters or shellfish waters; reductions in outbreaks and incidents of water related disease; identification and remediation of contaminated sites affecting water.

5.8.2 Marine Environment

The European Union participates in various international Conventions relating to the protection of the marine environment and the prevention of oil spills; another part of its work is the harmonisation of national programmes regarding the elimination of pollution. With the enlargement of the EU, bringing in countries bordering the Mediterranean, efforts are also being directed towards the protection of that region, where the environment is sensitive and already severely overloaded locally (see also this chapter, 5.20).

IMPLEMENTATION AND ENFORCEMENT AUTHORITIES

Overall responsibility for the maintenance and management of water resources in England and Wales rests with the Secretary of State for the Environment, Transport and the Regions: this includes responsibility for national policy on all matters of conservation and supply, sewerage and sewage disposal; the control of pollution in both inland and coastal waters; the use of inland waters for recreation and navigation; the control of marine pollution by oil. The Minister of Agriculture, Fisheries and Food is responsible for land drainage, the protection of freshwater and marine fisheries, the dumping of waste at sea, and the safe use of agricultural pesticides.

The effects of individual acts of pollution are usually most noticeable within the locality where they take place and it was considered that they could best be controlled by authorities with a detailed knowledge of the area; thus the first statute to control water pollution - the *Rivers Pollution Prevention Act 1876* - laid down the statutory framework for controlling water pollution but gave the responsibility for enforcement to local government bodies, such as town and district councils.

The River Boards Act 1948 had established river boards for the whole of England (except the Thames and London area); these were superseded by river authorities following the *Water Resources Act 1963*, which were in turn replaced by ten regional water authorities (nine in England and one in Wales) by the *Water Act 1973*.

Following privatisation of the water industry, the ten water authorities were transferred to the private sector (water undertakers), together with their responsibilities for water supply and sewerage, and sewage disposal. Responsibility for pollution control of rivers and watercourses passed to the National Rivers Authority following its establishment on 1 September 1989. In Scotland the River Purification Authorities were given similar responsibilities.

On 1 April 1996 the responsibilities and functions of the NRA and RPAs were transferred to the Environment Agency and the Scottish Environment Protection Agency, respectively.

5.9 ENGLAND AND WALES

5.9.1 Environment Agency

The Environment Agency for England and Wales was established by the *Environment Act 1995* which received the Royal Assent on 19 July 1995. On 1 April 1996 the Agency assumed all the responsibilities and functions of the National Rivers Authority which was abolished. The Agency also has responsibility for Integrated Pollution Control, Integrated Pollution Prevention and Control and waste regulation (see chapters 1 and 4 respectively).

The Environment Agency is charged with preventing deterioration of water quality and seeking its improvement; it has a duty to promote, as it considers desirable, the conservation and enhancement of the water environment (inland and coastal waters). As well as pollution control, the Agency's responsibilities include water resource management, planning and conservation, flood defence, forecasting and warning, abstraction licences, fisheries and in some areas navigation. It also has certain duties in relation to promoting conservation; amenity and recreational facilities. The Agency and SEPA should consult and collaborate on matters of common interest.

5.9.2 Drinking Water Inspectorate

This Inspectorate was established within the Department of Environment (now Department of the Environment, Transport and the Regions - DETR) in January 1990; its principal task is to ensure that water undertakers in England and Wales are fulfilling their statutory requirements for the supply of wholesome drinking water.

The Inspectorate carries out annual technical audits of each water company; this includes an assessment (based on information supplied by the company) of the quality of water in each supply zone, arrangements for sampling and analysis, and progress made on achieving compliance with UK and EU requirements.

The Inspectorate monitors compliance with the standards set in the *Water Supply (Water Quality) Regulations 1989* (as amended) - see 5.17.1c below. The Inspectorate investigates incidents affecting water quality and water companies are required to notify the Inspectorate of any significant pollution incidents.

The DWI's annual report *(Drinking Water, 1999)* shows that 99.82% (1998: 99.78%) of the 2.8 million drinking water tests carried out in 1999 met national and EU standards.

5.10 SCOTLAND

5.10.1 Scottish Environment Protection Agency

SEPA was also established by the *Environment Act 1995* and assumed the responsibilities and functions of the river purification authorities on 1 April 1996. Its functions mirror those of the Environment Agency - see 5.9.1 above. SEPA also has responsibility for Integrated Pollution Control, IPPC, Local Air Pollution Control (Part I, EPA 1990) and waste regulation (see chapters 1, 2 and 4 respectively).

The Water Act 1989 introduced new provisions into the *Water (Scotland) Act 1980* so as to make provision in Scotland in relation to the quality of water broadly equivalent to the quality of water provisions for England and Wales. The control of water pollution in Scotland is regulated by Part II of the *Control of Pollution Act 1974*, as amended.

Regulations implementing various EU Directives on water quality, and similar to those for England and Wales, have been made in Scotland and are referred to throughout this chapter.

5.10.2 Drinking Water

Monitoring and policy on drinking water in Scotland is the responsibility of the Scottish Office. Unitary authorities are responsible for the supply of "wholesome" water for domestic and other purposes (*Water (Scotland) Act 1980*).

In 1998, 98.3% (1997: 98.1%) drinking water tests in Scotland met the required standards (*Drinking Water Quality in Scotland 1998*, The Stationery Office).

5.11 NORTHERN IRELAND

The control of water pollution and water quality, together with drinking water, is the responsibility of the Environment and Heritage Service (Water Quality Unit); water supply and sewerage services are managed by the Water Service. Both are Agencies of the Department of the Environment (NI).

The main legislation for controlling water pollution is the *Water Act (Northern Ireland) 1972*. This will be repealed following full implementation of the *Water (Northern Ireland) Order 1999*, made on 10 March 1999. This updates current legislation to take account of developments both in science and policy and will, when implemented, introduce a similar system for controlling water pollution to that already in force in the rest of the UK.

In 1998, 98.86% of drinking water samples met legal standards.

Reference is made to the forthcoming legislation as appropriate as: WNIO: Art.00.

5.12 LOCAL AUTHORITIES

Under ss.77 & 78 of the *Water Industry Act 1991*, local authorities have a statutory duty to take all such steps as they consider appropriate for keeping themselves informed about the wholesomeness and sufficiency of both public and private supplies of water in their area.

If the public supply is likely to become unwholesome or insufficient, the local authority must advise the water undertaker who must take appropriate remedial action (s.79). In the case of private supplies, the *Water Industry Act* gives local authorities the power to serve a notice requiring improvements (s.80). *The Private Water Supplies Regulations 1991* set out local authorities' duties with regard to safeguarding water quality (see 5.17.1c below).

Local authorities are also responsible for the quality of bottled mineral waters for drinking. Sources have to be approved and standards as set out in the *Natural Mineral Waters Regulations 1985* complied with.

As from April 1992, local authorities also took over responsibility from MAFF for enforcing certain provisions of the *Control of Pesticides Regulations 1986*, as amended (see 5.30.3 below).

In Scotland water supplies, sewage disposal and sewerage are the responsibility of regional/unitary authorities, operating under the *Sewerage (Scotland) Act 1968*.

REGULATORY CONTROLS

Privatisation of the water industry in England and Wales in 1989 resulted in major changes to the legislation dealing with the control of water pollution. *The Water Act 1989*, which received the Royal Assent on 6 July 1989, largely replaced the water section (Part II) of the *Control of Pollution Act 1974* in England and Wales. On 30 November 1991 the *Water Act 1989,* together with a number of other statutes controlling water pollution in England and Wales, was repealed and their provisions consolidated in the following:

* *Water Resources Act 1991*
* *Water Industry Act 1991*
* *Land Drainage Act 1991*
* *Statutory Water Companies Act 1991*

A fifth Act - *the Water Consolidation (Consequential Provisions) Act 1991* - provides for consequential amendments and repeals and other transitional matters. These Acts took effect on 1 December 1991.

In Scotland, legislation dealing with water is contained in the *Water (Scotland) Act 1980* and Part II of the *Control of Pollution Act 1974*; both have been amended by ss.168 & 169 of the *Water Act 1989* to make provision, respectively, for water quality and the control of water pollution in Scotland similar to those in England and Wales. COPA has also been amended by the *Environment Act 1995* (Sch. 16 & Sch. 22, para 29). Reference is made to the appropriate provisions of COPA etc in the text below covering the *Water Resources Act 1991* and the *Water Industry Act 1991*.

In Northern Ireland the relevant legislation is the *Water Act (Northern Ireland) 1972* which is to be replaced by the *Water (Northern Ireland) Order 1999*. This is administered by the Water Quality Unit of the Environment and Heritage Service.

5.13 PUBLIC HEALTH ACT 1936

Section 259 makes the following matters statutory nuisances in England and Wales for the purposes of water pollution:

a) any pond, pool ditch, gutter or watercourse which is so foul or in such a state as to be prejudicial to health or a nuisance;

b) any part of a watercourse, not being a part ordinarily navigated by vessels employed in the carriage of goods by water, which is so choked or silted up as to obstruct or impede the proper flow of water and thereby to cause a nuisance, or give rise to conditions prejudicial to health.

Complaints about statutory nuisances are dealt with by local authorities who may take action through the Magistrates' Court for abatement of a nuisance (see also chapter 1, 1.16.1).

Section 260 enables parish and community councils to take action to deal with filthy or stagnant water which may be prejudicial to health.

5.14 ENVIRONMENTAL PROTECTION ACT 1990

Certain processes discharging to water are subject to Integrated Pollution Control (or in due course, Integrated Pollution Prevention and Control) as a result of their potential to pollute the air and/or land – see chapter 1, 1.13 and 1.14.

5.15 WATER RESOURCES ACT 1991

This Act which applies in England and Wales came into effect on 1 December 1991 and replaced corresponding sections of the *Water Act 1989*. It has subsequently been amended by the *Environment Act 1995*. The WRA deals with some of the responsibilities of the Environment Agency. (Sections 1-14 covering the functions of the NRA were repealed on 1 April 1996 following the abolition of the NRA and the establishment of the Environment Agency; its functions are set out in the *Environment Act 1995* - see chapter 1, 1.7.1.)

In Scotland water pollution is controlled under Part II of the *Control of Pollution Act 1974*, as amended by the *Environment Act 1995*, and is the responsibility of the Scottish Environment Protection Agency (SEPA) - see also chapter 1, 1.7.2.

In Northern Ireland, Part II of the *Water (Northern Ireland) Order 1999* (referred to in the following text as the WNIO) will replace the current 1972 legislation.

5.15.1 Control of Pollution of Water Resources (Part III)

This part of the WRA is concerned with maintaining and enhancing the quality of "controlled waters" (i.e. relevant territorial, coastal, inland freshwaters (including lakes and ponds) and groundwaters.

The Controlled Waters (Lakes and Ponds) Order 1989 (SI 1149) which came into force on 1 September 1989 brings within the definition of "controlled waters" reservoirs not discharging into a watercourse, other than those containing water which has been treated prior to entering the supply.

5.15.2 Quality Objectives (ss.82-84)

(a) Statutory Water Quality Objectives (ss.82-83)

Section 82 of the *Water Resources Act* provides for the establishment, via regulations, of systems of classifying water quality according to various criteria; s.83 provides for the setting of statutory water quality objectives (SWQOs) for individual stretches of water, on the basis of one or more of the classifications, together with a date by which the classification should be achieved. SWQOs will eventually be set for some 40,000 km of rivers and canals, as well as estuaries, coastal waters, lakes and groundwaters.

For Scotland, similar powers are contained in ss.30B, C, D & E of COPA (see Sch. 23, para 4 of *Water Act 1989* as amended by the *Environment Act 1995*, Sch. 22, para 29(1)-(5)). In Northern Ireland, Articles 5 & 6 of the 1999 Order contain the appropriate provisions.

The Surface Waters (Dangerous Substances) (Classification) Regulations 1989 (SI 2286), amended 1992

These Regulations, applicable in England and Wales, came into effect on 1 January 1990. They implement various EU Daughter Directives relating to inputs to inland and coastal and territorial waters of specific Black List (List I) substances listed in Directive 76/464 (see 5.6 above). The substances concerned and the standards set are at Appendix 5.4. These Regulations have been amended by 1992 Regulations made under s.83 of the *Water Resources Act 1991*. These implement statutory environmental quality standards for four substances covered by the 1990 EU Daughter Directive - ethylene dichloride, trichloroethylene, perchloroethylene and trichlorobenzene (see this chapter, 5.6.1). Similar 1990 Regulations (SI 126) apply in Scotland.

The Surface Waters (Dangerous Substances) (Classification) Regulations 1997 (SI 2560) and 1998 (SI 389)

These Regulations for England and Wales set water quality objectives for a total of 20 List II substances in EU Directive 76/464/EEC (see 5.6 above). Schedules to the Regulations specify the limits of dangerous substances which must not be exceeded to meet criteria for classification as inland freshwaters and for coastal waters and relevant territorial waters - see Appendix 5.4; the aim is to reduce pollution by the dangerous substances listed in the Schedules. The 1997 Regulations came into force on 26 November 1997 and the 1998 Regulations on 25 March 1998.

The Environment Agency is responsible for ensuring compliance with the Regulations, including sampling and analysis and monitoring the effect on waters of discharges containing the dangerous substances and of determining whether the requirements of each classification are being met.

In Scotland, the *Surface Waters (Dangerous Substances) (Classification) (Scotland) Regulations 1998* (SI 250), which came into force on 1 April 1998 and further 1998 regulations (SI 1344), which came into force on 1 July 1998, mirror the 1997 and 1998 E&W Regulations. Similar 1998 Regulations (SR 397) took effect in Northern Ireland on 1 February 1999.

The Bathing Waters (Classification) Regulations 1991 (SI 1597)

These Regulations implementing EU Directive 76/160/EEC came into force in August 1991 in England and Wales (see above, 5.7.3). There are similar 1991 Regulations in Scotland (SI 1609) and 1993 Regulations in Northern Ireland (SR 205). They set out a system for classifying the quality of UK territorial, coastal and inland waters which are designated bathing waters (currently 505 in the UK) - classified as BW1 waters - in compliance with the Directive. Schedule 1 to the Regulations specifies criteria for BW1 classifications and Schedule 2 sampling requirements. Schedule 3 (see Appendix 5.2b) sets out quality and additional sampling requirements.

The criteria for BW1 classification include:

a) at least 95% of samples taken and tested in accordance with sampling requirements must conform to the parametric values in Schedule 3;

b) no sample which fails when tested for compliance with the phenols parameter by the absorption method or with the transparency parameter should have a value which deviates by more than 50% from that in Schedule 3;

c) consecutive samples taken at suitable intervals should not deviate from the parametric values specified in Schedule 3.

Sampling should be carried out at the same place and as specified in Schedule 3 from 1 May - 30 September with a minimum of 20 samples taken at each site; additional samples should be taken if it is suspected that the water quality is deteriorating. Sampling results can be disregarded if they do not meet the requirements due to abnormal weather conditions.

Water companies are also required to comply with the Environment Agency's *Policy for Consents for Sewage Effluent Discharges Affecting Bathing Waters* (1997); under this policy treatment plants must use high standards of conventional treatment and discharge from an outfall well away from bathing waters; if an outfall near a bathing water is used, then very high standards of treatment followed by ultraviolet light disinfection is required. The Agency also requires water companies to meet the requirements of the EU's urban waste water Directive (and of the UK regulations) to ensure identified bathing waters meet the standards set in the bathing water Directive - see 5.7.3, 5.7.6 and 5.18.

The Surface Waters (River Ecosystem) (Classification) Regulations 1994 (SI 1057)

These Regulations, covering England and Wales, came into force on 10 May 1994. They prescribe a system for classifying inland rivers and watercourses, replacing a previous classification devised by the National Water Council (see this chapter, 5.4). The classifications are:

RE1   Water of very good quality suitable for all fish species

RE2   Water of good quality suitable for all fish species

RE3   Water of fair quality suitable for high class coarse fish populations

RE4   Water of fair quality suitable for coarse fish populations

RE5   Water of poor quality which is likely to limit coarse fish populations.

Eight parameters are used for assessing quality: dissolved oxygen; BOD; total ammonia; un-ionised ammonia; pH; hardness; dissolved copper; and total zinc - see Appendix 5.5. Frequency, location, methods of sampling and other procedures for compliance were set out in the NRA's *Water Quality Objectives: Procedures used by the National Rivers Authority for the purpose of the Surface Waters (River Ecosystem) (Classification) Regulations 1994* (30 March 1994).

In addition river and canal quality is surveyed every five years using the "General Quality Assessments Scheme" -

see 5.4 above. Under s.93 of the WRA, the Secretary of State can designate specific stretches of water as water protection zones to prevent pollution of drinking water sources - see 5.15.3(b).

The Surface Waters (Abstraction for Drinking Water) (Classification) Regulations 1996 (SI 3001)

These Regulations, made under ss.82 & 102 of the WRA, came into force on 6 January 1997, with similar 1996 legislation in Northern Ireland. They implement EU Directive 75/440/EEC on the quality of surface water intended for the abstraction of drinking water, which set mandatory and guideline quality requirements (see above, 5.7.2). Earlier 1989 Regulations (SI 1148), which dealt with the mandatory requirements of the Directive have been revoked.

The Regulations prescribe the system of classifying the quality of inland freshwaters according to their suitability for abstraction by water undertakers for supply (after treatment) as drinking water (see Appendix 5.6). Sampling must be carried out at points chosen by the Environment Agency with the frequency for each parameter set in Schedule 3 to the Regulations; Schedule 2 details the measurement method to be used for each parameter. Analysis of the samples must be carried out to ascertain compliance with the parameters in Schedule 1 (see Appendix 5.6) - i.e. 95% of the samples should comply with the limit, none exceed it by more than 50%, and where any of the samples exceed the limit, there should be no danger to public health. The Environment Agency can decide to reduce sampling frequency where there is no pollution of waters, no risk of deterioration in quality or it is of a better quality than the parameter required for waters classified as DW1 (see Appendix 5.6).

The Surface Waters (Fishlife) (Classification) Regulations 1997 (SI 1331)

These Regulations for England and Wales came into force in June 1997, with similar Regulations (SI 2471) for Scotland coming into force on 18 November 1997, and for Northern Ireland (SR 448). They implement the EU freshwater fish Directive (see above 5.7.4), prescribing a system for classifying the quality of inland waters which need protection or improvement to support fishlife. A Schedule to the Regulations lists 13 parameters and the requirements to be satisfied for salmonid and for cyprinid waters, as well as methods of analysis or inspection and minimum sampling and measurement frequency.

The Surface Waters (Shellfish) (Classification) Regulations 1997 (SI 1332)

These Regulations came into force on 12 June 1997 and apply in England and Wales. Similar Regulations (SI 2470) for Scotland came into force on 18 November 1997, and for Northern Ireland (SR 449). They implement the 1979 Shellfish Waters Directive (see above 5.7.4) by prescribing a system for classifying the quality of controlled waters which are coastal or brackish waters and which need protection or improvement in order to support shellfish life and growth. A Schedule to the Regulations lists 11 parameters and the mandatory values assigned to them in the Directive; it lists reference methods of measurement, and the minimum frequency required for sampling and analysis, also laid down in the Directive.

Following consultation in July 1998, the Government is designating a further 76 shellfish waters in accordance with the 1979 Directive (House of Commons, written answer, 8 July 1999).

(b) Protection of Groundwater (s.84)

Section 84 of the *Water Resources Act* gives the Agency a duty to protect the quality of groundwater and conserve its use for water resources.

The NRA's *Policy and Practice for the Protection of Groundwater* (published in 1992) outlined policy for protecting groundwater supplies from various sources of pollution and defined source protection zones as zone I (inner source protection); zone II (outer source protection) and zone III (source catchment). Also detailed are those activities which it is considered would pose a threat to groundwater within each source protection zone and should therefore be stopped or restricted.

The NRA's policy paper is not a statutory document and thus its status is to provide advice for industry, developers, planners and regulatory authorities on the effect of a particular activity on a groundwater source. While the Environment Agency has no direct control over how an area is used, it can try to influence, for example planning decisions, through its position as a statutory consultee, or for conditions to protect groundwater quality to be included in an authorisation.

Scotland's strategy for protection of groundwater was published in 1995 and uses the same approach as the NRA in identifying protection zones.

The Groundwater Regulations 1998 (SI 2746)

These Regulations, covering England, Scotland and Wales, came into force on 1 January 1999, with similar Regulations applying in Northern Ireland (SR 401) from the same date. They are designed to protect groundwater from pollution from mainly industrial and farming activities (including disposal of sheepdip or wastes and pesticides to land), thus implementing in full the 1980 groundwater Directive (see above 5.6.3). Activities controlled under the provisions of the *Waste Management Licensing Regulations* (see 4.19.3) are excluded from these Regulations.

Activities likely to lead to direct or indirect discharges to groundwater of List I or List II substances (defined in the Groundwater Directive) required authorisation from 1 April 1999. Direct discharges of List I substances are prohibited; activities which may result in indirect discharges (from tipping or disposal) may only be authorised if prior

investigation shows the groundwater is permanently unsuitable for other uses (e.g. domestic or agricultural). Such authorisations should include conditions to ensure all necessary technical precautions are taken to prevent the indirect discharge of a List I substance. List II discharges will only be authorised, with conditions, if prior investigation shows that groundwater pollution can be prevented. Where a discharge is authorised, the authorisation will specify where the discharge may be made, and the method to be used, precautions to be taken, as well as quantities of any substance and monitoring requirements. The authorisation will be granted for a limited period and must be reviewed every four years. Draft Guidance (E & W only) published in November 1999 includes a list of 79 List I substances whose entry to groundwater is prohibited. Similar Guidance will be issued for Scotland.

The Agency may serve a Notice on any person proposing to carry on an activity on or in the ground which might lead to an indirect discharge of a List I substance or pollution of groundwater as a result of an indirect discharge of a List II substance. The Notice may prohibit the activity, or authorise it subject to conditions specified in the Notice. The Regulations also enable statutory codes of practice to be drawn up providing guidance on preventing such discharges. A statutory code of practice is being drawn up defining environmental standards for new and existing underground petrol and diesel tanks and thus preventing any leaks or spills that could allow List I substances to enter groundwater.

The Regulations are enforced by the Environment Agency/SEPA and in Northern Ireland by the Environment and Heritage Service; they also include requirements for compliance monitoring, powers to serve variation and enforcement notices and revocation notices and introduce a cost recovery scheme. There is a right of appeal if the Agency refuses an authorisation and against enforcement notices. Details of all authorisations will be kept on the appropriate Agency's public register.

5.15.3 Pollution Offences (ss.85-91)

Under s.85 of the WRA (Scotland - s.30F of COPA: see *Env. Act 1995*, Sch. 16, para 1), it is an offence to cause or knowingly permit

a) any poisonous, noxious or polluting matter or any solid waste matter to enter any controlled waters;

b) any matter, other than trade effluent or sewage effluent, to enter controlled waters by being discharged from a drain or sewer in contravention of a relevant prohibition;

c) any trade effluent or sewage effluent to be discharged -

    into any controlled waters; or

    from land in England and Wales (or Scotland), through a pipe, into the sea outside the seaward limits of controlled waters;

d) any trade effluent or sewage effluent to be discharged, in contravention of any relevant prohibition, from a building or from any fixed plant on to or into any land or into any waters of a lake or pond which are not inland waters;

e) any matter whatever to enter any inland waters so as to tend (either directly or in combination with other matter which he or another person causes or permits to enter those waters) to impede the proper flow of the waters in a manner leading or likely to lead to a substantial aggravation of pollution due to other causes, or of the consequences of such pollution.

Contravention of this section of the Act or of conditions attached to a consent to discharge given under the Act may result in a fine not exceeding £20,000 and/or three months' imprisonment on summary conviction or an unlimited fine and/or two years' imprisonment on conviction on indictment.

Defences include:

- that the discharge or entry of matter into water was caused or permitted in an emergency to safeguard life or health;

- that all such steps as were reasonably practicable were taken to minimise the extent and effect of the discharge or entry;

- that the Environment Agency were given details of the entry or discharge as soon as reasonably practicable.

Under s.88 of the Act (Scotland, s.30I of COPA, see *Env. Act 1995*, Sch. 16), it is a defence to prove that a discharge to controlled waters did not contravene conditions imposed in accordance with other legislation under which the process is regulated - e.g. IPC authorisations under Part I of the *Environmental Protection Act 1990*. Section 89 of the WRA (as amended by s.60 of the *Env. Act 1995*, effective 1 July 1998), (Scotland, s.30J of COPA - Env. Act, Sch. 16), excludes from s.85 (s.30F COPA, Env. Act, Sch. 16) any person who allows water from a mine or part of a mine abandoned before 31 December 1999 to enter controlled waters; thus, mines abandoned after this date will be subject to control through discharge consents etc.

Articles 7-10 (to be implemented) of the *Water (Northern Ireland) Order 1999* contain similar provisions.

The Environment Agency has issued a consultation paper (August 2000) reviewing its policy for issuing consents to take account of the 1976 Directive on pollution caused by certain dangerous substances discharged into the aquatic environment (see 5.6); as well as requiring the prior authorisation prior to discharge containing any List I or II substances, the Directive also requires the prior authorisation of any discharge "liable to contain" a List I or II substance. The Agency is proposing a four-tiered regulatory regime, to be implemented from April 2001; all apply the Agency's "No deterioration and the Precautionary Principle" policy, with consents including a "change condition", which will require the consent holder to tell the Agency about any factors that change the discharge:

- **Regime A:** to be applied to all discharges known to contain dangerous substances and which could lead to non-compliance with EU legislation, environmental quality standards or international obligations; substances will be placed under Regime A if there is less than 95% confidence that an EQS will be met in the receiving water, or the impact of the discharge on the local environment is greater than 10% of the EQS. Under Regime A the Agency itself will carry out compliance monitoring.

- **Regime B:** applies to discharges containing List I substances or liable to contain a List I substance but at sufficiently low levels not to threaten the achievement of the targets set out for Regime A; the consent for the discharge will include a special condition requiring that the level of List I discharge does not exceed a specified limit. Discharges will be monitored by the consent holder and reported to the Agency.

- **Regime C:** will apply to discharges containing List II substances or liable to contain a List II substance but at sufficiently low levels not to threaten the achievement of the targets set out for Regime A. As for Regime B, conditions attached to the consent will require that the discharge shall not contain any List II substance in sufficient quantities to cause or contribute to exceedance of the relevant EQS downstream. Compliance will be mainly assessed from data collected from environmental monitoring programmes.

- **Regime D:** will be used for substances without a statutory EQS (to be called "operational standards"); discharges will be controlled using the "change condition", with compliance checked through the Agency's environmental monitoring programme.

It is proposed to implement the new policy from April 2001 for consents for discharges known to contain dangerous substances, and for other consents as they fall due for review.

(a) The Control of Pollution (Applications, Appeals and Registers) Regulations 1996 (SI 2971)

Discharges of trade or sewage effluent and other matter to water are regulated through a system of consents. (See also 5.17.3 below relating to trade effluents.)

The above Regulations came into force on 31 December 1996 and apply in England and Wales; they were made under ss.90A, 91, 190, 191 and Sch. 10 of the WRA, as amended by the *Environment Act 1995*, Sch. 22, paras 142-144 and 183 (which replaces the original Schedule 10 to the WRA). The Regulations revoke the *Control of Pollution (Consents for Discharges) Regulations 1989, the Control of Pollution (Consents for Discharges by the National Rivers Authority) Regulations 1989* and the *Control of Pollution (Registers) Regulations 1989*.

In Scotland, consents to discharge are issued by SEPA under Regulations made under Part II of the *Control of*

Pollution Act, s.34 - the *Control of Pollution (Consents for Discharges) (Secretary of State Functions) Regulations 1984* (SI 865) and the *Control of Pollution (Discharges by Islands Councils) (Scotland) Regulations 1993*. The procedure is similar to that outlined below.

In Northern Ireland Article 9(3) and Schedule 1 of the *Water (Northern Ireland) Order 1999* contain similar provisions in respect of applications for consents, their determination, consents without applications, revocations and modifying consents, variations and transfers; Article 12 covers enforcement notices, Article 13 appeals and Articles 30-32 the pollution control registers. All have yet to be brought into force; further requirements and details will be included in Regulations to be made under the Order.

(i) Application for a Consent to Discharge

An application for a consent to discharge has to be made on a form provided by the Agency, and submitted to it with any other information required together with the appropriate fee (see below). The Agency may refuse to process the application if all the information requested has not been provided (WRA, s.90A, see *Env. Act.* Sch.22, para 142).

A notice that an application for, or variation of, a discharge consent has been made must be advertised in one or more local newspapers and in the *London Gazette*; this should normally be done within 42 days, but not before 14 days after its receipt by the Agency. Exceptions to this are:

- where the Agency notifies the applicant that it refuses to proceed with the application or variation until further information is received, the period for advertising begins 14 days after receipt by the Agency of the additional information;

- where it is agreed that the application has implications for national security or is commercially confidential, the period for advertising begins 14 days later; where the applicant requests exclusion from the public register of those parts of the application considered to be commercially confidential, the date for advertising will begin when the Agency has notified the applicant of its decision, the date on which the period allowed for appeal expires, is determined or withdrawn.

The Agency may decide that the application may not be advertised if it is to be excluded from the public register on grounds of national security or that the activities to which the application relate "are unlikely to have an appreciable effect on controlled waters in the locality...".

Where it appears to the Agency that a discharge has been caused in contravention of s.85 or 86 of the WRA and is likely to happen again, it can issue a discharge consent (together with conditions) without having first received an application. Schedule 1 to the Regulations sets out the procedure (advertising, consultation, etc) which is similar to that for normal applications to discharge.

Where the Agency itself wishes to apply for a discharge consent, this should be done in writing to the Secretary of State; Schedule 2 to the Regulations sets out the procedure to be followed; this is similar to that for applicants to the Agency.

(ii) Consultation and Determination

A copy of the application should be sent to all affected local authorities and water undertakers in whose area it is proposed to discharge; to relevant ministers if it is proposed to discharge to coastal waters or relevant territorial waters; to any harbour authority or local fisheries committees whose waters might be affected by the discharge. Unless otherwise specified, a period of six weeks will normally be allowed for representations.

Copies of all applications will be put on the public register kept by the Agency. However, an applicant may apply to the Secretary of State for data to be withheld on the grounds of commercial confidentiality or that publishing such data would not be in the public interest.

An application for a consent must be considered within four months of receipt; if it is not and a longer period has not been agreed with the applicant, it is deemed to have been refused. In considering whether to grant a consent, the Agency will take into account whether statutory water quality objectives will be met; it will also need to be assured that the discharge will not result in deterioration of water quality or adversely affect uses of the water downstream.

The Secretary of State may call in the application for determination as a result of objections or representations made; a local inquiry or hearing will then be arranged as a means of enabling a decision to be made on the application.

If consent is granted, conditions will be included to ensure compliance with statutory water quality objectives (including EU legislation), absolute limits set for discharges and other conditions such as

a) the place to which the consent to discharge relates;

b) the nature, origin, composition, temperature, volume and rate of discharge, and the periods during which the discharge may be made;

c) steps to be taken to minimise the polluting effects of the discharge;

d) provision of facilities for sampling and monitoring;

e) provision, maintenance and testing of meters for measuring or recording discharges;

f) keeping of detailed records relating to the discharge and conditions attaching to the consent;

g) provision of information to the enforcing authority in respect of the discharge.

Consents and their conditions are reviewed from "time to time" and, following review, the Agency may serve a notice revoking or modifying a consent, modifying its conditions or adding some conditions to it; however, apart from a notice revoking a consent, such a notice will not normally be served within four years of the consent being issued without the agreement of the discharger; exceptions to this are to ensure compliance with EU legislation, other international obligations, or health or environmental protection reasons.

The holder of a consent may apply (on a form provided by the Agency) for it to be varied; the consent may also be transferred to another person with the person transferring it advising the Agency within 21 days. A person taking responsibility for a consent following the death or bankruptcy of the holder should advise the Agency of the fact within 15 months. (Holders of consents transferred prior to 1 April 1996 had until 1 October 1996 to register their ownership with the Environment Agency; failure to register renders the current holder liable to prosecution as the discharge is deemed to be illegal as the consent to discharge is in the name of another person.)

(iii) Appeals

Where an application for consent to discharge has been refused, revoked or otherwise varied, a variation has been refused, or an enforcement notice served, the applicant has a right of appeal to the Secretary of State. In Scotland appeals should be addressed to Scottish Ministers and copied to SEPA. Any appeal should be submitted in writing (together with supporting documentation) to the Secretary of State within three months of the decision which is being appealed against, with copies also being sent to the Agency at the same time. Appeals in respect of a revocation notice should be submitted before the revocation takes effect; in respect of an enforcement notice or refusal for information to be excluded from the public register, within 21 days.

The Secretary of State may then require the appellant to submit further documentation supporting the appeal within 28 days and will also advise the Agency that an appeal has been lodged. The Agency has 21 days in which to submit its own representations in respect of the appeal.

The Agency should notify all those who made representations concerning the application for discharge consent or variation and statutory consultees within 14 days of receiving notice of the appeal; it must also inform the Secretary of State within a further 14 days to whom it has sent notification of an appeal. Any representations (which will be copied to the Agency, the appellant and put on the register) should be sent to the Secretary of State within 21 days.

The appellant may choose to have the appeal dealt with by written representation or a hearing. In the case of written representation, information supporting an appeal should be submitted within 28 days (or 14 days in respect of an enforcement notice). If there is to be a hearing, the Secretary of State should give both the appellant and the Agency 28 days' notice of its date, time and place and at least 21 days before should publish a notice in a local newspaper and send notice of it to all who have submitted representations. Section 114 and Schedule 20 of the Environment Act 1995 enable the Secretary of State to appoint someone to carry out all or some aspect of the appeal on his behalf, including arranging a hearing or local inquiry. With effect from 1 January 1997, appeals relating to discharge consents, works and enforcement notices were transferred to the Planning Inspectorate. The Secretary of State will notify the appellant in writing of his decision concerning the appeal, as well as notify the Agency and others who made representations.

It should be noted that the terms of an enforcement notice, must be complied with pending determination of the appeal. Revocations, variations or the addition of conditions to consents will not take effect until determination or withdrawal of the appeal unless the Agency is of the opinion that to delay might result in the entry of any polluting, poisonous or noxious matter into controlled water or harm to human health.

In Scotland the relevant sections of COPA are s.39 and s.49B (Env. Act, Sch. 22, para 29(26)). The appeals procedure is set out in the Control of Pollution (Consents for Discharges) (Secretary of State Functions) Regulations 1984 (SI 865); draft Regulations, issued for consultation in August 2000 – The Control of Pollution (Registers) and (Consents for Discharges) (Secretary of State Functions) Amendment Regulations – will amend the 1984 Regulations to provide for appeals against the service of an enforcement notice similar to that in England and Wales.

(iv) Consents for Discharges by the Agency

Applications etc by the Agency itself to discharge into controlled waters are made in writing to the Secretary of State. Schedule 2 of the Regulations outlines the requirements and procedures, which are similar to those for applicants to the Agency.

(v) Pollution Control Registers

The Agency is required to maintain registers, open to public inspection, with details of

a) notices of water quality objectives and other Secretary of State notices and directions;

b) applications for discharge consents or for their variation and supporting data;

c) consents for discharges and any conditions, and information obtained or given in pursuance of conditions, and any variations thereof;

d) data relating to samples of water or effluent, including results of analysis, and steps taken by the Agency or another person as a consequence;

e) prohibition and enforcement notices, revocations, appeals and details of relevant convictions;

e) results of analysis of samples of effluent and of samples of water taken by the enforcing authority in carrying out their pollution control functions;

f) information acquired by the enforcing authority with respect to samples taken by other persons.

Information should normally be placed on the register within 28 days, or seven days in the case of enforcement notices. Information relating to a withdrawn application for a consent or variation should be removed from the register not less than two months and not more than three months after its withdrawal.

The Agency should inform the Secretary of State of any information excluded on the grounds of national security; or a person wishing to have information excluded on these grounds may notify the Secretary of State direct and, pending his decision, the information concerned should not be put on the register (*Env. Act 1995*, Sch. 22, para 170, adds s.191A to the WRA).

Where a person requests that certain information given in connection with an application for a discharge consent be excluded for commercially confidential reasons, the Agency must determine the request within 14 days; if it does not the information automatically becomes commercially confidential. Where the Agency has obtained information in pursuit of its duties which it considers could be commercially confidential, it should notify the appropriate person "giving him reasonable opportunity" to object to its inclusion. If the Agency considers information not to be commercially confidential, it should notify the relevant person, allowing 21 days before putting the information on the register, during which time an appeal may be made to the Secretary of State. Following determination or withdrawal of the appeal, seven days should elapse before the information is placed on the register (*Env. Act 1995*, Sch. 22, para 170 adds new s.191B to the WRA).

Where information is excluded from the Register, for instance on the grounds of commercial confidentiality, a notice should appear on the register to that effect.

The Agency is required to keep information on the Register for up to four years after it has been superseded; it is also required to keep monitoring information for up to four years.

The corresponding regulations in Scotland are the *Control of Pollution (Registers) (Scotland) Regulations 1993* (SI 1155) and ss.41& 42A-B of COPA (*Env. Act 1995*, Sch. 22, para 29(17)-(20)). These Regulations are to be amended by *The Control of Pollution (Registers) and (Consents for Discharges) (Secretary of State Functions) Amendment Regulations*, a draft of which was issued for consultation in August 2000; these will prescribe the information to be included on the public register in respect of enforcement notices, including appeals, convictions, compliance proceedings, etc.

(b) Enforcement Notices (s.90B)

This section of the WRA is added by the *Environment Act 1995*, Sch. 22, para 142. It was brought into force by Commencement Order (No. 8, SI 2909) on 1 January 1997. For Scotland the relevant section of COPA is s.49A (*Env. Act*, Sch. 22, para 29(26)) which it is proposed to implement

during 2001. In Northern Ireland, the relevant Article is Article 12 of the *Water (Northern Ireland) Order 1999*.

The Agency may serve an enforcement notice if it is of the opinion that the conditions of a consent are being, or may be contravened; the notice will specify the nature of the contravention or why it is considered that a contravention is likely, the steps to be taken to remedy the matter and the period within which this must be done. The Agency will normally give ten days' notice of its intention to serve an enforcement notice. A copy of the enforcement notice should be placed on the public register within seven days of service. There is a right of appeal against an enforcement notice (see iii above), which is not suspended during the course of the appeal.

Failure to comply with a notice is an offence subject to a fine not exceeding £20,000 and/or up to three months' imprisonment on summary conviction or up to two years' imprisonment and/or a fine on conviction on indictment.

5.15.4 Abandoned Mines

Sections 91A and 91B were added to the WRA by s.58 of the *Environment Act 1995* which was brought into force on 1 July 1998. They cover mines (including tourist mines and those for commercial mineral extraction) in England and Wales abandoned on or after 1 January 1999. For Scotland, s.59 of the Act adds ss.30Y-Z to the *Control of Pollution Act 1974* and has the same effect for abandoned mines in Scotland. Article 35 (which has yet to be brought into force) of the *Water (Northern Ireland) Order 1999* contains similar legislation for Northern Ireland.

"Abandoned" includes stopping all or some of the mining or related activities at a mine, or stopping or substantially changing operations for the removal of water from a mine.

The Mines (Notice of Abandonment) Regulations 1998 (SI 892)

These Regulations apply in England and Wales and came into force on 1 July 1998, with similar Regulations (SI 1572) taking effect in Scotland on 31 July.

A mine operator is required to give at least six months' notice of intention to abandon a mine to the appropriate Agency. The Notice should include the following details:

- name and address of the mine operator, and of the owner if this is different;
- location and description of the mine, pumping rates, etc;
- consequences of abandonment;
- proposals for monitoring groundwater quality and water quality in the mine;
- proposals for treating, lessening or preventing discharges from the mine.

Details of the proposed closure should also be published in at least one local newspaper.

Failure to give the required notice is an offence except if the mine is abandoned in an emergency to safeguard life or health or in some cases of insolvency. Notice of abandonment should be sent to the appropriate Agency as soon as practicable.

If the appropriate Agency considers that the proposed or actual abandonment is likely to result in surrounding land becoming contaminated as defined by Part IIA of the EPA 1990 (see chapter 4, 4.28.3), the relevant local authority should be advised.

It should be noted that ss.161A-C (Scotland - COPA, ss.46A-C) enable the Agencies to serve a works notice requiring certain anti-pollution works to be carried out to prevent or deal with polluting matter entering controlled waters from, inter alia, abandoned mines; it applies only to mines abandoned after 31 December 1999 - see below 5.15.6b.

Articles 16-19 of the *Water (Northern Ireland) Order 1999* relate to anti-pollution works and the service of notices.

5.15.5 Powers to Prevent and Control Pollution (ss.92-97)

(a) The Control of Pollution (Silage, Slurry and Agricultural Fuel Oil) Regulations 1991 (SI 324)

These Regulations to prevent water pollution from farms, were made under s.110 of the *Water Act*. This has been replaced by s.92 of the WRA. The Regulations, which apply in England and Wales, came into effect on 1 September 1991, with equivalent Regulations made under COPA applying in Scotland (SI 346).

New silage, slurry and agricultural fuel oil storage facilities have to be designed and built to minimum standards to prevent the pollution of controlled waters. Existing installations - i.e. those in use or constructed before 1 March 1991, or a contract for construction, or actual construction begun, before 1 March 1991 and completed before 1 September 1991 - are largely exempt from the Regulations except where the Agency considers that there is a serious risk of pollution. In such instances the Agency may require (subject to a right of appeal) that all or some of the standards for new installations are met. Substantially extended or reconstructed facilities must meet the new standards.

Silage can only be made in a silo with an impermeable base surrounded by a system to collect any effluent and take it to a storage tank. Silage can also be made in bales in a tower silo or an existing installation. Any other methods of silage making (e.g. field silage making) had to be registered with the Agency under transitional arrangements and could continue until 31 August 1996 unless considered to be a serious pollution risk. Farms producing slurry must have a minimum four months storage capacity unless the Agency is satisfied that less does not represent a serious pollution risk. There are also minimum standards for loading and height limits for slurry lagoons. Tanks for storing more than 1500 litres of fuel oil on a farm must be surrounded by an impervious wall called a bund to prevent leaks reaching watercourses.

1997 Amendment Regulations (SI 547, E & W only) permit field silage making - production and storage is prohibited within a 50 metre radius of the nearest relevant abstraction point of a protected water supply source and within 10 metres of any inland freshwaters or coastal waters. Farmers must give the Environment Agency 14 days' notice of any place where silage is to be made or stored and similar notice of their intention to use a new site for the purpose. The Regulations also enable the Agency to serve a notice (instead of immediate prosecution) on a farmer requiring measures to be taken to prevent pollution of water from all slurry, silage and agricultural fuel oil stores.

The penalty for contravening the Regulations is a fine of up to £20,000 and/or three months in prison on summary conviction or an unlimited fine and/or two years in prison on conviction on indictment

The Scottish Executive has issues proposals for amending the Regulations in Scotland; as well as enabling SEPA to issue works notices to farmers requiring improvements to structures for silage etc to prevent pollution, SEPA would be able to require the farmer to draw up a Farm Waste Management Plan in accordance with the Code of Good Practice for the Prevention of Pollution from Agricultural Activity. It is also proposed to extend the period for notifying SEPA before a new or substantially enlarged or reconstructed structure is brought into use to 28 days. The Regulations will also take account of the latest British Standard specifying design and construction standards, as well as enabling SEPA to take a site specific view on type of pollution controls needed.

(b) The Control of Pollution (Oil Storage) (England) Regulations *(Draft)*

Draft Regulations aimed at reducing the pollution of water from oil stores in England were issued for consultation by the DETR in April 2000. The Regulations will apply to anyone storing more than 200 litres of oil above ground on industrial commercial and institutional (residential and non-residential) premises; they would not apply to farms (which are covered by *The Control of Pollution (Silage, Slurry and Agricultural Fuel Oil) Regulations 1991*), to single private dwellings, oil stores at refineries or onward distribution centres and waste oil stores. The storage of oil in underground facilities (e.g. at petrol and diesel stations) is covered by the *Groundwater Regulations 1998*.

The Regulations will require all tanks for storing oil to be surrounded by a bund capable of holding 110% of the contents of a tank. It was hoped that the Regulations would come into force before the end of 2000, with new oil stores required to comply with them six months later; existing oil stores at "significant risk" would need to comply within two years of the Regulations taking effect, and the rest within five years.

(c) Water Protection Zones (s.93)

This section provides powers for areas to be designated water protection zones, enabling the Agency to have control over the application of pesticides and other potential pollutants in surrounding areas to prevent discharge of polluting matter into controlled waters to protect drinking waters. To date only one stretch of river has been given statutory protection - the River Dee, which flows through North East Wales, Cheshire and Merseyside.

Water Protection Zone (River Dee Catchment) Designation Order 1999 (SI 915)

This took effect on 21 June 1999 and requires all those carrying on a "controlled activity" - i.e. keeping or using controlled substances - within the zone to apply for a protection zone consent from the Environment Agency. The application and appeals procedures are contained in the *Water Protection Zone (River Dee Catchment) (Procedural and other Provisions) Regulations 1999* (SI 916), which also came into force on 21 June 1999.

An application for a protection zone consent must be made on a form provided by the Agency and must include a site map, substance location map and details of the controlled substances and emergency and safety statement; this latter should describe the potential sources of an incident which might result in a discharge to land or inland waters; how such an incident might occur and the measures taken or proposed to be taken to prevent, control or minimise the consequences of any incident to inland waters; and finally emergency procedures for dealing with an incident at the site. A fee of £250 should accompany the application (£50 if it relates to 10 or fewer controlled substances).

Within seven days of receipt, the EA should copy the application to relevant local authorities and water undertakers within the control area seeking their comments on the application; the Agency should also consult the Health and Safety Executive and, in relation to sites within SSSIs or designated special conservation areas, the Nature Conservancy Council for England or Countryside Council for Wales, as appropriate, allowing 42 days for the receipt of comments. An application for a consent will normally be determined within four months of its receipt by the Agency. Where the Agency is minded to grant a consent, it should by notice inform all those who have made representations or objected to the application, allowing 21 days before issuing the consent. A protection zone consent ceases to have effect where the person in control of the site changes, unless an application has been made for the continuation of the consent.

The protection zone consent should include details of the catchment control site, description of the substances to which the consent relates, together with maximum quantities to be kept or used at any one time and storage controls; any conditions attached to the consent should ensure the use of BATNEEC to prevent the direct or indirect release of controlled substances in circumstances which could cause pollution of "inland waters at any point where such waters are abstracted for the purposes of public water supply". The Agency may, by notice, revoke a consent or alter or add conditions if it considers it

expedient to do so. It may also, by notice, revoke a consent if planning permission results in a material change of use of the catchment control site, or in the case of a consent relating to one substance, it has not been kept or used for at least five years at the site to which the consent relates.

The Regulations make provision for consents to be varied, for appeals to the Secretary of State and for consents to be kept on a public register - these are similar to those in other Regulations.

Under the River Dee Designation Order it is an offence to carry on a controlled activity within a protection zone without a consent, if the quantity of controlled substances kept or used exceeds that permitted in a consent, or conditions in a consent are not being complied with. Summary conviction may result in imprisonment up to three months and/or a maximum fine of £20,000; conviction on indictment may result in up to two years' imprisonment and/or a fine.

(d) Nitrate Sensitive Areas (ss.94-95)

These sections provide powers for the establishment of nitrate sensitive areas (NSAs) in England and Wales in which controls can be introduced over agricultural activity in order to reduce the amount of nitrate leaching from agricultural land into water sources.

The Nitrate Sensitive Areas (Designation) Order 1990 (revoked with effect from 1 June 1996 by 1995 Regulations - see below) established a pilot scheme of ten NSAs in North East and Central England under which farmers were eligible for payments if they adopted measures to reduce nitrate leaching. Under the basic option they could continue their usual cropping systems but were restricted as to the amounts of fertiliser and manure they could apply; under the premium option, farmers were compensated for converting arable production to grassland and could also claim towards the cost of storage and transportation of manure from pig and poultry units. The scheme was due to end in 1995 but was extended for a further five years.

The Nitrate Sensitive Areas Regulations 1994 (SI 1729)

These Regulations (as amended in 1995 SI 1708 & 2095, 1996 SI 3105, 1997 SI 990 and 1998 SI 79 & 2138) establish 32 NSAs (including the 10 in the pilot scheme) around water supply boreholes mainly in the East Midlands, North Yorkshire, Lincolnshire and Staffordshire. Annual payments are made to farmers in NSAs who satisfy the conditions of whichever of the following schemes under which they apply for aid:

- **Basic scheme:** since 31.12.91 (apart from when it has been set-aside), the land has been used for the production of any agricultural crop other than a permanent crop; or grass grown for more than five consecutive years;

- **Premium arable scheme:** since 31.12.91 (apart from when it has been set-aside), the land has not been woodland or permanent grassland and has been used only for the production of any agricultural crop other than a permanent crop, or grass grown for more than one consecutive year;

- **Premium grass scheme:** the land is grassland which has been receiving more than 250 kg of nitrogen in the form of inorganic nitrogen fertiliser per hectare per year in each of the three years immediately preceding the date on which the undertakings given or are to be given, commence.

Farmers participating in the scheme must agree to comply with the requirements of a scheme for five consecutive years commencing on 1 October of the year in which his application is made; they are also expected to observe other environmental requirements, such as retention of hedges, trees, woodlands, etc. Farmers in the pilot scheme were able to transfer to the new scheme.

Participation in this scheme is voluntary and additional to the mandatory measures being introduced in compliance with the nitrates Directive to protect nitrate vulnerable zones - see above 5.7.7.

In Scotland, s.31(b) of COPA includes powers to designate nitrate sensitive areas.

(e) Codes of Practice (s.97)

This section of the Act enables the Secretary of State to approve codes of practice which give practical guidance to those engaged in agricultural activities that may affect controlled waters, and to promote desirable practices to control pollution. Breach of a code would not be an offence, but may be taken into account by the Agency in determining whether to serve a notice to prohibit pollution by discharges to water, or to require that precautions are taken against potential pollution.

The Code of Good Agricultural Practice for the Protection of Water, published in 1998, replaces a similar 1991 code, *the Water (Prevention of Pollution) (Code of Practice) Order 1991*. Drawn up by MAFF and the Welsh Office, it is a statutory code of practice covering England and Wales. The code provides guidance on avoiding water pollution from various farming practices, such as pesticide and fertiliser use, silage, sheep dip and disposal of animal carcases; it also provides advice on development of a farm waste management plan and outlines the legislation farmers need to be aware of. Breach of the code is not an offence although it can be used as evidence in any prosecution for polluting water. There are also codes covering air pollution from agricultural sources and on soil pollution, revised versions of which were also published in 1998 (see chapter 2, 2.19).

In Scotland the *Code of Practice' on the Prevention of Environmental Pollution from Agricultural Activity* covers air, soil and water pollution. It came into effect in March 1992 and a revised version was published in 1997. Only those sections covering water pollution have been given statutory backing under the *Water (Prevention of*

Pollution) (Code of Practice) (Scotland) Order 1992. Compliance with the Code is not a defence in any action for water pollution. The water sections of the Code cover similar issues to that for England and Wales, and also recommend good practices to prevent water pollution from nitrates. This is in line with EU Directive 91/676/EEC which places restrictions on the use of certain fertilisers (see this chapter, 5.7.7).

5.15.6 Miscellaneous Provisions Relating to Water Pollution

(a) Radioactive Substances (s.98)

The Control of Pollution (Radioactive Waste) Regulations 1989 (SI 1158) were brought into force on 1 September 1989. They apply in England and Wales and brought radioactive waste within the scope of the following sections of the *Water Act* (now *Water Resources Act*):

- classification of quality of waters (s.82);
- general duties to achieve and maintain objectives etc (s.84);
- offences of polluting controlled waters etc (ss.85-87);
- requirements to take precautions against pollution (s.92);
- consents and application to the Agency (s.99);
- anti-pollution works and operations (s.161);
- registers (s.190);
- information and assistance (s.202);
- exchange of information with respect to pollution incidents etc (s.203);
- local inquiries (s.213).

The radioactive properties of such waste remain subject to control under the *Radioactive Substances Act 1993*.

The corresponding Regulations in Scotland are the *Control of Pollution (Radioactive Waste) (Scotland) Regulations 1991*.

(b) Anti-Pollution Works (s.161)

Under this section of the *Water Resources Act*, the Agency is empowered to take remedial action to deal with actual or potential pollution affecting controlled waters. It could be used to deal with pollution from sources such as contamination from landfill sites, old mine workings, chemical discharges etc. (Scotland, COPA, s.46)

Section 60(3) of the *Environment Act 1995* (effective 1 July 1997, Commencement Order No. 9) amends this section of the Act to enable the Agency to carry out an investigation to establish the source of the polluting matter and the person responsible. Costs and expenses in respect of the investigation and in dealing with the pollution may be recovered from the person who caused or knowingly permitted the pollution. (It should be noted that the recovery of costs in respect of investigating or dealing with pollution from legally abandoned mines is specifically excluded from the Act s.161(4) & *Env. Act 1995*, s.60(5)).

Sections 161A-D (*Env. Act 1995*, Sch. 22, para 162) - Scotland, COPA 46A-D (*Env. Act*, Sch. 22, para 29(22)) -

enable the Agencies to serve a "works notice" on the person responsible for causing or knowingly permitting poisonous, polluting or noxious matter to enter controlled waters or to be likely to enter controlled waters.

Before serving the notice the Agency should make reasonable efforts to consult the responsible person on the works to be undertaken. If the person responsible for the actual or potential pollution cannot be found, or if the Agency considers the situation should be dealt with "forthwith", it may carry out the works itself and recover the costs and expenses incurred.

A works notice may not be served on an operator in respect of water from mines or part of a mine abandoned before 31 December 1999.

The Environment Agency's *Policy and Guidance on the Use of Anti-Pollution Works Notices* provides guidance on the interface and overlap between the powers contained in s.161 of the WRA and those in Part IIA (contaminated land) of the *Environmental Protection Act 1990*. Where land has been identified as being contaminated and is potentially affecting controlled waters, Part IIa of the EPA requires the service of a remediation notice; the Agency will usually use its powers to serve a works notice to deal with historic pollution.

Articles 16-19 of the *Water (Northern Ireland) Order 1999* will have the same effect, once implemented.

The Anti-Pollution Works Regulations (SI 1006)

These Regulations, which apply in England and Wales, came into force on 29 April 1999. A draft of similar Regulations for Scotland was issued for consultation by the Scottish Executive in January 2000.

The Regulations specify the content of the works notice and outline appeal procedures in respect of such notices.

As well as the name and address of the person on whom the notice is being served, and identifying the controlled waters to which the notice applies, the notice should specify

- that in the opinion of the Agency, poisonous, noxious or polluting matter or solid waste matter has entered, or is likely to enter, the identified waters;

- the works or operations to be carried out to remedy the situation, and the period within which each action specified in the notice must be carried out;

- that the person on whom the notice is served has a right of appeal within 21 days from the date the notice is received to the Secretary of State;

- the Agency's entitlement to recover costs in carrying out its investigations;

- consequences of non-compliance with a works' notice; i.e. that is an offence which on summary conviction may result in a fine not exceeding £20,000 and/or three months imprisonment; conviction on indictment may result in up to two years imprisonment and/or a

fine. Where a notice has not been complied with the Agency may carry out the work and recover the costs and expenses incurred.

Works Notices are not suspended during determination of an appeal; in sending written notice of appeal to the Secretary of State, the appellant should send relevant documents and should state whether the appeal is to be determined by written representations or a hearing; in the former case the Agency has 14 days to respond to any enquiries from the Secretary of State regarding the matter.

Where a person is required to grant rights of entry to a person on whom a works notice has been served in order that that person can comply with the notice, compensation is payable; the Regulations deal with the way in which compensation payments are to be calculated. Disputes over compensation payments are determined by the Lands Tribunal.

Copies of works notices, appeals and relevant documentation and appeal decisions, as well as convictions under the Regulations are held on the pollution control register maintained by the Environment Agency.

(c) Powers of Entry and Collecting Evidence

Sections 169 and 170 of the WRA empower an authorised person to enter any premises to determine whether any provisions of the *Water Resources Act* have been or are being contravened. Where entry is required for enforcement purposes, no advance notice need be given though, except in emergencies, entry should be sought at a "reasonable time"; in all other cases seven days' notice should be given (Schedule 20 to the WRA). The inspector may carry out tests, install monitoring equipment or take away samples for further analysis.

Under s.111 of the *Environment Act 1995* any apparatus used for recording or registering information shall be deemed to be accurate unless the contrary is proved. Where an authorised person has been unable to gain entry to monitor observance with a condition, this will be taken as evidence that the condition is not being complied with.

There is no longer a requirement for samples to be divided into three - one each for the discharger, the regulator and one for future comparison - as was the case under s.209 of the WRA, repealed by the *Env. Act*. In practice the Agency does still follow this procedure where "reasonably practicable" for samples to be used in court evidence.

Where entry is required in relation to the Agency's pollution control functions (including s.161-161D) of the WRA, the powers of entry provisions of the *Environment Act 1995* (ss.108-109) apply (*Env. Act*, Sch. 22, para 165); these provisions are set out in chapter 1, 1.14.2.

SCHEDULES

The *Water Resources Act 1991* has 26 Schedules appended to it, of which the following are of particular relevance to pollution control:

- **Schedule 10:** Discharge Consents (Schedule in WRA superseded by new Schedule 10 in *Environment Act 1995*, see Sch. 22, para 183);
- **Schedule 11:** Water Protection Zone Orders;
- **Schedule 12:** Nitrate Sensitive Area Orders - Part I, Applications by the Authority for Designation Orders and Part II, Orders Containing Mandatory Provisions;
- **Schedule 13:** Transitional Water Pollution Provisions;
- **Schedule 20:** Supplementary Provisions with Respect to Powers of Entry.

5.16 ENVIRONMENT ACT 1995

Charging Scheme

Section 41 of the *Environment Act* empowers the Agencies to make charging schemes in respect of environmental licences (including consents to discharge), variations of such licences etc; such schemes are approved by the Secretary of State under s.42 of the Act. The original Scheme for England and Wales was made under ss.131 & 132 of the *Water Resources Act 1991*.

The purpose of charging for applications and consents for discharges of sewage and trade effluent to controlled waters is to enable the Environment Agency to recover its costs in respect of monitoring, sampling, analysing and other regulatory functions related to discharge consents. The current scheme came into effect on 1 July 1991 and was reviewed in March 1994. Charges are reviewed annually.

Applications for a new or revised discharge consent are subject to a standard charge per effluent. In addition an annual fee, also per effluent, is payable; when treatment or monitoring is carried out together the annual fee will be calculated on the basis of the highest content and aggregated volume of the discharge. The annual fee is based on the volume and content of the discharges as specified in the consent, and on the nature of the receiving waters with the amount payable depending on the complexity of the discharge and the sensitivity of the receiving waters: each of the three categories of the annual charge has been banded into factors reflecting complexity and sensitivity or in the latter case, type of receiving water; the annual charge payable is the number of factors multiplied, multiplied again by the financial factor.

In Scotland charges are based on the volume and content of the discharge and the nature of the receiving water, multiplied by a financial factor.

In Northern Ireland, a charging scheme will be made under Article 11 of the *Water (Northern Ireland) Order 1999*.

5.17 WATER INDUSTRY ACT 1991

This Act came into force on 1 December 1991 and applies in England and Wales only. It consolidates various enactments relating to the appointment of water and sewerage undertakers, conditions of appointment, supply of water and the provision of sewerage services. It also sets

out the functions of the Director General of Water Services, and the duties of local authorities with regard to the supply of wholesome and sufficient water.

In Scotland, the *Water (Scotland) Act 1980* as amended by the *Water Act 1989* covers similar areas. Sewerage and drainage services are covered by the *Sewerage (Scotland) Act 1968*. This legislation is the responsibility of the North, East, and West of Scotland Water Authorities.

5.17.1 Quality and Sufficiency of Supplies (ss.67-86)

(a) General Obligations of Undertakers (ss.68-70)

Section 68 places a duty on water undertakers to supply only water which is "wholesome at the time of supply" to any premises for domestic purposes. Section 69 empowers the Secretary of State through Regulations to specify minimum requirements for the monitoring and recording of water quality, to forbid or regulate the use of substances, processes and products which might affect the quality of water supplied, and to require provision of certain information to the public about its quality.

Section 70 makes it an offence to supply water which is unfit for human consumption unless it can be shown that there were no reasonable grounds for suspecting that the water would be used for human consumption, or took all reasonable steps to ensure it was fit, or was not used for human consumption.

(b) Waste, Contamination, Misuse of Water (ss.71-75)

Under these sections, it is an offence for an owner or occupier of premises either through negligence or intentionally to allow water fittings to remain in disrepair so as to cause the contamination, wasting or misuse of water. The Secretary of State is empowered to make Regulations with regard to water fittings, and representatives of water undertakers or local authorities will be able to enter any premises to ensure compliance with those regulations and to check the installation of any water fittings. To prevent damage to persons or property, or contamination or waste of water, water authorities will be entitled either to cut off a supply of water, or to serve a notice on a consumer requiring action to remedy the problem.

(c) Local Authority Functions (ss.77-85)

Where existing supplies of water are insufficient or unwholesome, and piped water supplies would not be practicable at reasonable cost, s.79 entitles local authorities to require water undertakers to supply water for domestic purposes other than through pipes. Sections 78-82 place a general duty on local authorities to monitor the quality and sufficiency of water supplies in their area and where this is found to be below standard, empowers them to serve a notice on the water undertaker specifying what steps they consider necessary to effect improvements. There is a right of appeal to the Secretary of State against any action by a local authority in relation to private supplies.

Under s.86 the Secretary of State may appoint technical assessors to carry out investigations of drinking water quality matters and advise whether any duty imposed on a water undertaker in relation to such matters has been or might be contravened.

The Water Supply (Water Quality) Regulations 1989 (SI 1147) (as amended)

These Regulations were made under ss.52, 53, 56 & 65 of the *Water Act 1989* (WIA: ss.67-69, 77-78) and apply to England and Wales. Most of the provisions of the Regulations came into effect on 1 September 1989, and the remainder on 1 January 1990. Similar Regulations (1990 - SI 119, amended 1991 - SI 1333) apply in Scotland, and in Northern Ireland (1994). Draft new Regulations for England were issued for consultation in April 2000 to implement the 1998 EU Drinking Water Directive (see this chapter, 5.7.5), and are summarised below (see also introduction to this edition of the Pollution Handbook).

Parts II and III of the 1989 Regulations will be revoked on 25 December 2003, and the remainder and subsequent amendments on 1 January 2004.

The 1989 Regulations are primarily concerned with the quality of public supplies of water for drinking, washing and cooking and with arrangements for the publication of information about water quality. They also give effect to EU Directive 80/778/EEC which relates to the quality of water intended for human consumption, and in part, to EU Directive 75/440/EEC (quality required of surface water intended for the abstraction of drinking water).

Part II of the Regulations prescribes standards of wholesomeness in respect of water supplied by the water companies for drinking, washing or cooking. In particular, it provides that water is to be regarded as wholesome if it contains concentrations or values in respect of various properties, elements, organisms and substances (including pesticides and related products) which do not contravene prescribed maximum and, in some cases, minimum concentrations or values, as specified in Directive 80/778/EEC - see Appendix 5.2.

Part III enables the Secretary of State or the appropriate local authority, to relax the requirements of Part II in certain circumstances; these are

- in an emergency to maintain supplies for human consumption;
- in exceptional meteorological conditions;
- because of the nature or structure of the ground from which the supply emanates;
- where the supply is used solely for the purpose of food production.

Part IV provides for the monitoring of water supplies by reference to analysis of samples taken from consumers'

taps, with Part V providing additional provisions with regard to sampling. Part VI deals with the treatment of water and regulates the substances, processes and products that may be used by water undertakers in connection with the supply of water.

Part VII of the Regulations relates to the provision of information by water companies and Part VIII imposes requirements on local authorities in the performance of their duties in relation to the quality of water supplied by water companies.

The 1991 Amendment Regulations, separate versions of which apply in England/Wales and in Scotland, extend the scope of the 1989 Regulations to include the quality of water used for food production. There are also more stringent requirements relating to the sampling of water to establish its wholesomeness for drinking water. Local authorities are also empowered to comment on any application by a water undertaker for relaxation of obligations under the Regulations. In England and Wales only, the Amendment Regulations require water undertakers to give customers information regarding the public register of authorisations, discharge consents etc and how it can be consulted. This must be done at least once a year and, it is suggested should be sent out with customers' bills.

1999 Amendment Regulations (SI 1524) which came into force in England and Wales on 30 June 1999 require water companies to carry out a risk assessment at their water works to establish whether there is a "significant risk" from cryptosporidium - this is defined as one or more oocysts in ten litres of treated water. Assessment results must be reported to the Secretary of State; the Regulations contain stringent continuous monitoring and analysis requirements to ensure that any water posing a "significant risk" is dealt with quickly.

The Water Supply (Water Quality) (England) Regulations *(draft April 2000)*

These Regulations consolidate and will replace the 1989 *Water Quality Regulations* and subsequent amendments and implement the 1998 EU Directive concerning the quality of water intended for human consumption (the drinking water Directive) – see this chapter 5.7.5 and introduction to this edition of the Pollution Handbook. The Regulations will be enforced by the Drinking Water Inspectorate. Part of the Regulations were due to come into force on 1 January 2001 (see introduction to this Pollution Handbook) to ensure that water companies undertake the necessary work to meet the standards by the required dates (mostly 25 December 2003 – but see Appendix 5.3b); the Regulations affecting monitoring arrangements will take effect on 1 January 2004. Schedule 1 to the Regulations lists prescribed concentrations and values (microbiological & chemical parameters); Schedule 2 indicator parameters; Schedule 3 – monitoring, including parameters and circumstances for check monitoring & annual sampling frequencies); Schedule 4 analytical methodology.

Similar proposals in respect of **Scotland** were issued for consultation in May 2000.

Part I of the Regulations details when individual Regulations will come into force and what is meant by the terminology used in the Regulations (how they should be interpreted); Part II of the Regulations requires water undertakers, before the beginning of each year, to designate "water supply zones" within its area; these may cover a population of no more than 100,000 and may not be altered during the year.

Part III is concerned with the requirements for wholesomeness. Water supplied for domestic purposes and to premises in which food is produced must not contain any micro-organism, parasite or other substance – other than a permitted parameter (listed in schedules to the Regulations) – at a concentration or value which could be a potential danger to human health, or any substances (whether a parameter or not) which together could be a potential danger to human health.

Parts IV and V and Schedule 3 of the Regulations are concerned with monitoring of water supplies, sampling points, the way in which samples should be taken and the frequency, as well as analysis of samples. Part VI sets out the responsibilities of water undertakers in the event that water fails, or is likely to fail, to meet the required standards. As well as identifying which of the parameters are likely to exceed permitted concentrations, the water undertaker must identify to what the fault can be attributed – i.e. to the domestic distribution system, or to the maintenance of that system, or some other reason. The Secretary of State should be notified of any failures and the action being taken to rectify the faults. Where the failure is attributed to the domestic distribution system or to its maintenance, consumers in the affected area must be notified and given advice on action to be taken to safeguard their health.

Where a water undertaker is unable to meet the prescribed standards, he may apply to the Secretary of State for an authorisation permitting a departure from the provisions of Part III of the Regulations for any of its water supply zones. The application should include details of the grounds for the authorisation, for which water supply zones and the number of people affected; the parameters for which the authorisation is sought and results of sampling over the previous 12 months, and the period for which the authorisation is sought. The application should include details of further monitoring of the quality of the water to be supplied during the period of the authorisation. With the application, the water undertaker should submit a programme of works, estimated cost and timetable for bringing the water supply up to standard. A copy of the application and accompanying documents should be sent to the appropriate local authority and district health authority and to the customer services committee, who all have 30 days in which to make representations on the application to the Secretary of State. A departure will not be authorised unless the Secretary of State is satisfied that there is no potential danger to human health and that there is no other reasonable way in which water can be supplied to the zone. Details of the authorisation should be published in an appropriate local paper as soon as reasonably practicable unless the Secretary of State considers the contravention of the standard to be "trivial" and the situation is remedied within 30 days. The Secretary of State should normally give six months' notice of intention to modify or revoke an authorisation to the water undertaker and those to whom it was copied. He may revoke or modify an authorisation without notice in the interests of public health; an authorisation may also be revoked without notice where a water undertaker advises the Secretary of State that the circumstances for which the authorisation was granted no longer exist.

Part VII of the Regulations covers water treatment, including risk assessment and treatment for cryptosporidium (see 1999 amendment to the 1989 Regulations above), and the treatment of water as a result of contamination from copper or lead pipes.

Part VIII deals with maintenance of records and provision of information to the public. Water undertakers are required to maintain full records of water supply zones, authorised departures and action being taken to bring supplies up to standard, as well as monitoring and sampling results. Such information should be available for public inspection and copies available free of charge to residents for records relating to their own zone. Each year water undertakers should include with customers' bills a statement of where they may inspect, free of charge, records of water quality. No later than 30 June 2005, and no later than 30 June in subsequent years, water undertakers should send to local authorities full particulars of the water supplied during the previous year to each water supply zone in the authority's area. Water undertakers are also required to notify the appropriate local authority and district health authority and the customer services committee as soon as possible after an occurrence to the water which it supplies which gives rise, or may give rise, to a significant health risk to people in the area.

Finally, the Regulations require all water undertakers who intend to supply water on or after 25 December to submit to the Secretary of State, no later than 31 March 2001, a programme of work aimed at compliance with Part III of the Regulations by 25 December 2003 (or for lead by 25 December 2013); if a water undertaker is of the opinion that he will be unable to meet any of the requirements of Part III by 25 December 2003, he should apply for an authorisation permitting a departure from the standard no later than 25 September 2003.

The Private Water Supplies Regulations 1991 (SI 2790)

These Regulations (made under ss.67 & 77 of the *Water Industry Act 1991*) relate to the quality of water from private supplies for drinking, washing, cooking or for food production. They apply in England and Wales only and came into force on 1 January 1992. They contain similar requirements to those of Parts II and III of the *Water Supply (Water Quality) Regulations 1991*. Similar (1992, SI 575) Regulations apply in Scotland, and 1994 Regulations in Northern Ireland. New Regulations will be needed to implement the 1998 Drinking Water Directive.

Local authorities are required to monitor the quality of private water supplies by reference to two categories: water supplied for domestic purposes; and water supplied for food production, to staff canteens, hospitals, hostels, boarding schools etc and camp sites. The Regulations specify factors to be taken into account in monitoring programmes - sampling frequency, point of sampling, analysis, and charging for sampling and analysis. Where quality is found to be below standard, local authorities must ensure that the necessary remedial action is taken. They are also required to keep a register of all private water supplies in their area.

Private supplies are those not provided by a water undertaker (company) - i.e. not connected to a mains pipe (for example, borehole into an underground aquifer, a surface reservoir).

Sampling of Water

British Standard 6068, section 6.5, 1991, gives guidance on sampling drinking water and water used for food and beverage processing. It includes guidance on the design of sampling programmes and techniques, handling and preservation of samples, water processing treatment plant (including the analysis of raw water), supervision of the treatment plant and the distribution system, and the identification of defects in the system.

5.17.2 Sewerage Services (ss.94-117)

Provision of Sewerage Services (ss.94-101)

Every sewerage undertaker has a general duty to provide and maintain a system of public sewers and sewage disposal, and to have regard to its existing and likely obligations to allow for the discharge of trade effluent into its public sewers, and the disposal of such trade effluent. The Secretary of State may make Regulations detailing the extent to which breaches of specific sewerage service obligations are to amount to breaches of the general duty. Regulations may also prescribe individual standards of performance in relation to the sewerage service. If these standards are not met, payments are to be made by the undertaker to the persons affected. Sewerage undertakers must comply within six months with any request to provide a public sewer to be used for drainage of premises for domestic purposes, provided that certain financial conditions are met.

5.17.3 Trade Effluent (ss.118-134)

Occupiers of trade premises may not discharge any trade effluents into a public sewer unless authorised by the sewerage undertaker. An application to discharge should include details of the effluent, quantity to be discharged in any one day, and the highest rate at which it is proposed to discharge. (The sewerage undertaker must refer all applications covering special category effluent - see below - to the Environment Agency who will decide if the discharge should be prohibited or permitted subject to conditions.)

In granting an application, the sewerage undertaker may impose conditions covering the rate, quantity and composition of effluent and the sewer into which it may be discharged, and the time or times of day. Conditions may also relate to provision and maintenance of inspection chambers and meters and of other apparatus for testing the effluent, record keeping and payments to the sewerage undertaker.

There is a right of appeal to the Director of Water Services where an application is refused, has not been considered within two months, or conditions are considered unreasonable. In the case of special category effluent, appeals should be directed to the Secretary of State. A sewerage undertaker may vary conditions attached to a consent; again there is a right of appeal to the Director General of Water Services.

Where a process regulated under Part I of the *Environmental Protection Act 1990* proposes to discharge trade effluent into a sewer, it also requires a consent from the sewerage undertaker.

Trade Effluents (Prescribed Processes and Substances) Regulations 1989 (SI 1156) (amended 1990, 1992)

These Regulations came into force on 1 September 1989 and were made under ss.74 & 185 of the *Water Act*; they apply to England and Wales only and enable compliance with EU Directives on pollution caused by discharges to the aquatic environment (76/464/EEC) and the prevention and reduction of environmental pollution by asbestos (87/217/EEC).

The Regulations specify two categories of trade effluent which are subject to control over their discharge into public sewers and for which an authorisation to discharge is required from the Environment Agency.

The first category for which authorisation to discharge is required is effluent which contains concentrations of "red list" substances (see Appendix 1.2 - substances controlled for release to water under IPC) exceeding those that would be present regardless of the activities within the premises from which the effluent is discharged. The second "special" category consists of effluent from the following prescribed processes:

- any process for the production of chlorinated organic chemicals;
- any process for the manufacture of paper pulp;
- any industrial process in which cooling waters or effluents are chlorinated;
- any process for the manufacture of asbestos cement;
- any process for the manufacture of asbestos paper or board.

The 1992 Regulations added effluent containing more than 30 kg/year of trichloroethylene or perchloroethylene to "special category" effluent.

The Regulations also require sewerage undertakers to notify the Environment Agency if they propose to vary existing trade effluent discharge consents so as to permit the discharge of effluent containing "red list" substances at levels in excess of background concentrations. This will enable the Agency to exercise stricter controls over discharges to watercourses via the sewage system, thus enabling the UK to meet its commitment (agreed at the North Sea Conference - see 5.23 below) to reduce such discharges by 50% between 1985 and 1995.

The 1990 amending Regulations tightened up the notification procedure further to require agreements by which sewerage undertakers can accept trade effluents under the *Public Health (Drainage and Trade Premises) Act 1937*, also to be notified to the Agency. Under the Regulations, the Agency must also be notified where it is proposed to vary a consent for a trade effluent discharge containing asbestos or chloroform from any of the processes mentioned above at a level in excess of background concentrations.

In addition, a Department of Environment Circular (7/89) contains advice on implementation of the EU Directive on environmental pollution by asbestos. Water authorities were required to satisfy themselves that producers of asbestos cement, and of paper and board products, had appropriate effluent treatment or recycling technology in operation by mid-1991, or had phased out the use of raw asbestos by then.

In Scotland the 1987 EU Directive on the prevention and reduction of environmental pollution by asbestos has been implemented through the *Trade Effluents (Asbestos) (Scotland) Regulations 1993* (SI 1446). Asbestos discharges should be "reduced at source and prevented ... using BATNEEC, including where appropriate recycling or treatment". Specified limits on asbestos discharges can be included in discharge authorisations, with specific conditions to be included where the discharge relates to "special category" activities (see above).

5.18 URBAN WASTE WATER TREATMENT (ENGLAND & WALES) REGULATIONS 1994 (SI 2841)

These Regulations, made under the *European Communities Act 1972*, came into force on 30 November 1994, with similar (1994, SI 2842) Regulations applying in Scotland and in Northern Ireland (1995, SR 12). They implement the 1991 EU municipal waste water Directive (91/271/EEC) - see above 5.7.6.

Regulation 3 required the Secretary of State to review the identification of "sensitive areas" and "high natural dispersion areas" before 31 December 1997 and then at intervals of no more than four years. Schedule 1 to the Regulations lists criteria for identification: sensitive areas

include natural freshwater lakes, estuaries and coastal waters and surface freshwaters intended for the abstraction of drinking waters. A high natural dispersion area is a marine body or area where the discharge of waste water will not adversely affect the environment as a result of morphology, hydrology or specific hydraulic conditions in the area; in identifying a high natural dispersion area account should be taken of the discharge being transferred to an area where it could have an adverse effect.

Unless it would have no environmental benefit or would involve excessive cost, collecting systems satisfying Schedule 2 to the Regulations must be in place (Regulation 4) -

- by 31 December 1998 where the discharge is into receiving waters in a sensitive area for agglomeration with a population equivalent (pe) of more than 10,000;

- by 31 December 2000 for agglomeration with pe of more than 15,000;

- by 31 December 2005 for agglomeration with pe of 2,000-15,000.

Regulation 5 specifies the dates by which suitable treatment plant must be provided, with Schedule 3 detailing the requirements for discharges from treatment plants.

The Regulations also impose requirements relating to discharges of industrial waste water with sewerage undertakers being empowered to modify trade effluent consents and agreements to ensure compliance. The dumping of sewage sludge at sea had to be phased out by 31 December 1998 and its toxic, persistent and bioaccumulable properties progressively reduced before then.

The appropriate Agency must ensure that monitoring and other studies of discharges is carried out and certain documents made available for public inspection.

MARINE POLLUTION

5.19 UN CONVENTION ON THE LAW OF THE SEA

The importance of protecting the marine environment is now recognised as a priority by many governments. Inadequate sewage disposal, the build-up of chlorinated hydrocarbons from pesticides, the dumping of polychlorinated biphenyls (PCBs) and other chemicals, as well as the incineration of hazardous waste at sea all pose a threat to human health and to marine life.

The 1982 UN Convention on the Law of the Sea defines pollution of the marine environment as

"... the introduction by man, directly or indirectly, of substances or energy into the marine environment, including estuaries, which results or is likely to result in such deleterious effects as harm to living resources and marine life, hazards to human health, hindrance to marine activities, including fishing and other legitimate uses of the sea, impairment of quality for use of sea water and reduction of amenities."

The Convention covers all aspects of the preservation and protection of the marine environment and sets out the duties of states in this respect, as well as "the legal framework within which all activities in the oceans and seas must be carried out". Some of its articles - or aims - are similar to those in other conventions (see below) or have already been incorporated into national legislation.

This Convention came into force in 1994 following ratification by the required number (60) of countries. On 23 March 1998 the Council of Ministers adopted a decision which approves the Convention and Agreement of 28 July 1994 on implementation of Part XI of it, and the Convention thus came into force in the European Union on 1 May 1998.

The way in which the Convention is working is discussed annually by the UN General Assembly; in November 1999 the General Assembly adopted a Resolution providing for an annual consultative meeting open to all UN member states, parties to the Convention and relevant intergovernmental organisations. This meeting will discuss the UN Secretary General's report on oceans and the law with particular "emphasis on identifying areas where coordination and cooperation at intergovernmental and interagency levels should be enhanced".

5.20 THE LONDON CONVENTION

The London Convention on the Prevention of Marine Pollution by Dumping of Wastes and other Matter was signed in London in 1972; it entered into force on 30 August 1975 and applies worldwide. It aims to ban or restrict the dumping (i.e. deliberate disposal) of various polluting substances according to their potential to harm either human or marine life or otherwise impair the marine environment. As well as the disposal of waste from ships, aircraft and manmade structures at sea, the Convention bans the disposal of ships, aircraft and manmade structures and the residues of incineration at sea.

The London Convention also imposed an immediate ban on the dumping of high level radioactive waste at sea and in 1983 agreed a 10 year voluntary moratorium on the dumping of low level radioactive waste. In February 1994 a further amendment agreed in November 1993 banned the dumping of low level radioactive waste at sea, the incineration at sea of industrial wastes and agreed to phase out the dumping of industrial wastes at sea by 31 December 1995.

A 1996 Protocol to the Convention, which when ratified will replace the 1972 Convention, adopts the precautionary principle requiring that "appropriate preventative measures be taken when there is reason to believe that wastes or other matter introduced into the marine environment are likely to cause harm even when there is no conclusive evidence to prove a causal relation between inputs and their effects". As such the Protocol will ban the dumping at sea of all wastes except those listed in Annex I to the Protocol; the list includes dredged material; sewage sludge; fish waste; vessels, platforms and other manmade structures; inert, inorganic geological material; and organic material of natural origin. The Protocol will prohibit the export of waste to another country for dumping or incineration at sea. Finally only those wastes listed in an annex to the Protocol may be dumped at sea

5.21 MARPOL

This Convention - the International Convention for the Prevention of Pollution from Ships - was adopted following the 1973 international conference on marine pollution held under the auspices of the International Maritime Organisation. Included were articles dealing with oil, chemical, sewage and other pollution from ships, and requiring provision of adequate port reception facilities to deal with such wastes. However, it was not ratified because many governments felt it would be too difficult to implement. A further conference in 1978 agreed a protocol to the Convention which included a number of amendments and improved the annex relating to oil pollution. The Convention and its protocol (MARPOL 73/78) have now been ratified by a number of governments. In the UK it has been implemented through the 1996 *Merchant Shipping (Prevention of Oil Pollution) Regulations* - see below, 5.25.1.

Further measures aimed at reducing pollution from ships have now been agreed by the IMO and were incorporated in MARPOL for implementation from January 1992. These measures include reducing pollutants in ships' exhaust gases, banning the use of CFCs in refrigeration units and of halons in new fire extinguishers.

A new Annex VI to the MARPOL Convention was signed in London in September 1997; this aims to control emissions of air pollutants from shipping. The sulphur content of bunker oil is limited to 4.5%, with a lower limit of 1.5% to apply in the Baltic Sea which has been designated a "SOx Emission Control Area"; in April 2000 it was agreed that the North Sea should have similar status. Limits on emissions of nitrogen oxides from diesel engines are also set and the incineration at sea of contaminated packaging materials and PCBs is banned. Voluntary emissions of ozone depleting gases are also banned as are new installations with ozone depleting substances on board ships although those containing hydrochlorofluorocarbons are permitted until 1 January 2020. Before it can come into force, the Annex requires ratification by 15 (out of a possible 100) member states who together account for 50% of the world's merchant tonnage. However as at June 2000, only Norway and Sweden had ratified it.

The MARPOL Convention, in allowing certain oil discharges from ships, also allows for special areas to be declared in which stricter rules for discharges apply. The

IMO has agreed that the seas around the UK and north west European coastline should have special area status; thus from 1 August 1999 almost all oil pollution from ships in this area has been banned. Other special areas include the Gulf of Aden (1989), North Sea (1991), the Antarctic (1992) and the Wider Caribbean (1993).

A further treaty put forward by the IMO was agreed in London at the end of 1990. *The International Convention on Oil Pollution Preparedness Response and Cooperation 1990* lays down the principles of prompt and effective action in the event of an oil spill. Ships, off-shore installations, ports and other facilities which handle oil should establish emergency plans and all pollution incidents should be reported. This Convention came into force on 13 May 1995, 12 months after ratification by the required 15 states; as at 13 May 1995, 21 member states had ratified the Convention. In the UK this Convention has been partly implemented through the *Merchant Shipping (Oil Pollution Preparedness, Response and Cooperation Convention) Regulations 1998* (SI 1056); these came into force on 15 May 1998 - see 5.25.3 below.

5.22 THE OSPAR CONVENTION

The Convention on the Protection of the North Sea and North East Atlantic, which was signed in Paris in September 1992, entered into force in 1998. It replaces the 1972 Oslo *Convention for the Prevention of Marine Pollution by Dumping from Ships and Aircraft* and the 1974 Paris *Convention for the Prevention of Marine Pollution from Land-Based Sources*. Both Conventions covered the North Sea and North East Atlantic and were monitored by London based Commissions which also took a leading role in ensuring follow-up of actions agreed at the North Sea Conferences (see below). A Commission - the OSPAR Commission (i.e. drawn from the Oslo and Paris Commissions) - has been set up to implement and monitor the 1992 Convention; the members of OSPAR are Belgium, Denmark, Finland, France, Germany, Iceland, Ireland, Luxembourg, The Netherlands, Norway, Portugal, Spain, Sweden, Switzerland, the UK and the European Community.

The main objective of the 1992 Convention is the protection of the marine environment so as to safeguard human health through the elimination or prevention of pollution. Conservation and repair of the marine ecosystem are equally important objectives and a strategy to combat eutrophication is to be drawn up. Potentially polluting activities covered by the Convention are listed as are the substances for which control programmes must be implemented with a view to continuously reducing marine concentrations to background values and ceasing releases of such substances by 2020; these include pesticides, heavy metals, oil and hydrocarbons, organohalogen compounds and various chemicals. A list of priority substances for control to which the 2020 target will apply has been agreed. Both dumping and incineration at sea are to be banned, as are radioactive discharges thus giving

extra weight to the agreements reached at the North Sea Conferences (see below).

At the 1998 meeting of the Commission in Portugal, Ministers agreed a total ban on sea dumping of large steel installations (gas and oil rigs); it was also agreed that

- by the year 2000, the OSPAR Commission will, for the whole maritime area, work towards achieving further substantial reductions or elimination of discharges, emissions and losses of radioactive substances;

- by the year 2020, the OSPAR Commission will ensure that discharges, emissions and losses of radioactive substances are reduced to levels where the additional concentrations in the marine environment above historic levels resulting from such discharges, emissions and losses, are close to zero.

The UK and France also withdrew their opt-out from a ban on dumping nuclear waste at sea, which is to be phased out by 2020. However both the UK and France have not accepted a majority decision (taken at a meeting in Copenhagen in June 2000) that nuclear fuel reprocessing be terminated (and thus nuclear fuel be stored on land). At the 2000 meeting it was also agreed that each country should, by 2002, draw up an action plan for reducing radioactive discharges. A further Annex (Annex V) was also added to the Convention dealing with the protection and conservation of maritime ecosystems and biological diversity.

In drawing up action programmes to deal with polluting discharges, signatories must apply the precautionary principle and the polluter pays principle, as well as having regard to both BAT (Best Available Technique) and BEP (Best Environmental Practice); this latter includes information to the public, product labelling and collection and disposal systems. One of the tasks of the Commission implementing and monitoring the Convention will be to draw up documents specifying BAT for disposal, reduction and elimination of a range of substances from various industrial sectors.

The European Community gave its approval to the OSPAR Convention through Council Decision 98/249/EC. The Community formally approved Annex V through a Decision dated 8 May 2000.

In June 2000, the Government published a draft UK Strategy for Radioactive Discharges (DETR, 2000) which outlines how it is intended to implement the OSPAR agreements.

5.23 NORTH SEA CONFERENCES

In Europe, apart from the Directives which apply throughout the EU (see 5.6 & 5.7 above and Appendix 6.5), further initiatives have been taken by the countries bordering the North Sea which is the receiving water for a number of effluent-laden rivers which flow into it; these rivers include the Rhine, Elbe, Humber, Forth, Tyne, Tees and the Thames.

This growing concern resulted, in 1984, in the Government of the former West Germany convening a conference of countries bordering the North Sea (Belgium, Britain, Denmark, France, The Netherlands, Norway, Sweden and Germany) to draw up measures aimed at reducing pollution of the North Sea. This was followed by a second conference in 1987 in London; among other measures, agreement was reached on ending the dumping of harmful wastes by the end of 1989 and ending incineration by 1994.

The Third North Sea Conference was held in The Hague in 1990, and was attended by all the North Sea States plus Switzerland, whose industries along the Rhine contributed significantly to pollution levels. For the first time, the cuts agreed at the meeting are to be legally binding. Among the measures agreed were:

- by 1995, to make cuts of 50% or more (on 1985 levels) in inputs via rivers and estuaries of 39 hazardous substances;

- by 1995, a 50% cut (on 1985 levels) of inputs of dangerous substances from the air;

- by 1995, a 70% cut (on 1985 levels) of substances deemed to pose a major threat, and including dioxins, mercury, cadmium and lead;

- to aim for a substantial reduction in the quantities of pesticides reaching the North Sea;

- to phase out and to destroy in an environmentally safe manner all identifiable PCBs as soon as possible with the aim of complete destruction by 1995; and by 1999 at the latest, to ensure that the time between taking out of service and destruction is as short as practicable. It was also agreed that each country should provide its own destruction facilities;

- municipal sewage discharges, as well as effluent discharges from industry, should receive secondary treatment before discharge.

The European Commission's Fifth Action Programme on the Environment, Towards Sustainability (see also Appendix 6) includes as an objective to reduce emissions of cadmium, lead and mercury in line with the North Sea Agreement.

In the UK, the reductions will largely be achieved through controls on discharges under Integrated Pollution Control (see chapter 1) and by controls on discharges under the *Water Resources Act 1991* (see 5.15 above). The *Urban Waste Water Treatment (England and Wales) Regulations 1994* (and similar in Scotland) required the phasing out of the disposal of sewage sludge to sea by 31 December 1998 (5.18 above).

Commitments relating to the phasing out and destruction of PCBs and PCTs are to be met by voluntary action on the part of industry and other users. The UK action plan, which also takes into account the requirements of the EU Directive (96/59/EC) on the disposal of PCBs and PCTs,

circulated by the DOE (now DETR) in March 1997 proposes

- progressive withdrawal of existing exemptions from the ban on the sale and use of PCBs;

- requirement to register PCBs with a competent authority by 16 March 1996 and to agree a date for their destruction;

- a complete ban on supply, use and storage of PCBs from 31 December 1999;

- the compilation of an inventory of equipment containing PCBs of more than 5 dm³.

The *Environmental Protection (Disposal of Polychlorinated Biphenyls and Other Dangerous Substances) (England and Wales) Regulations 2000* implement EC Directive 96/59 and also give statutory backing to the UK commitment to phase out PCBs; similar Regulations apply in Scotland, and in Northern Ireland – see chapter 4, 4.24.

At the Fourth North Sea Conference in June 1995, there was a further commitment to achieve the reduction targets agreed at the Third Conference with a number of measures agreed for reducing discharges of priority substances (cadmium, mercury etc); there was also a call for on-going reductions in discharges and emissions of hazardous substances leading to their cessation within 25 years.

5.24 FOOD AND ENVIRONMENT PROTECTION ACT 1985, PART II

This part of the Act repealed the *Dumping at Sea Act 1974* which was the first UK legislation to impose statutory controls on the dumping of waste at sea; it gave effect to various international conventions (London, 1972 and Oslo - 5.20 & 5.22 above) imposing obligations relating to the disposal of waste, the dumping of hazardous pollutants and incineration at sea. The Act applies to the whole of the United Kingdom. (The UK ended incineration at sea in 1990 and the dumping of industrial waste in 1992.)

Part II of the *Food and Environment Protection Act* (FEPA) which covers dumping and incineration at sea and/or under the seabed within UK waters, and also the scuttling of vessels, was amended by s.146 of the *Environmental Protection Act 1990*. (The amendment mainly relates to the inclusion of UK controlled waters as well as UK waters.) FEPA applies to dumping etc whether by a UK or foreign ship, aircraft, hovercraft, marine structure or floating container.

5.24.1 Licensing Requirements for Dumping at Sea

Under the Act, the prescribed activities require prior approval by licence from the Ministry of Agriculture, Fisheries and Food. In most instances, the requirement for a licence includes activities prior to the dumping or incineration, such as the loading of ships and aircraft etc within the UK, UK waters or UK controlled waters. Exempted activities are listed in the *Deposits in the Sea*

(Exemptions) Order 1985 (SI 1699), and include activities such as returning to the water matter taken out during fishing and dredging or deposited for coastal protection or harbour works, and the disposal of "victual or domestic waste" from ships and hovercraft etc. As from 31 December 1994 exempted activities had to be registered with MAFF (amendment to Exemptions Order by *Waste Management Regulations 1994*).

In considering whether to issue a licence, MAFF will take into account the need to protect the marine environment, the living resources which it supports, and human health. The licence may include conditions to meet these requirements, and the Act provides for fees to be charged in respect of administrative expenses, monitoring and sampling. Where a licence has been breached, MAFF may revoke it and criminal proceedings may be instituted. Summary conviction carries a fine not exceeding £50,000; conviction on indictment carries a fine and/or imprisonment not exceeding two years.

5.24.2 Public Registers

Part II of FEPA requires each licensing authority to maintain a public register containing details of licences issued relating to deposits and incineration at sea. This provision has been amended by s.147 of the *Environmental Protection Act 1990* which specifies that the register must contain applications for licences, those issued, variations and revocations as well as details of convictions for breaches of licence conditions. Information may be excluded from the register on grounds of commercial confidentiality or national security. These requirements have been given effect through *The Deposits in the Sea (Public Registers of Information) Regulations 1996* (SI 1427) which came into force on 1 July 1996. The Regulations apply in England and Wales only. The register is to be held by MAFF in London with access available at reasonable times. A charge may be levied for copies of entries on the register.

5.25 OIL POLLUTION

5.25.1 Prevention of Oil Pollution Act 1971

This Act makes it an offence (subject to various defences) to discharge oil or any substance containing oil into UK territorial waters, either from a place on land or from sea-based explorations or into harbour waters; discharges under and escapes authorised by Part I of the *Environmental Protection Act 1990* are not subject to this part of the Act (*Env. Act 1995*, Sch. 22, para 15, England, Scotland & Wales only). The Act introduced requirements for record keeping covering transfers of oil and placed restrictions on when such transfers can take place; it also covers liability for soil pollution and requires compulsory insurance against liability. A 1986 Act extended the 1971 Act to cover discharges from vessels.

Section 148 of the *Environmental Protection Act 1990* amended the 1971 Act to enable action to be taken against foreign owned ships for illegally discharging oil into UK territorial waters or ports and harbours.

Merchant Shipping (Prevention of Oil Pollution) Regulations

These Regulations implement the MARPOL Convention (see above); they apply to UK ships worldwide and to others while in UK waters.

The *Merchant Shipping (Prevention of Oil Pollution) (Limits) Regulations 1996* (SI 2128), which came into force on 5 September 1996, establish a UK "pollution zone"; this extends beyond the 12 nautical mile territorial limit to up to 200 nautical miles from the coastline. Any foreign ship suspected of committing a pollution offence within the pollution zone which calls at a port in the UK will then be liable to prosecution by the UK courts.

The *Merchant Shipping (Prevention of Oil Pollution) Regulations 1996* (SI 2154), as amended 1997 (SI 1910) came into force on 17 September; they provide for the enforcement of oil pollution offences committed within the pollution zone and consolidate earlier 1983 and 1993 Regulations. These introduced record keeping requirements as well as survey and certification for oil tankers and other UK ships above a certain size. There is a duty to maintain ships and their equipment in compliance with the Regulations; other provisions relate to powers of inspection and penalties. New oil tankers must be fitted with double hulls and existing ones must be fitted with additional protection against grounding or collision once they are 25 years old. Oil pollution emergency plans must be carried and stricter rules regarding discharges of oil complied with. The 1996 Regulations also include measures aimed at improving the provision and use of port waste reception facilities, tighten the regulations on legal discharges from ships, improve the enforcement of the Regulations and increase the maximum fines for illegal discharges.

5.25.2 Merchant Shipping (Salvage and Pollution) Act 1994

This Act received the Royal Assent in July 1994; from 1 October 1994 the owners of all vessels (except laden oil tankers) became liable for any oil pollution and resultant pollution prevention measures. It also implemented, with effect from 1 January 1995, a number of international marine conventions and declarations, including:

- the 1990 Convention on Oil Pollution Preparedness, Response and Cooperation (see 5.21 above);

- a 1992 Declaration from the North Sea Conference calling for implementation of various provisions of the 1982 UN Convention on the Law of the Sea (see above 5.19).

5.25.3 Merchant Shipping (Oil Pollution Preparedness, Response and Cooperation Convention) Regulations 1998 (SI 1056)

These Regulations, which apply throughout the UK, came into force on 15 May 1998; they implement in part the 1990 IMO Convention of the same name (see above 5.21). They apply to harbours and oil handling facilities with an annual turnover of more than £1 million, and to those which are able to handle tankers above a certain threshold or are designated by the Secretary of State; they also apply to off-shore installations in UK waters.

The Regulations required harbour authorities and operators of oil handling facilities to prepare and submit an oil spill contingency plan to the Government's Marine Pollution Control Unit by 15 August 1999; off-shore installations had until the same date to submit a similar plan to the Department of Trade and Industry's Oil and Gas Office in Aberdeen; local people and organisations, local authorities and environmental organisations had to be consulted during the plan's preparation. Plans must be reviewed every five years.

Ships' masters and those in charge of harbours, oil handling facilities and off-shore installations must report any oil spills to their nearest Coastguard station.

5.26 MERCHANT SHIPPING AND MARITIME SECURITY ACT 1997

This Act, which received the Royal Assent in late March 1997, aims to tighten UK controls on shipping which poses a pollution risk, e.g. because of an accident, collision or other internal or external damage. It includes provisions to:

- require the Secretary of State to draw up and implement a national marine pollution contingency plan;

- establish temporary exclusion zones at sea to allow safety zones to be placed around ships or structures on grounds of safety and/or pollution;

- widen the Coastguard's intervention powers to cover any risk of significant pollution;

- permit charging for maritime functions such as emergency pollution response and standard setting activity in line with the polluter pays and user pays principles;

- enable regulations to be made requiring port and harbour authorities to prepare waste management plans and to charge ships for the use of waste reception facilities;

- enable regulations to be made requiring local authorities to draw up contingency plans to deal with oil spills;

- give powers to move ships on if they pose a threat to safety or the environment;

- increase the maximum penalty for marine pollution offences from £50,000 to £250,000.

5.27 SHIP GENERATED WASTE

5.27.1 Merchant Shipping (Port Waste Reception Facilities) Regulations 1997 (SI 3018)

These Regulations, which came into force on 27 January 1998, require port and harbour authorities to prepare waste management plans which have to be approved by the Secretary of State. The Regulations also require the authorities to ensure they have adequate facilities (having regard to their waste management plan and to Guidance from the Secretary of State) for receiving prescribed wastes from ships.

The *Merchant Shipping (Prevention of Pollution by Garbage) Regulations 1998* (SI 1377) require all ships above 400 gross tonnage and those certified to carry more than 15 people to have a garbage management plan, and to keep disposal records. Illegal disposal carries a maximum fine of £25,000.

5.27.2 Proposal for a Directive on Ship Generated Waste

In September 2000, the European Parliament formally approved the text of the Directive on port reception facilities for ship generated waste and cargo residues – COM(98) 4458 - agreed by the Council of Ministers and Parliament under the Conciliation Procedure. An aim of the Directive is to reduce the discharge of ship generated waste at sea, by requiring Member States to ensure there are adequate waste reception facilities at ports and marinas. This Directive builds on the requirements of MARPOL which prohibits dumping of waste at sea – see 5.21. The Directive will require such facilities to be licensed and will also require ports to draw up a waste handling and reception plan. Ships calling at a port will have to deposit ship generated waste in the reception facility unless it has enough storage capacity to do so at a subsequent port. Costs for such facilities will be recovered through fees levied on ships calling at the port.

PESTICIDES
5.28 INTRODUCTION

Pesticides are toxic chemicals intended to control insect, rodent and other pest infestations. Their main use is for agricultural purposes where benefits can be said to include less disease and increased yields. However, their overuse and misuse in some instances has resulted in various pests becoming resistant to certain pesticides; the widespread use of pesticides can also mean that some crops may receive multiple applications; and while workers may risk occupational exposure, the general public may be exposed to spraydrift from aerial applications of pesticides. Pesticide use can also result in environmental damage to rivers, wildlife and vegetation.

The term "pesticides" commonly includes insecticides, rodenticides, fungicides, herbicides etc as well as substances used as growth regulators, fumigants, insect repellants or attractors and defoliants and desiccants. In addition the European Commission uses the term "biocides" to cover a range of non-agricultural pesticides such as disinfectants, textile and consumer product preservatives and air conditioning biocides; it proposes regulating these in much the same way as the more traditional pesticides.

5.29 EUROPEAN UNION AND INTERNATIONAL MEASURES

At EU level, there are a number of Directives relating to the discharge of dangerous substances, including pesticides to water (see 5.6 above and Appendix 6.6). In addition there are various Directives covering pesticide residues in products of plant origin (e.g. fruit and vegetables) and in animal feeds and products. A 1979 Directive (79/117/EEC) which has subsequently been amended a number of times prohibits the placing on the market and use of plant protection products (i.e. pesticides etc) containing certain active substances; among the substances so far covered are the "drins" group of pesticides, DDT, chlordane, hexachlorocyclohexane, heptachlor, hexachlorobenzene and various mercury compounds. The marketing and use of various dangerous substances, including pentachlorophenol (PCP), is also controlled under Directive 76/769/EEC; in the UK the marketing and use of PCP and its supply for domestic use (which is banned) is regulated under the *Environmental Protection (Control of Injurious Substances) Regulations 1993*.

In 1991, a Directive (91/414/EEC) concerning the placing of plant protection products on the market was adopted; its main purpose is to regulate agricultural pesticides through the establishment of an EU-wide list of approved active ingredients, harmonise approval procedures and to allow for mutual recognition of individual Member States' authorisation procedures. The list of active ingredients will be drawn up progressively as pesticides currently on sale within the EU are examined on human and environmental health and safety grounds. The Directive has been amended a number of times with Directive 94/43 outlining uniform principles for evaluating and authorising pesticides to ensure uniformity throughout the Community. Following a complaint from the European Parliament, the European Court of Justice annulled Directive 94/43 on the basis that it did not adequately protect groundwater, a requirement of the 1991 Directive. The 1994 Directive has now been replaced by Directive 97/57/EC which was adopted in mid-1997. These Directives have been implemented by the *Plant Protection Products Regulations 1995* (SI 887) and subsequent amendments.

A Directive on the placing of biocidal products on the market - 98/8/EC - was adopted on 16 February 1998 and should have been implemented by Member States by 14 May 2000. This Directive uses a similar approach to the plant products Directive in aiming to standardise the way in which biocides are registered throughout the EU, protecting human health and the environment; the Directive covers chemicals, including disinfectants, "avicides", "piscicides" and dirt inhibitors (but not biocides for agricultural use) not covered by existing legislation. An annex to the Directive sets out the common principles, including risk assessment criteria, to be applied when authorising biocidal products to enable mutual recognition of authorisations throughout Member States. Member States may however apply stricter standards to protect human health or the environment. Only biocidal products containing an active substance approved under the Directive (on the basis of how safe it is for human health and the environment) may be authorised for use. However products already on the market remain authorised for use until the active substance they contain has been reviewed; the Directive allows Member States ten years to review existing active substances.

The European Commission's Fifth Action Programme, *Towards Sustainability*, also includes as an objective the "significant reduction of pesticide use . . . and conversion of farmers to methods of integrated pest control".

In the UK, the pesticide related Directives have been implemented mainly through Part III of the *Food and Environment Protection Act 1985* and the *Control of Pesticide Regulations 1986 and 1997* Amendment Regulations made under the Act, and the *Plant Protection Product Regulations 1995* (SI 887). The pesticide residues Directives are implemented through the *Pesticides (Maximum Residue Levels in Food) Regulations 1988* in England, Scotland and Wales, with similar Regulations applying in Northern Ireland.

In July 1999, the Health and Safety Executive published proposals for Regulations and an Approved Code of Practice to implement the biocides Directive. These have now been redrafted and agreed by the Health and Safety Commission which now submits its proposals to Ministers for approval. Technical guidance on all aspects of the Regulations is to be prepared. A new committee of the HSE – the Biocides Consultative Committee – will be the UK competent authority, providing expert advice on the evaluation of biocidal products under the Regulations.

In 1990 the Third North Sea Conference (see 5.23 above) also agreed measures to reduce discharges of certain pesticides into the North Sea. In 1985 the United Nations Food and Agriculture Organisation adopted a *Code of Practice on the International Distribution and Use of Pesticides*. This is mainly concerned with ensuring that pesticides restricted or banned in the country of origin are not freely available or dumped on other countries.

In September 1998, the International Convention on Trade in Hazardous Chemicals and Pesticides was approved with 95 signatories, including the EU. Amongst other things, the Convention bans the export of any chemical or pesticide which has itself been banned or severely restricted in at least two other countries, unless the importing country gives its specific (prior) consent; the Convention will initially apply to a list of 22 pesticides and five industrial chemicals. The Convention will need ratification by 50 states before it can come into force, but is likely to be implemented on a voluntary basis until it formally comes into force.

5.30 REGULATORY CONTROLS

The main legislation controlling the use of pesticides is Part III of the *Food and Environment Protection Act 1985* (FEPA), as amended by the *Pesticides Act 1998*, and Regulations made under it. Also of relevance are the *Control of Substances Hazardous to Health Regulations 1999* which are intended to safeguard employees' health (see this chapter, below, and chapter 2, 2.16.2). The disposal of pesticides and pesticides containers is covered by Part II of the *Environmental Protection Act 1990* and by the *Water Resources Act 1991* (Scotland - COPA) (see this chapter and chapter 4). The *Water Supply (Water Quality) Regulations 1989* include maximum admissible concentrations for pesticides and related products - see this chapter 5.17.1c and Appendix 5.3 – these Regulations are to be replaced by new Regulations which are due to begin coming into force on 1 January 2001 – see introduction to the *Pollution Handbook*.

Additional controls on the use of pesticides in designated Environmentally Sensitive Areas are contained in the *Agriculture Act 1986*.

5.30.1 Food and Environment Protection Act 1985, Part III

This Part of the Act aims to protect the health of human beings, creatures and plants, to safeguard the environment and to secure safe, efficient and humane methods of controlling pests. Pesticides are defined as any substance, preparation or organism prepared or used for destroying any pest. The definition therefore includes herbicides, fungicides, insecticides, wood preservatives etc.

The Act provides Ministers with power, by regulation or order, to control the import, sale, supply, storage, use and advertisement of pesticides; to set maximum pesticide residue levels in food, crops and feeding stuffs; to make information supplied in connection with the control of pesticides available to the public. Under the Act an Advisory Committee on Pesticides was established and Codes of Practice published.

The Advisory Committee on Pesticides (ACP) consists of government appointed experts. The ACP considers manufacturers' applications for approval of pesticides and makes recommendations to government; it also reviews existing approvals, reviews safety and can make recommendations regarding revocation or amendments to approvals. A number of expert advisory panels advise the ACP on various issues relating to pesticide approvals.

There is limited public access to information on pesticides data: since 1986 evaluation data on newly approved or reviewed pesticides has been published, with manufacturers' supporting data available on request. In 1992, public access was extended to cover pesticides approved before 1986; fact sheets on older pesticides are also to be published. It should be noted that access to manufacturers' data is limited: information is not available on active ingredients and formulation specification and composition; production methods; names and addresses of laboratories, sites, personnel and individual medical records. People requesting access have to sign an undertaking that they will make no commercial use of the information; access is by "reading room facility" and while notetaking is allowed, photocopying is not; see, however, proposed amendments to the *Control of Pesticides Regulations 1986*, summarised below at 5.30.3.

The monthly Pesticides Register gives information on regulatory and other policy issues and the ACP publishes reports on items discussed at its meetings.

5.30.2 Pesticides Act 1998

This Act, which also extends to Northern Ireland, amends FEPA to enable regulations to be made to give local authorities (as well as Ministers) powers to seize and destroy pesticides, and for information on pesticides to be made available to the public, subject to conditions which Ministers consider appropriate. The *Control of Pesticides Regulations* (see below) are to be amended to provide access to data on pesticides approved before 1986, as well as to provide access to scientific data submitted by manufacturers; the amended Regulations will also clarify local authority seizure powers.

5.30.3 Control of Pesticides Regulations 1986 (SI 1510), as amended

These Regulations, define the types of pesticides subject to control; they apply in England, Scotland and Wales and came into force in October 1986, with similar legislation (1987) applying in Northern Ireland. The Regulations implement those sections of FEPA relating to the approval, advertisement, sale, supply, storage and use (including aerial spraying) of pesticides - all these activities are prohibited unless products have been formally approved for use, conditions of approval observed and additional conditions set out in "Consents" are met. Two statutory codes of practice - see below – originally issued by MAFF in 1990, provide guidance on implementation of the Regulations.

The *Control of Pesticides (Amendment) Regulations 1997* (SI 188), which came into force on 31 January 1997, amend the 1986 Regulations to:

- clarify that they apply to: any pesticide, or substance, preparation or organism prepared or used as plant or wood protection product; plant growth regulator; to give protection from harmful creatures or to make them harmless; to control organisms with harmful or unwanted effects on water systems or buildings, other structures or manufactured products; to protect animals against ectoparasites;

- require Consents for the advertisement of pesticides, the sale, supply, storage of pesticides, and for their use (including aerial use - see also 5.30.5b below) to include the conditions which are set out in Schedules 1 - 4 of the Regulations;

- clarify that in the event of breach of an approval or of a Consent, Ministers may require persons to recover pesticides from the market; empower Ministers to seize and dispose of a pesticide or require the holder of an approval or other person to dispose of it; where a pesticide has been imported into Great Britain or Northern Ireland in contravention of the Regulations (1987 Regulations in NI), to require, in writing, that it is exported again within a specified period;

- amend the rules covering access to information: Ministers may make evaluation documents available to the public and may charge a fee for supplying a copy; a person who has either inspected or paid or received a copy of an evaluation document may then make a request to the Minister to inspect the relevant study report; access to studies commissioned by government (including those produced to meet data requirements set in the course of reviews or approvals are included; the use for commercial purposes or publication of any data is prohibited unless approval in writing has been received from the Minister.

"Consents" are prepared by the Pesticides Safety Division of the Ministry of Agriculture, Fisheries and Food and updated from time to time. They are regularly updated and published in the Pesticides Register and the annual MAFF/HSE reference book on Pesticides - this latter also lists the pesticides approved under the Regulations. MAFF also publishes *The COPR Handbook - a Guide to the Policies, Procedures and Data Requirements relating to their Control under the Control of Pesticides Regulations 1986*. This also provides detailed information on pesticide legislation and guidance on registration under the Regulations.

Since April 1992 local authorities have been responsible for enforcing those sections of the Regulations which relate to the advertisement, sale, supply, storage and use of pesticides from a variety of commercial premises (e.g. shops, garden centres, sports grounds, hotels) and also domestic premises. Those parts of the Regulations relating to health and safety (e.g. storage and use) are dealt with by environmental health departments; the advertising, sale and supply of pesticides are the responsibility of trading standards departments.

The actual enforcement powers are contained in s.19 of FEPA. Authorised officers of the local authorities have powers of entry and inspection where they suspect infringement of the Regulations. While they may take photocopies of documents and records and photographs, they do not have powers to seize and destroy pesticides - only Ministers have this power, although proposals have now been issued for amending the Regulations to extend this power to local authorities - see below. Where the local authority enforcement officer is of the opinion that an offence has been committed in respect of Regulation 4, e.g. breach of consent, it can serve a notice detailing infringements, and time within which remedial action should be taken.

It is proposed to amend the Regulations (consultation document from MAFF's Pesticides Safety Directorate, July 2000) to widen public access to pesticides data. Additional information to be made available will include:

- information on experimental, provisional and full approvals;
- information on individual products or groups of products as well as active ingredients;
- information on reviewed, amended and revoked approvals;
- information on applications for approval and on those which have been refused;
- information about parallel products imported by growers for their own use.

As at present no copying of data will be allowed, but notetaking will be allowed; those seeking access will be required to sign an undertaking that they will not make commercial use of the data or publish any of it without written consent of Ministers. There will be no access to personal data or that deemed commercially confidential. The PSD will aim to respond to "simple" requests within 15 working days and to more complex requests involving searches or collation of material in 40 working days.

The Regulations are also be amended to include a power for local authorities to seize and dispose of pesticides in the event of a breach of statutory requirements.

5.30.4 Control of Substances Hazardous to Health Regulations 1999 (SI 437)

These Regulations came into force on 25 March 1999, replacing and consolidating 1994 Regulations (SI 3246) (which replaced the original 1988 Regulations). They apply in England, Scotland and Wales and cover a wide range of substances, including agricultural and non-agricultural pesticides; their purpose is to prevent exposure to all toxic or hazardous substances used in the work place which can harm health. A summary of requirements under COSHH is given in chapter 2, 2.16.2. The Regulations are enforced by the Health and Safety Executive.

Suspected cases of poisoning or death from exposure to pesticides in the course of work should be reported to the HSE and to the Pesticides Incidents Appraisal Panel (PIAP). Incidents within the home or outside should be reported to the local environmental health department and to the PIAP.

5.30.5 Codes of Practice

(a) Code of Practice for Suppliers of Pesticides to Agriculture, Horticulture & Forestry 1998

This Code, published by MAFF, covers construction of storage facilities, transportation of pesticides and disposal.

Anyone involved in supplying or selling pesticides, or who stores more than 200 kg or litres of pesticides must hold a certificate of competence from the British Agrochemical Standards Inspection Scheme. Before storing pesticides, the relevant water authority, water undertakers, environmental health departments and emergency services must be consulted over safety and pollution control requirements.

While failure to observe both this Code and the one following is not in itself an offence, breach of them may be taken as evidence in any proceedings for breach of the Regulations.

(b) Code of Practice for the Safe Use of Pesticides on Farms & Holdings 1998

This Code, published by MAFF, deals with responsibilities under both the *Control of Pesticide Regulations 1986* and the *Control of Substances Hazardous to Health Regulations 1999* (see chapter 2). The main areas of the Code of relevance to pollution control are the prevention of spraydrift and the disposal of waste pesticides and containers. Other areas covered by the Code include user training and certification, application methods, protection of wildlife and protection of local residents and walkers, and record keeping. A similar Code (1992) applies in Northern Ireland.

Prevention of Spraydrift

Aerial application of pesticides requires an Aerial Application Certificate under the *Air Navigation Order 1985* and approval of the pesticide specifically for aerial application under the *Control of Pesticides Regulations* (see above, 5.30.3). Additional conditions to be complied with are set out in Schedule 4 to the 1997 COP Amendment Regulations and will be reiterated in the Code of Practice.

Among the organisations and individuals to be notified in writing in advance if spraying is to take place within a specified distance or adjacent to their land or buildings are:

- local, marine or national nature reserves and Sites of Special Scientific Interest (not less than 72 hours' notice);

- if spraying is adjacent to or within 250 metres of water, the appropriate area office of the Environment Agency or SEPA (not less than 72 hours' notice); specific consent must be obtained if it is intended to spray aquatic weeds or weeds on the banks of watercourses or lakes;

- local chief environmental health officer, farmers, growers, landowners, residents, hospitals and schools (24 - 48 hours' notice); local beekeepers spray warning scheme (not less than 48 hours' notice).

Details to be included on the notification include name, address and telephone number of person carrying out spraying; pesticide to be used; time and date of spraying; confirmation that similar information has been sent to the chief environmental health officer. Records of aerial spraying (including details of the pesticide used, aircraft, name and address of pilot, flight times, unusual occurrences which affected the application) must be retained for not less than three years. The conditions of the Consent also specify that aircraft be at least 200 feet above and 60 metres horizontally (30 metres with written consent of the occupier) from any occupied building and its curtilage, children's playgrounds, sportsgrounds and buildings with livestock; the aircraft should also be no less than 250 feet from ground level when over a motorway, or no less than 100 feet from other public highways. Other requirements relate to wind velocity, ground markers and warning signs for pedestrians and motorists.

Land-based spraying is also subject to controls, with farmers required to allow a gap of six metres from a river bank or watercourse if spraying with organophospates or synthetic pyrethroid insecticides to prevent water pollution; a 1997 leaflet from MAFF, *Is your sprayer fit for work*, provides advice on preparing, calibrating and maintaining spraying equipment to prevent damage to wildlife. The gap to be left if spraying other pesticides will depend on the outcome of a "Local Environmental Risk Assessment for Pesticides" (LERAP); this takes into account the size of the watercourse, the type of sprayer being used and the need to reduce the pesticide dosage near the watercourse. A 1999 leaflet from MAFF explains these arrangements; in some cases there is a legal obligation to carry out and record the results of a LERAP.

Disposal of Waste Pesticides and Containers

In this respect, both the *Water Resources Act 1991* and Part I of the *Control of Pollution Act 1974* (re-enacted in Part II of the *Environmental Protection Act 1990*) are also applicable.

Under s.85 of the *Water Resources Act*, it is an offence to abandon or dispose of poisonous, noxious or polluting waste on any land (including agriculture premises) where it is likely to pose an environmental hazard; it is also an offence to cause or knowingly permit any poisonous, noxious or polluting matter to enter controlled waters, and in any case this requires a Consent to Discharge from the Environment Agency (see 5.15.3a above). Discharge of pesticide waste to sewers requires a trade effluent consent.

The Code of Practice says that on the whole, empty containers should not be re-used, but should be thoroughly cleaned, and then punctured or crushed; such containers can then usually be disposed of at licensed disposal sites.

In certain cases, pesticide containers may be buried on site with special attention being paid to ensuring no risk of pollution to surface or groundwater; the burial site should also be clearly marked for future identification.

Where it is proposed to burn pesticide containers, care must be taken to adhere to relevant clean air legislation and the Code gives guidance on minimising smoke and nuisance from any burning.

(c) Code on the Safe Use of Pesticides for Non-Agricultural Purposes

This Code drawn up by the Health and Safety Executive was published in 1991 and provides advice on compliance with the COSHH Regulations (see chapter 2, 2.16.2). It is aimed at all those involved in the use of non-agricultural pesticides, including those engaged in amenity horticulture, wood preservation, the application of anti-fouling paints, public hygiene pest control and commercial forestry. Topics covered include undertaking a COSHH assessment, prevention or control of exposure, use of control measures, health surveillance and information, and instruction and training for operators.

Appendices

Bibliography

Index

APPENDIX 1.1

ENVIRONMENTAL PROTECTION (PRESCRIBED PROCESSES AND SUBSTANCES) REGULATIONS 1991 (as amended)

Schedule 1 to the 1991 Regulations (as amended, 1992, 1993, 1994 and 1995) details the processes subject to integrated pollution control (Part A processes), and those subject to air pollution control (Part B processes). The Regulations and Schedule will be revoked following full implementation of Integrated Pollution Prevention and Control.

Process Guidance Notes for Part A and Part B processes are listed in Appendices 1.3 and 2.1, respectively.

PRESCRIBED PROCESSES

CHAPTER 1: FUEL PRODUCTION PROCESSES, COMBUSTION PROCESSES (INCLUDING POWER GENERATION)

1.1 Gasification and Associated Processes

PART A

(a) Reforming natural gas.

(aa) Refining natural gas if that process is related to another Part A process or is likely to involve the use in any 12 month period of 1000 tonnes or more of natural gas.

(b) Odorising natural gas or liquified petroleum gas if that process is related to another Part A process.

(c) Producing gas from coal, lignite, oil or other carbonaceous material or from mixtures thereof other than from sewage or the biological degradation of waste, unless carried on as part of a process which is a combustion process (whether or not that process falls within section 1.3 of this schedule).

(d) Purifying or refining any product of any of the processes described in paragraphs (a), (b) or (c) or converting it into a different product.

In this section "carbonaceous material" includes such materials as charcoal, coke, peat and rubber.

PART B

(a) Odorising natural gas or liquified petroleum gas, except where that process is related to a Part A process.

(b) Blending odorant for use with natural gas or liquified petroleum gas.

(c) Any process for refining natural gas not falling within paragraph (aa) of Part A of this Section.

In paragraph (c) of Part B of this section "refining natural gas" does not include refining mains gas.

1.2 Carbonisation and Associated Processes

PART A

(a) The pyrolysis, carbonisation, distillation, liquefaction, partial oxidation or other heat treatment of coal (other than the drying of coal), lignite, oil, other carbonaceous material (as defined in section 1.1) or mixtures thereof otherwise than with a view to gasification or making of charcoal.

(b) The purification or refining of any of the products of a process mentioned in paragraph (a) or its conversion into a different product.

Nothing in paragraph (a) or (b) refers to the use of any substance as a fuel or its incineration as a waste or to any process for the treatment of sewage.

In paragraph (a), the heat treatment of oil does not include heat treatment of waste oil or waste emulsions containing oil in order to recover oil.

PART B

No Processes.

1.3 Combustion Processes

PART A

(a) Burning any fuel in a combustion appliance with a net rated thermal input of 50 megawatts or more;

(b) [omitted - 1995 amendment Regulations]

(c) Burning any of the following in an appliance with a net rated thermal input of 3 megawatts or more otherwise than as a process which is related to a Part B process -
   (i)   waste oil;
   (ii) recovered oil;
   (iii) any fuel manufactured from, or comprising, any other waste.

For the purposes of paragraph (a) above, where

(i) two or more boilers or furnaces with an aggregate net rated thermal input of 50 megawatts or more (disregarding any boiler or furnace with a net rated thermal input of less than 3 megawatts); or

(ii) two or more gas turbines or compression ignition engines with an aggregate net rated thermal input of 50 megawatts or more (disregarding any such turbine or engine with a net rated thermal input of less than 3 megawatts),

are operated by the same person at the same location those boilers or furnaces or, as the case may be, those turbines or engines, shall be treated as a single combustion appliance with a net rated thermal input of 50 megawatts or more.

Nothing in this part of this section applies to the burning of any fuel in a boiler, furnace or other appliance with a net rated thermal input of less than 3 megawatts.

PART B

The following processes unless carried on in relation to and as part of any Part A process -

(a) Burning any fuel in a boiler or furnace with a net rated thermal input of not less than 20 megawatts (but less than 50 megawatts);

(b) Burning any fuel in a gas turbine or compression ignition engine with a net rated thermal input of not less than 20 megawatts (but less than 50 megawatts);

(c) Burning as fuel in an appliance with a net rated thermal input of less than 3 megawatts waste oil or recovered oil;

(d) Burning, in an appliance with a net rated thermal input of less than 3 megawatts solid fuel which has been manufactured from waste by a process involving the application of heat;

(e) Burning, in any appliance, fuel manufactured from, or including, waste (other than waste oil or recovered oil or such fuel as is mentioned in paragraph (d)) if the appliance has a net rated thermal input of less than 3 megawatts but at least 0.4 megawatts or is used together with (whether or not it is operated simultaneously with) other appliances which each have a net rated thermal input of less than 3 megawatts and the aggregate net rated thermal input of all the appliances is at least 0.4 megawatts.

In paragraph (c) of Part A and paragraph (e) of Part B, "fuel" does not include gas produced by biological degradation of waste; for the purpose of this section -

"net rated thermal input" is the rate at which fuel can be burned at the maximum continuous rating of the appliance multiplied by the net calorific value of the fuel and expressed as megawatts thermal; and

"waste oil" means any mineral based lubricating or industrial oil which has become unfit for the use for which it was intended and, in particular, used combustion engine oil, gearbox oil, mineral lubricating oil, oil for turbines and hydraulic oil; and

"recovered oil" means waste oil which has been processed before being used.

1.4 Petroleum Processes

PART A

(a) The loading, unloading or other handling of, the storage of or the physical, chemical or thermal treatment of -

(i)   crude oil;
(ii) stabilised crude petroleum;
(iii) crude shale oil;
(iv) if related to another process described in this paragraph, any associated gas or condensate.

(b) [omitted - 1994 amendment Regulations.]

(c) Any process not falling within any other description in this Schedule by which the product of any process described in paragraph (a) above is subject to further refining or conversion or is used (otherwise than as a fuel or solvent) in the manufacture of a chemical.

PART B

The following processes unless falling within a description in Part A of this Section -

(a) the storage of petrol in stationary storage tanks at a terminal, or the loading or unloading of petrol into or from road tankers, rail tankers or inland waterway vessels at a terminal;

(b) the unloading of petrol into stationary storage tanks at a service station, other than an exempt service station, if the total quantity of petrol unloaded into such tanks at the service station in any 12 month period is likely to be equal to or greater than 100 m³.

Paragraph 2(1) of Schedule 2 shall not apply to a process described in paragraph (b) of this Section.

In this part of this section:

"inland waterway vessel" means a vessel, other than a sea-going vessel, having a total dead weight of 15 tonnes or more;

"petrol" means any petroleum derivative, with or without additives, having a reid vapour pressure of 27.6 kilopascals or more which is intended for use as a fuel for motor vehicles, other than liquefied petroleum gas;

"service station" means any premises where petrol is dispensed to motor vehicle fuel tanks from stationary storage tanks;

"exempt service station" means a service station:

(a) which was not in operation, and for the construction of which planning permission was not granted, before 31 December 1995;

(b) at which the total quantity of petrol unloaded into stationary storage tanks does not exceed 500 m³ in any twelve month period; and

(c) which

   i   is situated in one of the following local government areas established by section 1 of the Local Government etc (Scotland) Act 1994:

      - Argyll and Bute;
      - Moray;
      - Orkney Islands;
      - Shetland Islands;
      - Western Isles; or

   ii is situated in the local government area of Aberdeenshire established by that section and outside the Aberdeen area the boundary of which is shown as "the derogated boundary: Aberdeen area" on the maps contained in the volume of maps entitled "Volume of maps indicating the extent of derogated areas for new small petrol stations under the *Environmental Protection (Prescribed Processes and Substances Etc) (Amendment) (Petrol Vapour Recovery) Regulations 1996*" ("the maps"); or

iii is situated in the local government area of Highland established by that section and outside the Inverness area the boundary of which is shown on the maps as "the derogated boundary: Inverness area"; or

iv is situated in the local government area of Angus, Perth and Kinross or Stirling established by that section and to the north of the line shown on the maps as "the derogated boundary: Central Scotland";

"terminal" means any premises which are used for the storage and loading of petrol into road tankers, rail tankers or inland waterway vessels;

and other expressions which are also used in European Parliament and Council Directive 94/63/EC on the control of VOC emissions resulting from the storage of petrol and its distribution from terminals to service stations have the same meaning as in that Directive.

CHAPTER 2: METAL PRODUCTION AND PROCESSING

2.1 Iron and Steel

PART A

(a) Loading, unloading or otherwise handling or storing iron ore except in the course of mining operations;

(b) Loading, unloading or otherwise handling or storing burnt pyrites;

(c) Crushing, grading, grinding, screening, washing or drying iron ore or any mixture of iron ore and other materials;

(d) Blending or mechanically mixing grades of iron ore or iron ore with other materials;

(e) Pelletising, calcining, roasting or sintering iron ore or any mixture of iron ore and other materials;

(f) Making, melting or refining iron, steel or any ferrous-alloy in any furnace other than a furnace described in Part B of this Section;

(g) Any process for the refining or making of iron, steel or any ferrous-alloy in which air or oxygen or both are used unless related to a process described in Part B of this Section;

(h) The desulphurisation of iron, steel or any ferrous-alloy made by a process described in this Part of this Section;

(i) Heating iron, steel or any ferrous-alloy (whether in a furnace or other appliance) to remove grease, oil or any other non-metallic contaminant (including such operations as the removal by heat of plastic or rubber covering from scrap cable), if related to another process described in this Part of this Section;

(j) Any foundry process (including ancillary foundry operations such as the manufacture and recovery of moulds, the reclamation of sand, fettling, grinding and shot-blasting) if related to another process described in this Part of this Section;

(k) [omitted - 1994 amendment Regulations.]

(l) Handling slag in conjunction with a process described in paragraph (f) or (g).

(m) Any process for rolling iron, steel or any ferrous alloy carried on in relation to any process described in paragraph (f) or (g), and any process carried on in conjunction with such rolling involving the scarfing or cutting with oxygen of iron, steel or any ferrous alloy.

Nothing in paragraph (a) or (b) of this Part of this Section applies to the handling or storing of other minerals in association with the handling or storing of iron ore or burnt pyrites.

A process does not fall within paragraph (a), (b), (c) or (d) of this Part of this Section unless -

(i) it is carried on as part of or is related to a process falling within a paragraph of this Part of this Section other than paragraph (a), (b), (c) or (d); or

(ii) it consists of, forms part of or is related to a process which is likely to involve the unloading in any 12 month period of more than 500,000 tonnes of iron ore or burnt pyrites or, in aggregate, both.

PART B

(a) Making or refining iron, steel or any ferrous-alloy in -

(i) an electric arc furnace with a designed holding capacity of less than 7 tonnes; or

(ii) a cupola, crucible furnace, reverberatory furnace, rotary furnace, induction furnace or resistance furnace;

(b) Any process for the refining or making of iron, steel or any ferrous alloy in which air or oxygen or both are used, if related to a process described in this Part of this Section;

(c) The desulphurisation of iron, steel or any ferrous-alloy, if the process does not fall within paragraph (h) of Part A of this Section;

(d) Any such process as is described in paragraph (i) of Part A above, if not falling within that paragraph but a process does not fall within this paragraph if -

(i) it is a process for heating iron, steel or any ferrous-alloy in one or more furnaces or other appliances the primary combustion chambers of which have in aggregate a net rated thermal input of less than 0.2 megawatts;

(ii) it does not involve the removal by heat of plastic or rubber covering from scrap cable or of any asbestos contaminant; and

(iii) it is not related to any other process described in this Part of this Section.

(e) Any foundry process (including ancillary foundry operations such as the manufacture and recovery of moulds, the reclamation of sand, fettling, grinding and shot-blasting) if related to another process described in this Part of this Section;

(f) Any other process involving the casting of iron, steel or any ferrous alloy from deliveries of 50 tonnes or more at one time of molten metal.

Any description of a process in this Section includes, where the process produces slag, the crushing, screening or grading or other treatment of the slag if that process is related to the process in question.

In this Section "net rated thermal input" has the same meaning as in Section 1.3.

In this Section and Section 2.2; "ferrous alloy" means an alloy of which iron is the largest constituent, or equal to the largest constituent, by weight, whether or not that alloy also has a non-ferrous metal content greater than any percentage specified in Section 2.2 below, and "non-ferrous metal alloy" shall be construed accordingly.

2.2 Non-ferrous Metals

PART A

(a) The extraction or recovery from any material -

(i) by chemical means or the use of heat of any non-ferrous metal or alloy of non-ferrous metal or any compound of a non-ferrous metal: and

(ii) by electrolytic means, of aluminium,

if the process may result in the release into the air of particulate matter or any metal, metalloid or any metal or metalloid compound or in the release into water of a substance described in Schedule 5 [see Appendix 1.2] and does not fall within a description set out within paragraph (b) of Part B of this Section.

In this paragraph "material" includes ores, scrap and other waste.

(b) The mining of zinc or tin where the process may result in the release into water of cadmium or any compound of cadmium.

(c) The refining of any non-ferrous metal (other than the electrolytic refining of copper) or non-ferrous metal alloy except where the process is related to a process falling within a description in paragraphs (a), (c) or (d) of Part B of this Section.

(d) Any process other than a process described in paragraphs (b), (c) or (d) of Part B of this Section for making or melting any non-ferrous metal or non-ferrous metal alloy in a furnace, bath or other holding vessel if the furnace, bath or vessel employed has a designed holding capacity of 5 tonnes or more.

(e) Any process for producing, melting or recovering by chemical means or by the use of heat lead or any lead alloy, if -

(i) the process may result in the release into the air of particulate matter or smoke which contains lead; and

(ii) in the case of lead alloy, the percentage by weight of lead in the alloy in molten form exceeds 23% if the alloy contains copper and 2% in other cases.

(ee) Any process for recovering any of the elements listed below if the process may result in the release into the air of particulate matter or smoke which contains any of those elements -

gallium   indium
palladium   tellurium
thallium.

(f) Any process for producing, melting or recovering (whether by chemical means or by electrolysis or by the use of heat), cadmium or mercury or any alloy containing more than 0.05% by weight of either of those metals or of both of those metals in aggregate.

(g) Any manufacturing or repairing process involving the manufacture or use of beryllium or selenium or any alloy of one or both of those metals if the process may occasion the release into the air of any substance described in Schedule 4 [see Appendix 1.2]; but a process does not fall within this paragraph by reason solely of its involving the melting of any alloy or beryllium if that alloy contains less than 0.1% by weight of beryllium in molten form and the process falls within a description in paragraph (a) or (d) of Part B of this Section.

(h) The heating in a furnace or other appliance of any non-ferrous metal or non-ferrous metal alloy for the purpose of removing grease, oil or any other non-metallic contaminant (including such operations as the removal by heat of plastic or rubber covering from scrap cable) if related to another process described in this Part of this Section.

(i) Any foundry process (including ancillary foundry operations such as the manufacture and recovery of moulds, the reclamation of sand, fettling, grinding and shot-blasting) if related to another process described in this Part of this Section.

(j) [omitted - 1994 amendment Regulations.]

(k) Pelletising, calcining, roasting or sintering any non-ferrous metal ore or any mixture of such ore and other materials.

PART B

(a) The making or melting of any non-ferrous metal or non-ferrous metal alloy (other than tin or any alloy which, in molten form, contains 50% or more by weight of tin in any furnace, bath or other holding vessel with a designed holding capacity of less than 5 tonnes (together with any incidental refining).

(b) The separation of copper, aluminium, magnesium or zinc from mixed scrap by differential melting.

(bb)The fusion of calcined bauxite for the production of artificial corundum.

(c) Melting zinc or a zinc alloy in conjunction with a galvanising process.

(d) Melting zinc, aluminium or magnesium or an alloy of one or more of these metals in conjunction with a die-casting process.

(e) Any such process as is described in paragraph (h) of Part A above, if not related to another process described in that Part; but a process does not fall within this paragraph if -

   (i) it involves the use of one or more furnaces or other appliances the primary combustion chambers of which have in aggregate a net rated thermal input of less than 0.2 megawatts; and

   (ii) it does not involve the removal by heat of plastic or rubber covering from scrap cable or of any asbestos contaminant.

(f) Any foundry process (including ancillary foundry operations such as the manufacture and recovery of moulds, the reclamation of sand, fettling, grinding and shot-blasting) if related to another process described in this Part of this Section.

(g) [omitted - 1995 amendment Regulations]

The processes described in paragraph (a), (c) and (d) above include any related process for the refining of any non-ferrous metal or non-ferrous metal alloy.

Nothing in this section shall be taken to prescribe the processes of hand soldering or flow soldering.

In this section "net rated thermal input" has the same meaning as in Section 1.3.

2.3 Smelting Processes

[omitted - 1994 amendment Regulations.]

CHAPTER 3: MINERAL INDUSTRIES

3.1 Cement & Lime Manufacture and Associated Processes

PART A

(a) Making cement clinker.

(b) Grinding cement clinker.

(c) Any of the following processes, where the process is related to a process described in paragraph (a) or (b), namely blending cement; putting cement into silos for bulk storage; removing cement from silos in which it has been stored in bulk; and any process involving the use of cement in bulk, including the bagging of cement and cement mixtures, the batching of ready-mixed concrete and the manufacture of concrete blocks and other cement products.

(d) The heating of calcium carbonate or calcium magnesium carbonate for the purpose of making lime where the process is likely to involve the heating in any 12 month period of 5,000 tonnes or more of either substance or, in aggregate, of both.

(e) The slaking of lime for the purpose of making calcium hydroxide or calcium magnesium hydroxide where the process is related to a process described in paragraph (d) above.

PART B

(a) Any of the following processes, if not related to a process falling within a description in Part A of this Section -

   (i) storing, loading or unloading cement or cement clinker in bulk prior to further transportation in bulk;

   (ii) blending cement in bulk or using cement in bulk other than at a construction site, including the bagging of cement and cement mixtures, the batching of ready-mixed concrete and the manufacture of concrete blocks and other cement products.

(b) The slaking of lime for the purpose of making calcium hydroxide or calcium magnesium hydroxide unless related to and carried on as part of a process falling within another description in this Schedule.

(c) The heating of calcium carbonate or calcium magnesium carbonate for the purpose of making lime where the process is not likely to involve the heating in any 12 month period of 5,000 tonnes or more of either substance or, in aggregate, of both.

3.2 Processes involving Asbestos

PART A

(a) Producing raw asbestos by extraction from the ore except where the process is directly associated with the mining of the ore.

(b) The manufacture and, where related to the manufacture, the industrial finishing of the following products where raw asbestos is involved -

asbestos cement
asbestos cement products
asbestos fillers
asbestos filters
asbestos floor coverings
asbestos friction products

asbestos insulating board
asbestos jointing, packaging and reinforcement material
asbestos packing
asbestos paper or card
asbestos textiles

(c) The stripping of asbestos from railway vehicles except -

(i) in the course of the repair or maintenance of the vehicle;

(ii) in the course of recovery operations following an accident; or

(iii) where the asbestos is permanently bonded in cement or in any other material (including plastic, rubber or a resin).

(d) The destruction by burning of a railway vehicle if asbestos has been incorporated in, or sprayed on to, its structure.

PART B

The industrial finishing of any product mentioned in paragraph (b) of Part A of this Section if the process does not fall within that paragraph.

In this section, "asbestos" means any of the following fibrous silicates -

actinolite, amosite, anthophyllite, chrysotile, crocidolite and tremolite

3.3 Other Mineral Fibres

PART A

Manufacturing

(i) glass fibre;
(ii) any fibre from any mineral other than asbestos.

PART B

No Processes.

3.4 Other Mineral Processes

PART A

No Processes.

PART B

(a) The crushing, grinding or other size reduction (other than the cutting of stone) or the grading, screening or heating of any designated mineral or mineral product except where -

(i) the process falls within a description in another Section of this Schedule;

(ii) the process is related to and carried on as part of another process falling within such a description; or

(iii) the operation of the process is unlikely to result in the release into the air of particulate matter.

(b) Any of the following processes unless carried on at an exempt location or as part of a process falling within another description in this Schedule -

(i) crushing, grinding or otherwise breaking up coal or coke or any other coal product;

(ii) screening, grading or mixing coal, or coke or any other coal product;

(iii) loading or unloading petroleum coke, coal, coke or any other coal product except unloading on retail sale.

(c) The crushing, grinding or other size reduction with machinery designed for that purpose of bricks, tiles or concrete.

(d) Screening the product of any such process as is described in paragraph (c).

(e) Coating roadstone with tar or bitumen.

(f) Loading, unloading, or storing pulverised fuel ash in bulk prior to further transportation in bulk, unless carried on as part of or in relation to a process falling within another description in this Schedule.

In this section -

"coal" includes lignite;

"designated mineral or mineral product" means -

(i) clay, sand and any other naturally occurring mineral other than coal or lignite;

(ii) metallurgical slag;

(iii) boiler or furnace ash produced from the burning of coal, lignite, coke or any other coal product;

(iv) gypsum which is a by-product of any process; and

"exempt location" means -

(i) any premises used for the sale of petroleum coke, coal, coke or any coal product where the throughput of such substances at those premises in any 12 month period is in aggregate likely to be less than 10,000 tonnes; or

(ii) any premises to which petroleum coke, coal, coke or any coal product is supplied only for use there.

"retail sale" means sale to the final consumer.

Nothing in this section applies to any process carried on underground.

3.5 Glass Manufacture and Production

PART A

The manufacture of glass frit or enamel frit and its use in any process where that process is related to its manufacture and the aggregate quantity of such substances manufactured in any 12 month period is likely to be 100 tonnes or more.

PART B

(a) The manufacture of glass at any location where the person concerned has the capacity to make 5,000 tonnes or more of glass in any 12 month period, and any process involving the use of glass which is carried on at any such location in conjunction with its manufacture.

(b) The manufacture of glass where the use of lead or any lead compound is involved.

(c) The making of any glass product where lead or any lead compound has been used in the manufacture of the glass except -

   (i) the making of products from lead glass blanks;

   (ii) the melting, or mixing with another substance, of glass manufactured elsewhere to produce articles such as ornaments or road paint;

(d) Polishing or etching glass or glass products in the course of the manufacturing process if -

   (i) hydrofluoric acid is used;

   (ii) hydrogen fluoride may be released into the air.

(e) The manufacture of glass frit or enamel frit and its use in any process where that process is related to its manufacture if not falling within Part A of this Section.

3.6 Ceramic Production

PART A

Firing heavy clay goods or refractory material in a kiln where a reducing atmosphere is used for a purpose other than coloration.

PART B

(a) Firing heavy clay goods or refractory material (other than heavy clay goods) in a kiln where the process does not fall within a description in Part A of this Section.

(b) Vapour glazing earthenware or clay with salts.

"clay" includes a blend of clay with ash, sand or other materials;

"refractory material" means material (such as fireclay, silica, magnesite, chrome-magnesite, sillimanite, sintered alumina, beryllia and boron nitride) which is able to withstand high temperatures and to function as a furnace lining or in other similar high temperature applications.

CHAPTER 4: THE CHEMICAL INDUSTRY

Except where paragraph 2 or 8 of Schedule 2 applies, nothing in this chapter of this Schedule applies to the operation of waste treatment plant.

4.1 Petrochemical Processes

Where a process in this chapter falls within descriptions in different sections, it should be taken to fall within the description in whichever relevant section is first mentioned in the sequence 4.5; 4.2; 4.1; 4.4; 4.3; 4.6; 4.7; 4.8; 4.9.

PART A

(a) Any process for the manufacture of unsaturated hydrocarbons.

(b) Any process for the manufacture of any chemical which involves the use of a product of a process described in sub-paragraph (a).

(c) Any process for the manufacture of any chemical which involves the use of a product of a process described in paragraph (b) otherwise than as a fuel or solvent.

(d) Any process for the polymerisation or co-polymerisation of any unsaturated hydrocarbons (other than the polymerisation or co-polymerisation of a pre-formulated resin or pre-formulated gel coat which contains any unsaturated hydrocarbons, or which contains any product of a process mentioned in paragraph (b) or (c) of Part A of this section) which is likely to involve, in any 12 month period, the polymerisation or co-polymerisation of 50 tonnes or more of unsaturated hydrocarbons or of any such products or, in aggregate, of any combination of those materials or, in aggregate, of any combination of those materials and products.

(e) Any process, if related to and carried on as part of a process falling within another paragraph of this Part of this Section, for the polymerisation or co-polymerisation of any pre-formulated resin or pre-formulated gel coat which contains any unsaturated hydrocarbons, or which contains any product of a process mentioned in paragraph (b) or (c) of Part A of this section, which is likely to involve, in any 12 month period, the polymerisation or co-polymerisation of 100 tonnes or more of unsaturated hydrocarbons or of any such products or, in aggregate, of any combination of those materials and products.

PART B

Any process, unless related to and carried on as part of a process falling within Part A of this section, for the polymerisation or co-polymerisation of any pre-formulated resin or pre-formulated gel coat which contains any unsaturated hydrocarbons, or which contains any product of a process mentioned in paragraph (b) or (c) of Part A of this section, which is likely to involve, in any 12 month period, the polymerisation or co-polymerisation of 100 tonnes or more of unsaturated hydrocarbons or of any such products or, in aggregate, of any combination of those materials and products.

In this section and in section 4.2 "pre-formulated resin or pre-formulated gel coat" means any resin or gel coat which has been formulated before being introduced into the polymerisation or co-polymerisation process (whether or not the resin or gel coat contains a colour pigment, activator or catalyst).

4.2. The Manufacture and Use of Organic Chemicals

PART A

Any of the following processes unless falling within a description set out in Section 6.8 -

(a) The manufacture of styrene or vinyl chloride.

(aa) The polymerisation or co-polymerisation of styrene or vinyl chloride (other than the polymerisation or co-polymerisation of a pre-formulated resin or pre-formulated gel coat which contains any styrene) where the process is likely to involve, in any 12 month period, the polymerisation or co-polymerisation of 50 tonnes or more of either of those materials or, in aggregate, of both.

(ab) Any process, if related to and carried on as part of a process falling within another paragraph of this section, for the polymerisation or co-polymerisation of any pre-formulated resin or pre-formulated gel coat which contains any styrene, which is likely to involve, in any 12 month period, the polymerisation or co-polymerisation of 100 tonnes or more of styrene;

(b) Any process of manufacture involving the use of vinyl chloride.

(c) The manufacture of acetylene, any aldehyde, amine, isocyanate, nitrile, any carboxylic acid or any anhydride or carboxylic acid, any organic sulphur compound or any phenol if the process may result in the release of any of these substances into the air.

(d) Any process for the manufacture of a chemical involving the use of any substance mentioned in paragraph (c) if the process may result in the release of any such substance into the air.

(e) The manufacture or recovery of carbon disulphide.

(f) Any manufacturing process which may result in the release of carbon disulphide into the air.

(g) The manufacture or recovery of pyridine, or of any substituted pyridines.

(h) The manufacture of any organo-metallic compound.

(i) The manufacture, purification or recovery of any designated acrylate.

(j) Any process for the manufacture of a chemical which is likely to involve the use in any 12 month period of 1 tonne or more of any designated acrylate or, in aggregate, of more than one such designated acrylate.

In this part of this Section, "designated acrylate" means any of the following, namely, acrylic acid, substituted acrylic acids, the esters of acrylic acid and the esters of substituted acrylic acids.

PART B

Any process, unless related to and carried on as part of a process falling within Part A of this section, for the polymerisation or co-polymerisation of any pre-formulated resin or pre-formulated gel coat which contains any styrene, which is likely to involve, in any 12 month period, the polymerisation or co-polymerisation of 100 tonnes or more of styrene.

4.3 Acid Processes

PART A

(a) Any process for the manufacture, recovery, concentration or distillation of sulphuric acid or oleum.

(b) Any process for the manufacture of any oxide of sulphur but excluding any combustion or incineration process other than the burning of sulphur.

(c) Any process for the manufacture of a chemical which uses, or may result in the release into the air of, any oxide of sulphur but excluding any combustion or incineration process other than the burning of sulphur and excluding also any process where such a release could only occur as a result of the storage and use of SO_2 in cylinders.

(d) Any process for the manufacture or recovery of nitric acid.

(e) Any process for the manufacture of any acid-forming oxide of nitrogen.

(f) Any other process (except the combustion or incineration of carbonaceous material as defined in section 1.1 of this Schedule) which is not described in Part B of this Section, does not fall within a description in Section 2.1 or 2.2 of this Schedule and is not treated as so falling by virtue of the rules in Schedule 2, and which is likely to result in the release to air of any acid forming oxide of nitrogen.

(g) Any process for the manufacture or purification of phosphoric acid.

PART B

Any process for the surface treatment of metal which is likely to result in the release into the air of any acid-forming oxide of nitrogen and which does not fall within a description in Section 2.1 or 2.2. of this Schedule and is not treated as so falling by virtue of the rules in Schedule 2.

4.4 Processes Involving Halogens

PART A

The following processes if not falling within a description in any other Section of this Schedule -

(a) Any process for the manufacture of fluorine, chlorine, bromine or iodine or of any compound comprising only -

(i) two or more of these halogens; or
(ii) any one or more of those halogens and oxygen.

(b) Any process of manufacture which involves the use of, or which is likely to result in the release into the air or water of, any of the four halogens or any of the compounds mentioned in paragraph (a) other than the use of any of them as a pesticide (as defined in Schedule 6 [see Appendix 1.2]).

(c) Any process for the manufacture of hydrogen fluoride, hydrogen chloride, hydrogen bromide or hydrogen iodide or any of their acids.

(d) Any process for the manufacture of chemicals which may result in the release into the air of any of the four compounds mentioned in paragraph (c);

(e) Any process of manufacture (other than the manufacture of chemicals) involving the use of any of the four compounds mentioned in paragraph (c) or any of their acids, which may result in the release of any of those compounds into the air other than the coating, plating or surface treatment of metal.

PART B

No Processes.

4.5 Inorganic Chemical Processes

PART A

(a) The manufacture of hydrogen cyanide or hydrogen sulphide other than in the course of fumigation.

(b) Any manufacturing process involving the use of hydrogen cyanide or hydrogen sulphide.

(c) Any process for the manufacture of a chemical which may result in the release into the air of hydrogen cyanide or hydrogen sulphide.

(d) The production of any compound containing any of the following -

Antimony	Arsenic	Beryllium
Gallium	Indium	Lead
Palladium	Platinum	Selenium
Tellurium	Thallium,	

where the process may result in the release into the air of any of those elements or compounds or the release into water of any substance described in Schedule 5 [see Appendix 1.2] in a quantity which, in any 12 month period, exceeds the background quantity by more than the amount specified in relation to the description of substance in column 2 of that Schedule.

(e) The recovery of any compound referred to in paragraph (d) where the process may result in any such release as is mentioned in that paragraph.

(f) The use in any process of manufacture other than the application of a glaze or vitreous enamel, of any element or compound referred to in paragraph (d) where the process may result in such a release as is mentioned in that paragraph.

(g) The production or recovery of any compound of cadmium or mercury.

(h) Any process of manufacture which involves the use of cadmium or mercury or of any compound of either of those elements or which may result in the release into the air of either of those elements or any of their compounds.

(i) The production of any compound of -

Chromium	Manganese
Nickel	Zinc.

(j) The manufacture of any metal carbonyl.

(k) Any process for the manufacture of a chemical involving the use of a metal carbonyl.

(l) The manufacture or recovery of ammonia.

(m) Any process for the manufacture of a chemical which involves the use of ammonia or may result in the release of ammonia into the air other than a process in which ammonia is used only as a refrigerant.

(n) The production of phosphorus or of any oxide, hydride or halide of phosphorus.

(o) Any process for the manufacture of a chemical which involves the use of phosphorus or any oxide, hydride or halide of phosphorus or which may result in the release into the air of phosphorus or of any such oxide, hydride or halide.

(p) The extraction of any magnesium compound from sea water.

PART B

No Processes.

4.6 Chemical Fertiliser Production

PART A

(a) The manufacture of chemical fertilisers.

(b) The conversion of chemical fertilisers into granules.

In this section "chemical fertilisers" means any inorganic chemical to be applied to the soil to promote plant growth; and "inorganic chemical" includes urea; and "manufacture of chemical fertilisers" shall be taken to include any process for blending chemical fertilisers which is related to a process for their manufacture.

PART B

No Processes.

4.7 Pesticide Production

PART A

The manufacture or the formulation of chemical pesticides if the process may result in the release into water of any substance described in Schedule 5 [see Appendix 1.2] in a quantity which, in any 12 month period, exceeds the background quantity by more than the amount specified in relation to the description of substance in column 2 of that Schedule.

PART B

No Processes.

In this section "pesticide" has the same meaning as in Schedule 6 [see Appendix 1.2].

4.8 Pharmaceutical Production

PART A

The manufacture or the formulation of a medicinal product if the process may result in the release into water of any substance described in Schedule 5 [see Appendix

1.2] in a quantity which, in any 12 month period, exceeds the background quantity by more than the amount specified in relation to the description of substance in column 2 of that Schedule.

PART B

No Processes.

In this section, "medicinal product" means any substance or article (not being an instrument, apparatus or appliance) manufactured for use in one of the ways specified in section 130(1) of the *Medicines Act 1968*.

4.9 The Storage of Chemicals in Bulk

PART A

No Processes - reclassified as Part B - 1994 Amendment Regulations.

PART B

The storage in a tank or tanks, other than as part of a Part A process, and other than in a tank for the time being forming part of a powered vehicle, of any of the substances listed below except where the total capacity of the tanks installed at the location in question in which the relevant substance may be stored is less than the figure specified below in relation to that substance:

any one or more designated acrylates	20 tonnes
acrylonitrile	20 tonnes
anhydrous ammonia	100 tonnes
anhydrous hydrogen fluoride	1 tonne
toluene di-isocyanate	20 tonnes
vinyl chloride monomer	20 tonnes
ethylene	8,000 tonnes

In this Section, "designated acrylate" has the same meaning as in Part A of Section 4.2.

CHAPTER 5: WASTE DISPOSAL AND RECYCLING

5.1 Incineration

PART A

(a) The destruction by burning in an incinerator of any waste chemicals or waste plastic arising from the manufacture of a chemical or the manufacture of a plastic.

(b) The destruction by burning in an incinerator, other than incidentally in the course of burning other waste, of any waste chemicals being, or comprising in elemental or compound form any of the following -

bromine	cadmium
chlorine	fluorine
iodine	lead
mercury	nitrogen
phosphorus	sulphur
zinc.	

(bb) The incineration of hazardous waste in an incineration

plant, other than in an exempt hazardous incineration plant.

(c) The destruction by burning of any other waste, including animal remains, otherwise than by a process related to and carried on as part of a Part B process, on premises where there is plant designed to incinerate such waste at a rate of 1 tonne or more per hour.

(d) The cleaning for reuse of metal containers used for the transport or storage of a chemical by burning out their residual content.

PART B

(a) The destruction by burning in an incinerator other than an exempt incinerator of any waste, including animal remains, except where related to a Part A process.

(b) The cremation of human remains.

In this section -

"exempt hazardous waste incineration plant" means:

(i) an incineration plant for animal carcases or remains;

(ii) an incineration plant for infectious clinical waste, provided that such waste is not rendered hazardous as a result of the presence of constituents listed in Annex II to Directive 91/689/EEC on hazardous waste other than constituents C35 in that list (infectious substances); or

(iii) a municipal waste incineration plant also burning infectious clinical waste which is not mixed with other wastes which are rendered hazardous as a result of one of the properties listed in Annex III to Directive 91/689/EEC other than property H9 in that list (infectious);

"exempt incinerator" means any incinerator on premises where there is plant designed to incinerate waste, including animal remains, at a rate of not more than 50 kgs per hour, not being an incinerator employed to incinerate clinical waste, sewage sludge, sewage screenings or municipal waste (as defined in Article 1 of EC Directive 89/369/EEC); and for the purposes of this section, the weight of waste shall be determined by reference to its weight as fed into the incinerator;

"hazardous waste" means any solid or liquid waste as defined in Article 1(4) of Directive 91/689/EEC but shall not include the following waste:

(i) combustible liquid wastes, including waste oils as defined in Article 1 of Directive 75/439/EEC on the disposal of waste oils, provided that they meet the following three criteria:

(a) the mass content of polychlorinated aromatic hydrocarbons, e.g. polychlorinated biphenyls or pentachlorinated phenol, amounts to concentrations not higher than those set out in the relevant Community legislation;

(b) these wastes are not rendered hazardous by virtue

of containing other constituents listed in Annex II to Directive 91/689/EEC in quantities or concentrations which are inconsistent with the achievement of the objectives set out in Article 4 of Directive 75/442/EEC on waste; and

(c) the net calorific value amounts to at least 30 MJ per kilogramme;

(ii) any combustible liquid wastes which cannot cause, in the flue gas directly resulting from their combustion, emissions other than those from gas oil, as defined in Article 1(1) of Directive 75/716/EEC relating to the sulphur content of liquid fuels or a higher concentration of emissions than those resulting from the combustion of gas oil as so defined;

(iii) hazardous waste resulting from the exploration for and the exploitation of oil and gas resources from off-shore installations and incinerated on board;

(iv) municipal waste covered by Directives 89/369/EEC and 89/429/EEC relating to air pollution from, respectively, new and existing municipal waste incineration plants;

(v) sewage sludges from the treatment of municipal waste waters which are not rendered hazardous by virtue of containing constituents listed in Annex II to Directive 91/689/EEC in quantities or in concentrations which are inconsistent with the achievement of the objectives set out in Article 4 of Directive 75/442/EEC on waste.

"incineration of hazardous waste in an incineration plant" means the incineration by oxidation of hazardous wastes, with or without recovery of the combustion heat generated, including pretreatment as well as pyrolysis or other thermal treatment processes, for example, plasma process, insofar as their products are subsequently incinerated, and includes the incineration of such wastes as a regular or additional fuel for any industrial process;

"waste" means solid, liquid wastes or gaseous wastes (other than gas produced by biological degradation of waste); and

"clinical waste" in the definition of exempt incinerator means waste (other than waste consisting wholly of animal remains) which falls within sub-paragraph (a) or (b) of the definition of such waste in paragraph (2) of regulation 1 of the *Controlled Waste Regulations 1992* (or would fall within one of those sub-paragraphs but for paragraph (4) of the regulation).

5.2 Recovery Processes

PART A

(a) The recovery by distillation of any oil or organic solvent.

(b) The cleaning or regeneration of carbon, charcoal or ion exchange resins by removing matter which is, or includes, any substance described in Schedule 4, 5 or 6.

Nothing in this part of this Section applies to -

(i) The distillation of oil for the productionn or cleaning of vaccum pump oil; or

(ii) A process which is ancillary and related to another process which involves the production or use of the substance which is recovered, cleaned or regenerated.

PART B

No Processes.

5.3 The Production of Fuel from Waste

PART A

Making fuel from waste by any process involving the use of heat other than making charcoal.

PART B

No Processes.

CHAPTER 6: OTHER INDUSTRIES

6.1 Paper and Pulp Manufacturing Processes

PART A

(a) The making of paper pulp by a chemical method if the person concerned has the capacity at the location in question to produce more than 25,000 tonnes of paper pulp in any 12 month period.

(b) Any process associated with making paper pulp or paper (including processes connected with the recycling of paper such as de-inking) if the process may result in the release into water of any substance described in Schedule 5 [see Appendix 1.2] in a quantity which, in any 12 month period, exceeds the background quantity by more than the amount specified in relation to the description of substance in column 2 of that Schedule.

In this paragraph "paper pulp" includes pulp made from wood, grass, straw and similar materials and references to the making of paper are to the making of any product using paper pulp.

PART B

No Processes.

6.2 Di-Isocyanate Processes

PART A

(a) Any process for the manufacture of any di-isocyanate or a partly polymerised di-isocyanate.

(b) Any manufacturing process involving the use of toluene di-isocyanate or partly polymerised toluene di-isocyanate if -

(i) 1 tonne or more of toluene di-isocyanate monomer is likely to be used in any 12 month period; and

(ii) The process may result in a release into the air which contains toluene di-isocyanate.

(c) [omitted - 1994 amendment Regulations]

(d) The flame bonding of polyurethane foams or polyurethane elastomers, and the hot wire cutting of such substances where such cutting is related to any other Part A process.

PART B

(a) Any process not falling within any other description in this Schedule where the carrying on of the process by the person concerned at the location in question is likely to involve the use in any 12 month period of 5 tonnes or more of any di-isocyanate or of any partly polymerised di-isocyanate or, in aggregate, of both.

(b) Any process not falling within any other description in this Schedule involving the use of toluene di-isocyanate or partly polymerised toluene di-isocyanate if -

(i) less than 1 tonne of toluene di-isocyanate monomer is likely to be used in any 12 month period; and

(ii) The process may result in a release into the air which contains toluene di-isocyanate.

(c) The hot wire cutting of polyurethane foams or polyurethane elastomers, except where this process is related to any other Part A process.

6.3 Tar and Bitumen Processes

PART A

Any process not falling within any other description in this Schedule involving -

(a) The distillation of tar or bitumen in connection with any process of manufacture; or

(b) The heating of tar or bitumen for the manufacture of electrodes or carbon-based refractory materials,

where the carrying on of the process by the person concerned at the location in question is likely to involve the use in any 12 month period of 5 tonnes or more of bitumen or, in aggregate, of both.

PART B

Any process not falling within Part A of this Section or within any other description in this Schedule involving -

(a) The heating, but not the distillation, of tar or bitumen in connection with any process of manufacture; or

(b) (unless the process is related to and carried on as part of a process falling within Part A of Section 1.4 of this Schedule) the oxidation of bitumen by blowing air through it,

where the carrying on of the process by the person concerned at the location in question is likely to involve the use in any 12 month period of 5 tonnes or more of tar or of bitumen or, in aggregate, of both.

In this Section the expressions "tar" and "bitumen" include pitch.

6.4 Processes Involving Uranium

[omitted - 1994 amendment Regulations.]

6.5 Coating Processes and Printing

PART A

(a) The application or removal of a coating material containing one or more tributyltin compounds or triphenyltin compounds, if carried out at a shipyard or boatyard at which vessels of a length of 25 metres or more can be built, or maintained or repaired.

(b) The treatment of textiles if the process may result in the release into water of any substance described in Schedule 5 [see Appendix 1.2] in a quantity which, in any 12 month period, exceeds the background quantity by more than the amount specified in relation to the description of substance in column 2 of that Schedule.

(c) [omitted - 1994 amendment Regulations.]

PART B

(a) Any process (other than for the repainting or respraying of or of parts of aircraft or road or railway vehicles) for the application to a substrate of, or the drying or curing after such application of, printing ink or paint or any other coating material as, or in the course of, a manufacturing process where -

(i) the process may result in the release into the air of particulate matter or of any volatile organic compound; and

(ii) the carrying on of the process by the person concerned at the location in question is likely to involve the use in any 12 month period of -

(aa) 20 tonnes or more applied in solid form of any printing ink, paint or other coating material; or

(bb) 20 tonnes or more of any metal coatings which are sprayed on in molten form; or,

cc) 25 tonnes or more of organic solvents in respect of any cold set web offset printing process or any sheet fed litho printing process or, in respect of any other process, 5 tonnes or more of organic solvents.

(b) Any process for the repainting or respraying of or of parts of road vehicles if the process may result in the release into the air of particulate matter or of any volatile organic compound and the carrying on of the process by the person concerned at the location in question is likely to involve the use of 1 tonne or more of organic solvents in any 12 month period.

(c) Any process for the repainting or respraying of or of parts of aircraft or railway vehicles if the process may result in the release into the air of particulate matter or of any volatile organic compound and the carrying on of the process by the person concerned at the location in question is likely to involve the use in any 12 month period of -

(i) 20 tonnes or more applied in solid form of any paint or other coating material; or

(ii) 20 tonnes or more of any metal coatings which are sprayed on in molten form; or

(iii) 5 tonnes or more of organic solvents.

In this section -

(i) 20 tonnes or more applied in solid form of any paint or other coating material; or

(ii) 20 tonnes or more of any metal coatings which are sprayed on in molten form; or

(iii) 5 tonnes or more of organic solvents.

In this section -

"aircraft" includes gliders and missiles;

"coating material" means paint, printing ink, varnish, laquer, dye, any metal oxide coating, any adhesive coating, any elastomer coating and any metal or plastic coating and any other coating material; and the amount or organic solvents used in a process shall be calculated as -

(a) The total input of organic solvents into the process, including both solvents contained in coating materials and solvents used for cleaning or other purposes; less

(b) Any organic solvents that are removed from the process for re-use or for recovery for re-use.

6.6 The Manufacture of Dyestuffs, Printing Ink & Coating Materials

PART A

Any process for the manufacture of dyestuffs if the process involves the use of hexachlorobenzene.

PART B

Any process

(a) For the manufacture or formulation of a printing ink or any other coating material containing, or involving the use of, an organic solvent, where the carrying on of the process by the person concerned at the location in question is likely to involve the use of 100 tonnes or more of organic solvents in any 12 month period;

(b) For the manufacture of any powder for use as a coating material where there is the capacity to produce 200 tonnes or more of such powder in any 12 month period.

In this section "coating material" has the same meaning as in section 6.5, and the amount of organic solvents used in a process shall be calculated as -

(a) The total input of organic solvents into the process, including both solvents contained in coating materials and solvents used for cleaning or other purposes; less

(b) Any organic solvents (not contained in coating materials) that are removed from the process for re-use or for recovery for re-use.

6.7 Timber Processes

PART A

(a) The curing or chemical treatment as part of a manufacturing process of timber or of products wholly or mainly made of wood if any substance described in Schedule 5 [see Appendix 1.2] is used.

(b) [omitted - 1994 amendment Regulations.]

PART B

The manufacture of products wholly or mainly of wood at any works if the process involves the sawing, drilling, sanding, shaping, turning, planing, curing or chemical treatment of wood relevant processes and the throughput of the works in any 12 month period is likely to exceed -

(i) 10,000 cubic metres, in the case of works at which wood is sawed but is not subjected to any other relevant processes or is subjected only to relevant processes which are exempt processes; or

(ii) 1,000 cubic metres in any other case.

For the purposes of this paragraph relevant processes other than sawing are "exempt processes" where, if no sawing were carried out at the works, the activities carried on there would be treated as not falling within this Part of this Section by virtue of Regulation 4(2). "Throughput" shall be calculated by reference to the amount of wood which is subjected to any of the relevant processes: but where, at the same works, wood is subject to two or more of the relevant processes, no account shall be taken of the second or any subsequent processes; "wood" includes any product consisting wholly or mainly of wood; and "works" includes a sawmill or any other premises on which relevant processes are carried out on wood.

6.8 Processes Involving Rubber

PART A

No Processes.

PART B

(a) The mixing, milling or blending of: -

(i) natural rubber; or

(ii) synthetic organic elastomers, if carbon black is used.

(b) Any process which converts the product of a process falling within paragraph (a) into a finished product if related to a process falling within that paragraph.

6.9 The Treatment & Processing of Animal or Vegetable Matter

PART A

Any of the following processes, unless falling within a description in another Section of the Schedule or an exempt process, namely the processing in any way whatsoever, storing or drying by the application of heat of any dead animal (or part thereof) or any vegetable matter if the process may result in the release into water of any substance described in Schedule 5 [see Appendix 1.2] in a quantity which, in any 12 month period, exceeds the background quantity by more than the amount specified in relation to the description of substance in column 2 of that Schedule; but excluding any process for the treatment of effluent so as to permit its discharge into controlled waters or into a sewer unless the treatment process involves the drying of any material with a view to its use as an animal feed stuff.

PART B

(a) Any process mentioned in Part A, of this Section unless an exempt process - but

   (i) where the process has the characteristics described in regulation 4(1)(ii); but

   (ii) may release into the air a substance described in Schedule 4 [see Appendix 1.2] or any offensive smell noticeable outside the premises on which the process is carried on.

(b) Breeding maggots in any case where 5 kg or more of animal or of vegetable matter or, in aggregate, of both are introduced into the process in any week.

In this section -

"animal" includes a bird or a fish; and

"exempt process" means -

(i) any process carried on on a farm or agricultural holding other than the manufacture of goods for sale;

(ii) the manufacture or preparation of food or drink for human consumption but excluding -

   (a) the extraction, distillation or purification of animal or vegetable oil or fat otherwise than as a process incidental to the cooking of food for human consumption;

   (b) any process involving the use of green offal or the boiling of blood except the cooking of food (other than tripe) for human consumption;

   (c) the cooking of tripe for human consumption elsewhere than on premises on which it is to be consumed;

(iii) the fleshing, cleaning and drying of pelts of fur-bearing animals;

(iv) any process carried on in connection with the operation of a knacker's yard, as defined in article 3(1) of the *Animal By-Products Order 1992*;

(v) any process for the manufacture of soap not falling within a description in Part A of Section 4.2 of this Schedule;

(vi) the storage of vegetable matter otherwise than as part of any prescribed process;

(vii) the cleaning of shellfish shells;

(viii) the manufacture of starch;

(ix) the processing of animal or vegetable matter at premises for feeding a recognised pack of hounds registered under article 10 of the *Animal By-Products Order 1992*;

(x) the salting of hides or skins, unless related to any other prescribed process;

(xi) any process for composting animal or vegetable matter or a combination of both, except where that process is carried on for the purposes of cultivating mushrooms;

(xii) any process for cleaning, and any related process for drying or dressing, seeds, bulbs, corms or tubers;

(xiii) the drying of grain or pulses;

(xiv) any process for the production of cotton yarn from raw cotton or for the conversion of cotton yarn into cloth;

"food" includes drink, articles and substances of no nutritional value which are used for human consumption, and articles and substances used as ingredients in the preparation of food. And "green offal" means the stomach and intestines of any animal, other than poultry or fish, and their contents.

APPENDIX 1.2

ENVIRONMENTAL PROTECTION (PRESCRIBED PROCESSES AND SUBSTANCES) REGULATIONS 1991 (as amended)

Schedules 4, 5 and 6 of the Regulations list the prescribed substances for releases to, respectively, air, water and land. Schedule 4 applies to those processes which are regulated for air pollution only (Part B processes); all three schedules apply to processes regulated for Integrated Pollution Control.

Following full implementation of the *Pollution Prevention and Control Regulations 2000*, the above Regulations will be revoked. The same substances are however prescribed for control under the PPC Regulations – see Schedule 1, Part 2, paras 12, 13 and 14.

These substances are also prescribed for control under the *Industrial Pollution Control (Prescribed Processes and Substances) Regulations (Northern Ireland) 1998*.

Schedule 4: Releases into the Air

Oxides of sulphur & other sulphur compounds
Oxides of nitrogen & other nitrogen compounds
Oxides of carbon
Organic compounds & partial oxidation products
Metals, metalloids & their compounds
Asbestos (suspended particulate matter & fibres), glass fibres & mineral fibres
Halogens & their compounds
Phosphorus & its compounds
Particulate matter

Schedule 5: Releases into Water

Substance	Amount in excess of background quantity released in any 12 month period (Grammes)
Mercury & its compounds	200 (expressed as metal)
Cadmium & its compounds	1000 (expressed as metal)
All isomers of	20

hexachlorocyclohexane

All isomers of DDT	5
Pentachlorophenol & its compounds	350 (expressed as PCP)
Hexachlorobenzene	5
Hexachlorobutadiene	20
Aldrin	2
Dieldrin	2
Endrin	1
Polychlorinated biphenyls	1
Dichlorvos	0.2
1,2-Dichloroethane	2000
All isomers of trichlorobenzene	75
Atrazine	350*
Simazine	350*
Tributyltin compounds	4 (expressed as TBT)
Triphenyltin compounds	4 (expressed as TPT)
Trifluralin	20
Fenitrothion	2
Azinphos-methyl	2
Malathion	2
Endosulfan	0.5

*Where both Atrazine and Simazine are released, the figure in aggregate is 350 grammes.

Schedule 6: Releases to Land

Organic solvents
Azides
Halogens & their covalent compounds
Metal carbonyls
Organo-metallic compounds
Oxidising agents
Polychlorinated dibenzofuran & any cogener thereof
Polychlorinated dibenzo-p-dioxin & any cogener thereof
Polyhalogenated biphenyls, terphenyls & naphthalenes
Phosphorus

Pesticides, that is to say, any chemical substance or preparation prepared or used for destroying any pest, including those used for protecting plants or wood or other plant products from harmful organisms; regulating the growth of plants; giving protection against harmful creatures; rendering such creatures harmless; controlling organisms with harmful or unwanted effects on water systems, buildings or other structures, or on manufactured products; or protecting animals against ectoparasites.

Alkali metals and their oxides and alkaline earth metals and their oxides.

APPENDIX 1.3

CHIEF INSPECTOR'S GUIDANCE TO INSPECTORS

These notes are applicable to processes currently prescribed for integrated pollution control; new technical guidance is being prepared for installations regulated under integrated pollution prevention and control.

INDUSTRY SECTOR GUIDANCE NOTES

These notes are intended to give general guidance to the Environment Agency in England and Wales on specific industry sectors to enable them to deal with applications for authorisations for new processes and for substantial changes to existing processes. More detailed guidance is given in the process guidance notes.

IPR 1	Fuel and Power Industry
IPR 2	Metal Industry
IPR 3	Mineral Industry
IPR 4	Chemical Industry
IPR 5	Waste Disposal Industry

PROCESS GUIDANCE NOTES

IPR Process Guidance Notes are available from The Stationery Office. IPR Notes are normally reviewed every four years to take account of new technology etc - revised notes have been given a prefix S2 and S3 (Series 2 and 3). The Notes listed here only apply to processes in England and Wales; there are no comparable notes for processes in Scotland. These Notes will eventually be superseded by guidance notes applicable to the Integrated Pollution Prevention and Control regime, which is being implemented over the next 6-7 years.

Combustion Processes (1.3)

S2 1.01	Large boilers & furnaces 50 MW(th) & over (1995) [supersedes IPR 1/1]
S3 1.01	Combustion processes – supplementary guidance note [draft 5.4.00]
IPR 1/2	Gas turbines (revised September 1994)
S2 1.03	Compression ignition engines 50 MW(th) & over (1995) [supersedes IPR 1/3]
S2 1.04	Waste and recovered oil burners 3 MW(th) & over (1995) [supersedes IPR 1/4]
S2 1.05	Combustion of fuel manufactured from or comprised of solid waste in appliances 3 MW(th) and over (1995) [supersedes IPR 1/5, 1/6, 1/7 and 1/8]
S2 1.12	Reheat and heat treatment furnaces 50 MW(th) and over (1995) [supersedes IPR 1/17]

Carbonisation & Associated Processes (1.2)

S2 1.06	Coke manufacture (1995) [supersedes IPR 1/09]
S2 1.07	Smokeless fuel, activated carbon and carbon black manufacture (1995) [supersedes IPR 1/10]

Gasification Processes (1.1)

S2 1.08	Gasification of solid & liquid feedstocks including gasification combined cycle (1995) [previously IPR 1/11]
S2 1.09	Refining of natural gas (1995) [previously IPR 1/12]; to be read in conjunction with update S3 1.02
IPR 1/13	The refining of natural gas at liquified natural gas sites

Petroleum Processes (1.4)

S2 1.10   Oil refining and associated processes (1995) [incorporates IPR 1/14 on the odorising of natural gas or liquified petroleum gas and IPR 1/15 crude oil refineries]; to be read in conjunction with update S3 1.02

S2 1.11   On-shore oil production (1995) [supersedes IPR 1/16]; to be read in conjunction with update S3 1.02

S3 1.02   Oil and gas processes: supplementary note, consolidates and updates S2 1.09, 1.10 and 1.11 (draft June 2000)

Iron and Steel (2.1)

S2 2.01   Integrated iron and steel works (1999) [replaces IPR 2/1]

IPR 2/2   Ferrous foundry processes

S2 2.02   Ferrous foundries: supplementary guidance (1999)

IPR 2/3   Processes for electric arc steelmaking, secondary steelmaking and special alloy production

S2 2.03   Non-ferrous metals: supplementary guidance note (1999)

Non-Ferrous Metals (2.2); Smelting Processes (2.3)

IPR 2/4   Processes for the production of zinc and zinc alloys

IPR 2/5   Processes for the production of lead and lead alloys

IPR 2/6   Processes for the production of refractory metals

IPR 2/7   Processes for the production, melting, recovery of cadmium, mercury and their alloys

IPR 2/8   Processes for the production of aluminium

IPR 2/9   Processes for the production of copper and copper alloys

IPR 2/10   Processes for the production of precious metals and platinum group metals

IPR 2/11   The extraction of nickel by the carbonyl process and the production of cobalt and nickel alloys

IPR 2/12   Tin and bismuth processes

Cement & Lime Manufacture & Associated Processes (3.1)

S2 3.01   Cement manufacture, lime manufacture & associated processes (1996)

Processes Involving Asbestos (3.2)

S2 3.02   Asbestos processes (1996) [supersedes IPR 3/2]

Other Mineral Fibres (3.3) and Glass Manufacture & Production (3.5)

S2 3.03   Manufacture of glass fibres, other non-asbestos mineral fibres, glass frit, enamel frit and associated processes (1996) [incorporates former IPR 3/4 and 3/5]

Ceramic Production (3.6)

S2 3.04   Ceramic processes (1996) [formerly 3/6]

Organic and Inorganic Chemicals Industries

S2 4.01   Large volume organic chemicals (1999) [replaces 4/1, 4/2, 4/3, 4/4 & 4/6]

S2 4.02   Speciality organic chemicals (1999) [replaces 4/5, 4/7, 4/8, 4/9, 4/12 & 4/15]

S2 4.03   Inorganic acids and halogens (1999) [replaces 4/10, 4/11, 4/13 & 4/14]

S2 4.04   Inorganic chemicals (1999) [replaces 4/16, 4/18, 4/19, 4/20, 4/21, 4/22, 4/23, 4/24 & 4/25]

IPR 4/17   Bulk storage installations

Incineration (5.1)

S2 5.01   Waste to energy plants and incineration plant for the following wastes: chemical and hazardous; clinical; municipal; animal carcasses; sewage sludge; and drum residues (1996) [replaces 5/1, 5/2, 5/3, 5/4, 5/5 and 5/11]

Recovery Processes (5.2)

S2 5.03   Cleaning and regeneration of carbon (1996) [replaces IPR 5/7]

S2 5.04   Recovery of organic solvents and oil by distillation (1996) [replaces IPR 5/8 & 5/10]

IPR 5/9   Regeneration of ion exchange resins [not being revised; only one IPC authorisation. HMIP research report DOE/HMIP/RR/95/028 Technical & Economic Study of Recovery Processes contains up to date information on their environmental performance]

Production of Fuel from Waste (5.3)

S2 5.02   Making solid fuel from waste (1996) [replaces IPR 5/6]

Other Industries (chapter 6)

IPR 6/1   Application or removal of tributyltin, or triphenyltin coatings at shipyards or boatyards

IPR 6/2   Tar and bitumen processes

IPR 6/3   Timber preservation processes

IPR 6/4   Di-isocynate manufacture

IPR 6/5   Toluene di-isocyanate use and flame bonding of polyurethanes

IPR 6/6   Textile treatment processes

IPR 6/7   Processing of animal hides and skins

IPR 6/8   The making of paper pulp by chemical methods

IPR 6/9   Papermaking and related processes, including mechanical pulping, recycled fibres and de-inking

APPENDIX 1.4

TECHNICAL GUIDANCE NOTES

These notes provide further guidance to those involved in implementing Part I of the *Environmental Protection Act*; they will however also be of interest to process operators and others with an interest in the operation of the EPA. Further TG notes are planned. They are available from The Stationery Office.

Dispersion

D1   Guidelines on discharge stack heights for polluting emissions (1993)

Monitoring

M1   Sampling facility requirements for the monitoring of particulates in gaseous releases to atmosphere (1993)

M2   Monitoring emissions of pollutants at source (1994)

M3   Standards for IPC monitoring: Part 1 - standards organisations and the measurement infrastructure (1995)

M4   Standards for IPC monitoring: Part 2 - standards in support of IPC monitoring (1995)

M5   Routine measurement of gamma ray air kerma rate in the environment (1995)

M   The Measurement of di-isocyanates in stack emissions (draft, 1998)

M   The Monitoring of tar fume (draft, 1998)

M9   Monitoring methods for ambient air (2000)

Abatement

A1   Guidance on effective flaring in the gas, petroleum, petrochemical and associated industries (1993)

A2   Pollution abatement technology for the reduction of solvent vapour emissions (1994)

A3   Pollution abatement technology for particulate and trace gas removal (1994)

A4   Effluent treatment techniques (1997)

A5   Abatement of atmospheric radioactive releases from nuclear facilities

A6   Abatement of atmospheric radioactive releases to water from nuclear facilities

Environmental

E1   Best Practicable Environmental Option Assessments for Integrated Pollution Control; Vol. I: Principles and Methodology; Vol. II: Technical Data (for consultation) (1997)

APPENDIX 2.1

AIR POLLUTION CONTROL: SECRETARY OF STATE'S GUIDANCE NOTES

GENERAL GUIDANCE NOTES

These notes (GG Notes) give guidance to local authorities and port health authorities in England and Wales and to the Scottish Environment Protection Agency in Scotland on their responsibilities under Part I of the *Environmental Protection Act 1990*.

GG1(91)   Introduction to Part I of the Act
GG2(91)   Authorisations
GG3(91)   Applications and Registers
GG4(91)   Interpretation of terms used in process guidance notes
GG5(91)   Appeals

PROCESS GUIDANCE NOTES

Process Guidance (PG) Notes are issued by the Secretary of State under section 7 of the *Environmental Protection Act 1990*; they provide guidance on BATNEEC for each category of process, and will usually include emission limits, monitoring and sampling requirements etc. PG Notes were originally produced in 1991 and 1992 in advance of processes applying for authorisation from their local authority and most have now been revised. The revised notes supersede any earlier versions. PG notes are reviewed approximately every four years. PG Notes are published by The Stationery Office for the DETR, Welsh Office and Scottish Office; however, following devolution (1999), consideration is given on a case by case basis as to the applicability of PG notes to each region.

Details of all PG Notes can be accessed on: www.aeat.co.uk/netcen.airqual/info/labrief.html

PG 1/1(95)   Waste oil burners, less than 0.4 MW net rated thermal input

PG 1/2(95)   Waste oil or recovered oil burners, 0 .4-3 MW net rated thermal input

PG 1/3(95)   Boilers and furnaces, 20-50 MW net rated thermal input

PG 1/4(95)   Gas turbines, 20-50 MW net rated thermal input; see also AQ 1(97)

PG 1/5(95)   Compression ignition engines, 20-50 MW net rated thermal input

PG 1/10(92)   Waste derived fuel burning processes less than 3 MW net rated thermal input

PG 1/11(96)   Reheat and heat treatment furnaces, 20-50 MW net rated thermal input [revised draft August 2000]

PG 1/12(95)   Combustion of fuel manufactured from or comprised of solid waste in appliances between 0.4 and 0.3 MW net rated thermal input [replaces 1991 PG 1/6, 1/7, 1/8 and 1/9]

PG 1/13(96)   Processes for the storage, loading and

unloading of petrol at terminals; see also AQ 6(97); see also AQ 10(99)

PG 1/14(96) Unloading of petrol into storage at service stations; see also AQ 6(97); see also AQ 10(99)

PG 1/15(97) Odorising natural gas and liquefied petroleum gas

PG 2/1(96) Furnaces for the extraction of non-ferrous metal from scrap

PG 2/2(96) Hot dip galvanising processes

PG 2/3(96) Electrical, rotary, crucible and reverberatory furncaces

PG 2/4(96) Iron, steel and non-ferrous metal foundry processes

PG 2/5(96) Hot and cold blast cupolas

PG 2/6(96) Processes for melting and producing aluminium, magnesium and their alloys

PG 2/7(96) Zinc and zinc alloy processes

PG 2/8(96) Copper and copper alloy processes

PG 2/9(96) Metal decontamination processes

PG 3/1(95) Blending, packing, loading and use of bulk cement

PG 3/2(95) Manufacture of heavy clay goods and refractory goods

PG 3/3(95) Glass (excluding lead glass) manufacturing processes

PG 3/4(95) Lead glass, glass frit and enamel frit manufacturing processes

PG 3/5(95) Coal, coke, coal product and petroleum coke processes [revised draft, 2000]

PG 3/6(95) Processes for the polishing or etching of glass or glass products using hydrofluoric acid

PG 3/7(95) Exfoliation of vermiculite and expansion of perlite [revised draft, 2000]

PG 3/8(96) Quarry processes

PG 3/12(95) Plaster processes

PG 3/13(95) Asbestos processes; see also AQ 3(96)

PG 3/14(95) Lime processes

PG 3/15a(96) Roadstone coating processes [amends and replaces 3/15(96)] [revised draft, 2000]

PG 3/16(96) Mobile crushing and screening processes [revised draft, 2000]

PG 3/17(95) China and ball clay processes including the spray drying of ceramics [amends and replaces 3/10(91) and 3/11(91)] [revised draft, 2000]

PG 4/1(94) Processes for the surface treatment of metals

PG 4/2(96) Processes for the manufacture of fibre reinforced plastics; see also AQ 1(97)

PG 5/1(95) Clinical waste incineration processes under 1 tonne an hour

PG 5/2(95) Crematoria

PG 5/3(95) Animal remains incineration processes under 1 tonne an hour

PG 5/4(95) General waste incineration processes under 1 tonne an hour

PG 5/5(91) Sewage sludge incineration processes under 1 tonne an hour [not being updated: no

relevant incinerators; if any enquiries or applications, DETR suggest also refer to IPR 5/11]

PG 6/1(00) The processing of animal remains and by-products (E, S & W) (see also AQ 3(00) for amendment to clause 13)

PG 6/2(95) Manufacture of timber and wood based products

PG 6/3(97) Chemical treatment of timber and wood based products

PG 6/4(95) Processes for the manufacture of particleboard and fibreboard

PG 6/5(95) Maggot breeding processes; see also AQ 1(97)

PG 6/7(97) Printing and coating of metal packaging

PG 6/8(97) Textile and fabric coating and finishing processes

PG 6/9(96) Manufacture of coating powder

PG 6/10(97) Coating manufacturing processes

PG 6/11(97) Manufacture of printing ink

PG 6/12(91) Production of natural sausage casings, tripe, chitterlings and other boiled green offal products

PG 6/13(97) Coil coating processes

PG 6/14(97) Film coating processes

PG 6/15(97) Coating in drum manufacturing and reconditioning processes

PG 6/16(97) Printworks

PG 6/17(97) Printing of flexible packaging

PG 6/18(97) Paper coating processes; see also AQ 4(98)

PG 6/19(97) Fish meal and fish oil processes

PG 6/20(97) Paint application in vehicle manufacturing; see also AQ 4(98)

PG 6/21(96) Hide and skin processes

PG 6/22(97) Leather finishing processes

PG 6/23(97) Coating of metal and plastic

PG 6/24(96) Pet food manufacturing processes

PG 6/25(97) Vegetable oil extraction and fat and oil refining processes

PG 6/26(96) Animal feed compounding processes; see also AQ 1(97)

PG 6/27(96) Vegetable matter drying processes

PG 6/28(97) Rubber processes

PG 6/29(97) Di-isocyanate processes ; see also AQ 3(97)

PG 6/30(97) Production of mushroom substrate

PG 6/31(96) Powder coating processes, including sheradising [revised draft 2000]

PG 6/32(97) Adhesive coating processes

PG 6/33(97) Wood coating processes

PG 6/34(97) Respraying of road vehicles; see also AQ 4(98)

PG 6/35(96) Metal and other thermal spraying processes

PG 6/36(97) Tobacco processing

PG 6/40(94) Coating and recoating of aircraft and aircraft components [revised draft, 2000]

PG 6/41(94) Coating and recoating of rail vehicles [revised draft, 2000]

PG 6/42(94) Bitumen and tar processes, as amended by

"green note" dated November 1996 [revised draft, 2000]

UG-1 (92)   Revisions/additions to existing process and general guidance notes: no. 1. However, this is now relevant only inrelation to PG 1/10 - all other references in UG-1 having been included in PG Note revisions.

APPENDIX 2.2

LOCAL AIR POLLUTION CONTROL: ADDITIONAL GUIDANCE NOTES

These notes are prepared by the Air and Environment Quality Division at the Department of the Environment, Transport and the Regions (until mid-1997, the Department of the Environment) on behalf of the DETR, Scottish Executive and the National Assembly for Wales; they supplement and clarify information contained in Process Guidance Notes and provide additional guidance on the way in which Part I of the Environmental Protection Act 1990 and its Regulations should be interpreted. Only those notes which remain valid as at 25 July 2000 are listed here.

Details of Additional Guidance Notes can be found on: www.environment-agency.gov.uk/epns/lapchome.html

AQ 5(91)   Registers - Rehabilitation of Offenders Act
AQ 7(91)   Meaning of "existing process"
AQ 8(91)   Obtaining further information: specimen notice
AQ 9(91)   VAT on charges

AQ 3(92)   Radioactive substances
AQ 5(92)   Foundries - triviality
AQ 7(92)   Amendments to applications
AQ 8(92)   Rubber processes - meaning of "if carbon black is used"
AQ 9(92)   Mobile plant
AQ 14(92)   Cement processes

AQ 1(93)   EPA Part I - advising operators on their rights of appeal. See also AQ 7(94) and 8(96)
AQ 3(93)   Triviality and zinc diecasters
AQ 4(93)   Transfer of authorisations under s.9 of EPA
AQ 7(93)   Small coal mines - triviality
AQ 8(93)   Mobile plant - necessity for consultation with English Nature and Countryside Council for Wales
AQ 9(93)   Variation notices - consolidation of authorisations
AQ 10(93)   Notification of publication of TG note *Guidelines on Discharge Stack Heights for Polluting Emissions* (see also AQ 18(93))
AQ 12(93)   Obtaining additional information
AQ 14(93)   Service of notices etc - advice on
AQ 15(93)   Commercial confidentiality (advice on appeal costs no longer current)
AQ 16(93)   Submission of draft authorisations to operators
AQ 18(93)   Errors in Technical Guidance D1 (see also AQ 10(93))

AQ 1(94)   Notification (to operators) of triviality exemption, together with specimen
AQ 2(94)   Solvent substitution [of 1,1,1 trichloroethane or methyl chloroform to another solvent] in vapour degreasing equipment
AQ 3(94)   Animal by-product rendering (PG 6/1(91)) - amendment of para 2 of clause 33 relating to self-closing doors
AQ 4(94)   Availability of HMIP Technical Guidance Note M2 of monitoring of pollutants at source
AQ 5(94)   Content of public registers (should only include information specified in Reg. 15 of Applications, Appeals & Registers Regs 1991; working files not to be used as public registers)
AQ 6(94)   Notification of availability of HMIP TG Note A2 *Pollution Abatement Technology for the Reduction of Solvent Vapour Emissions*
AQ 7(94)   Appeals arrangements: initial stages of appeals in England under Part I of EPA to be handled by Planning Inspectorate
AQ 9(94)   Availability of HMIP TG Note A3 *Pollution Abatement Technology for Particulate and Trace Gas Removal*
AQ 11(94)   Additional guidance on *Waste Management Licensing Regulations 1994* and their implications for LAAPC
AQ 12(94)   Establishment of Environmental Technology Best Practice Programme
AQ 15(94)   Explicitly informing operators of their right to appeal against EPA Part I decisions of the LA and suggested form of wording
AQ 17(94)   Recirculation of workroom air and triviality - exemption from LAPC authorisations (so long as satisfy COSHH requirements)
AQ 18(94)   Triviality

AQ 2(95)   Delays in deciding applications and considering upgrading submissions (should aim to deal with within 4 months of receipt of all relevant information)
AQ 3(95)   Refractory materials: further guidance on defining; see also section 3.6 of Schedule 1 to 1994 Prescribed Processes & Substances Regulations
AQ 4(95)   Inspection frequency - basic principles: to check compliance with conditions usually every 6 months, announced or unannounced; in connection with applications etc, prearranged visit
AQ 5(95)   Four-yearly review of authorisations under s. 6(6) of EPA: aspects to be considered
AQ 7(95)   Placing of commercially confidential information on public register on expiry of 4 year limit; see also AQ 1(93), 15(93) & 15(94).
            Removal of details of convictions from public register in accordance with *Rehabilitation of Offenders Act 1994*

AQ 10(95)   PG 5/5(91) not being updated as no sewage sludge incinerators under 1 tonne/hr in operation

AQ 11(95)   Amendments to LAAPC as a result of *Environment Act 1995* and note re air quality provisions of the Act

AQ 14(95)   Publication of HMIP Technical Guidance Notes M3 and M4 on standards for IPC Monitoring

AQ 16(95)   Authorisation conditions relating to odour

AQ 17(95)   Summary of recent LAPC appeals decisions (see also 10(96) & 7(98))

AQ 18(95)   Amended EPA sections 10 and 13 relating to variation and enforcement notices effective 12.10.95 - see *Environment Act 1995,* Sch. 22, paras 51 and 53

AQ 20(95)   Monitoring of processes and emissions by local authorities

AQ 1(96)   The determination of chimney heights for process heaters

AQ 2(96)   Amendments to LAPC coming into force on 1 April as result of *Environment Act 1995*

AQ 3(96)   Asbestos processes (PG 3/13(95)) - clause 14, second sentence should read "A fibre is defined as any object of length greater than 5 μm, breadth less than 3 μm ..."

AQ 8(96)   Amendment to specimen notes on appeal (dated November 1992) and AQ 1(93); appeals should be received by the Secretary of State within the appropriate time limit (not sent within the limit)

AQ 10(96)   Summary of recent LAPC appeal decisions (see also 17(95) & 7(98))

AQ 1(97)   Corrections to PG 1/4(95), 4/2(96), 6/5(95) and 6/26(96)

AQ 3(97)   Corrections to PG 6/29(97)

AQ 4(97)   Categories of process operated by different local authorities

AQ 5(97)   Appeals (Secretary of State powers delegated to Planning Inspectorate wef 1 September 1997); guidance on appeals procedure

AQ 6(97)   Petroleum processes (PG 1/13(96) & PG 1/14(96)): definition of petrol and advice on when modifying of existing process should trigger "new process" requirements

AQ 7(97)   Categories of process operated by different local authorities (additions to AQ 4(97)

AQ 4(98)   Corrections to PG 6/18(97), PG 6/20(97) and PG 6/34(97)

AQ 7(98)   Summary of recent appeal decisions (see also 17(95) & 10(96))

AQ 9(98)   BATNEEC for unloading petrol at stations with older types of tank gauging (modification of advice given in PG 1/14(96)

AQ 10(98)   Procedures for tank connections at petrol stations (confirmed as stated in PG 1/14(96)

AQ 11(98)   Guidance in response to LAPC action plan

AQ 12(98)   Application of the emission limit value for amines in PG 2/4

AQ 1(99)   Application of process guidance notes to the printed circuit board industry

AQ 2(99)   Transfer efficiency for spraying coatings

AQ 3(99)   List of current and outdated AQ notes as at March 1999

AQ 4(99)   Amendments to PG 6(23) 97 – coating of constructional steelworks

AQ 5(99)   Explanation of 1999/00 increase in LAPC fees and charges

AQ 6(99)   Manufacture of heavy clay goods and refractory goods (PG 3.2(95)) - fluoride limit

AQ 7(99)   Transfer of LAPC Local Authority Unit to Environment Agency; Address: Block 1, Government Buildings, Burghill Road, Westburyon-Trym, Bristol BS10 6BF; Contact: Steve Shrewsbury, Tel: 0117 914 2703; Fax: 0117 914 2827; Email: steve.shrewsbury@environment-agency.gov.uk

AQ 8(99)   Dr. Alison Simmons joins LAU; Tel: 0117 914 2778; Fax: 0117 914 2827; Email: alison.simmons@environment-agency.gov.uk

AQ 10(99)   Use of dipsticks on mobile containers put into operation after 31.12.99 (supplments guidance notes PG1/13(96) and PG 1/14(96)

AQ 1(00)   Categories of process regulated by different local authorities

AQ 2(00)   Summary of recent High Court Judgement (Dudley MBC v Henley Foundries Ltd – 26.4.99); clarifies the meaning of the word "persistency" in context of emission of fumes from a prescribed process; and the applicability of authorisation conditions when a process is not malfunctioning

AQ 3(00)   Amendments to PG6/1(00) Processing of animal remains and by-products (clause 13)

AQ 4(00)   Preparation of court cases – note prepared by Environment Agency's Chief Prosecutor

AQ 5(00)   New DETR and LAU contact details

AQ 6(00)   Updated list of current and out of date AQ notes (updating 3/99)

AQ 7(00)   Guidance from DETR & Nat Assembly for Wales – Link Authorities (for the purpose of inter-authority networking on individual LAPC sectors)

AQ 8(00)   Climate Change Levy

APPENDIX 2.3

THE RINGELMANN CHART

The method of visual assessment of smoke emission by comparison of the darkness of the smoke with the standard shades of grey on a chart placed in a suitable position was devised by Professor Ringelmann of Paris towards the end of the 19th century. Professor Ringelmann obtained the shades of grey by cross-hatching in black on a white background so that a known percentage of the white was obscured.

The British Standard Ringelmann Chart (BS 2742C) is printed for the BSI so that the shades obtained in use are both consistent and near the average of those to which users were accustomed when using the previously available commercially-printed Ringelmann Charts, including those issued by the US Bureau of Mines.

The Chart consists of a cardboard sheet 581 mm x 127 mm on which are printed five 101 mm squares, four of which are cross-hatched by 20 horizontal and 20 vertical lines so that in use the cross-hatched black lines merge into the white background and produce for each shade, apparently, a uniform grey.

The number of shades - the Ringelmann numbers - range from 0 to 4, each shade increasing by comparison with the previous number by 20% obscuration so that

Ringelmann 1 = 20% obscuration
Ringelmann 2 = 40% obscuration
Ringelmann 3 = 60% obscuration
Ringelmann 4 = 80% obscuration

"Dark smoke" is smoke which is as dark or darker than shade 2 on the Chart; "black smoke" is smoke which is as dark or darker than shade 4 on the Chart.

The Use of the Ringelmann Chart

The use of the Ringelmann Chart is described in BS 2742:1969.

The Ringelmann Chart should be firmly mounted onto a backing holder - aluminium is suitable - similar to that described in BS 2742. Protective coverings must not be applied to the Chart in use and nothing should impair the luminance of its working surface.

It should be used under daylight conditions and held in a vertical plane in line between the observer and the chimney top, at a distance of more than 15 metres to ensure that cross-hatched lines merge into shades of grey.

Where possible the general illumination of the sky should be uniform, but if the sun is shining or the sky bright on one side, the British Standard recommends that the bright source of illumination should be approximately at right angles to the line of vision and not in front of or behind the observer. Under hazy conditions observations should not be taken at extreme distance as there will be a tendency for the readings to be low. The angle of view of the Chart and smoke should be as low as possible; observations at a steep angle should be avoided.

The darkness of the smoke at the chimney terminal should be compared with the Chart; the Ringelmann number which most closely matches the darkness of the smoke, and the time and duration of the emission, should be noted. In favourable conditions it is possible to estimate smoke darkness to the nearest quarter Ringelmann.

Ringelmann Smoke Chart

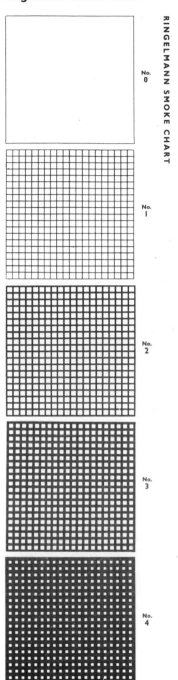

APPENDIX 2.4

THE CLEAN AIR ACT (EMISSION OF GRIT AND DUST FROM FURNACES) REGULATIONS 1971

Schedule 1 - Furnaces Rated by Heat Output

This Schedule applies to boilers and also indirect heating appliances in which the material being heated is a gas or a liquid (e.g. an air heater); where an indirect heating appliance falls also within the provisions of Schedule 2, it should be treated as a Schedule 1 furnace.

Max. continuous rating in lbs of steam/hr (from & at 100°C (212°F) in thousands BTU/hr) *		Max. permitted quantities of grit and dust per hour Furnaces burning			
		solid matter		liquid matter	
000 Btu/hr	MW	lbs	kg	lbs	kg
825	0.24	1.10	0.55	0.25	0.11
1,000	0.29	1.33	0.60	0.28	0.12
2,000	0.58	2.67	1.21	0.56	0.25
3,000	0.87	4.00	1.81	0.84	0.38
4,000	1.17	5.33	2.41	1.12	0.50
5,000	1.46	6.67	3.02	1.4	0.63
7,000	2.19	8.50	3.85	2.1	0.95
10,000	2.93	10.00	4.53	2.8	1.27
15,000	4.39	13.33	6.04	4.2	1.90
20,000	5.86	16.67	7.56	5.6	2.54
25,000	7.32	20.0	9.07	7.0	3.17
30,000	8.79	23.4	10.61	8.4	3.81
40,000	11.72	30	13.60	11.2	5.08
50,000	14.65	37	16.78	12.5	5.66
100,000	29.30	66	29.93	18	8.16
150,000	43.96	94	40.97	24	10.88
200,000	58.61	122	55.37	29	13.15
250,000	73.42	149	67.58	36	16.32
300,000	87.92	172	78.01	41	18.59
350,000	102.57	195	88.45	45	20.41
400,000	117.22	217	98.42	50	22.67
450,000	131.88	239	108.40	54.5	24.72
475,000	139.20	250	113.39	57	25.85

1 Watt = 3.41214 Btu/hr

Schedule 2 - Furnaces Rated by Heat Input

This schedule applies to indirect heating appliances and to furnaces in which combustion gases are in contact with the material being heated, but that material does not in itself contribute to the grit and dust in the combustion gases.

		Max. permitted quantities of dust emissions per hour Furnaces burning			
		solid matter		liquid matter	
in millions BTU/hr)	MW	lbs	kg	lbs	kg
1.25	0.36	1.1	0.49	0.28	0.12
2.5	0.73	2.1	0.95	0.55	0.24
5.0	1.46	4.3	1.95	1.1	0.49
7.5	2.19	6.8	3.08	1.7	0.77
10	2.93	7.6	3.44	2.2	0.99
15	4.39	9.7	4.39	3.3	1.49
20	5.86	11.9	5.39	4.4	1.99
25	7.32	14.1	6.40	5.5	2.49
30	8.79	16.3	7.39	6.6	2.99
35	10.25	18.4	8.34	7.7	3.49
40	11.72	20.6	9.34	8.8	3.99
45	13.18	22.8	10.34	9.8	4.44
50	14.65	25	11.33	10.9	4.94
100	29.30	45	20.51	16	7.25
200	58.61	90	40.82	26	11.79
300	87.92	132	59.87	35	15.87
400	117.22	175	79.37	44	19.95
500	146.53	218	98.88	54	24.49
575	168.51	250	113.39	57	25.85

Note: typically, a large power station is 2000-4000 MW

The Regulations limit the grit in the sample of grit and dust to the following proportions:

- **Schedule 1 furnaces:**

  Grit not to exceed 33% where maximum continuous rating does not exceed 16,800 lbs/hr of steam or 16,800,000 Btu/hr (4.92 MW);
  Grit not to exceed 20% in any other case.

- **Schedule 2 furnaces:**

  Grit not to exceed 33% where designed heat input of the furnace does not exceed 25,000,000 Btu/hr (7.32 MW);
  Grit not to exceed 20% in any other case.

Notes:

1. Multiflue chimneys are defined and for the purpose of the Regulations each flue is to be taken as a separate chimney for the purpose of calculating acceptable emissions.

2. Where a chimney serves a furnace to which the Regulations apply and also a furnace to which the Regulations do not apply, the emissions from the latter shall be disregarded.

3. The prescribed limits apply to any period of standard operation of the furnace, including periods during which it is at or close to the loading to which it is subject for the greater part of its working time, or at any higher loading to which it is regularly subject for a limited time (whether or not this exceeds the furnace maximum combustion rating or designed heat input).

APPENDIX 2.5
CALCULATION OF CHIMNEY HEIGHT

This appendix supplements the details given in chapter 2, 2.14.2 relating to chimney height, ss.14-16 of the *Clean Air Act 1993,* and also has relevance to the requirements for BATNEEC in s.7(2) of the *Environmental Protection Act 1990.*

Chimney heights offer a means of local control of pollutants discharged to the atmosphere from combustion and incineration plant and from industrial processes. They may be used to control the deposition of pollutants to the ground or their ambient concentrations over either long or short time scales, and for a variety of purposes including health effects and nuisance (due to odour for example). There are often additional controls on the scale of discharges from particular processes, both because of the requirements of BATNEEC to minimise discharge where practically possible and also to limit polluting discharges where the accumulation of a multiplicity of discharges may cause problems on larger scales, for example over the background level of pollutants in urban areas or where the accumulation of pollutants on continental or global scales is important. However, even when there are high levels of abatement, there is likely to be a residual discharge which must be effectively dispersed by means of an adequate chimney height.

Chimneys act as a means of control over local pollution levels by raising the polluting source to a sufficient height above the ground for the initial dispersion of the discharge plume, where pollutant concentrations are high, to occur away from the ground where most pollution problems occur. The chimney height is arranged so that the eventual contact of the plume with the ground results in pollutant concentrations at the ground within some prescribed limit value. This process is only effective within distances of about 50-100 chimney heights, much beyond which the effects of discharge height are no longer distinguishable. The highest pollutant concentrations usually occur within this range.

The calculation of effective chimney heights is thus a matter of great practical importance and there are a variety of methods of doing this, either by direct dispersion modelling or by using one of a number of guides for this purpose. For large plant, for example that defined as Part A processes (regulated for Integrated Pollution Control), it is common for individual dispersion modelling studies to be requested as a part of the authorisation process. Direct dispersion modelling may also be used for calculating chimney heights for smaller plant where there are complex problems due to the character of the dispersion or the nature of the discharge. However this is not usually practicable and there are several guides which allow chimney heights to be calculated more quickly and easily. These are discussed below. The majority of direct dispersion modelling uses computer models of varying sophistication. The USEPA models are the most commonly used (in the UK, along with the NRPB models), though they have distinct limitations in dealing with the more complex dispersion problems. Some complex dispersion problems also use small scale wind tunnel modelling to determine chimney heights.

For the great majority of smaller polluting discharges, chimney heights are determined using the published guides for this purpose. For many years chimney heights for conventional combustion plant (mainly heating and steam raising plant running on coal, fuel oil or gas) have been calculated using the 3rd Edition of the *Clean Air Act Memorandum "Chimney Heights"* which is still recommended for this purpose. More recently there has been a need to deal with newer types of combustion plant (combined cycle for example) and with the requirements for adequate discharge stack heights for the wide variety of smaller process plant classified as Part B processes under the *Environmental Protection Act*. This has been met with the HMIP Guidance Note D1, *Guidelines for Discharge Stack Heights for Polluting Emissions* (HMSO, 1993), which provides a systematic procedure for dealing with almost any type of polluting discharge. There is also specific advice on minimum chimney heights for discharge stacks in the Process Guidance Notes issued by the DETR Local Authority

Unit dealing with the requirements for authorisation of various Part B processes. These also contain maximum pollutant emission limits for the processes. Guidance Note D1 is also used occasionally for setting chimney heights for Part A processes, but this requires specific approval in individual cases.

More information on the *Memorandum of Chimney Heights* and on Guidance Note D1 can be found in the background report (*Background Report to the HMIP Guidelines on Discharge Stack Heights for Polluting Emissions*, D.J. Hall, V. Kukadia, Building Research Establishment Report No. CR200/95); specific advice on calculating chimney heights for odorous discharges can be found in Clean Air, Vol. 24, No. 2, pp74-92, and in AEA Technology Report No. AEA/CS/REMA-038; on dealing with chimneys with low velocity discharges in *Clean Air*, Vol. 25, No. 3, pp128-339; and on chimney heights for emissions of volatile organic compounds in *Clean Air*, Vol. 25, No. 4.

(*This appendix prepared by D.J. Hall at the Building Research Establishment*, 1995)

APPENDIX 2.6

CLEAN AIR ACT 1993: SMOKE CONTROL

Section 18 of the *Clean Air Act 1993* allows a local authority to make Smoke Control Orders. When operative, it is an offence for an occupier of premises to allow smoke to be emitted from a chimney, unless the smoke is caused by an authorised fuel or the fireplace which the chimney serves is exempt from the order. The Department of the Environment, Transport and the Regions is responsible for authorising fuels and exempted fireplaces.

Authorised fuels are listed below at Appendix 2.6a, and exempted fireplaces at Appendix 2.6b.

Appendix 2.6a: Smoke Control Areas (Authorised Fuels) Regulations 1991

Regulations covering authorised fuels were made under section 34(1) of the *Clean Air Act 1956* (*Clean Air Act 1993*, section 20) and apply to England, Wales and Scotland. The 1991 Regulations, which came into force on 1 July 1991 (amended 1992, 1993, 1996, 1997, and 1998), consolidate all the Regulations covering authorised fuels made since 1956. All the earlier Regulations are revoked. Amendment Regulations made in 2000 cover England only, with similar Regulations applying in Scotland.

In addition to anthracite, semi-anthracite, electricity, gas and low volatile steam coals, the following are authorised under the Act:

1. **Phurnacite Plus**, manufactured by Coal Products Limited at Aberaman, Mid Glamorgan, which

(a) comprise anthracite and coke breeze (as to approximately 75% of the total weight) and coking coal (as to the remaining weight):

(b) were manufactured from those constituents by a process involving heat treatment, roll-pressing and further heat treatment at about 400°C;

(c) are unmarked cushion-shaped briquettes and have an average weight of 40 grammes (Ancit 40) or 60 grammes (Ancit 60); and

(d) have a sulphur content not exceeding 1.5% of the total weight.

1A **Aimcor Excel briquettes**, manufactured by Applied Industrial Materials UK Limited at Newfield, Co. Durham, which

(a) comprise petroleum coke as to 60% to 75% of the total weight), low volatile coal and reactive coke (as to 20% to 25% of the total weight) and cold-setting resin binder (as to the remaining weight);

(b) were manufactured from those constituents by a process involving roll pressing;

(c) are unmarked pillow-shaped briquettes and have an average weight of 73 grammes; and

(d) have a sulphur content not exceeding 2% of the total weight.

1B **Aimcor Pureheat briquettes**, manufactured by Applied Industrial Materials UK Limited at Immingham, North East Lincolnshire, which

(a) comprise anthracite (as to approximately 60% of the total weight), petroleum coke (as to approximately 25% of the total weight) and binder (as to the remaining weight);

(b) were manufacturered from those constituents by a process involving roll pressing and heat treatment at about 250°C;

(c) are pillow-shaped briquettes with a single line indentation on one side and a double line indentation on the reverse side and have an average weight of 75 grammes; and

(d) have a sulphur content not exceeding 2% of the total weight.

1C **Ancit briquettes**, manufactured by CPL Industries Limited at Immingham, North East Lincolnshire, which

(a) comprise anthracite (as to approximately 60-85% of the total weight), petroleum coke (up to approximately 30% of the total weight), bituminous coal (up to approximately 15% of the total weight) and a molasses and phosphoric binder (as to the remaining weight);

(b) were manufactured from those constituents by a process involving roll pressing and heat treatment at about 300°C;

(c) are unmarked cushion-shaped briquettes with an average weight of 48 grammes; and

(d) have a sulphur content not exceeding 1.5% of the total weight.

2. **Anthracine N20 briquettes**, manufactured by Agglonord, Agglomération du Nord, at Oignies, France, which

(a) comprise anthracite (as to approximately 95% of the total weight) and starch as binder (as to the remaining weight);

(b) were manufactured from those constituents by a process involving roll-pressing and heat treatment at about 150°C;

(c) are ovoids marked with one arrow and have an average weight of 20 grammes; and

(d) have a sulphur content not exceeding 0.8% of the total weight.

3. **Anthranor briquettes & Energlo briquettes**, manufactured by Agglonord, Agglomération du Nord, at Oignies, France, which

(a) comprise anthracite (as to approximately 95% of the total weight) and starch as binder (as to the remaining weight);

(b) were manufactured from those constituents by a process involving roll-pressing and heat treatment at about 150°C;

(c) are cushion-shaped briquettes with rounded corners and have an average weight of 30 grammes; and

(d) have a sulphur content not exceeding 0.8% of the total weight.

4. **Antrex briquettes**, manufactured by Agglonord, Agglomération du Nord, at Oignies, France, which

(a) comprise anthracite;

(b) were manufactured from the anthracite by a process involving roll-pressing and heat treatment at about 180°C;

(c) are pillow-shaped ovoids with three small grooves on one side and have an average weight of 40 grammes; and

(d) have a sulphur content not exceeding 1% of the total weight.

4A. **Black Diamond Gem briquettes**, manufactured by Coal Products Limited at Immingham Briquetting Works, Immingham, Humberside, which

(a) comprise anthracite duff (as to 20-30% of the total weight), petroleum coke (as to 40-45% of the total weight), bituminous coal (as to 12-22% of the total weight) and molasses and phosphoric acid binder (as to the remaining weight);

(b) were manufactured from those constituents by a process involving roll-pressing and heat treatment at about 300°C;

(c) are pillow-shaped briquettes marked with two parallel indented lines running latitudinally around the briquette and have an average weight of 160 grammes; and

(d) have a sulphur content not exceeding 1.5% of the total weight.

4B. **BFL Fireside**, marketed by British Fuels Limited and are the same as Supertherm briquettes as described in para 18 below.

4C. **Jewel briquettes**, manufactured by Eldon Colliery Limited at Newfield Works, Bishop Auckland, County Durham which

(a) comprise anthracite (as to approximately 30-50% of the total weight) and Long Beach petroleum coke (as to approximately 50-70% of the total weight) and a carbohydrate binder (as to the remaining weight);

(b) were manufactured from those constituents by a process involving roll pressing and heat treatment at at about 150°C;

(c) are unmarked pillow-shaped briquettes and have an average weight of 33 grammes; and

(d) have a sulphur content not exceeding 1.5% of the total weight.

5. **Centurion briquettes**, manufactured by Greystone Heating Marketing Limited at Hamilton, Lanarkshire, which

(a) comprise anthracite (as to approximately 90% of the total weight) and molasses and phosphoric acid as binder (as to the remaining weight);

(b) were manufactured from those constituents by a process involving roll-pressing and heat treatment at about 250°C;

(c) are unmarked ovoids and have an average weight of 35 grammes; and

(d) have a sulphur content not exceeding 1.5% of the total weight.

6. **Clean Flame briquettes**, manufactured by NSM Mining (South Wales) Limited at Llanelli, Dyfed which

(a) comprise a blend of anthracite and semi-anthracite coal (as to approximately 94.5% of the total weight) and hard grade bitumen binder (as to the remaining weight);

(b) were manufactured from those constituents by a process involving roll-pressing and heat treatment at about 250°C;

(c) are unmarked pillow-shaped briquettes and have an average weight of 100 grammes; and

(d) have a sulphur content not exceeding 1.5% of the total weight.

7. **Coalite** manufactured by Coalite Products Limited at Bolsover, near Chesterfield, Derbyshire and at Grimethorpe, Yorkshire using a low temperature carbonisation process.

8. **Coke** manufactured by

(a) Coal Products Limited at Cwm Coking Works, Llantwit Fardre, Pontypridd, Mid Glamorgan and sold as "Sunbrite";

(b) Monckton Coke & Chemical Company Limited at Royston, near Barnsley, South Yorkshire and sold as "Sunbrite" or "Monckton Boiler Beans";

(c) Association Cooperative Zelandaise de Carbonisation at Sluiskil, The Netherlands and sold as "Dutch (Sluiskil) Coke Doubles";

(d) Centrala Handlu Zagraniczengo Weglokoks, and sold as "Glowbrite";

(e) SSM Coal Limited at Immingham Dock, Grimsby, South Humberside and sold as "Gloco";

(f) British Steel Plc at Teesside Works, Redcar, Cleveland and sold as "Redcar Coke Nuts (Doubles)";

(g) Coal Products Limited at Cwm Coking Works, Pontypridd, South Wales and sold as "Cwm Coke Doubles".

8AA **Cosycoke (also marketed as Lionheart Crusader or Sunbrite Plus)**, manufactured by Monckton Coke & Chemical Company Limited at Royston, near Barnsley, South Yorkshire, and Aimcor Supercoke (also marketed as Supercoke), manufactured by M & G Fuels Limited at Hartlepool Docks, Hartlepool, Cleveland, which (in each case)

(a) comprise sized hard coke (as to approximately 45-65% of the total weight) and sized petroleum coke (as to the remaining weight);

(b) were manufactured from those constituents by blending;

(c) are unmarked random shapes; and

(d) have a sulphur content not exceeding 2% of the total weight.

8A. **Ecobrite briquettes**, manufactured by Arigna Fuels Limited at Arigna, Carrick-on-Shannon. County Roscommon, which

(a) comprise anthracite fines (as to approximately 96% of the total weight) and starch as binder (as to the remaining weight);

(b) were manufactured from those constituents by a process involving roll-pressing and heat treatment at about 250°C;

(c) are unmarked pillow-shaped briquettes in two sizes having an average weight of 37 grammes for the smaller size and 48 grammes for the larger size; and

(d) have a sulphur content not exceeding 1.5% of the total weight.

9. **Extracite briquettes**, manufactured by Sophia-Jacoba Handelsgesellschaft GmbH at Hückelhoven, Germany, which

(a) comprise anthracite duff (as to approximately 95.5% of the total weight) and ammonium lignosulphonate lye as binder (as to the remaining weight);

(b) were manufactured from those constituents by a process involving roll-pressing and heat treatment at about 260°C;

(c) are cushion-shaped briquettes with a silvery appearance and are marked with the letters "S" and "J" and have an average weight of 40 grammes; and

(d) have a sulphur content of approximately 1.2% of the total weight.

10. **Fireglo briquettes**, manufactured by Les Combustibles de Normandie at Caen, France, and by La Société Rouennaise de Defumage at Rouen, France which

(a) comprise washed Welsh duffs (as to approximately 92% of the total weight) and coal pitch binder (as to the remaining weight);

(b) were manufactured from those constituents by a process involving roll-pressing and heat treatment at about 330°C;

(c) are ovoids with three lines on one side and are smooth

on the other side and have an average weight of 30 grammes; and

(d) have a sulphur content not exceeding 0.8% of the total weight.

11. **Flamelite pellets**, manufactured by Alfred McAlpine Energy Limited at Rheola Works, Resolven, West Glamorgan, which

(a) comprise pre-mixed anthracite duff and filter cake combined with a fixed proportion of starch-based binder;

(b) were manufactured from those constituents by a process involving extrusion and heat treatment at about 100°C;

(c) are unmarked pellets approximately 25mm in diameter and between 20mm and 35mm in length; and

(d) have a sulphur content not exceeding 1% of the total weight.

12. **Homefire briquettes**, manufactured by Coal Products Limited at Coventry, Warwickshire, which

(a) comprise crushed bituminous coal;

(b) were manufactured from the coal by a process involving heat treatment at about 450°C and extrusion;

(c) are unmarked hexagonal briquettes and have an average weight of 200 grammes; and

(d) have a sulphur content not exceeding 1.5% of the total weight.

12A. **Kola briquettes**, manufactured by Allied Smokeless Fuels Limited at Foynes, County Limerick, which

(a) comprises anthracite fines and coal blends (as to approximately 70% of the total weight), petroleum coke (as to approximately 70% of the total weight), and molasses and phosphoric acid as binder (as to the remaining weight);

(b) were manufactured from those constituents by a process involving roll-pressing and heat treatment at between 250°C and 280°C;

(c) are pillow-shaped briquettes, with one indented line running latitudinally around the briquette, in two sizes having an average weight of 42 grammes for the smaller size and 85 grammes for the larger size; and

(d) have a sulphur content not exceeding 1.5% of the total weight.

12AA. **Homefire (R) briquettes**, manufactured by Coal Products Limited at Coventry, Warwickshire, which

(a) comprise anthracite fines (as to 40-60% of the total weight), char (as to 40-60% of the total weight), bituminous coal (as to 0-10% of the total weight) and an organic binder as to the remaining weight;

(b) were manufactured from those constituents by a process involving extrusion;

(c) are unmarked hexagonal briquettes having an average weight of 240 grammes; and

(d) have a sulphur content not exceeding 1.5% of the total weight.

12AB. **Island Lump and Island Nuts**, manufactured by

Unocal Refinery, California, United States of America, which

(a) comprise petroleum coke;

(b) were manufactured from petroleum coke by a process involving heat treatment and steam injection;

(c) are unmarked random shapes and have an average weight of 80 grammes (Island Lump) or 30 grammes (Island Nuts); and

(d) have a sulphur content not exceeding 2% of the total weight.

12AAA. **Homefire Ovals (R)**, manufactured by Coal Products Limited at Chesterfield, Derbyshire, which

(a) comprise anthracite fines (as to approximately 50-75% of the total weight), petroleum coke (as to approximately 20-45% of the total weight), bituminous coal (as to approximately 5-17% of the total weight) and an organic binder (as to the remaining weight);

(b) were manufactured from those constituents by a process involving roll pressing;

(c) are pillow-shaped briquettes with two parallel indented lines running latitudinally around the briquette and have an average weight of 130 grammes; and

(d) have a sulphur content not exceeding 1.5% of the total weight.

12AAB. **Homefire (Improved) briquettes**, manufactured by Coal Products Limited at Coventry, Warwickshire, which

(a) comprise anthracite fines (as to approximately 40-70% of the total weight), petroleum coke (as to approximately 20-45% of the total weight), char (as to approximately 0-10% of the total weight), bituminous coal (as to approximately 5-30% of the total weight) and an organic binder (as to the remaining weight);

(b) were manufactured from those constituents by a process involving roll pressing;

(c) have a volatile content in the finished briquette of not less than 9% nor more than 15% of the total weight on a dry basis;

(d) are unmarked hexagonal briquettes and have an average weight of 140 grammes; and

(e) have a sulphur content not exceeding 1.5% of the total weight.

12B. **Long Beach Lump nuts** (otherwise known as LBL nuts), manufactured by Aimcor Carbon Corp. at Long Beach, California, USA, which

(a) comprise petroleum coke (as to approximately 85-100% of the total weight), limestone (as to approximately 0-10% of the total weight) and coal tar pitch (as to the remaining weight);

(b) were manufactured from those constituents by a process involving heat treatment and steam injection;

(c) are unmarked random shapes; and

(d) have a sulphur content not exceeding 2% of the total weight.

13. **Maxibrite briquettes**, manufactured by Maxibrite Limited at Llantrisant, Mid Glamorgan, which

(a) comprise anthracite fines (as to approximately 99% of the total weight) and bitumen as binder (as to the remaining weight);

(b) were manufactured from those constituents by a process involving roll-pressing and heat treatment at between 270°C and 300°C;

(c) are cushion-shaped briquettes marked with the letter "M" and have an average weight of 35 grammes; and

(d) have a sulphur content of approximately 1% of the total weight.

13A. **Maxiflame briquettes**, manufactured by Maxibrite Limited at Llantrisant, Mid Glamorgan, which

(a) comprise anthracite fines (as to approximately 99% of the total weight) and bitumen as binder (as to the remaining weight);

(b) were manufactured from those constituents by a process involving roll-pressing and heat treatment at between 270°C and 300°C;

(c) are cushion-shaped briquettes marked with the letters "MF" and have an average weight of 80 grammes; and

(d) have a sulphur content of approximately 1% of the total weight.

13B. Revoked by 1998 Regulations, SI 2154.

13BB. **Natura briquettes**, manufactured by NSM Mining (South Wales Limited at Taybrite Plant, Llanelli, Dyfed, which

(a) comprise anthracite fines (as to approximately 90% of the total weight) and molasses and phosphoric binder (as to the remaining weight);

(b) were manufactured from those constituents by a process involving roll pressing and heat treatment at about 250°C;

(c) are cushion-shaped briquettes with a red coating having a central line running latitudinally around the briquette and have an average weight of 48 grammes; and

(d) have a sulphur content not exceeding 1.5% of the total weight.

14. **New Taybrite briquettes**, manufactured by NSM Mining (South Wales) Limited at Llanelli, Dyfed, which

(a) comprise anthracite fines (as to approximately 94% of the total weight) and bitumen as binder (as to the remaining weight);

(b) were manufactured from those constituents by a process involving agglomeration with steam, roll-pressing and heat treatment at about 280°C;

(c) are cushion-shaped briquettes imprinted with a flame motif and have an average weight of 47 grammes; and

(d) have a sulphur content of approximately 1% of the total weight.

14A. **Newflame briquettes**, manufactured by Maxibrite Limited, at Llantrisant, Mid-Glamorgan, which

(a) comprise anthracite (as to approximately 75% of the total weight), petroleum coke (as to approximately 21% of the total weight) and starch with a catalyst binder (as to the remaining weight);

(b) were manufactured from those constituents by a process involving roll pressing and heat treatment at about 250°C;

(c) are unmarked pillow-shaped briquettes and have an average weight of 78 grammes; and

(d) have a sulphur content not exceeding 2% of the total weight.

15. **Phurnacite briquettes**, manufactured by Coal Products Limited at Immingham Briquetting Works, Immingham, Humberside, which

(a) comprise anthracite duff (as to approximately 65% to 85% of the total weight), petroleum coke (up to approximately 20% of the total weight) and a molasses and phosphoric acid as binder (as to the remaining weight);

(b) were manufactured from those constituents by a process involving roll-pressing and heat treatment at about 300°C;

(c) are ovoid-shaped briquettes with two parallel indented lines running longitudinally around the briquette and have an average weight of 40 grammes; and

(d) have a sulphur content not exceeding 1.5% of the total weight.

16. Revoked by 1998 (Amendment No. 2) Regulations, SI 3096.

16A. **Homefire ovals**, manufactured by Coal Products Limited at Immingham Briquetting Works, Immingham, Humberside, which

(a) comprise anthracite duff (as to approximately 57% of the total weight), petroleum coke (as to approximately 17% of the total weight), bituminous coal (as to approximately 13% of the total weight) and molasses and phosphoric acid as binder (as to the remaining weight);

(b) were manufactured from those constituents by a process involving roll-pressing and heat treatment at about 300°C;

(c) are pillow-shaped briquettes with two parallel indented lines running latitudinally around the briquette and have an average weight of 135 grammes; and

(d) have a sulphur content not exceeding 1.5% of the total weight.

16B. **Safelight Firelogs**, manufactured by Advanced Natural Fuels Limited, at Pocklington, East Yorkshire, which

(a) comprise woodchip (as to approximately 40% to 55% of the total weight) and Palm Wax binder (as to approximately 45% to 60% of the total weight);

(b) were manufactured from those constituents by a process involving pressing of the mixed ingredients at about 40° to 50°C;

(c) are rectangular hard finish Firelogs with two deep overlapping slots in the top surface, a single continuous slot in the base surface, and have an average weight of 1.8 kilogrammes; and

(d) have a sulphur content not exceeding 2% of the total weight.

17. **Sovereign briquettes**, manufactured by the Monckton Coke & Chemical Company Limited at Royston, near Barnsley, South Yorkshire, which

(a) comprise anthracite (as to approximately 75% of the total weight), coal and reactive coke (as to approximately 21% of the total weight) and cold-setting resin binder (as to the remaining weight);

(b) were manufactured from those constituents by a process involving extrusion;

(c) are unmarked hexagonal briquettes and have an average weight of 130 grammes; and

(d) have a sulphur content not exceeding 2% of the total weight.

17A.**Sunbrix briquettes**, manufacture by Yarraboldy Briquette Company Limited at Rockhampton, Queensland, Australia, which

(a) comprise anthracite (as to approximately 90% of the total weight) and cold setting organic binder as to the remaining weight;

(b) were manufactured from those constituents by a process involving roll pressing;

(c) are unmarked ovoids which have an average weight of 50 grammes; and

(d) have a sulphur content not exceeding 1% of the total weight.

17AB**Supabrite coke doubles**, manufactured by H.J. Banks & Company Limited at Inkerman Road Depot, Tow Law, County Durham, which

(a) comprise metallurgical coke (as to approximately 40 to 60% of the total weight) and petroleum coke (as to the remaining weight);

(b) were manufacturered from those constituents by a process involving blending and screening;

(c) are unmarked random shapes; and

(d) have a sulphur content not exceeding 1.95% of the total weight.

17B.**Supacite briquettes**, manufactured by Maxibrite Limited at Llantrisant, Mid-Glamorgan, which

(a) comprise anthracite (as to approximately 95% of the total weight) and starch and catalyst as binder (as to the remaining weight);

(b) were manufactured from those constituents by a process involving roll pressing and heat treatment at about 240°C;

(c) are unmarked ovoids and have an average weight of 45 grammes; and

(d) have a sulphur content not exceeding 1.5% of the total weight.

18. **Supertherm briquettes**, manufactured by Coal Products Limited at Shildon, County Durham, which

(a) comprise a blend (in the proportion of 19:1) of anthracite and medium volatile coal (as to approximately 93% of the total weight) and cold-setting organic binder (as to the remaining weight);

(b) were manufactured from those constituents by a process involving roll-pressing;

(c) are unmarked ovoids and have an average weight of 160 grammes; and

(d) have a sulphur content not exceeding 1.5% of the total weight.

18A.**Supertherm II briquettes**, manufactured by Coal Products Limited at Shildon, County Durham, which

(a) comprise anthracite (as to approximately 36-51% of the total weight), petroleum coke (as to approximately 40-55% of the total weight) and an organic binder (as to the remaining weight);

(b) were manufactured from those constituents by a process involving roll pressing at the ambient temperature;

(c) are unmarked ovoids and have an average weight of 140 grammes; and

(d) have a sulphur content not exceeding 2% of the total weight.

18B.**Taybrite briquettes** (otherwise known as Surefire briquettes), manufactured by Coal Products Limited at Immingham Briquetting Works, North East Lincolnshire, which

(a) comprise anthracite (as to approximately 60% to 80% of the total weight), petroleum coke (as to approximately 10% to 30% of the total weight) and a molasses and phosphoric acid binder (as to the remaining weight);

(b) were manufactured from those constituents by a process involving roll pressing and heat treatment at about 300EC;

(c) are pillow-shaped briquettes marked with a single indented line running longitudinally along each face, offset from its counterpart by 10 millimetres or unmarked, and in either case have an average weight of 75 grammes; and

(d) have a sulphur content not exceeding 2% of the total weight.

19. **Thermac briquettes**, manufactured by Coal Products Limited at Shildon, County Durham, which

(a) comprise anthracite (as to approximately 90% of the total weight) and cold-setting organic binder (as to the remaining weight);

(b) were manufactured from those constituents by a process involving roll-pressing;

(c) are unmarked pillow-shaped briquettes and have an average weight of 48 grammes; and

(d) have a sulphur content not exceeding 1.5% of the total weight.

20. **Thermobrite briquettes & Thermaglow briquettes**, manufactured by Volkseigener Betrieb Gaskombinat "Fritz Selbmann" Schwarze Pumpe at Lauchhammer, Germany, which

(a) comprise milled lignite;

(b) were manufactured from the lignite by a process involving extrusion, drying and heat treatment at a temperature greater than 900°C;

(c) are unmarked briquettes which are produced in three sizes: Thermobrite or Thermaglow Large, Thermobrite or Thermaglow Doubles and Thermobrite or Thermaglow Beans; and

(d) have a sulphur content not exceeding 2% of the total weight.

Appendix 2.6b: Smoke Control (Exempted Fireplaces) Orders

(These Orders cover England and Wales. Similar Orders have been made for Scotland)

Class of Fireplace	*Conditions*
1970 Order (SI 1970 No. 615)	
1. Any fireplace specially designed or adapted for combustion of liquid fuel.	
2. Any fireplace (other than a fireplace fired by pulverised fuel) constructed on or after 31st December 1956 and installed before 1st May 1970 and equipped with mechanical stokers, or adapted between those dates for use with such stokers.	No fuel shall be used other than that for which the mechanical stoker was designed.
3. Any fireplace designed to burn coal (other than a fireplace fired by pulverised coal) with a heating capacity exceeding 150,000 Btu/hr constructed and installed on or after 31st December 1956 and equipped with mechanical stokers or adapted on or after that date for use with such stokers.	No fuel shall be used other than that for which the mechanical stoker was designed.
*4. The fireplace known as the Solid Fuel Ductair Unit, manufactured by Radiation Ltd.	
5. The fireplace known as the Fulgora slow combustion Stove, manufactured by Fulgora Stoves Ltd.	No fuel shall be used other than wood waste in clean condition.
*6. The fireplace known as the Housewarmer manufactured for the National Coal Board by Ideal Standard Limited and latterly by Stelrad Group Ltd.	No fuel shall be used other than selected washed coal marketed under the name Housewarm" by agreement with the National Coal Board.
*7. The fireplace known as Wood Chip Fired Air Heater, manufactured by Air Plants (Sales) Ltd.	No fuel shall be used other than clean wood waste of a size within the limits referred to in the manufacturer's instructions.
*8. The fireplace known as the Hounsell Sawdust Burning Stove, manufactured by John Hounsell (Engineers) Ltd.	No fuel shall be used other than wood waste in clean condition.

1970 No. 2 Order (SI 1970 No. 1667)

The Fireplace known as the Triancomatic T 80 and manufactured by Trianco Ltd.

***1971 Order (SI 1971 No. 1265)**

The fireplace known as the Rayburn CB 34 and manufactured by Glynwed Foundries Ltd.

1972 Order (SI 1972 No. 438)

The fireplace known as the Parkray Coalmaster and manufactured by Radiation Parkray Ltd, now T. I. Parkray Ltd.

No fuel shall be used other than selected washed coal marketed under the name "Housewarm" by agreement with the National Coal Board.

1972 No. 2 Order (SI 1972 No. 955)

The fireplace known as the Trianco TGB 17 and manufactured by Trianco Ltd.

1973 Order (SI 1973 No. 2166)

The fireplace known as the Rayburn Prince 101 and the fireplace known as the Rayburn Prince 301, both manufactured by Glynwed Foundries Ltd.

* No longer in production, but where such fireplaces continue in use they remain exempt

Class of Fireplace	*Conditions*

1975 No. 2 Order (SI 1975 No. 1001)

The fireplace known as the Riley Nihot Woodchip Fired Air Heater type NM011 manufactured by Clarke Chapman Ltd, latterly by NEI International Combustion Ltd, Riley Equipment.

No fuel shall be used other than clean wood waste of a size within the limits of the manufacturer's specifications and containing not more than 5% sander dust.

1975 No. 3 Order (SI 1975 No. 1111)

The fireplace known as the Rayburn Prince 76, manufactured by Glynwed Domestic and Heating Appliances Ltd.

No fuel shall be used other than selected washed coal doubles and trebles.

1978 Order (SI 1978 No. 1609)

The fireplace known as the Spanex Wood Fired Air Heater (types UL50, UL75 and UL100 only), manufactured by Spanex Sander GmbH KG of Volpriehausen, Solling, in the Federal Republic of Germany

1. The Fireplace shall be installed, maintained and operated so as to minimise the emission of smoke and in accordance with Issue No 1 of the manufacturer's instructions dated May 1978.
2. No fuel shall be used other than clean wood waste containing not more than 5% sander dust and not more than 1% plastic contamination.

1982 Order (SI 1982 No. 1615)

The fireplace known as the APE Saffire Boiler (in the sizes, expressed in BTUs per hour, as 1M to 8M, 10M and 12M) manufactured by Air Pollution Engineering Limited, now Air Pollution Equipment Ltd.

1. The fireplace shall be installed, maintained and operated so as to minimise the emission of smoke at all times and in accordance with the manufacturer's instructions dated 27 August 1982 and bearing the reference "SAF 250-3000/HW & /S".
2. No fuel shall be used other than sawdust or shavings, or mixtures of sawdust, shavings and offcuts, being fuel containing (by weight) not more than 1 % of plastic material.

1983 Order (SI 1983 No. 277)

The fireplace known as the Rayburn Coalglo C-30 and manufactured, both as an inset model and as a freestanding model, by Glynwed Domestic & Heating Appliances Ltd, now Glynwed Appliances Ltd.

1. The fireplace shall be installed, maintained and operated so as to minimise the emission of smoke at all times and in accordance with the manufacturer's instructions which -
a) in the case of the inset model, bear the date 1 September 1981 and the reference "Code 510" or
b) in the case of the freestanding model, bear the date 1 December 1982 and the reference "Code 510 F".
2. No fuel shall be used other than selected washed coal doubles and trebles (also known as nuts and large nuts).

1983 No. 2 Order (SI 1983 No. 426)

The fireplace known as the Talbott 500 Hot-air Heater (afterburn model) and manufactured by Talbott's Heating Ltd.

1. The fireplace shall be installed, maintained and operated so as to minimise the emission of smoke at all times and in accordance with the manufacturer's instructions dated 1 January 1983 and bearing the reference A1000.
2. No fuel shall be used other than wood off-cuts, woodwaste, pellets, chipboard, plastic covered chip-board (the plastic content of the covering being not more than 1% by weight), cardboard or paper.
3. The afterburn cycle shall last not less than 25 mins. and shall come into operation each time the loading door is opened.

Class of Fireplace	*Conditions*

1983 No. 3 Order (SI 1983 No. 1018)

The fireplace known as the Trianco Coal King' Boiler and manufactured by Trianco Redfyre Ltd.	1. The fireplace shall be installed, maintained and operated so as to minimise the emission of smoke at all times, and in accordance with the manufacturer's instructions dated May 1983 and which - a) in the case of installation instructions bear the reference '47664' and b) in the case of the user, instructions bear the reference '47665'. 2. No fuel shall be used other than selected washed coal doubles or Union Coal Briketts, manufactured by Rheinbraun AG of Germany and comprising lignite compressed into briquettes of approximately 15 centimetres in length with square ends and with a sulphur content not exceeding 1 per cent.

1984 Order (SI 1984 No. 1649)

The Parkray Coalmaster II manufactured by T.I. Parkray Limited, both as an inset model and as a free standing model.	a) installation instructions for for the inset model: reference "List No. 1048/June 1983 8402"; b) installation instructions for the free-standing model: reference "List No. 1058/February 1984"; and c) user's instructions for both models: reference "List No. 1049/September 1983".
The Spacewarmer B200 manufactured by Clean Air Systems.	installation operation and maintenance instructions: reference "B200/DEC 1983".
The Spacewarmer B500 manufactured by Clean Air Systems.	installation operation and maintenance instructions: reference "B500/DEC 1983".

1985 Order (SI 1985 No 864)

The SE60 Coalburner Stove manufactured by Jetmaster Fires Limited.	a) installation instructions: reference "SE60/18/84"; b) operating and maintenance instructions: reference "SE 60/28/84".
The Worcester Centair 40 Solid Fuel Warm Air Heater manufactured by Worcester Engineering Co. Limited	a) installation instructions: reference "BC40.1.2 July 1983"; b) operating and maintenance instructions: reference "BC40.OM2 July 1983".

1986 Order (SI 1986 No. 638)

The Triancomatic 60 boiler manufactured by Trianco Redfyre Limited.	1. The fireplace shall be installed, maintained and operated so as to minimise the emission of smoke at all times, and in accordance with the manufacturer's instructions dated 24 July 1985 and which - a) in the case of the installation instructions bear the reference "No. 45576"; and b) in the case of the user instructions bear the reference "No. 45574".

Class of Fireplace

Conditions

	2. No fuel shall be used other than the washed coals recommended in the manufacturer's user instructions: reference "No. 45574".
The Worcester Coalstream 17.5 kw underfeed stoker manufactured by Worcester Engineering Company Limited	1. The fireplace shall be installed, maintained and operated so as to minimise the emission of smoke at all times, and in accordance with the manufacturer's instructions dated 1 August 1985 and which a) in the case of the installation instructions bear the reference No. "ZKLIT 140"; and b) in the case of the user instructions bear the reference No." ZKLIT 139". 2. No fuel shall be used other than the washed coals recommended in the manufacturer's user instructions: reference No. "ZK LIT 139".
The Corsair 300HW, 500HW and 750HW boilers manufactured by Erithglen Limited.	The fireplace shall be installed, maintained and operated so as to minimise the emission of smoke at all times, and in accordance with the manufacturer's instructions: reference "001 August 1985".

1988 Order (SI 1988 No. 2282)

The Babcock Worsley Fluidised Bed Combuster manufactured by Babcock Robey Limited.	1. The fireplace shall be installed, maintained and operated so as to minimise the emission of smoke at all times, and in accordance with the manufacturer's instructions dated 30 April 1986 and which bear the reference No. "C06/0016". 2. No fuel shall be used other than the waste derived fuel recommended in the manufacturer's instructions. 3. The fireplace shall be operated as a single unit with - a) the Tollemache Drier manufactured by Newell Dunford Limited; and b) The Venturi Scrubber manufactured by Air Pollution Control Limited.
The CBR Flexifuel Heater, models 300, 400 and 600 manufactured by CBR Fabrications Limited	1. The fireplaces shall be installed, maintained and operated so as to minimise the emission of smoke at all times, and in accordance with the manufacturer's instructions, which bear the reference FF/CBR Turbo Heat 88. 2. No fuel shall be used other than hard or soft wood off-cuts, chipboard or plastic coated chipboard. 3. The fireplace shall not be used to burn sawdust in bulk or plastic materials other than plastic coated chipboard.
The Eclipse Junior, Standard, Senior, Jumbo 30 and Jumbo 50 incinerators, manufactured by Northern Incinerators Limited.	1. The fireplaces shall be installed, maintained and operated so as to minimise the emission of smoke at all times, and in accordance with the manufacturer's instructions dated 21 June 1988 and which bear the reference "NORCIN/ TECH/88". 2. No fuel shall be used, other than fuel consisting of paper, cardboard cartons, scrap wood, foliage, combustible floor sweepings and other waste from

Class of Fireplace	*Conditions*

	domestic, commercial and industrial activities containing no more than 20% of restaurant and cafeteria waste, and containing less than 5% by weight of coated papers, plastic or rubber waste.
The Haat LD, MD and HD Incinerators manufactured by Haat Incineration Limited.	1. The fireplaces shall be installed, maintained and operated so as to minimise the emission of smoke at all times, and in accordance with the manufacturer's instructions dated March 1988 and which bear the reference "HAAT/I/CAA". 2. No fuel shall be used, other than fuel consisting of paper, cardboard cartons, scrap wood, foliage, combustible floor sweepings and other waste from domestic, commercial and industrial activities containing no more than 20% of restaurant and cafeteria waste, and containing less than 5% by weight of coated papers, plastic or rubber waste.
The Holden Heat House 29.3kw and 45.4kw underfeed bituminous coal burning boilers manufactured by Holden Heat plc.	1. The fireplaces shall be installed, maintained and operated so as to minimise the emission of smoke at all times, and in accordance with the manufacturer's instructions which - a) in the case of the installation instructions bear the reference "HH861B"; and b) in the case of the user instructions bear the reference "HH861A". 2. No fuel shall be used other than the washed coals recommended in the manufacturer's user instructions.
The RanHeat Boiler Type RHA20, manufactured by RanHeat, Energy A/S.	1. The fireplace shall be installed, maintained and operated so as to minimise the emission of smoke at all times, and in accordance with the manufacturer's instructions dated 30 March 1988 and which bear the reference "RHGBEA 30388". 2. No fuel shall be used other than hard and soft wood shavings.
The Talbott Pirojet P150 Heater manufactured by Talbott's Heating Limited.	1. The fireplace shall be installed, maintained and operated so as to minimise the emission of smoke at all times, and in accordance with the manufacturer's instructions dated February 1987 and which bear the reference No. "P150-2-87". 2. No fuel shall be used other than hard or soft wood off-cuts, chipboard or plastic coated chipboard. 3. When the fireplace is used to burn chipboard and plastic coated chipboard, an afterburner which is supplied with the fireplace and which must be capable of continuously producing 20 megajoules of heat per hour, shall be used. 4. The fireplace shall not be used to burn sawdust in bulk or plastic materials other than plastic coated chipboard.

Class of Fireplace	*Conditions*
The Talbott Pirojet P300 Heater manufactured by Talbott's Heating Limited.	1. The fireplace shall be installed, maintained and operated so as to minimise the emission of smoke at all times, and in accordance with the manufacturer's instructions dated February 1987 and which bear the reference No. "P300-2-87". 2. No fuel shall be used other than hard or soft wood off-cuts, chipboard or plastic coated chipboard. 3. When the fireplace is used to burn chipboard and plastic coated chipboard an afterburner which is supplied with the fireplace and which must be capable of continuously producing 40 megajoules of heat per hour, shall be used. 4. The fireplace shall not be used to burn sawdust in bulk or plastic materials other than plastic coated chipboard.
The Talbott Pirojet P600 Heater manufactured by Talbott's Heating Limited.	1. The Fireplace shall be installed, maintained and operated so as to minimise the emission of smoke at all times, and in accordance with the manufacturer's instructions dated December 1986 and which bear the reference "P600-12-86" 2. No fuel shall be used other than hard or soft wood off-cuts, or chipboard or plastic coated chipboard. 3. When the fireplace is used to burn chipboard, and plastic coated chipboard an afterburner which is supplied with the fireplace and which must be capable of continuously producing 75 megajoules of heat per hour, shall be used. 4. The fireplace shall not be used to burn sawdust in bulk or plastic materials other than plastic coated chipboard.
The Triancomatic 90 boiler manufactured by Trianco Redfyre Limited	1. The fireplace shall be installed, maintained and operated so as to minimise the emission of smoke at all times, and in accordance with the manufacturer's instructions dated July 1987 and which - a) in the case of the installation instructions bear the reference "No. 46576"; and b) in the case of the user instructions bear the reference "No. 46574". 2. No fuel shall be used other than the washed coals recommended in the manufacturer's user instructions.
The Triancomatic 140 boiler manufactured by Trianco Redfyre Limited.	1. The fireplace shall be installed, maintained and operated so as to minimise the emission of smoke at all times, and in accordance with the manufacturer's instructions dated November 1986 and which - a) in the case of the installation instructions bear the reference No. 48375"; and b) in the case of the user instructions bear the reference No. 48374". 2. No fuel shall be used other than the washed coals recommended in the manufacturer's user instructions.

Class of Fireplace

Conditions

1989 Order (SI 1989 No. 1769)

The Talbott T5-1M Automatic Heater manufactured by Talbott's Heating Ltd.

1. The fireplace shall be installed, maintained and operated so as to minimise the emission of smoke at all times, and in accordance with the manufacturer's instructions bearing the reference Jan. 89 T5-A-1-89.
2. No fuel other than softwood shavings, hardwood shavings or chipboard dust shall be used.

The Nordist Waste Fired System models 10, 11, 12, 13, 14, 15, 16, 17, 18, 19, 20, 21, 22 and 23 manufactured in part by Nordfab A/S and in part by Danstoker A/S.

1. The fireplace shall be installed, maintained and operated so as to minimise the emission of smoke at all times, and in accordance with the manufacturer's instructions bearing the reference P.S.501 9.12.88.
2. No fuel other than softwood shavings, hardwood shavings or sawdust shall be used.

The CBR Flexifuel Heater, models 150 and 200 manufactured by CBR Fabrications Ltd.

1. The fireplace shall be installed, maintained and operated so as to minimise the emission of smoke at all times, and in accordance with the manufacturer's instructions bearing the reference FF/CBR Flexifuel 150/200 1989.
2. No fuel other than hardwood or softwood offcuts, chipboard or plastic coated chipboard shall be used.
3. The fireplace shall not be used to burn sawdust in bulk or plastic materials other than plastic coated chipboard.

The Silent Glow Incinerator, models CCD 450, 600 and 750 manufactured by Silent Glow Incinerators Ltd.

1. The fireplace shall be maintained and operated so as to minimise the emission of smoke at all times, and in accordance with the manufacturer's instructions dated May 1989.
2. No fuel other than solid waste of the types specified in the manufacturer's instructions dated May 1989 shall be used.

The Hughes Edwards 45 Coalflow Boiler manufactured by Hughes Edwards Heating Ltd.

1. The fireplace shall be installed, maintained and operated so as to minimise the emission of smoke at all times, and in accordance with the manufacturer's instructions which:
a) in the case of the installation instructions bear the reference II/02D/07-89, and
b) in the case of the user instructions bear the reference UI/02D/07-89.
2. No fuel other than the washed coals recommended in the manufacturer's instructions bearing the reference II/02D/07-89 shall be used.

1990 Order (SI 1990 No. 345)

The Haat Pioneer ABI Incinerators, models 12, 20, 28 and 36 manufactured by Haat Incineration Limited.

1. The fireplaces shall be installed, maintained and operated so as to minimise the emission of smoke at all times, and in accordance with the manufacturer's instructions bearing the reference "HAAT/2/CAA/10/89".

Class of Fireplace	*Conditions*
	2. No fuel shall be used other than the following fuels used in the mixtures by volume recommended in Appendix A of the manufacturer's instructions: paper, cardboard, corrugated paper, office or domestic waste, wood, polythene sheet or foam, polypropylene, nylon, polyethylene, rubber foam backed carpet, polystyrene, polyurethane and glass fibre reinforced plastics.
The Triancomatic 45 boiler manufactured by Trianco Redfyre Limited.	1. The fireplace shall be installed, maintained and operated so as to minimise the emission of smoke at all times, and in accordance with the manufacturer's instructions dated September 1989 and which - (a) in the case of the installation instructions bear the reference "No. 44359"; and (b) in the case of the user instructions bear the reference "No. 44358". 2. No fuel shall be used other than the washed coals recommended in the manufacturer's user instructions.

1990 Order (SI No. 2457)

Class of Fireplace	*Conditions*
The Intrepid II woodstove manufactured by Vermont Castings, Inc.	1. The fireplace shall be installed, maintained and operated in accordance with the manufacturer's instructions bearing the reference "AMENDED No. 20917C U.K. MAY 1990". 2. No fuel shall be used other than 16" firewood that has been split, stacked and air-dried.
The Spacewarmer B200 manufactured by Clearair Limited.	1. The fireplace shall be installed, maintained and operated in accordance with the manufacturer's instructions bearing the reference "B200/DEC 83". 2. No fuel shall be used other than hardwood or softwood offcuts, a mixture of offcuts (hardwood or softwood) and sawdust with no more than 50% of the mixture being sawdust, chipboard offcuts or plastic coated chipboard offcuts. 3. The fireplace shall not be used to burn chipboard or plastic coated chipboard unless an afterburner, supplied by the manufacturer of the fireplace and capable of producing 50 megajoules of heat per hour, has been fitted to the fireplace.
The Spacewarmer B500 manufactured by Clearair Limited.	1. The fireplace shall be installed, maintained and operated in accordance with the manufacturer's instructions bearing the reference "B500/DEC 83". 2. No fuel shall be used other than hardwood or softwood offcuts.
The Turbo Heat, models 1000 and 1200 manufactured by CBR Engineers Limited.	1. The fireplace shall be installed, maintained and operated in accordance with the manufacturer's

Class of Fireplace	*Conditions*

| | instructions bearing the reference "CBR TURBO' HEAT 1000 TO 1200 1990".
2. No fuel shall be used other than hardwood or softwood offcuts, chipboard offcuts or plastic coated chipboard offcuts. |
| The Talbott's Energy Saving Wood Waste Burning Automatic Warm Air Heaters, models T1.5/A, T3/A, T5/A and TM/A manufactured by Talbotts Heating Limited. | 1. The fireplaces shall be installed, maintained and operated in accordance with the manufacturer's instructions bearing the reference "T/A JANUARY 1990".
2. No fuel shall be used other than hardwood or softwood shaving or sawdust. |

1991 Order (SI No. 2892)

The Hughes Edwards Model 65 hot water boiler manufactured by Hughes Edwards Heating Limited.	1. The fireplace shall be installed, maintained and operated in accordance with the manufacturer's instructions bearing the reference "II/02D/11-90 and UI/02D/11-90". 2. No fuel shall be used other than bituminous Coalflow pearls distributed by the British Coal Corporation.
The Jansen Design stove, using the five channel system, manufactured by Kakkel Ovnsmakeriet as.	1. The fireplace shall be installed, maintained and operated in accordance with the manufacturer's instructions bearing the reference "CSC-JDS-OI dated 21/10/91". 2. No fuel shall be used other than wood.
The Resolute Acclaim woodstove manufactured by Vermont Castings, Inc.	1. The fireplace shall be installed, maintained and operated in accordance with the manufacturer's instructions bearing the reference "AMENDED No. 200 - 0908 U.K. OCTOBER 1991". 2. No fuel shall be used other than 16" firewood that has been split, stacked and air-dried.
The Talbott's Warm Air Heaters Down Firing range models D250, D500 and D700 manufactured by Talbotts Heating Limited.	1. The fireplaces shall be installed, maintained and operated in accordance with the manufacturer's instructions bearing the reference "MAY 1991 Ref No: D257". 2. No fuel shall be used other than hardwood or softwood offcuts, chipboard, plastic coated chipboard or cardboard.

1992 Order (SI No. 2811)

| The Cronspisen stove, using the five channel chimney system, manufactured by Cronspisen Produktion AB. | 1. The fireplace is installed, maintained and operated in accordance with the manufacturer's instructions bearing the reference "January 1992. Serial No: UM 351B".
2. No fuel is used other than firewood that has been split, stacked and air-dried. |
| The RanHeat Boiler Types RHA 160, 200 and 250, manufactured by RanHeat Energy GB Limited. | 1. The fireplaces are installed, maintained and operated in accordance with the manufacturer's instructions dated 30th March 1988 bearing the reference "RHGBEA 30388".
2. No fuel is used other than hard and soft wood shavings. |

Class of Fireplace	*Conditions*
The Defiant Encore manufactured by VCW International Limited.	1. The fireplace is installed, maintained and operated in accordance with the manufacturer's instructions dated "November 1991 bearing the reference 200-8632". 2. No fuel is used other than firewood that has been split, stacked and air-dried.

1993 Order (SI No. 2277)

The Apollo incinerator types 10, 25 and 50 manufactured by Apollo Incineration Systems Limited.	1. The incinerators shall be installed, maintained and operated in accordance with the manufacturer's instructions dated 2nd November 1992 and bearing the reference "Apollo 10-25-50". 2. No fuel shall be used other than wood, wood shavings, cardboard and polythene.
The Clearview models 650 and 750, and the Vision 500 model, manufactured by Clearview Stoves.	1. The fireplaces shall be installed, maintained and operated in accordance with the manufacturer's instructions dated 1st January 1993 and, in the case of the Clearview models 650 and 750, bearing the reference "1/42" and, in the case of the Vision 500 model, bearing the reference "V1/42". 2. No fuel shall be used other than firewood which has been split, stacked and air dried.
The Farm 2000 boilers HT60, HT70, HT80 and BB154/2V manufactured by Farm 2000 Limited.	1. The boilers shall be installed, maintained and operated in accordance with the manufacturer's instructions which, in the case of models HT60, HT70 and HT80, are dated 1st July 1993 and bear the reference "HT60/70/80", and, in the case of model BB154/2V, are dated 1st September 1993 and bear the reference "9/93". 2. No fuel shall be used other than cereal straw.

1996 Order (SI No. 1108)

The Dovre woodstove models 500CBW and 700CBW manufactured by Dovre Castings Limited, including those models when referred to by their former reference numbers 500G and 700G respectively.	1. The fireplaces shall be installed, maintained and operated in accordance with the manufacturer's instructions dated October 1993 and bearing the following reference :– (a) model 500G: "500G"; (b) model 700G:"700G". 2. No fuel shall be used other than wood.
The Farm 2000 boiler models BB154, BB154A and BB154/2 (when used with the Farm 2000 conversion kit BB154/2Vcx), maunufactured by Farm 2000 Limited.	1. The boilers shall be installed in accordance with the manufacturer's instructions dated May 1994 and bearing the reference "BB154/2VC", and maintained and operated in accordance with the manufacturer's instructions dated September 1993 and bearing the reference "BB154/2V". 2. No fuel shall be used other than cereal straw.
The Farm 2000 model HT6 (when used with the Farm 2000 conversion kit HT60cx), the HT6PLUS and HT600 (when each is used with the Farm conversion kit HT70cx), and the HT7 and HT8 (when each is used with the Farm	1. The boilers shall be installed in accordance with the manufacturer's instructions dated May 1994 and bearing the reference "HT6780" and "HT 6781", and maintained and operated in accordance with the manufacturer's

Class of Fireplace	*Conditions*

2000 conversion kit HT80cx), manufactured by Farm 2000 Limited.	instructions dated 1 July 1993 and bearing the reference "HT60/70/80". 2. No fuel shall be used other than cereal straw.

The Jotul catalyst stove models 8TDIC and 12TDIC manufactured by Jotul Limited.	1. The fireplaces shall be installed, maintained and operated in accordance with the manufacturer's instructions dated November 1995 and bearing the following references :–
	    (a) model 8TDIC: "JT8/001" and "J/S/001";
	    (b) mode12TDIC: "JT12/001" and "JT/S/001".
	2. No fuel shall be used other than wood.

The RanHeat appliances models MSU150, MSU300, MSU500, WA150, WA300 and WA500, manufactured by RanHeat Engineering Limited.	1. The appliances shall be installed, maintained and operated in accordance with the manufacturer's instructions dated July 1995 bearing the following references :– (a) models MSU150, MSU300 and MSU500: "MSU150/5001994"; (b) models WA150, WA300 and WA500: "WA150/5001994". 2. No fuel shall be used other than chipboard, fibreboard, melamine coated chipboard, wood offcuts, softwood or hardwood shavings or dust.
The Talbott's Combustion Units, models C1, C2, C3 and C4, manufactured by Talbott's Heating Limited.	1. The fireplaces shall be installed, maintained and operated in accordance with the manufacturer's instructions dated August 1995 and bearing the reference "Issue: C1000/C/Range". 2. No fuel shall be used other than chipboard, or wood shavings, forestry chips or paper briquettes.
The Talbott's Heating models T75, T150, T300, D250B, D500B and D700B, manufactured by Talbott's Heating Limited.	1. The fireplaces shall be installed, maintained and operated in accordance with the manufacturer's instructions dated 1st January 1995 and bearing the following references :– (a) models T75, T150 and T300: "gen/sttech"; (b) models D250B, D500B and D700B: "Gen/Tech". 2. No fuel shall be used other than the following; (a) models T75, T150 and T300: wood offcuts, woodwaste pallets, chipboard, plastic coated chipboard, cardboard or paper; (b) models D250B, D500B and D700B: hardwood or softwood offcuts, chipboard, plastic coated chipboard or cardboard.

1997 Order (SI No. 3009)

The Talbott's Energy Saving Wood Waste Burning Automatic Hot Water Heaters, models T1.5/AB, T3/AB, T5/AB, manufactured by Talbott's Heating Limited.	1. The fireplaces shall be installed, maintained and operated in accordance with the manufacturer's instructions dated October 1993 and bearing the reference "Issue: A1001". 2. No fuel shall be used other than hardwood or softwood shavings or sawdust.

Class of Fireplace

Conditions

The Talbott's Combustion Units, models CM1, CM2, CM3 and CM4, manufactured by Talbott's Heating Limited.

1. The fireplaces shall be installed, maintained and operated in accordance with the manufacturer's instructions dated August 1997 and bearing the reference "Issue: CM897".
2. No fuel shall be used other than wood-waste pallets, medium density fibreboard, melamine faced chipboard, cardboard, paper or untreated and airdried wood offcuts

1999 Order (SI No. 1515)

The Dunsley Yorkshire Stove manufactured by Dunsley Heat Limited.

1. The fireplaces shall be installed, maintained and operated in accordance with the manufacturer's instructions dated 5th August 1998 and bearing the reference "A/22160".
2. No fuel shall be used other than-
(a) untreated dry wood;
(b) peat or peat briquettes with, in either case, less than 25 per cent moisture;
(c) Union Coal Briketts, manufactured by Rheinbraun AG of Germany and comprising lignite compressed into briquette of approximately 15 centimetres in length with square ends and with a sulphur content not exceeding 1 per cent of the total weight;
(d) CPL Wildfire, manufactured by Coal Products Limited, Coventry, which comprise bituminous coal with a volatile content of 32 per cent to 36 per cent (as to approximately 96 per cent of the total weight) and a cold cure resin binder (as to the remaining weight); are manufactured from those constituents by a progress involving roll-pressing; have an average weight of between 80 and 90 grammes or between 160 and 170 grammes; and have a sulphur content not exceeding 1.8 per cent of the total weight.

The I.D.L, M and H incinerators, manufactured by the Incinerator Doctor.

1. The fireplaces shall be installed, maintained and operated in accordance with the manufacturer's instructions dated February 1999 and bearing the reference "I.D.E.I".
2. No fuel shall be used other than paper, cardboard, untreated dry wood, foliage, floor sweepings, and other waste containing no more than 20 per cent by weight of restaurant and cafeteria waste and less than 5 per cent by weight of coated paper, plastic or rubber waste.

The Osier wood burning stove, manufactured by Reinhart von Zschock.

1. The fireplaces shall be installed, maintained and operated in accordance with the manufacturer's instructions dated 30th September 1997 and bearing the reference "CSC/OS/001".
2. No fuel shall be used other than untreated dry wood.

The Trash X Incinerator, models TX25, TX35, TX50, TX35L and TX50L manufactured by Roscoe Fabrications Limited.

1. The fireplaces shall be installed, maintained and operated in accordance with the manufacturer's instructions dated 1998 and bearing the reference "TX/1998".

Class of Fireplace

Conditions

2. No fuel shall be used other than paper, card, untreated dry wood and cotton waste.

The Wood Stone Ovens, models WS- MS-4-W (Mt. Chucknaut), WS-MS-5-W (Mt. Adams), WS-MS-6-W (Mt. Baker) and WS-MS-7-W (Mt. Rainier), manufactured by the Wood Stone Corporation, USA.

1. The fireplaces shall be installed, maintained and operated in accordance with the manufacturer's instructions dated 1998 and bearing the reference "BPWS version 1".
2. No fuel shall be used other than untreated dry wood.

NB. There are no appendices for Chapter 3, Noise.

APPENDIX 4.1
WASTE MANAGEMENT PAPERS

This series of papers provides guidance on all aspects of waste management. Section 35(8) of the Environmental Protection Act 1990 requires regulatory authorities to take account of guidance (such as WMPs) issued by the Secretary of State in the discharge of their licence functions. WMPs listed here were prepared by the Department of the Environment. They are published by The Stationery Office.

WMP 1   A review of options (second edition 1992)

WMP 2/3   [replaced by DOE Guidance, Waste Management Planning - Principles and Practice (1995)

WMP 4   The licensing of waste facilities (third edition 1994)

WMP 4A   Licensing of metal recycling sites (1995)

WMP 5   The relationship between waste disposal authorities and private industry (1976)

WMP 6   Polychlorinated biphenyl (PCB) wastes - a technical memorandum on reclamation, treatment and disposal (1994)

WMP 7   Mineral oil wastes - a technical memorandum on arisings, treatment and disposal (1976)

WMP 8   Heat treatment cyanide wastes - a technical memorandum on arisings, treatment and disposal (second edition 1985)

WMP 9   Halogenated hydrocarbon solvent wastes from cleaning processes - a technical memorandum on reclamation and disposal (1976)

WMP 10   local authority waste disposal statistics 1974/75 (1976)

WMP 11   Metal finishing wastes - a technical memorandum on arisings, treatment and disposal (1976)

WMP 12   Mercury bearing wastes - a technical memorandum on storage, handling, treatment, disposal and recovery (1979)

WMP 13   Tarry and distillation wastes and other chemical based wastes - a technical memorandum on arisings, treatment and disposal (1977)

WMP 14   Solvent wastes (excluding halogenated hydrocarbons) - a technical memorandum on reclamation and disposal (1977)

WMP 15   Halogenated organic wastes - a technical memorandum on arisings, treatment and disposal (1978)

WMP 16   Wood preserving wastes - a technical memorandum on arisings, treatment and disposal (1980)

WMP 17   Wastes from tanning, leather dressing and fellmongering - a technical memorandum on recovery, treatment and disposal (1978)

WMP 18   Asbestos waste - a technical memorandum on arisings and disposal (1979)

WMP 19   Wastes from the manufacture of pharmaceuticals, toiletries and cosmetics - a technical memorandum on arisings, treatment and disposal (1978)

WMP 20   Arsenic bearing wastes - a technical memorandum on recovery, treatment and disposal (1980)

WMP 21   Pesticide wastes - a technical memorandum on arisings and disposal (1980)

WMP 22   Local authority waste disposal statistics 1974/75 to 1977/78 (1978)

WMP 23   Special wastes - a technical memorandum providing guidance on their definition (1981; redraft due 9/97))

WMP 24   Cadmium bearing wastes - a technical memorandum on arisings, treatment and disposal (1984)

WMP 25   Clinical wastes - a technical memorandum on arisings, treatment and disposal (replaced 1999, HSC Guidance: Safe disposal of clinical waste

WMP 26   Landfilling wastes - a technical memorandum on landfill sites (1986)

WMP 26A   Landfill completion - a technical memorandum providing guidance on assessing the completion of licensed landfill sites (1994)

WMP 26B   Landfill design, construction and operation (1995)

WMP 26D   Landfill monitoring (draft published 1/96; publication due Spring 1998)

WMP 26E   Landfill restoration and post closure management (draft 9/96; publication due 7/97)

WMP 26F   Landfill co-disposal (publication due 7/97)

WMP 27   Landfill gas - a memorandum for local authorities on recycling (1991)

WMP 28   Recycling - a memorandum for local authorities on recycling (1991)

*   Waste Policy Guidance: Preparing and revising local authority recycling strategies and recycling plans (DETR, 1998)

WMP 401   Guidance note: Policy on licence surrender (Environment Agency, 1999)

APPENDIX 5.1

FRAMEWORK DIRECTIVE ON WATER POLICY

Draft Priority List of Water Pollutants

The Framework Directive on water policy was finally adopted in September 2000. The draft priority list of water pollutants for control under the Directive was published in February 2000. These substances have been selected on the basis of toxicity, persistence and bioaccumulation and thus the risk they pose to the aquatic environment and to human health. Once agreed, quality standards and discharge controls will be set for all the substances on the List.

Alachlor
Anthracene
Atrazine
Benzene
Brominated diphenylether
Cadmium and its compounds
C_{10-13}-chloralkanes
Chlorfenvinphos
Chlorpyrifos
1,2-Dichloroethane
Dichloromethane

Di(2-ethylhexyl)phthalate
Diuron
Endosulfan (alpha-endosulfan)*
Hexachlorobenzene
Hexachlorobutadiene
Hexachlorocyclohexane (gamma isomer, lindane)*
Isoproturon
Lead and its compounds
Mercury and its compounds
Naphthalene
Nickel and its compounds
Nonylphenols (4-(para)-nonylphenol)*
Octylphenols (para-tert-octylphenol)*
Polyaromatic hydrocarbons (Benzo(a)pyrene, Benzo(b)fluoranthene, Benzo(g, h, i)perylene, Benzo(k)fluoranthene, fluoranthene, indeno (1,2,3-cd)pyrene)*
Pentachlorobenzene
Simazine
Pentachlorophenol
Tributyltin compounds (tributyltin-cation)*
Trichlorobenzenes (1,2,4-Trichlorobenzene)*
Trichloromethane (Chloroform)*
Trifluralin

*   indicative parameter for that group of substances; controls to be placed on the indivdual substances with others in that group to be added if appropriate.

APPENDIX 5.2a

QUALITY REQUIREMENTS FOR BATHING WATER (76/160/EEC)

Parameters		G (Guideline)	I (Mandatory)	Minimum sampling frequency	Method of analysis and inspection
MICROBIOLOGICAL					
1	Total coliforms /100 ml	500	10000	Fortnightly (1)	Fermentation in multiple tubes subculturing of the positive tubes on a confirmation medium.
2	Faecal coliforms /100 ml	100	2000	Fortnightly (1)	Count according to MPN (most probable number) or membrane filtration and culture on an appropriate medium such as Tergitol lactose agar, endo agar. 0.4% Teepol broth, subculturing and identification of the suspect colonies.
					In the case of 1 and 2, the incubation temperature is variable according to whether total or faecal coliforms are being investigated.
3	Faecal streptococci /100ml	100	-	(2)	Litsky method. Count according to MPN (most probable number) or filtration on membrane. Culture on an appropriate membrane.
4	Salmonella / 1 litre	-	0	(2)	Concentration by membrane filtration. Inoculation on a standard membrane. Enrichment - subculturing on isolating - agar identification.
5	Entero viruses PFU/10 litres	-	0	(2)	Concentrating by filtration, flocculation or centrifuging and confirmation.
PHYSICO-CHEMICAL:					
6	pH	-	6 to 9 (0)	(2)	Electrometry with calibration at pH 7 and 9.
7	Colour	-	No abnormal change in colour (0)	Fortnightly (1)	Visual inspection or photometry with standards on the Pt. Co scale.
		-	-	(2)	
8	Mineral oils mg/litre	-	No film visible on the surface of the water and no odour	Fortnightly (1)	Visual and olfactory inspection or extraction using an adequate volume and weighing the dry residue.
		<0.3	-	(2)	
9	Surface-active substances reacting with methylene blue	mg/litre (lauryl-sulfate)	-	No lasting foam	Fortnightly (1)
		<0.3		(2)	Visual inspection or absorption spectrophotometry with methylene blue.
10	Phenols (phenolindices)	mg/litre C_6H_5OH	-	No specific odour	Fortnightly (1)
		≤0.005	≤0.05	(2)	Verification of the absence of specific odour due to phenol or absorption spectrophotometry 4-aminoantipyrine (4 AAP) method.
11	Transparency m	2	1(0) (1)	Fortnightly	Secchi's disc.
12	Dissolved oxygen % saturation O_2	80 to 190	-	(2)	Winkler's method or electrometric method (oxygen meter).
13	Tarry residues and floating materials such as wood, plastic articles, bottles, containers of glass, plastic, rubber or any other substance. Waste or splinters.	Absence		Fortnightly (1)	Visual inspection.

Parameters		G (Guideline)	I (Mandatory)	Minimum sampling frequency	Method of analysis and inspection
14 Ammonia	mg/litre NH4			(3)	Absorption spectrophotometry. Nessler's method, or indophenol blue method.
15 Nitrogen Kjeldahl	mg/litre N			(3)	Kjeldahl method.
16 Pesticides (parathion, HCH, dieldrin)	mg/litre			(2)	Extraction with appropriate solvents and chromatographic determination.
17 Heavy metals such as – arsenic As – cadmium Cd – chrom VI CrVI – lead Pb – mercury Hg	mg/litre			(5)	Atomic absorption possible preceded by extraction
18 Cyanides	mg/litre CN			(2)	Absorption spectrophotometry using a specific reagent
19 Nitrates and phosphates	mg/litre NI, PO$_4$			(2)	Absorption spectrophotometry using a specific reagent

G guide; I mandatory; (0) provision exists for exceeding the limits in the event of exceptional geographical or meteorological conditions; (1) When a sampling taken in previous years produced results which are appreciably better than those in this Annex and when no new factor likely to lower the quality of the water has appeared, the competent authorities may reduce the sampling frequency by a factor of 2; (2) Concentration to be checked by the competent authorites when an inspection in the bathing area shows that the substance may be present or that the quality of the water has deteriorated; (3) These parameters must be checked by the competent authorites when there is a tendency towards the eutrophication of the water.

APPENDIX 5.2b

THE BATHING WATERS (CLASSIFICATION) REGULATIONS 1991

Quality and Additional Sampling Requirements in Compliance with Directive 76/160/EEC

Parameter	Parametric value	Minimum sampling frequency	Method of analysis and inspection
MICROBIOLOGICAL			
1 Total coliforms	10,000/ 100ml	Fortnightly (1)	Fermentation in multiple tubes. Sub-culturing of the positive tubes on a confirmation medium. Either counting according to MPN (most probable number) or membrane filtration, culturing on an appropriate medium, subculturing and identification of the suspect colonies.
2 Faecal coliforms	2,000/ 100ml	Fortnightly (1)	The incubation temperature is variable according to whether total or faecal coliforms are being investigated.
3 Salmonella	Absent in 1 litre	(2)	Membrane filtration, culturing on an appropriate medium, sub-culturing and identification of the suspect colonies.
4 Entero viruses	No plaque forming units in 10 litres	(2)	Concentration (by filtration, flocculation or centrifuging) and confirmation.
PHYSICO-CHEMICAL:			
5 pH	6 to 9	(2)	Electrometry with calibration at pH 7 and 9.
6 Colour	No abnormal change in colour	Fortnightly (1)	Visual inspection or photometry with standards on the platinum cobalt scale.

Parameter	Parametric value	Minimum sampling frequency	Method of analysis and inspection
7 Mineral oils	No film visible on the surface of the water and no odour	Fortnightly (1)	Visual and olfactory inspection.
8 Surface-active substances reacting with methylene blue	No lasting foam	Fortnightly (1)	Visual inspection.
9 Phenols (phenol indices)	No specific odour ≤0.05 mg/litre (C_6H_5OH)	Fortnightly (1) (2)	Olfactory inspection. Absorption spectrophotometry 4-aminoantipyrine (4 AAP) method.
10 Transparency	1 metre	Fortnightly (1)	Secchi's disc.

Notes

1. Samples may be taken at intervals of four weeks where samples taken in previous years show that the waters are of an appreciably higher standard than that required for the classification in question and the quality of the waters has not subsequently deteriorated and is unlikely to do so.
2. Samples must be taken in relation to this parameter when there are grounds for suspecting that there has been a deterioration in the quality of the waters or the substance is likely to be present in the waters.

APPENDIX 5.3a

WATER SUPPLY (WATER QUALITY) REGULATIONS 1989 AND PRIVATE WATER SUPPLIES REGULATIONS 1991

These Regulations will be revoked following full impementation of the 2000 Regulations

Schedule 2: Prescribed Concentrations or Values

Table A

Item	Parameters	Units of Measurement	Concentration or Value (maximum unless otherwise stated)
1.	Colour	mg/l Pt/Co scale	20
2.	Turbidity (including suspended solids)	Formazin turbidity units	4
3.	Odour (including hydrogen sulphide)	Dilution number	3 at 25°C
4.	Taste	Dilution number	3 at 25°C
5.	Temperature	°C	25
6.	Hydrogen ion	pH value	9.5 5.5 (minimum)
7.	Sulphate	mg SO4/l	250
8.	Magnesium	mg Mg/l	50
9.	Sodium	mg Na/l	150
10.	Potassium	mg K/l	12
11.	Dry residues	mg/l	1500 (after drying at 180°C)
12.	Nitrate	mg NO23/l	50
13.	Nitrite	mg NO22/l	0.1
14.	Ammonium (ammonia and ammonium ions)	mg NH24/l	0.5
15.	Kjeldahl nitrogen	mg N/l	1
16.	Oxidizability (permangantate value)	mg O_2/l	5
17.	Total organic carbon	mg C/l	No significant increase over that normally observed
18.	Dissolved or emulsified hydrocarbons (after extraction with petroleum ether); mineral oils	µg/l	10
19.	Phenols	µg C_6H_5OH/l	0.5

20.	Surfactants (as lauryl sulphate)	µg/l	200
21.	Aluminium	µg Al/l	200
22.	Iron	µg Fe/l	200
23.	Manganese	µg Mn/l	50
24.	Copper	µg Cu/l	3000
25.	Zinc	µg Zn/l	5000
26.	Phosphorus	µg P/l	2200
27.	Fluoride	µg F/l	1500
28.	Silver	µg Ag/l	10(i)

Note: (i) If silver is used in a water treatment process, 80 may substituted for 10.

Table B

Item	Parameters	Units of Measurement	Maximum Concentration
1.	Arsenic	µg As/l	50
2.	Cadmium	µg Cd/l	5
3.	Cyanide	µg CN/l	50
4.	Chromium	µg Cr/l	50
5.	Mercury	µg Hg/l	1
6.	Nickel	µg Ni/l	50
7.	Lead	µg Pb/l	50
8.	Antimony	µg Sb/l	10
9.	Selenium	µg Se/l	10
10.	Pesticides and related products:		
	(a) individual substances	µg/1	0.1
	(b) total substances (i)	µg/1	0.5
11.	Polycyclic aromatic hydrocarbons (ii)	µg/1	0.2

Notes: (i) The sum of the detected concentrations of individual substances.
(ii) The sum of the detected concentrations of fluoranthene, benzo 3.4 fluoranthene, benzo 11.12 fluoranthene, benzo 3.4 pyrene, benzo 1.12 perylene and indeno (1,2,3-cd) pyrene.

Table C

1.	Total coliforms	number/100 ml	0
2.	Faecal coliforms	number/100 ml	0
3.	Faecal streptococci	number/100 ml	0
4.	Sulphite-reducing clostridia	number/20ml	≤1(i)
5.	Colony counts	number/1 ml at 22°C or 37°C	No significant increase over that normally observed

Note: (i) Analysis by multiple tube method.

Table D(1)

Item	Parameters	Units of Measurement	Maximum Concentration or Value
1.	Conductivity	µS/cm	1500 at 20°C
2.	Chloride	mg Cl/l	400
3.	Calcium	mg Ca/l	250
4.	Substances extractable in chloroform	mg/l dry residue	1
5.	Boron	µg B/l	2000
6.	Barium	µg Ba/l	1000
7.	Benzo 3,4 pyrene	ng/l	10
8.	Tetrachloromethane	µg/l	3
9.	Trichloroethene	µg/l	30
10.	Tetrachlorothene	µg/l	10

Note: (i) See regulation 3(3)(d).

Table E

Item	Parameters	Units of Measurement	Minimum Concentration(i)
1.	Total hardness	mg Ca/l	60
2.	Alkalinity	mg HCO₃/l	30

Note: (i) See regulation 3(4).

APPENDIX 5.3b
WATER SUPPLY (WATER QUALITY) REGULATIONS 2000

These Regulations will begin coming into force from 1 January 2001, replacing the 1989 (and amendment) Regulations – see chapter 5, 5.17.1. They implement the 1998 EC Drinking Water Directive (98/83/EC) - see chapter 5, 5.7.5.

Schedules 1 and 2 to the Regulations, shown below, list prescribed concentrations and values, and indicator parameters, respectively. Schedules 3 and 4 cover monitoring and analytical methodology.

Schedule 1: Prescribed concentrations and values

Table A: Microbiological parameters

Item	Parameters	Concentration or value (max)	Units of Measurement
	Part I: Directive requirements		
1.	Enterococci	0	number/100 ml
2.	Escherichia coli (E.coli)	0	number/100 ml

[point of compliance: consumers' taps]

	Part II: National requirements		
1.	Coliform bacteria	0	number/100 ml
2.	Escherichia coli (E. coli)	0	number/100 ml

[point of compliance: service reservoirs and water treatment works; 95% of samples to comply from each service reservoir]

Table B: Chemical parameters

Part I: Directive requirements

1.	Acrylamide (i)	0.10	µg/l
2.	Antimony	5.0	µgSb/l
3.	Arsenic	10	µgAs/l
4.	Benzene	1.0	µg/l
5.	Benzo(a)pyrene	0.010	µg/l
6.	Boron	1.0	mgB/l
7.	Bromate	10	µgBrO₃/l
8.	Cadmium	5.0	µgCd/l
9	Chromium	50	µgCr/l
10.	Copper (ii)	2.0	µg Cu/l
11.	Cyanide	50	µgCN/l
12.	1,2 dichloroethane	3.0	µg/l
13.	Epichlorohydrin (i)	0.10	µg/l
14.	Fluoride	1.5	µg F/l
15.	Lead (ii)		
	from 25.12.03-24.12.13	25	µgPB/l
	from 25.12.13	10	
16.	Mercury	1.0	µgHg/l
17.	Nickel (ii)	20	µgNi/l
18.	Nitrate (iii)	50	µgNO₃/l
19.	Nitrite (iii)	0.50	µgNO₂/l
		0.10	µgNO₂/l*
20.	Pesticides (iv, v) aldrin}		
	dieldrin}	0.030	µg/l
	heptachlor} heptachlor epoxide}		
	other pesticides	0.10	µg/l
21.	Total pesticides (vi)	0.50	µg/l
22.	Polycyclic aromatic hydrocarbons (vii)	0.10	µg/l
23.	Selenium	10	µgSe/l
24.	Tetrachloroethene & Trichloroethene (viii)	10	µg/l
25.	Trihalomethanes: total (ix)	100	µg/l
26.	Vinyl chloride (i)	0.50	µg/l

[point of compliance: consumers' taps]

Notes:

i   The parametric value refers to the residual monomer concentration in the water as calculated acccording to specifications of the maximum release from the corresponding polymer in contact with the water. This is controlled by product specification.

ii   See also Reg. 6(6) [Secretary of State to determine how these parameters to be monitored].

iii See also Reg. 4(2)d [when water is to be regarded as unwholesome].

iv   See also definition of "pesticides and related products" in Reg. 2.

v   The parametric value applies to each individual pesticide.

vi   "Pesticides: total" means the sum of the concentrations of the individual pesticides detected and quantified in the monitoring procedure.

vii The specified compounds are: benzo(b)fluoranthene; benzo(k)fluoranthene; benzo(ghi)perylene; and indeno(1,2,3-cd)pyrene.
The parametric value applies to the sum of the concentrations of the individual compounds detected and quantified in the monitoring process.

viii The parametric value applies to the sum of the concentrations of the individual compounds detected and quantified in the monitoring process.

ix   The specified compounds are: chloroform; bromoform; dibromochloromethane; and bromodichloromethane.
The parametric value applies to the sum of the concentrations of the individual compounds detected and quantified in the monitoring process.

Part II: National requirements

1.	Aluminium	200	μg Al/l
2.	Colour	20	μg/l Pt/Co
3.	Hydrogen ion	10.0	pH value
		6.5 (min.)	pH value
4.	Iron	200	mg/l
5.	Manganese	50	mg/l
6.	Odour	3 at 25 deg.C	Dilution number
7.	Sodium	200	μgNa/l
8.	Taste	3 at 25 deg.C	Dilution number
9.	Tetrachloromethane	3	μg/l
10.	Turbidity	4	NTU

[point of compliance: consumers' taps]

Schedule 2: Indicator parameters

Item	Parameters	Concentration or Value (max.)	Units of Measurement
1.	Ammonium	0.50	μgNH$_4$/l
2.	Chloride (i)	250	μgCl/l*
3.	Clostridium perfringes (inc. spores)	0	number/100 ml
4.	Coliform bacteria	0	number/100 ml
5.	Colony count	No abnormal change	no./1 ml at 22°C**
			no./1 ml at 37°C**
6.	Conductivity (i)	2500	mS/cm at 20°C*
7.	Sulphate (i)	250	μgSO$_4$/l*
8.	Total indicative dose (for radioactivity) (ii)	0.10	mSv/year*
9.	Total organic carbon (TOC)	No abnormal change	μgC/l*
10.	Tritium (for radioactivity)	100	Bq/l*
11.	Turbidity	1	NTU**

Notes:

(i) The water should not be aggressive.

(ii) Excluding tritium, potassium-40, radon and radon decay products.
1 & 4 Point of monitoring: consumers' taps.

*   Point of monitoring: may be monitored from samples of water leaving treatment works or other supply point, as no significant change during distribution.

**   Point of monitoring: service reservoirs and treatment works (11, treatment works only).

APPENDIX 5.4

THE SURFACES WATERS (DANGEROUS SUBSTANCES) (CLASSIFICATION) REGULATIONS 1989

Environmental quality standards relating to inputs of various EC "Black List" substances to inland, coastal and territorial waters.

	Inland	Coastal and territorial
	µg/l, annual mean	
Aldrin, dieldrin endrin & isodrin*	0.03 for total drins 0.005 for endrin	
Cadmium & compounds	5 (total)	2.5 (dissolved)
Carbon tetrachloride	12	12
Chloroform	12	12
DDT (all isomers)	0.025	0.025
pp-DDT	0.01	0.01
Hexachlorobenzene	0.03	0.03
Hexachlorobutadiene	0.1	0.1
Hexachlorocyclohexane (all isomers)	0.1	0.02
Mercury & compounds	1 (total)	0.3 (dissolved)
Pentachlorophenol & its compounds	2	2

* In July 1997 the Department of the Environment, Transport and the Regions expressed an intention to amend these standards as follows:

- aldrin   10 ng/l
- dieldrin   10 ng/l
- .endrin   5 ng/l
- isodrin   5 ng/l

THE SURFACE WATERS (DANGEROUS SUBSTANCES) (CLASSIFICATION) REGULATIONS 1997 AND 1998

Schedules to the Regulations list concentrations of certain dangerous substances which should not be exceeded for meeting criteria for classification of either inland freshwaters or coastal and relevant territorial waters - see chapter 5, 5.15.2.

Schedules 1 and 2 to 1997 Regulations

Dangerous Substance	Inland	Coastal and territorial
	µg/l, annual mean	
Arsenic	50	25
Atrazine & Simazine (for the two substances in total)	2	2
Azinphos-methyl	0.01	0.01
Dichlorvos	0.001	0.04
Endosulphan	0.003	0.003
Fenitrothion	0.01	0.01
Malathion	0.01	0.02
Trifluralin	0.1	0.1
Tributyltin	0.02 µg/l	0.002 µg/l
Triphenyltin & its derivatives	0.02 µg/l	0.008 µg/l
Dichlorvos (used as a treatment For sea-lice infestation)		0.6 µg/l

Schedules 1 and 2 to 1998 Regulations

Dangerous Substance	Inland µg/l, annual mean	Coastal and territorial
4-Chloro-3-methyl-phenol	40	40
2-Chlorophenol	50	50
2,4-Dichlorophenol	20	20
2,4-D (ester)	1	1
(Non-ester)	40	40
1,1,1-Trichloroethane	100	100
1,1,2-Trichloroethane	400	300
Bentazone	500	500
Benzene	30	30
Biphenyl	25	25
Chloronitrotoluenes	10	10
Demeton	0.5	0.5
Dimethoate	1	1
Linuron	2	2
Mecoprop	20	20
Naphthalene	10	5
Omethoate	0.01	-
Toluene	50	40
Triazaphos	0.005	0.005
Xylene	30	30

APPENDIX 5.5

THE SURFACE WATERS (RIVER ECOSYSTEM) (CLASSIFICATION) REGULATIONS 1994

These classifications apply to inland rivers and watercourses in England and Wales.

(1) Class	(2) Dissolved Oxygen % saturation 10 percentile	(3) BOD (ATU) mg/l 90 percentile	(4) Total Ammonia mg N/l 90 percentile	(5) Un-ionised Ammonia mg N/l 95 percentile	(6) pH lower limit as 5 percentile; upper limit as 95 percentile	(7) Hardness mg/l CaCO$_3$	(8) Dissolved Copper µg/l 95 percentile	(9) Total Zinc µg/l 95 percentile
RE1	80	2.5	0.25	0.021	6.0-9.0	≤ 10 > 10 and ≤ 50 > 50 and ≤ 100 > 100	5 22 40 112	30 200 300 500
RE2	70	4.0	0.6	0.021	6.0-9.0	≤ 10 > 10 and ≤ 50 > 50 and ≤ 100 > 100	5 22 40 112	30 200 300 500
RE3	60	6.0	1.3	0.021	6.0-9.0	≤ 10 > 10 and ≤ 50 > 50 and ≤ 100 > 100	5 22 40 112	300 700 1000 2000
RE4	50	8.0	2.5	—	6.0-9.0	≤ 10 > 10 and ≤ 50 > 50 and ≤ 100 > 100	5 22 40 112	300 700 1000 2000
RE5	20	15.0	9.0	—	—	—	—	—

APPENDIX 5.6

THE SURFACE WATERS (ABSTRACTION FOR DRINKING WATER) (CLASSIFICATION) REGULATIONS 1996

Schedule 1: Criteria for Classification of Waters

(The limits set out below are maxima)

Parameters	Units	Limits DW1	DW2	DW3
Coloration (after simple filtration)	mg/1 Pt Scale	20	100	200
Temperature	°C	25	25	25
Nitrates	mg/l NO_3	50	50	50
Fluorides	mg/l F	1.5		
Dissolved iron	mg/l Fe	0.3	2	
Copper	mg/l Cu	0.05		
Zinc	mg/l Zn	3	5	5
Arsenic	mg/l As	0.05	0.05	0.01
Cadmium	mg/l Cd	0.005	0.005	0.005
Total chromium	mg/l Cr	0.05	0.05	0.05
Lead	mg/l Pb	0.05	0.05	0.05
Selenium	mg/l Se	0.01	0.01	0.01
Mercury	mg/l Hg	0.001	0.001	0.001
Barium	mg/l Ba	0.1	1	1
Cyanide	mg/l CN	0.05	0.05	0.05
Sulphates	mg/l SO_4	250	250	250
Phenol (phenol index) paranitraniline 4-aminoantipyrine	mg/l C_6H_5OH	0.001	0.005	0.1
Dissolved or emulsified hydrocarbons	mg/l	0.05	0.2	1
Polycyclic aromatic hydrocarbons	mg/l	0.0002	0.0002	0.001
Total pesticides (parathion, hexachlorocyclohexane, dieldrin	mg/l	0.001	0.0025	0.005
Ammonium	mg/l NH_4		1.5	4

The classifications, DW1, DW2 and DW3, correspond to the 1975 Surface Water Directive's classifications of A1, A2 and A3; the limits specified are the maximum allowable for each classification; an annex to Directive 75/440 specifies the treatment required to bring the surface water up to drinking water standard in each classification:

- DW1: simple physical treatment and disinfection;
- DW2: normal physical treatment, chemical treatment and disinfection;
- DW3: intensive physical and chemical treatment and disinfection.

APPENDIX 6

THE EUROPEAN UNION AND THE ENVIRONMENT

The European Economic Community came into existence on 1 January 1958 following the signing of the 1957 *Treaty of Rome* by its six founder members - Belgium, France, West Germany, Italy, Luxembourg and The Netherlands. (These same six countries had, in 1951, formed the European Coal and Steel Community which created a common market in coal and steel.) The European Community was enlarged in 1973 when Denmark, Ireland and the United Kingdom joined; in 1981 Greece became a member, followed in 1986 by Spain and Portugal and by Austria, Finland and Sweden in 1995. The 1992 *Treaty on European Union* (the *Maastrict Treaty*) (see below) created the "European Union", the term by which the 15 member states are more usually called. In 1998 Cyprus, Hungary, Poland, Estonia, the Czech Republic and Slovenia began formal negotiations to join the EU.

The presidency of the European Union (EU) rotates every six months between Member States (as does chairmanship of the Council of Ministers). The 1957 *Treaty of Rome*, which has been amended a number of times, sets out the basic operating principles of the EU with the aim of ensuring a Common Market - that is the free movement of goods, people and services between Member States.

The European Union has become one of the most important international innovators on environmental issues and there are now over 600 legislative measures covering the whole spectrum of the environment; it should be noted however that a number of these are revisions or amendments of existing measures.

Although some of the EU's earliest environmental protection measures, on for example vehicle emissions, were adopted in 1970, it was not until 1973 that the *First Action Programme on the Environment* was adopted (see below). And it was not until 1986, when the *Single European Act 1986* was adopted, that the *Treaty of Rome* was also amended to make explicit mention of the environment.

Article 174 (formerly 130R), as amended, of the Treaty includes the following points:

a) Action by the Community relating to the environment shall have the following objectives:

• to preserve, protect and improve the quality of the environment;
• to contribute towards protecting human health;
• to ensure a prudent and rational utilisation of natural resources;

A further objective was added by the *Maastricht Treaty* (see below) and that was the need for EC environmental policies to contribute to international environmental measures to deal with regional and worldwide environmental problems:

b) Action by the Community relating to the environment shall be based on the principles that preventive action should be taken, that environmental damage should as a priority be rectified at source, and that the polluter should pay. Environmental protection requirements shall be a component of the Community's other policies.

In preparing its action relating to the environment, the Community shall take account of:

• available scientific and technical data;
• environmental conditions in the various regions of the Community;
• the potential benefits and costs of action or lack of action;
• the economic and social development of the Community as a whole and the balanced development of its regions.

This development, which had both legal and symbolic significance, was given further impetus through the *Treaty on European Union* (the *Maastricht Treaty*) signed in Maastricht in February 1992. Following ratification by all Member States, this came into force on 1 November 1993. The Treaty has as a principle objective "the promotion of sustainable and non-inflationary growth respecting the environment, including among the activities of the Community a policy in the sphere of the environment". The Treaty was further amended in 1997 to require the Union to promote "balanced and sustainable development of economic activities". It stresses that the policy should not only aim at a high level of protection for the environment but that environmental protection should be integrated into other areas of EU policy.

The *Maastricht Treaty* also gives further substance to the principle of "subsidiarity" and refers "to the process of creating an ever closer union among the peoples of Europe in which decisions are taken as closely as possible to the citizen". This principle has been included in the EU's Fifth Action Programme (see below).

Finally, the *Maastricht Treaty* created the European Union (i.e. all the countries within the Community) - this is made up of three sections: the European Community, Common Foreign & Security Policy and Home Affairs & Justice Policy. An amendment to the *Treaty of Rome* abolishes the European Economic Community (EEC) which becomes the European Community (EC). The Council of Ministers has become the Council of the European Community and the Commission of the European Communities the European Commission.

The *Amsterdam Treaty*, which came into force on 1 May 1999, strengthens requirements for EU proposals to promote a high level of protection for the environment and improvement in environmental quality, as well as to promote the objectives of sustainable development. The Treaty also made adoption of legislation through "co-decision" the procedure under which most EU legislation is adopted. Thus most legislation now requires the formal agreement of both the Council of Ministers and the European Parliament. The Treaty also consolidated and renumbered the Articles of the *Treaty of Rome*.

Legislative and Institutional Procedures

The *Single European Act 1986,* which came into force in July 1987, has as a principle objective the abolition of all barriers between Member States by 31 December 1992. To this end, new measures have been drafted and legislation amended with the aim of creating a single market in goods, services and employment - i.e. the right, subject to various safeguards, to trade and work in any Member State and the removal of technical, fiscal and other barriers. A fundamental objective to completion of the Single Market is that products and services legally sold or offered in one Member State should not be banned in another.

With regard to legislative proposals relating to the environment, those relating to product standards, competition or the "establishment and functioning of the internal market" (i.e. harmonising measures) are subject to majority voting under Article 95 (formerly 100A). Other Directives relating to action on the environment are proposed under Articles 174 and 175 (formerly 130) and thus require unanimous voting. An amendment agreed in Maastricht enables some environmental measures to be adopted on a qualified majority voting (QMV) – Article 205, and indeed most are. However, those incorporating, for example, fiscal, energy, planning and land use (excluding waste management) still require unanimous approval. Article 176 (formerly 130T) permits Member States to adopt or keep stricter environmental protection legislation under certain conditions. For QMV, each Member State has been allocated a certain number of votes depending on population.

The European Commission - which can be seen as the "civil service" of the EU - is split into a number of Directorates-General (DG), each responsible for a particular area of the Commission's work. DG XI, the Directorate-General for Environment, Nuclear Safety and Civil Protection, is responsible for most environmental policy. The Commission is headed by a President and there are 20 Commissioners; although Commissioners are nominated by Member States' governments, they are expected to act independently of national interests. The Commission is responsible for developing and proposing new legislation and other initiatives. Proposals are published usually with the prefix "COM" - i.e. Communication [from the Commission to the Council and Parliament concerning ...], followed by the year and a reference number, e.g. COM(2001) 00. Following adoption, they are published with a reference number preceded by the year of adoption (2001/00).

EU measures are finalised as either

- **Regulations:** these are binding on all Member States in their entirety and take precedence over national legislation.

- **Directives:** these are binding on Member States as to the result to be achieved, while leaving a degree of flexibility on how the measure will be implemented in national legislation.

- **Decisions:** these are binding in their entirety and may be addressed to government, private enterprise or individual.

- **Recommendations and opinions:** these are not binding.

The Council of the European Community (i.e. Council of Ministers) is responsible for agreeing, amending or referring back to the Commission its draft proposals. The Council formally consists of the Foreign Ministers of the Member States, with the chairmanship changing every six months in line with the Presidency of the Community. Where, for example, environmental matters are to be discussed, then the Council will usually comprise the environmental ministers of the Member States. Initial discussions will have taken place between national governments' officials and also in the Committee of Permanent Representatives (COREPER), who will aim to reach agreement on proposals prior to discussion in the Council of Ministers. COREPER consists of each Member States' Ambassador to the EU.

The European Parliament is directly elected by electors in each Member State. Prior to ratification of the *Maastricht Treaty,* the EP had a rather limited role, being restricted to offering an opinion on Commission proposals; it was unable to amend or reject decisions reached by the Council, but could only ask them to reconsider. The only exception to this was the budget which it could reject.

The European Parliament now has the right to approve the appointment of the European Commission and of its President. On a majority vote it may also ask the Commission to produce a proposal for legislation in furtherance of the objectives of the Treaty. Under the co-decision procedure the Parliament may block a measure, even if approved by the Council of Ministers, if it is of the opinion that the proposal does not meet the purpose for which it is intended (Article 251). If agreement cannot be reached on a proposal it is referred to a conciliation committee consisting of representatives of the EP and of the Council for further negotiation. The cooperation procedure (Article 252) enables the Parliament on a second reading to propose amendments to proposals even though the Council of Ministers has already adopted a common position. The Commission then decides which of the European Parliament's amendments it can accept before the proposal returns to the Council of Ministers. The Council of Ministers can only reject or further amend the European Parliament's amendments which have been accepted by the European Commission by unanimous vote.

Following adoption, the final text of Directives etc are published in the *Official Journal of the European Communities*. All legislation includes a date by which

Member States must have incorporated it into national legislation. The amount of time allowed largely depends on the impact of the measure on national practice and the cost of implementation. In some instances, individual Member States will be allowed a derogation - i.e. extra time in which to comply.

In the UK EU measures are implemented either under the appropriate primary legislation, or where no suitable legislation exists, under the *European Communities Act 1972*.

The European Commission is also responsible for monitoring the performance of Member States in complying with Directives etc. Where it feels that a Member State is in breach of EU legislation it will first try to resolve the matter through informal discussion, correspondence, etc - there is a procedure for doing this. If however the Commission is still not satisfied, it can initiate legal action in the European Court of Justice. This is situated in Luxembourg with judges drawn from all Member States. Individuals in Member States may also complain to the European Court if they feel EU legislation is being breached. The European Court of Justice has the power to fine or levy a financial penalty on offenders.

European Environment Agency

Although agreement was reached on the establishment of the European Environment Agency (Regulation 1210/90) in 1990, it did not formally begin work until late 1993. The EEA's main task is to record, collate and analyse data on the environment, drawing up expert reports. These will enable both the European Commission and Member States to formulate appropriate environmental protection policies. A further aim of the EEA, which is based in Copenhagen, is to develop ways of harmonising measurement and forecasting methods. The Agency's remit initially includes air, water, soil, wildlife, land use, waste management and noise. Following adoption of an amending Regulation (933/1999), the Agency's remit has been extended to include responsibility for ensuring the dissemination of methodologies for assessing environmental impacts, and on the use of environmentally-friendly technologies, particularly telematics; it has also been charged with disseminating results of environmental research in a way which enables the research to assist in policy development.

The Agency's information network - EIONET: European Information and Observation Network - will help to coordinate the work and establish links between policy and research institutes throughout the EC. Information collected by the Agency will be publicly available and a report on the state of the environment will be published every three years.

EC Network of Environmental Enforcement Agencies

The permanent Network of Environmental Enforcement Agencies was founded in 1992 with representatives from all EC Member States. Its aims are to "provide a mechanism for the exchange of information and experience between environmental agencies in the EC in order to address issues of mutual concern and to enhance the quality of the environment". The Network operates mainly through four permanent working groups with specific areas of interest:

- technical aspects of permitting;
- procedural and legal aspects of permitting;
- compliance monitoring, inspection and enforcement;
- managing the enforcement process.

Action Programmes on the Environment

The United Nations Conference on the Human Environment, held in Stockholm in 1972, marked the beginning of global recognition of environmental problems which could only be solved by a sustained effort in all countries.

The European Community responded by drawing up its *First Action Programme on the Environment*; it covered the period 1973-76 and was adopted by the Council of Ministers in November 1973. This *First Action Programme* was a wide-ranging document containing a large number of measures designed to deal with already urgent pollution problems; it also took a longer term view of the future and sought the positive management of human activities in such a way as to prevent further problems arising. The First Action Programme also set out goals and objectives, defined principles, such as the Polluter Pays Principle, and recognised that prevention is better than cure. It adopted a comprehensive approach, tackling both air and water pollution, the management of wastes, noise pollution and the protection of wildlife and habitats. These ideas and principles were given further substance in three subsequent Action Programmes covering 1977-81, 1982-86 and 1987-92.

In 1993 the Commission's *Fifth Action Programme - Towards Sustainability* was approved by the Council of Ministers and the Parliament. In their Resolution adopting the Programme, the EC Environment Ministers ask the Commission to "ensure that all proposals relating to the environment properly reflect the principle of subsidiarity". They also note that further measures will be needed if the desire for sustainable development is to be achieved. The Programme, covering 1993-2000 with a review in late 1995, stresses the need for all sectors of the community - governments, industry and citizens - to become involved in and to take responsibility for the protection of their environment. It says that environmental policies should be integrated into all areas of Community policy if the goal of sustainability is to be achieved. Sustainability in this context is defined as reflecting "a policy and strategy for continued economic and social development without detriment to the environment and the natural resources on the quality of which continued human activity and further development depend".

The 5th Programme also states that "the Community will

take action, in accordance with the principle of subsidiarity, only if and insofar as the objectives of the proposed action cannot be sufficiently achieved by the Member States and can therefore, by reason of the scale or effects of the proposed action, be better achieved by the Community". It also recognises that in many areas, objectives will best be achieved through "shared responsibility" using a mix of "actors and instruments at the appropriate levels" - i.e. that action should be taken at Community, national or local level as appropriate.

Five areas requiring major effort because of the stresses each can place on the environment have been targeted: industry, agriculture, energy, transport and tourism. The Commission suggests that these are all areas at which action for improvement can most efficiently and appropriately be taken at Community level. Within each of these target areas the Programme identifies a number of objectives aimed at achieving sustainable development while benefitting the sector concerned. The Programme also identifies a number of environmental issues which because of their transboundary or global nature should be dealt with at Community level. Again objectives and targets are set and a programme to be reviewed and developed is proposed. The environmental issues highlighted are climate change, acidification, air quality, urban environment (noise), waste management, protection of nature and biodiversity, management of water resources and coastal zones. The targets and actions proposed are summarised in the relevant chapters of the *Pollution Handbook*.

The Commission is now considering its *6th Action Programme*, which it suggests should focus on three key requirements:

- a healthy high quality environment which protects human health (with priority given to water and air quality, and effects of chemicals on human health);
- efficient use and management of resources (biodiversity and integrated waste management policies);
- climate change.

The 6th programme will also need to reflect Article 2 of the Amsterdam Treaty which requires the integration of environmental, social and economic objectives.

On the pages which follow, we list Community measures relating to air, noise, waste and water. Other measures of relevance are listed at Appendix 6.6.

Further Reading

A number of useful publications providing a more detailed discussion on the development of Community environmental policies and legislation, their implementation and the way in which the various Community institutions operate, are listed in the bibliography (General - European Issues) section of this Handbook.

APPENDIX 6.1:

Environmental Action Programmes

Number	Title	Date adopted	brought into force	OJ No. and date	Purpose
–	Declaration of the Council of the European Communities and of the Representatives of the Governments of the Member States meeting in the Council on the Action Programme of the European Communities of the Environment. (1973-1976)	22.11.73	22.11.73	C 112 20.12.73	To lay down the objectives and principles of a Community environment policy. To describe measures to be taken to reduce pollution and nuisances and to improve the environment.
–	Resolution of the Council of the European Communities and of the Representatives of the Governments of the Member States meeting within the Council on the continuation and implementation of a European Community policy and Action Programme on the Environment. (1977-1981)	17.05.77	17.05.77	C 139 13.06.77	To restate the policy objectives and principles. To describe measures to be undertaken to reduce pollution and nuisance, protect and manage land, the natural environment and resources and improve the environment.
–	Resolution of the Council of the European Communities and of the Representatives of the Governments of the Member States meeting in the Council on the continuation and implementation of a European Community policy and and Action Programme on the Environment (1982-86)	07.02.83	07.02.83	C 46 17.02.83	To develop an overall strategy. To describe measures to be taken to prevent and reduce pollution and nuisance in the different environments, as well as the protection and rational management of land, the environment and natural resources.
–	Resolution of the Council on the continuation and implementation of a European Community policy and action programme on the environment. (1987- 1992)	19.10.87	19.10.87	C328 07.12.87	To identify pollutants; to determine best focus for control measures; to set objectives to combat acid deposition and forest die-back; to reduce ambient pollutant concentrations; to develop appropriate management techniques.
	Resolution of the Council on the fifth Community Policy and Action Programme on the Environment and Sustainable Development. (1993-2000)	18.03.92		C138 17.05.93	Define objectives for tackling a number of issues and for achieving sustainable development. Issues include climate change, acidification, air and water pollution, waste management.

APPENDIX 6.2: AIR POLLUTION

Industrial Pollution

Number	Title	Date adopted	brought into force	OJ No. and date	Purpose
84/360/	"Framework" Directive on combating EEC air pollution from industrial plants.	28.06.84	30.06.87	L 188 16.07.84	To implement measures and procedures designed to prevent and reduce air pollution from industrial plants within the Community.
88/609/ EEC	Directive limiting emissions of certain pollutants into the air from large combustion plants.	24.11.88	30.06.90	L 336 07.12.88	Sets emission standards SO_2, NOx and dust for existing and new plant; Reduction targets are to be met progressively by 1993, 1998, 2003 using 1980 levels as a base.
96/61/ EC	Council Directive concerning integrated pollution prevention and control	24.09.96	30.10.96	L257 10.10.96	To introduce a system of permitting for certain industrial installations.
99/13/EC	Council Directive on limitation of emissions of VOCs due to the use of organic solvents in certain activities & installations	11.03.99	29.03.99	L85 29.03.99	To limit VOCs - part of strategy reducing VOC emissions from other sectors.

Motor Vehicles and Fuels

Number	Title	Date adopted	brought into force	OJ No. and date	Purpose
70/220/ EEC	Directive relating to measures to be taken against air pollution by gases from positive ignition engines of motor vehicles.	20.03.70	30.06.70	L 76 06.04.70	To set limit values for emissions of CO and HC from petrol-engined vehicles.
74/290/ EEC	Amendment Directive (1st)	28.05.74	01.10.74	L 159 15.06.74	To define specifications for acceptance tests, and reduce previous limits.
77/102/ EEC	Amendment Directive (2nd)	30.11.76	01.01.77	L 32 03.02.77	To fix permissible values for carbon monoxide, hydrocarbon fuels and nitrogen oxides and determine materials, conditions and methods for use in measuring levels of these substances.
78/665/ EEC	Amendment Directive (3rd)	14.07.78	01.01.79	L 233 14.08.78	To establish limits for exhaust emissions from road vehicles representing 35% for CO; 25% for HC; 15% for NOx.
83/351/ EEC	Amendment Directive (4th)	16.06.83	30.11.83	L 197 20.07.83	Reduce limits set in 78/665 of CO by 23%; HC and NOx by 20-30%; also limits pollutants from diesel engines.
88/76	Amendment Directive (5th): The Luxembourg Agreement".	03.12.87		L36 09.02.88	To set emission limits for CO, HC + NOx and NOx according to engine size.
89/458/ EEC	Amendment directive (7th) on gaseous emissions from private motor cars with a capacity of less than 1400cc	18.07.89		L226 03.08.89	To set mandatory limits on emissions of 19g/test CO and 5g/test HC + NOx for small sized cars. (Partially supersedes 88/76)
89/491/ EEC	Amendment Directive (15th)			L 238 15.08.89	Amends various directives with regard to fuel consumption.
91/441/ EEC	Amendment Directive (8th)	26.06.91	01.04.92	L 242	Extends emission standards set in 89/458
94/12/ EC	Amendment Directive (9th)	1994		L 100 19.04.94	Tightens limits for petrol cars & for diesels to be met in two stages.
98/69/ EC	Amendment Directive (11th)	09.98		L 350 28.12.98	Part of Auto-oil programme emission limits set for 2000 & 2005
93/59 EEC	Amendment directive. (18th)	28.06.93	01.10.93	L186 28.07.93	To place emission limits on light commercial vehicles, off-road vehicles and heavy cars.
96/69	Amendment Directive (20th)	8.10.96		L282 01.11.96	Tightens emission limits for light commercial vehicles
72/306/ EEC	Directive on measures to be taken against emissions of pollutants from diesel engines for use in motor vehicles.	02.08.72	10.02.74	L 190 20.08.72	To lay down requirements relating to the type approval of diesel motor vehicles. To define standards for acceptance tests. To fix permissible values for fumes and determine materials, conditions and methods for measuring levels of the fumes.

Number	Title	Date		OJ No. and date	Purpose
		adopted	brought into force		
88/436	Amendment Directive (6th) limiting gaseous pollutants from diesel vehicles up to 3.5 tonnes	16.06.88		L 214 06.08.88	To set standards for the emission of particulates of 1.1g/test for new engine types and 1.4g/test for new vehicles.
88/77	Directive on emission of gaseous pollutants from diesel lorries and buses.	03.12.87	01.10.90	L36 09.02.88	To control emissions of CO, HC and NOx in vehicles over 3.5 tonnes.
91/542	Amendment Directive of 88/77	01.10.91	01.01.92	L 295 25.10.91	Tightens limits set in 88/77 and introduces limits for particulates.
96/1	Amendment of Directive 88/77	22.01.96		L40 17.02.96	As above.
99/96	EP & Council Directive amending 88/77	13.12.99		L44 16.02.00	Tightens HGV emission limits & puts limits on those fuelled by natural gas & LPG
77/537/ EEC	Directive relating to measures to be taken against the emission of pollutants from diesel engines for use in wheeled agricultural forestry tractors.	28.06.77	30.12.78	L 220 29.08.77	To lay down requirements to the type approval of such vehicles. To fix permissible values for the fumes and determine materials, conditions and methods for measuring levels of the fumes.
97/98	Directive concerning emissions from non-road machinery	16.12.97	19.03.98	L59 27.02.98	To limit emissions of gaseous and particulate pollutants from internal combustion engines to be installed in non-road mobile macinery
2000/25	EP & Council Directive on emissions from agricultural or forestry tractors	22.05.00		L173 12.07.00	Controls emissions of gaseous and particulate pollutants
75/716/ EEC	Directive relating to the approximation of the laws of Member States on the sulphur content of certain liquid fuels.	24.11.75	26.08.76	L 307 27.11.75	Repealed 1.10.94
87/219/ EEC	Amends Directive 75/716.	20.03.87	31.12.88	L 091 03.04.87	Repealed 1.10.94
93/12 EEC	Directive relating to the sulphur content of certain liquid fuels.	23.03.93	1.10.94	L74 27.03.93	Reduces sulphur content of gasoils to 0.2% by weight by 01.10.94 and to 0.05% from 01.10.96.
98/70/ EC	Council Directive relating to quality of petrol & diesel fuels	09.98	28.12.98	L 350 28.12.98	Part of Auto-oil programme; bans marketing of leaded petrol, reduces amount of benzene & other compounds in fuels and amends 93/12
99/32/ EC	Council Directive relating to sulphur content of certain liquid fuels	26.04.99		L 121 11.05.99	Reduce sulphur content of gas oil & amends 93/12
78/611/ EEC	Directive concerning the lead content of petrol.	29.06.78	05.01.80	L 197 22.07.78	Replaced by 85/210 – 31.12.85
85/210/ EEC	Directive on the approximation of Member State legislation on lead content of petrol, and the introduction of lead-free petrol.	21.03.85	01.01.86	L 096 03.04.85	Replaces Directive 78/611. Also fixes benzene content of leaded and unleaded petrol at 5% max. by volume.
87/416/ EEC	Amendment of Directive 85/210/EEC.	21.07.87	-	L 225 13.08.87	To permit Member States to ban the sale of regular grade leaded petrol after giving 6 months notice.
92/6 EEC	Directive on the installation and use of speed limitation devices for certain categories of motor vehicles.	10.02.92	01.10.93	L57 02.03.92	Speed limiters to be fitted to HGVs, buses and coaches.
92/55 EEC	Directive on vehicle emission testing.	10.06.92		L225 10.08.92	To harmonise in-service testing of vehicle emissions.
93/116/ EEC	Directive relating to the fuel consumption of motor vehicles.			L369 30.12.93	To set down procedure for determining CO2 emissions and require these to be recorded in document kept by vehicle owner.
99/94	Directive relating to consumer information on fuel economy and CO$_2$ emissions	13.12.99		L12 18.01.00	To require information to be available in respect of marketing new cars.

Number	Title	Date			Purpose
		adopted	brought into force	OJ No. and date	
94/63/ EC	EP and Council Directive on the control of VOCs resulting from the storage of petrol and its distribution from terminals to service stations.	20.12.94	31.12.95	C365 31.12.94	To reduce evaporative fuel losses.

Air Quality

Number	Title	Date			Purpose
96/62/EC	Directive on air quality assessment and management	24.09.96	21.10.96	L296 01.11.96	Framework Directive outlining system of monitoring and assessing air quality.
99/30/ EC	Council Directive relating to limit values for SO2, NO2 & oxides of nitrogen particulate matter & lead	22.04.99	19.07.99	L 163 29.06.99	"Daughter" Directive under 96/62
97/101/EC	Decision (superseding 82/459), establishing a reciprocal exchange of information and data from networks and individual stations measuring ambient air quality within Member States.	27.01.97	01.01.97	L 35 5.02.97	To set up a procedure for exchanging information between the Member States' measuring stations on a number of substances causing air pollution. To nominate a coordinating body. To arrange for the publication of a summary report.
80/779/ EEC	Directive on air quality limit values and guide values for sulphur dioxide and suspended particulates.	15.07.80	17.07.82	L 229 30.08.80	To lay down standards for sulphur dioxide and suspended particulates in the air, as well as the conditions for their application. To lay down the reference methods for sampling and analysis to be used.
–	Resolution relating to transboundary air pollution by sulphur dioxide and suspended particulates.	15.07.80	-	C 222 30.08.80	Calls on Member States to limit, and as far as possible reduce or prevent transboundary pollution in line with Directive
81/462/ EEC	Decision on the conclusion of the Convention on long-range transboundary air pollution. (The Geneva Convention).	11.06.81	-	L 171 27.06.81	To limit and as far as possible reduce and prevent transboundary air pollution.
86/277/ EEC	Council Decision concluding a Protocol to the 1979 Geneva Convention on Long-Distance Transboundary Air pollution concerning the funding of a long-term programme of cooperation for the constant monitoring and evaluation of the long-distance atmospheric transfer of pollutants in Europe (EMEP).	12.06.86	-	L181 04.07.86	See Title.
93/361	Council decision on the accession of the community to the Protocol to the LRTAP Convention on the control of emissions of nitrogen oxides or their transboundary fluxes.	17.05.93		L.149 21.06.93	
77/312/ EEC	Directive on biological screening of the population for lead.	29.03.77	31.03.78	L 105 28.04.77	To conduct two blood lead surveys, coordinated across the Community and separated by two years. The Directive prescribes surveys of three groups of people and defines reference' levels expressed in µg/100ml of blood to be applied to each group of people in assessing the results of the survey.
82/884/ EEC	Directive on a limit value for lead in the air.	03.12.82	10.12.84	L 378 31.12.82	To fix a limit value of 2 micrograms Pb/m³ expressed as an annual mean concentration. To define characteristics to be complied with for choosing a sampling method and a reference method for analysing the concentration of lead.
85/203/ EEC	Directive on air quality standards for nitrogen dioxide.	07.03.85	01.01.87	L 087 27.03.85	To establish a limit value for NO_2 in air of 200 µg/m³, expressed as a 98 percentile of the mean of one-hour measurements made throughout a year; also lower "guide values" for special protection zones.

Number	Title	Date		OJ No. and date	Purpose
		adopted	brought into force		
87/217/ EEC	Directive on prevention and reduction of environmental pollution by asbestos.	28.03.87	31.12.88	L 085 28.03.87	To put controls on the pollution of air, water and land by asbestos from all significant point sources.
89/427/ EEC	Directive modifying 80/779 on limit values and guide values of air quality for sulphur dioxide and suspended particulates.	21.06.89			To harmonise measurement methods.
92/72 EEC	Directive on air pollution by ozone.	21.09.92		L297 13.10.92	To establish procedure for monitoring ground-level ozone, give information to the public and issue public alerts when levels are expected to be high.

Incinerators

Number	Title	adopted	brought into force	OJ No. and date	Purpose
89/369/ EEC	Directive on air pollution from new municiple waste incinerators.	08.06.89	01.01.90	L 163 14.06.89	To set emission limit values and operating requirements for new waste incinerators.
89/429/ EEC	Directive on air pollution from exisiting municipal waste incinerators.	08.06.89	01.01.90	L 203 15.07.89	To set emission limit values and operation requirements for existing waste incinerators

Chlorofluorocarbons

Number	Title	adopted	brought into force	OJ No. and date	Purpose
–	Resolution on chlorofluorocarbons in the environment.	30.05.78	30.05.78	C 133 07.06.78	To limit the production of CFCs in the Community. To encourage the search for substitute products. To promote elimination of CFCs.
87/412	Decision on the signing of a Protocol of the Vienna Convention for the protection of the ozone layer, relating to the control of chlorofluorocarbons.	10.09.87	-		See title
88/540/ EEC	Decision implementing the Vienna Convention on protection of the ozone layer and the Montreal Protocol on substances which deplete the ozone layer.	14.10.88	-	L 297 31.10.88	See title
594/91/ EEC	Regulation on substances that deplete the ozone layer.	04.03.91	15.03.91	L 67 14.03.91	Repealed.
3952/92	Regulation amending 594/91	30.12.92		L405 31.12.92	Repealed.
3093/94 EC	Regulation on substances that deplete the ozone layer	15.12.94		L333 22.12.94	Tightens controls on CFCs etc and introduces restrictions on HCFCs and methyl bromide.
2000/22	Commission Decision re. essential uses			L7 12.01.00	Covers allocation of quantities of controlled substances allowed for essential uses under Reg.3093/94.

Energy Efficiency

Number	Title	adopted	brought into force	OJ No. and date	Purpose
93/76 EEC	Directive to limit carbon dioxide emissions by improving energy efficiency (SAVE).	13.09.93	31.12.94	L237 23.09.93	

APPENDIX 6.3: NOISE POLLUTION

Vehicles/Construction Plant/Aircraft

Number	Title	adopted	brought into force	OJ No. and date	Purpose
70/157/ EEC	Directive on the approximation of laws in the Member States relating to the permissible sound level and the exhaust system of motor vehicles.	06.02.70	10.08.71	L 42 23.02.70	To fix the permissible limits for the sound level, the equipment, conditions and methods for measuring this level.
73/350/ EEC	Directive adapting 70/157 to technical progress.	07.11.73	01.03.74	L 321 21.11.73	To prescribe measures for exhaust systems.
77/212/ EEC	Council amendment to 70/157	08.03.77	01.04.77	L 66 12.03.77	(Now superseded by Directive 84/424).

Number	Title	Date		OJ No. and date	Purpose
		adopted	brought into force		
84/424/ EEC	Council amendment to 70/157	03.09.84	06.09.84	L 238 06.09.84	Amends noise limits set in 77/212; buses and lorries under 3.5 tonnes are categorised together, and those over categorised by horsepower.
92/97 EEC	Amendment to 70/157	10.11.92	01.07.92	L371 19.12.92	Reduces noise limits for cars, buses and HGVs by between 2-5 dB(A).
96/20 EC	Amends 92/97	27.03.96		L92 13.04.96	To make various changes to noise level testing method.
78/1015/ EEC	Directive relating to the permissible sound level and exhaust system of motorcycles.	23.11.78	01.10.80	L 349 13.12.78	To fix the permissible limits for the sound level, the equipment, conditions and methods for measuring this level. To prescribe measures for exhaust systems.
87/56/ EEC	Amendment to Directive 78/1015	18.12.86	01.10.88	L 24 27.01.87	To modify the test procedure.
89/235/ EEC	Modification of Directive 78/1015 on sound levels of motorbikes.	13.03.89	01.10.90	L 98 11.04.89	To lay down common technical standards for exhaust systems; to provide a model EC type approval certificate.
74/151/ EEC	Directive relating to certain parts and characteristics of wheeled agricultural or or forestry tractors.	04.03.74	07.04.75	L 84 28.03.74	To fix the permissible limits for the sound level, the equipment, conditions and methods for measuring this level.
77/311/ EEC	Directive related to the driver-perceived noise level of wheeled agricultural or forestry tractors. (Extended by Directive 82/80.)	29.03.77	01.10.79	L 105 28.04.77	To fix the permissible limits for the sound level, the equipment, conditions and methods for measuring this level.
80/51/ EEC	Directive relating to the limitation of noise emissions from subsonic aircraft.	20.12.79	21.06.80	L 18 24.01.80	To make it compulsory for the Member States to apply annex 16 to the Chicago Convention on Subsonic Aircraft to establish mutual recognition of validity certificates. To determine exemptions.
83/206/ EEC	Amendment to 80/51		26.04.84	L117 04.05.83	To ensure that aircraft landing in the Community since 21.04.84 respect standards laid down by ICAO Chicago Convention.
89/629/ EEC	Directive limiting noise emissions from subsonic aircraft.	04.12.89		L 363 13.12.89	To prohibit registraton after 01.11.90 of aircraft unable to meet specific noise limits.
92/14 EEC	Directive limiting aircraft noise.	02.03.92		L 76 23.03.92	To ban all aircraft unable to meet Chapter 3 standards from operating into or out of EC after 01.04.95 and all Chapter 2 aircraft after 01.04.92.
925/99	Council Regulation on registration and use of certain types of jet aeroplanes	24.04.99		L115 4.5.99	Bans use of aeroplanes fitted with hushkits from specific dates.
79/113/ EEC	Directive on the approximation of the laws of the Member States relating to the determination of the noise emission of construction plant and equipment.	19.12.78	21.06.80	L 33 08.02.79	To define the sound level for construction plant and equipment. To define the criteria to use for expressing results, equipment and conditons for carrying out measurements and calculation method.
81/1051/ EEC	Amendment to 79/113	07.12.81	14.06.83	L 376 30.12.81	To determine the noise emitted to the operator's position by all categories of machines.
2000/14	EP & Council Directive relating to noise emissions from equipment for use outdoors	08.05.00	3.7.00	L162 3.7.00	Requires equipment to conform to specific noise level and for manufacturers to guarantee noise level. Equipment covered ranges from concrete breakers to hedge trimmers.
84/533/ EEC	Directive on the limitation of the noise emitted by compressors.	17.09.84	26.09.89	L 300 19.11.84	To be repeated 03.01.06
84/534/ EEC	Directive on the approximation of the laws of the Member States relating to the permissible sound level for tower-cranes.	17.09.84	26.09.89	L 300 19.11.84	To be repeated 03.01.06

Number	Title	Date		OJ No. and date	Purpose
		adopted	brought into force		
84/535/ EEC	Directive on the approximation of the laws of the Member States relating to the permissible sound power level of welding generators.	17.09.84	26.09.89	L300 19.11.84	To be repeated 03.01.06
84/536/ EEC	Directive on the approximation of the laws of the Member States relating to the permissible sound power level of power generators.	17.09.84	26.09.89	L 300 19.11.84	To be repeated 03.01.06
84/537/ EEC	Directive on the approximation of the laws of Member States relating to the permissible sound power level of powered hand-held concrete-breakers and picks.	17.09.84	26.09.89	L 300 19.11.84	To be repeated 03.01.06
86/662/ EEC	Directive on the limitation of noise emitted by earthmoving machinery (amended 1994).	22.12.86	26.09.89	L 384 31.12.86	To be repeated 03.01.06
95/27	Directive on noise from earth moving machinery.	29.06.95	18.07.95	L168 18.07.95	To be repeated 03.01.06

Lawn Mowers

Number	Title	Date		OJ No. and date	Purpose
84/538/ EEC	Directive on the approximation of the laws of the Member States relating to noise emitted by lawn mowers.	17.09.84	01.07.87	L 300 19.11.84	To be repeated 03.01.06

Household Appliances

Number	Title	Date		OJ No. and date	Purpose
86/594/ EEC	Directive on airborne noise emitted by household appliances.	01.12.86	04.12.89	L 344 06.12.86	To harmonise the methods of measuring the noise, arrangements for checking, general principles for publishing information on the noise emitted by these appliances.

Protection of Workers

Number	Title	Date		OJ No. and date	Purpose
86/188/ EEC	Directive on the protection of workers from the risks related to exposure to noise at work.	12.05.86	01.01.90	L 137 24.05.86	To protect workers from risks to hearing by setting limits on noise levels at which preventative action is required.

APPENDIX 6.4: WASTE

Waste

Number	Title	Date		OJ No. and date	Purpose
		adopted	brought into force		
75/442/ EEC	Directive on waste.	15.07.75	18.07.77	L 194 25.07.75	To encourage the prevention and recycling of waste. To determine the arrangements to be made for the harmless disposal of waste. To provide administrative provisions for management and control. To provide a system of authorisations for firms responsible for collection, recycling or disposal.
91/156/ EEC	Directive amending 75/442/EEC on waste.	18.03.91	01.04.93	L78 26.03.91	Tightens up definition of waste and lists 16 specific categories. Obligations of 1975 Directive are expanded.
94/3	Commision decision establishing a list of wastes.	20.12.93		L5 07.01.94	Replaced by Decision 2000/532
94/62 EC	EP and Council Directive on packaging waste	20.12.94	31.12.94	C365 31.12.94	To harmonise measures, reduce amount of such waste and its environmental impact; set up collection, recovery and re-use systems.
75/439/ EEC	Directive on the disposal of waste oils.	16.06.75	18.06.77	L 194 25.07.75	To determine the arrangements to be made for the collection and harmless disposal of waste oils. To require that priority is given to the regeneration of waste oils. To require a system of authorisations for plant either regenerating or burning waste oil. To prevent waste oils being mixed with toxic and dangerous wastes, in particular with PCBs.

Number	Title	Date			Purpose
		adopted	brought into force	OJ No. and date	
87/101/ EEC	Amendment to above	13.01.87	01.01.90	L 42 12.02.87	
99/31/ EC	Council Directive on Landfill of Waste	26.04.99		L 182 16.07.99	To reduce the amount of biodegradable waste sent to landfill
2000/532	Commission Decision establishing a list of hazardous and non-hazardous waste.	03.05.00	–	L226 06.09.00	

Hazardous Waste

Number	Title	Date			Purpose
78/319/ EEC	Directive on toxic and dangerous wastes.	20.03.78	22.03.80	L 84 31.03.78	Repealed 27.6.95
91/689/ EEC	Directive on hazardous waste.	12.12.91	11.12.93	L 377 31.12.91	Updates 1978 Directive on hazardous waste management, defines various types of, and constituencies of hazardous wastes.
94/311/	Amendment of hazardous waste directive.				Sets implementation date of 91/689 at 31.3.95.
94/904/ EC	Decision establishing hazardous waste list	22.12.94	–	L356 31.12.94	Replaced by Decision 2000/532
84/631/ EEC	Directive on the supervision and control of transfrontier shipment of hazardous wastes within the European Community.	06.12.84	01.01.87	L 326 13.12.84	Repealed 6.5.94
90/170/ EEC	Decision on acceptance of OECD recommendation on control of trans-frontier shipment of hazardous waste.	02.04.90	-	L 92 07.04.90	See title.
91/157/ EEC	Directive on batteries and accumulators containing certain dangerous substances. Adapted by 93/72.	18.03.91	18.09.92	L 78 26.03.91	To reduce the amount of pollution from used batteries containing heavy metals; to encourage recycling and the production of batteries with lower levels of heavy metals.
259/93	Regulation on the supervision and control of shipments of waste into and out of the EC.	01.02.93	01.05.94	L30 06.02.93	Builds on and extends 1984 Directive and and implements Basel Convention on transboundary movements of hazardous waste.
93/98	Council decision on the conclusion of a convention of transboundary movements of hazardous waste and their disposal (the Basel Convention).	01.02.93		L39 16.02.93	
1420/ 1999	Council Regulation establishing common rules & procedures to apply to waste shipments to certain non-OECD countries	29.04.99		L 166 01.07.99	See title
94/67/ EC	Directive on the incineration of hazardous waste.	16.12.94	31.12.94	C365 31.12.94	To reduce or prevent adverse environmental effects.
96/59 EC	Directive on the disposal of PCBs andPCTs	16.09.96	16.09.96	L 243 24.09.96	To identify PCBs and to control their disposal and elimination by 31.12.10

Recycling

Number	Title	Date			Purpose
81/972/ EEC	Recommendation concerning the re-use of waste paper and the use of recycled paper.	03.12.81	-	L 355 10.12.81	To define and implement policies to promote the use of recycled paper and board.
85/339/ EEC	Directive on containers of liquids for human consumption.	27.06.85	03.07.87	L176 06.07.85	Repealed 30.6.96

Sewage Sludge

Number	Title	Date			Purpose
86/278/ EEC	Directive on the protection of the environ-ment, and in particular of the soil, when sewage sludge is used in agriculture.	12.06.86	17.06.89	L 181 04.07.86	To provide for a special regime concerning the spreading of sludge in agriculture and to fix sludge and soil analyses.

Number	Title	Date			Purpose
		adopted	brought into force	OJ No. and date	

APPENDIX 6.5: WATER POLLUTION

Surface Water

Number	Title	adopted	brought into force	OJ No. and date	Purpose
75/440/ EEC	Directive concerning the quality required of surface water intended for the abstraction of drinking water in Member States.	16.05.75	18.06.77	L 194 25.07.75	To define the quality requirements for surface fresh water used for or intended for abstraction of drinking water. Provision of plans to clean up water. To define the requirements with which the quality measurements must comply.
79/869/ EEC	Directive concerning the methods of measurement and frequencies of sampling and analysis of surface water intended for the abstraction of drinking water in the Member States.	09.10.79	09.10.81	L 271 29.10.79	To lay down reference measuring methods for the parameters contained in Directive 75/440/EEC and sampling frequencies. To lay down the requirements with which these measurements must comply.
77/795/ EEC	Decision establishing a common procedure for the exchange of information on the quality of surface fresh water in the Community. Amended by 86/574.	12.12.77	12.12.77	L 334 24.12.77	To designate a coordinating body. To designate the stations taking part in the exchange of information. To define the parameters to be measured. To provide for the publication of a summary report.

Drinking Water

Number	Title	adopted	brought into force	OJ No. and date	Purpose
80/778/ EEC	Directive relating to the quality of water intended for human consumption.	15.07.80	19.07.82	L 229 30.08.80	To lay down standards for water intended for human consumption. To lay down sampling frequency, measuring methods and the requirements with which the measurements must comply. To lay down the conditions in which this quality is to be achieved. To be repeated 25.12.03
98/83/ EC	Directive on the quality of water for human consumption.	03.11.98	25.12.98	L330 5.12.98	Tightens standards for drinking water; will replace 80/778.

Fresh Water

Number	Title	adopted	brought into force	OJ No. and date	Purpose
78/659/ EEC	Directive on the quality of fresh waters needing protection or improvement in order to support fish life.	18.07.78	20.07.80	L 222 14.08.78	To lay down the quality requirements for waters intended to support fish life. To lay down sampling frequency, measuring methods and the requirements with which the measurements must comply. To lay down the conditions in which this quality is to be achieved.

Shellfish Waters

Number	Title	adopted	brought into force	OJ No. and date	Purpose
79/923/ EEC	Directive on the quality required of shellfish waters.	30.10.79	30.10.81	L 281 10.11.79	To lay down the quality requirements for shellfish waters. To lay down the sampling frequencies, measuring methods and the requirements with which the measurements must comply. To lay down the conditions in which this quality is to be achieved

Bathing Water

Number	Title	adopted	brought into force	OJ No. and date	Purpose
76/160/ EEC	Directive concerning the quality of bathing water.	08.12.75	10.12.77	L31 05.02.76	To define the quality requirements for bathing water. To define the sampling frequency, the measuring methods and the requirements with which these measurements must comply. To lay down the conditions in which this quality is to achieved.

Number	Title	Date			Purpose
		adopted	brought into force	OJ No. and date	

Groundwater

Number	Title	adopted	brought into force	OJ No. and date	Purpose
80/68/ EEC	Directive on the protection of groundwater against pollution caused by certain dangerous substances.	17.12.79	19.12.81	L 20 26.01.80	To prevent the discharge of List I substances and restrict that of List II substances. To set up a system of authorisations and lay down the conditions for derogations. To prepare an inventory of discharge authorisations granted.

Dangerous Substances

Number	Title	adopted	brought into force	OJ No. and date	Purpose
76/464/ EEC	Framework directive on pollution caused by certain dangerous substances discharged into the aquatic environment of the Community.	04.05.76	04.05.78	L 31 05.02.76	To provide a system of authorisations for the discharge of dangerous substances into water. To provide limit values or quality objectives and monitoring procedures for List I substances. To provide quality objectives for List II substances. To adopt anti-pollution programmes for both types of substances and communicate them to the Commission. To draw up a list of discharges involving List I substances.
82/176/ EEC	Directive on limit values and quality objectives for mercury discharges by the chlor-alkali electrolysis industry.	22.03.82	01.07.83	L 81 27.03.82	To apply the Directive 76/464/EEC to the discharges from this industrial sector.
83/513/ EEC	Directive on limit values and quality objectives for cadmium discharges.	26.09.83	28.09.85	L 291 24.10.83	- as above -
84/156/ EEC	Directive on limit values and quality objectives for mercury discharges by sectors other than the chlor-alkali electrolysis industry.	18.03.84	12.03.86	L 74 17.03.84	- as above -
84/491/ EEC	Directive on limit values and quality objectives for discharges of hexachloro-cyclohexane (in particular lindane).	09.10.84	01.04.86	L 274 17.10.84	- as above -
86/280/ EEC	Directive setting out legal provisions applicable to various substances in List I of Annex to 76/464.	12.06.86	01.01.88	L 181 04.07.86	As above. To exend Directive 76/464/ EEC to cover discharges of DDT, carbon tetrachloride and pentachlorophenol.
88/347/ EEC	Directive on limit values and quality objectives for Hexachlorobenzene (HCB), Hexachlorabutadiene (HCBD), chloroform, isodrin, endrin, dieldrin and aldrin, discharges.	16.06.88	01.01.90	L 158 25.06.88	To extend Directive 76/464/EEC to cover discharges of the HCB, HCBD, chloroform and drins.
90/415/ EEC	Directive on limit values and quality objectives for certain List I substances.	31.07.90	01.01.92	L 219 14.08.90	To include 1,2 dichloroethane, trichloroethane, perchloroethane and trichlorobenzene.

Nitrates

Number	Title	adopted	brought into force	OJ No. and date	Purpose
91/676/ EEC	Directive on protection of fresh, coastal and marine waters from nitrate pollution.	12.12.91	19.12.93	L 375 31.12.91	To reduce and prevent nitrate pollution from agriculture, including nitrogen compounds on soils.

Waste Water

Number	Title	adopted	brought into force	OJ No. and date	Purpose
91/271/ EEC	Directive on urban waste water treatment.	21.05.91	30.06.93	L 135 30.05.91	To lay down minimum standards for the treatment of municipal waste water and the disposal of sludge.
98/51	Directive on urban waste water treatment.			L67 07.03.98	

Titanium Dioxide

Number	Title	adopted	brought into force	OJ No. and date	Purpose
78/176/ EEC	Directive on waste from the titanium dioxide industry.	20.02.78	22.02.79	L 54 25.02.78	To promote the prevention and recycling of such waste. To ensure its harmless disposal. To provide a system of authorisations for disposal operations. To lay down provisions governing immersion, discharge, storage and dumping. To enact provisions for monitoring long-established industries and to provide decontamination programmes with possible exceptions for new industries.

Number	Title	Date		OJ No.	Purpose
		adopted	brought into force	and date	
83/29/ EEC	Amendment	03.02.83		L 32 03.02.83	To provide a system of authorisation which will include a preliminary impact assessment. To determine the information to be notified to the Commission.
82/883/ EEC	Directive on procedures for the surveillance and monitoring of environments concerned by waste from the titanium dioxide industry.	03.12.82	10.12.84	L 378 31.12.78	To determine the parameters to be surveyed, the minimum sampling and analysis frequencies as well as the methods of measurement to be used in controlling the application of the Directive 78/176/EEC.
92/112/ EEC	Directive on procedures for the harmonisation of programmes for the reduction and eventual elimination of pollution caused by waste from the titanium dioxide industry.	15.12.92		L409 31.12.92	See title.

Barcelona Convention

Number	Title	Date		OJ No.	Purpose
77/585/ EEC	Decision concluding the Convention for the Protection of the Mediterranean Sea against Pollution and the Protocol for the Prevention of the Pollution of the Mediterranean Sea by Dumping from Ships and Aircraft. (Barcelona Convention).	25.07.77	-	L 240 19.09.77	See title.
81/420/ EEC	Decision on the conclusion of the Protocol concerning cooperation in combating pollution of the Mediterranean Sea by oil and other harmful substances in cases of emergency.	19.05.81	-	L 162 19.06.81	See title.
83/101/ EEC	Decision concluding the Protocol for the protection of the Mediterranean Sea against pollution from land-based sources.	28.02.83	-	L 67 12.03.83	See title.
87/1125	Decision on mercury and cadmium discharges.	21.09.87	-		To allow the Commission to negotiate on behalf of the EEC, the adoption of measures relating to mercury and cadmium discharges as well as organosilicate components, within the framework of the convention for the protection of the Mediterranean Sea against pollution.

Paris Convention

Number	Title	Date		OJ No.	Purpose
75/437/ EEC	Decision concluding the Convention for the Prevention of Marine pollution from Land-based Sources. (Paris Convention).	03.03.75	-	L 194 25.07.75	Ratification by the Community of the Convention.
75/438/ EEC	Decision concerning Community participation in the Interim Commission established on the basis of Resolution No. III of the Convention for the Prevention of Marine Pollution from Land-based Sources.	03.03.75	-	L 194 25.07.75	To authorise the Commission to represent the Community in the Interim Commission responsible for administering the Paris Convention.
87/57/ EEC	Decision concluding the protocol amending the convention for the prevention of marine pollution from land-based sources.	22.12.86	-	L 24 27.07.87	To extend its scope to include airborne pollution.
98/249	Decision on the conclusion of the Convention for the protection of the marine environment of the north-east Atlantic - OSPAR			L104 03.04.98	

Number	Title	Date			Purpose
		adopted	brought into force	OJ No. and date	

APPENDIX 6.6: OTHER EU MEASURES OF RELEVANCE TO POLLUTION CONTROL

Environmental Assessment/Access to Information

Number	Title	adopted	brought into force	OJ No. and date	Purpose
75/436/ Euratom ECSC/ EEC	Council Recommendation of cost allocation and action by public authorities on environmental matters.	03.03.75	03.03.75	L 194 25.07.75	To set out in detail the procedures for applying the Polluter Pays Principle, and to provide for some exceptions which may be made to this Principle.
79/3/ EEC	Council Recommendation to the Member States regarding methods of evaluating the cost of pollution control to industry.	09.12.78	09.12.78	L 5 09.01.79	To define the principles and methods to be followed by the Member States in assessing the costs of pollution control to industry.
85/337/ EEC	Directive concerning the assessment of the environmental effects of certain public and private projects.	27.06.85	03.07.88	L 175 05.07.85	To grant planning permission for projects which are likely to have significant effects on the environment only after an appropriate prior assessment of their environmental effects.
97/11 EC	Council directive amending 1985 directive			L 73	Amend 1985 Directive 14.03.97
85/338/ EEC	Decision on the adoption of a work programme for the first phase of the implementation of an information system on the state of the environment and the natural resources in the Community (1984-1987). (CORINE) (90/150 extends the programme pending establishment of European Environment Agency)	27.06.85	-	L 176 06.07.85	To fix a methodology framework and to apply it to: - biotopes of major importance for nature conservation. - protection of the Mediterranean environment. - acid deposition.
90/313/ EEC	Directive on freedom of access to information on the environment.	07.06.90	31.12.92	L 158 23.06.90	To oblige public authorities to provide access to environmental information, subject to certain restrictions.
1210/90	Regulation on the establishment of the European Environmental Agency and the European Environmental Information and Observation Network.	07.05.90	-	L 120 11.05.90	To set up a body to oversee the information network and ensure collection and objective data on environment.
880/92	Regulation on a Community eco-label award scheme.	23.03.92	23.03.92	L 99 11.04.92	To set up a Community scheme, define criteria and procedures, for awarding eco-labels; to promote the development of products with minimal environmental impact through their whole life-cycle.
1836/93	Regulation allowing voluntary participation by companies in the industry sector in a Community eco-management and audit scheme.			L168 10.07.93	To establish system of environmental management and auditing at industrial sites and provision of information to the public.

Chemicals

Number	Title	adopted	brought into force	OJ No. and date	Purpose
82/501/ EEC	Directive on the major accident hazards of certain industrial activities (The Seveso Directive).	24.06.82	08.01.84	L 230 05.08.82	To establish a notification system of all dangerous substances, installations and major accident hazards. To ensure a better flow of information not only to the national and Community authorities but also to the workers and to the population concerned. Repealed 3.2.99.
96/8/82	Directive on the control of major accident hazards (seveso 2))	09.12.96		L 10 14.01.97	Tightens and extends provisions of earlier 1982 Directive which it will replace in 1998.
87/216/ EEC	Amendment to 82/501	19.03.87	-	L 85 28.03.87	To reduce the threshold triggering of notification system for certain products. Repealed 3.2.99.

Number	Title	Date		OJ No. and date	Purpose
		adopted	brought into force		
88/610/ EEC	Amendment to 82/501			L 336 07.12.88	To increase scope of the Directive and clarify information to be made available to public. Repealed 3.2.99.

Pesticides

[see also water pollution: dangerous substances]

Number	Title	adopted	brought into force	OJ No. and date	Purpose
76/895/ EEC	Directive on the fixing of maximum levels for pesticide residues in and on fruit and vegetables.			L 340 19.12.76	To protect consumers by setting limits on pesticide amounts on food.
86/362/ EEC	Directive on the fixing of maximum residues in and on cereals.			L 221 07.08.86	To protect consumers by setting limits on pesticide amounts on food.
86/363/ EEC	Directive on the fixing of maximum residues in and on products of animal origin.			L 221 07.08.86	To protect consumers by setting limits on pesticide amounts on food.
90/642/ EEC	Directive fixing maximum levels of pesticides in and on certain products of plant origin including fruit and vegetables.		31.12.92	L 350 14.12.90	Framework Directive providing for setting of mandatory maximum residue levels.
91/132/ EEC	Directive relating to undesirable sub-stances and products in animal nutrition.		01.08.91	L 66 13.03.91	Sets maximum permitted pesticide residues on or in animal feeds.
79/117/ EEC	Directive prohibiting the marketing and use of plant protection products containing certain substances.	21.12.78		L 33 08.02.79	Prohibits use of five mercury compounds and eight organochlorine compounds; also nitrogen 1,2 dibromoethane and 1,2 dichloroethane prohibited by subsequent amendments.
78/631/ EEC	Directive on classification, packaging and labelling of dangerous preparations.			L 206 29.07.78	To specify packaging and labelling labelling requirements for pesticides.
91/414/ EEC	Directive concerning placing of plant pro-tection products on the market.	15.07.91	26.07.93	L 230 19.08.91	To harmonise EC-wide registration of pesticides.
98/8/EC	Directive on placing of biocidal products on the market	16.02.98		L123 24.04.98	To standardise way in which biocides are authorised throughout the EU; common principles, risk assesment criteria, etc.

Radioactivity

Number	Title	adopted	brought into force	OJ No. and date	Purpose
	Resolution relating to the technological problems of nuclear safety.	22.07.75	22.07.75	C 185 14.08.75	To define guidelines for the progressive harmonisation of safety requirements and criteria.
80/836/ Euratom	Directive amending the Directives laying down the basic safety standards for the health protection of the general public and workers against the dangers of ionising radiation.	15.07.80	03.12.83 03.06.84	L 246 17.09.80	To establish a system of prior authorisa-tion. To set doses for controllable expo-sures and principles governing operational protection of exposed workers.
87/600/ Euratom	Council Decision on Community arrang-ments for the early exchange of infor-mation in the event of a radiological emergency.	14.12.87	-	L 371 30.12.87	See title.
87/3954/ Euratom	Regulation laying down maximum per-mitted radioactivity levels for foodstuffs in the event of a nuclear accident.	22.12.87	-	L 371 30.12.87	See title.
89/618/ Euratom	Directive on informing the public in the event of a radiological emergency.	27.11.89	27.01.91	L 357 07.12.89	To require prior information on what to do in an emergency to general public likely to be affected and information about an accident to be communicated without delay to those affected; information on possible health risks to be given to all those giving emergency assistance.
90/143/ Euratom	Recommendation on the protection of the public against indoor exposure to radon.	21.02.90	-	L 80 27.03.90	See title.

Number	Title	Date		OJ No. and date	Purpose
		adopted	brought into force		
90/641/ Euratom	Directive concerning protection of outside workers.			L 349 13.12.90	Supplements 80/836 by setting standards for outside workers' exposure to ionising radiation.
96/29	Council Directive laying down basic safety standards relating to ionising radiation	14.05.96	13.05.00	L159 29.06.96	To protect workers and general public from dangers of ionising radiation
92/3/ Euratom	Directive on the supervision and control of shipments of radioactive waste.	13.02.92	01.01.94	L 35 12.02.92	To monitor and control transfrontier shipments of radioactive waste both between Member States and into and out of the Community.
1493/93	Regulation on Euratom shipments of radioactive substances between Member States.	08.06.93		L148 19.06.93	Similar to above.

Genetically Modified Organisms

Number	Title	adopted	brought into force	OJ No. and date	Purpose
90/219/ EEC	Directive on contained use of GMOs.	23.04.90	23.10.91	L 117 08.05.90	To establish notification, consent and emergency system to protect human health and the environment.
90/220/ EEC	Directive on deliberate release of GMOs into the environment.	23.04.90	23.10.91	L 117 08.05.90	To harmonise human health and environmental protection measures in Member States.

BIBLIOGRAPHY

GENERAL

European Issues

A Guide to EC Environmental Law – Dorothy Gillies, Earthscan, 1999.

Caring for our Future: Action for Europe's Environment - European Commission, 1997.

EC Treaty and Environmental Law (second edition) - Krämer, L. Sweet & Maxwell, 1995.

EU Environment Guide (updated annually) - EC Committee of the American Chamber of Commerce, Avenue des Arts 50, Bte 5, B-1040 Brussels.

European Community Environment Legislation (Vol. 2 Air, Vol. 5 Noise, Vol. 6 Waste, Vol. 7 Water) - Commission of the European Communities, DG XI, 1993.

Manual of Environmental Policy: the EC and Britain - Haigh, N. Longman, 1992. (Updated twice a year)

Health

Environmental Health Criteria. International Programme on Chemical Safety. Series of reports on various pollutants evaluating effects on human health and the Environment. Nearly 150 reports have been published under joint sponsoring of UNEP, ILO and WHO. Further information available from the Office of Publications. WHO, Switzerland.

Legislation

Annual Catalogue of Standards. British Standards Institution. (Published in January.)

Environmental Law - Burnett-Hall, R. Sweet & Maxwell, 1995.

Environmental Protection Act 1990, Part I. A Practical Guide - Central Control - Scottish Office, 1992.

Integrated Pollution Control - A Practical Guide. 1996. Environment, Department of. Available from DETR, 43 Marsham Street, London SW1P 3PY.

Integrated Pollution Prevention and Control – A Practical Guide – DETR, 2000. (Similar in preparation for Scotland).

The Environment Acts 1990-1995 - Tromans, S. Sweet & Maxwell, 1996. Texts and commentary.

The Green Triangle - an Environmental Legislation Guide for Businesses in Northern Ireland - ARENA Network (c/o Business in the Community, Airport Road West, Belfast BT2 9EA), 1997.

The Law of Nuclear Installations and Radioactive Substances - Tromans, S & Fitzgerald, J. Sweet & Maxwell, 1997.

Pollution Control: The Law in Scotland - Smith, C, Collar, N & Poustie, M. T & T Clark, Edinburgh, 1997.

Planning

Planning Pollution Prevention - Wood, C. Heinemann Newnes, 1989.

Planning Policy Guidance Notes - The Stationery Office. PPG 1: General Policy & Principles (1997); 3: Housing (2000); 6: Town Centres & Retail Development (1996); 7: The Countryside & the Rural Economy (1992, revised due April 1997); 8: Telecommunications (draft revision July 2000); 9: Nature Conservation (1994); 10: Waste Disposal

& Management (draft 1998); 11: Regional Planning (Oct. 2000); 12: Development Plans (1999); 13: Transport (1994, revised draft 1999); 14: Development on Unstable Land (1990); 18: Enforcing Planning Control (1991); 22: Renewable Energy & annexes (1993/94); 23: Planning and Pollution Control (1994); 24: Planning and Noise (1994); 25: Development & Flood Risk (draft 2000). PPGs are also available on the DETR website: www.planning.detr.gov.uk

National Planning Policy Guidance (Scotland) - General (1997); 1: The Planning System (draft, July 2000); Provision of Roadside Facilities on Motorways & Other Trunk Roads (1996); 10: Planning & Waste Management (1996); Sport, Physical Recreation & Open Spaces (1996); Land for Housing (1996); 8: Retail Development (draft 1997); Skiing (1997); Planning for the Coast (draft 1997); Rural Development (draft 1997); 17: Transport & Planning (1999).

Planning Guidance (Wales): Planning Policy – First revision, 1999.

Planning Policy Statements (Northern Ireland) - PPS 1: Planning System in NI (draft due 3/97); 2: Planning & Nature Conservation (due 3/97); 3: Development Control & Road Considerations (1996); 4: Industrial Development (draft due 3/97); 5: Retailing & Town Centres (1996). Other PPSs include Environmental Impact Assessment; Hazardous Substances.

Reference

Digest of Environmental Statistics (Annual) - Environment, Transport & The Regions Department of, The Stationery Office.

EC Eco-Management and Audit Scheme: A Participant's Guide - Department of Environment for UK Competent Body, 1995.

Environmental Health Reference Book - Jackson, MH and others. Butterworth, 1989.

Fundamentals of Environmental Chemistry - Manahan, SE. Lewis, 1993.

A Guide to Risk Assessment and Risk Management - HMSO, 1995.

Pollution: Causes, Effects and Control - Harrison, R (Ed). Second Edition. Society of Chemistry Cambridge, 1990.

Silent Spring - Carson, R. Hamish Hamilton, 1962.

Royal Commission on Environmental Pollution Reports. First Report (1971); 2nd: *Three Issues in Industrial Pollution* (1972); 3rd: *Pollution in some British Estuaries and Coastal Waters* (1972); 4th: *Pollution Control: Progress and Problems* (1974); 6th: *Nuclear Power and the Environment* (1976); 7th: *Agriculture and Pollution* (1979); 8th: *Oil Pollution of the Sea* (1981); 9th: *Lead in the Environment* (1983); 10th: *Tackling Pollution - Experience and Prospects* (1984); 11th: *Managing Waste: The Duty of Care* (1985); 12th: *Best Practicable Environmental Option* (1988); 13th:

The Release of Genetically Engineered Organisms to the Environment (1989); 14th: *GENHAZ - A System for the Critical Appraisal of Proposals to Release GMOs into the Environment* (1991); 15th: *Emissions from Heavy Duty Diesel Vehicles* (1991) 16th: *Freshwater Quality* (1992); 17th: *Incineration of Waste* (1993); 18th: *Transport and the Environment* (1994); 19th: *Sustainable Use of Soil* (1996) - all published by HMSO. 20th: *Transport and the Environment - Developments since 1994* (1997); 21st: *Setting Environmental Standards* (1998); 22nd: *Energy – The Changing Climate* (2000) - The Stationery Office.

Sustainable Development

Our Common Future - World Commission on Environment and Development, Oxford University Press, 1987.

Quality of Life Counts: Indicators for a Strategy for Sustainable Development for the United Kingdom: A Baseline Assessment. DETR, 1999.

AIR

Acid Pollution

Air Pollution, Acid Rain and the Environment - Mellanby, K (Ed). Elsevier for Watt Committee on Energy, London, 1988.

The Effects of Acid Deposition on Buildings and Building Materials in the UK - Buildings Effects Review Group. HMSO, 1989.

Sulphur Dioxide, Acid Aerosols and Particulates - Advisory Group on the Medical Aspects of Air Pollution Episodes. HMSO, 1992.

Air Pollution

Air Pollution and Plant Life - Treshow, M (Ed). John Wiley & Sons, 1984.

Air Pollution and Tree Health - Environment, Department of. HMSO, 1993.

Local Air Pollution Control: Management Guide – Chartered Institute of Environmental Health, 2000.

Principles of Air Pollution Meteorology, Lyons, T & Scott, B. Belhaven Press, 1990.

The Politics of Clean Air - Ashby, A & Anderson, M. Clarendon Press, Oxford, 1981.

Air Quality

Air Quality Guidelines for Europe - WHO Regional Office for Europe. WHO Regional Publications, European Series; No. 23, 1987. Revised edition in press 1999. See also WHO website at www.who.dk

Expert Panel on Air Quality Standards - 1st report: *Benzene* (1994); 2nd: *Ozone* (1994); 3rd: *1,3 Butadiene* (1994); 4th: *Carbon Monoxide* (1994); 5th: *Sulphur Dioxide* (1995); 6th: *Particles* (1995); 7th: *Nitrogen Dioxide* (1996); 8th: *Lead* (1998); 9th: *Polycyclic Aromatic Hydrocarbons* (1999). The Stationery Office.

Department of the Environment, Transport & The Regions & National Assembly for Wales - Local Air Quality Management Guidance: *Framework for Review and Assessment of Air Quality* (LAQM.G1(00)); *Developing Local Air Quality Action Plans and Strategies: the main considerations* (LAQM.G2(00)); *Air Quality and Transport* (LAQM.G3(00)); *Air Quality and Land-Use Planning* (LAQM.G4(00)).

DETR, National Assembly for Wales and Scottish Office - Technical Guidance for Review and Assessment: *Monitoring Air Quality* (LAQM.TG1(00)); *Estimating Emissions* (LAQM.TG2(00)); *Selection and Use of Dispersion Models* (LAQM.TG3(00)); *Pollutant Specific Guidance* (LAQM.TG4(00)).

Quality of Urban Air Review Group - 1st report: *Urban Air Quality in the United Kingdom* (1993); 2nd: *Diesel Vehicle Emissions and Urban Air Quality* (1993); 3rd: *Airborne Particulate Matter in the United Kingdom* (1996). HMSO.

Scottish Office: Local Air Quality Management Guidance – as for DETR/Wales Guidance but with reference no. LAQM.G1(S)(00), etc.

Smog Alert - Managing Urban Air Quality - Elsom D. Earthscan, 1996.

Source Apportionment of Airborne Particulate Matter in the United Kingdom – Report of the Airborne Particles Group, January 1999.

The Air Quality Strategy for England, Scotland, Wales and Northern Ireland – Working Together for Clean Air – DETR, Scottish Office, National Assembly for Wales and DOE (Northern Ireland). 2000.

Global Warming

The Greenhouse Effect, Climatic Change and Eco-systems (SCOPE 29) - Bolin, B & others (Eds). John Wiley & Sons, 1986.

The Potential Effects of Climate Change in the United Kingdom - UK Climate Change Impacts Review Group, First Report, HMSO, 1991.

Health

Air Pollution and Health - Holman, C. Friends of the Earth, London 1989, revised 1991.

Department of Health, Advisory Group on the Medical Aspects of Air Pollution Episodes - 1st report: *Ozone* (1991); 2nd: *Sulphur Dioxide, Acid Aerosols and Particulates* (1992); 3rd: *Oxides of Nitrogen* (1993); 4th: *Health Effects of Exposures to Mixtures of Air Pollutants.* HMSO.

Department of Health, Committee on the Medical Effects of Air Pollutants - *Asthma and Outdoor Air Pollution* (1995); *Non-Biological Particles and Health* (1995), HMSO. *Handbook on Air Pollution and Health* (1997);

Quantification of the Effects of Air Pollution on Health in the United Kingdom (1998), The Stationery Office.

Estimating Human Exposure to Air Pollutants - World Health Organisation. WHO Offset Publication No. 69. WHO, Geneva, 1982.

Lead, Mercury, Cadminum and Arsenic in the Environment (SCOPE 31) - Hutchinson, TC & Meema, KM (Eds). John Wiley & Sons, 1987.

Monitoring

Aerosol Sampling - Science and Practice - Vincent, JH. John Wiley & Sons, 1989.

Atmospheric Diffusion (3rd ed) - Pasquill, F and Smith, FB. Ellis Horwood Ltd, 1983.

Atmospheric Dispersion Modelling: Guidelines on the Justification of Choice and Use of Models and the Communication and Reporting of Results - Policy Statement by Royal Meteorological Society, published in collaboration with Department of Environment, 1995. Available from RMO, 104 Oxford Road, Reading, Berkshire RG1 7LJ.

Characterisation of Air Quality BS 6069: Parts 1-4: 1990-1992. British Standards Institution.

Global Environmental Monitoring System - Assessment of Urban air Quality - Prepared by Monitoring and Assessment Research Centre for WHO and UNEP, 1988.

Methods for the Measurement of Air Pollution BS 1747: Parts 1-12; 1969-1993. British Standards Institution.

Monitoring Ambient Air Quality for Health Impact Assessment – WHO Regional Office for Europe, Copenhagen, 1999.

Odour

Latest Developments in Odour Measurement - Gibson, RN. IAPSC, Warren Spring Laboratory, 1992.

Odour at the Process Boundary - Pratt, M. Clean Air Vol 22, no. 3, 1992.

Odour Measurement and Control - An Update - Woodfield, M & Hall, D (Eds). AEA Technology, NETCEN, 1994.

The Control of Airborne Odours - Elvidge, AF & Blitz, J. IAPSC, Warren Spring Laboratory, 1992.

Ozone, Stratospheric

UK Stratospheric Ozone Review Group - Stratospheric Ozone (Fourth Report). HMSO, 1991.

Ozone, Tropospheric

Ozone - Advisory Group on the Medical Aspects of Air Pollution Episodes, 1991.

Radiation

Environmental Radon - Cothern, CR & Smith, JE (Eds). Plenum Press, New York, 1987.

Living with Radiation - National Radiological Protection Board, HMSO. 1989.

Radiation Exposure of the UK Population - Hughes, JS & others. HMSO for National Radiological Protection Board, annual.

Transport

Atmospheric Emissions from the Use of Transport in the United Kingdom - Fergusson, M, Holman, C, Barrett, M. Earth Resources Research. Worldwide Fund for Nature, 1989.

The Impact of Airport Operations on Air Quality - Raper, D, Longhurst, J. Clean Air, Vol. 20, no. 1, 1990.

Transport and the Environment - OECD, 1988.

Transport Statistics Great Britain - The Stationery Office, annual.

NOISE

Acoustics and the Built Environment - Elsevier, 1989.

Fighting Noise in the 1990s - OECD, 1991.

Guidelines for Community Noise – World Health Organisation, 2000.

Noise and Noise Law: A Practical Approach - Adams MS & McManus F. Wiley Chancery Law, 1994.

Noise Assessment, Information and Control, Noise Guides 3-8 - Health and Safety Executive. HMSO, 1990

Noise at Work Regulations 1989. Noise Guides 1-2 - Legal duties to prevent damage to hearing - Health and Dafety Executive. HMSO 1989.

Noise Control: The Law and its Enforcement - Penn CN. Shaw & Sons, 1995.

Noise Pollution (SCOPE 24) - Saenz, AL & Stephens, RWB (Eds). John Wiley and Sons, 1986.

Planning and Noise (PPG 24). HMSO, 1994.

Rating Industrial Noise Affecting Mixed Residential and Industrial Areas, BS 4142. British Standards Institution, 1990.

PESTICIDES

Pesticide Related Law - Gilbert, D. & Macrory, R. The British Crop Protection Council, 1989.

The Pesticide Handbook - Hurst, P, Hay, A & Dudley, N. Journeyman, 1991.

Pesticide Users' Health and Safety Handbook - Watterson, A. Gower, 1988.

WASTE

Contaminated Land - Aspinwall & Co. for Institution of Environmental Health Officers. IEHO, 1989.

Cutting Your Losses: A further Guide to Waste Minimisation for Business - Trade and Industry, Department of. HMSO, 1992.

Guidance on Distinguishing Waste Scrap Metal from Raw Material – British Metals Federation (16 High Street, Brampton, Huntingdon PE28 4TU), 2000.

Reducing the Burden of Waste - Guidelines for Business - Confederation of British Industry, 1993.

The Environmental Impact of Refuse Incineration in the UK - Woodfield, M. Warren Spring Laboratory, 1987.

The Law of Waste Management - Pocklington, D. Shaw & Sons, 1997.

Waste Management Planning - Principles & Practice - Department of the Environment. HMSO, 1995.

WATER

Aquatic Pollution: An Introductory Text - Laws, WA, John Wiley & Sons, 1994.

Dangerous Substances in Water - A Practical Guide. Environmental Data Services Ltd, 1992.

The Law of the National Rivers Authority - Howarth, W. The National Rivers Authority/Centre for Law in Rural Areas, 1990.

Wisdoms Law of Watercourses, Fifth Edition - Howarth, W. Shaw and Sons, 1992.

JOURNALS

(Covering subjects relevant to material in the *Pollution Handbook*)

Air Quality Management (monthly). Information for Industry Ltd, 18-20 Ridgway, London SW19 4QN.

Atmospheric Environment (monthly). Pergamon Press, Headington Hill Hall, Oxford.

Clean Air (quarterly). Journal of the National Society for Clean Air.

ENDS Report (monthly). ENDS, Unit 24, Finsbury Business Centre, 40 Bowling Green Lane, London EC1R 0NE. News and analysis of current developments. Specialist reports on industry and the environment.

Environment Business (monthly). Information for Industry Ltd, 18-20 Ridgway, London SW19 4QN.

Environmental Health (monthly). Journal of the Institution of Environmental Health Officers, Chadwick House, Rushworth Street, London SE1 0QT.

Europe Environment (fortnightly). Europe Information Service, Av. Albert Elisabeth 46, 1200 Brussels.

Waste Manager. Environmental Services Association, 154 Buckingham Palace Road, London SW1W 9TR.

WEBSITES

www.detr.gov.uk: Department of Environment, Transport and the Regions, with links to all DETR areas of responsibility

www.environment-agency.gov.uk: Environment Agency

www.environment-agency.gov.uk/epns.lapchome.html: LAPC Additional Guidance Notes

www.hmso.gov.uk: Acts of Parliament, statutory orders and drafts, with links to Scottish, Welsh and Northern Ireland legislation

www.aeat.co.uk/netcen/aqarchive.archome.html: automatic and non-automatic monitoring data, and UK atmospheric emissions inventories

www.aeat.co.uk/netcen/airqual/info/labrief.html: LAPC guidance notes, together with links to other sites with information of relevance to LAPC

www.open.gov.uk: gateway to all central and local government bodies

www.sepa.org.uk: Scottish Environment Protection Agency

www.scotland.gov.uk: Scottish Executive, includes consultations in progress, and details of legislation

www.ehsni.gov.uk Northern Ireland Environment and Heritage Service – environmental protection site provides details of legislation and policy in each of EHS's areas of responsibility

http://europa.eu.int/index-en.htm: European Union news, press releases, basic information and links to official texts and legislation

POLLUTION HANDBOOK INDEX